MECHANICS FOR ENGINEERS: DYNAMICS

Mechanics for Engineers

DYNAMICS *Second Edition*

FERDINAND P. BEER
Professor and Head, Department of Mechanics
Lehigh University

E. RUSSELL JOHNSTON, JR.
Professor, Department of Civil Engineering
University of Connecticut

1962

McGRAW-HILL BOOK COMPANY
New York, San Francisco, Toronto, London

MECHANICS FOR ENGINEERS: DYNAMICS

07-004303-5

Library of Congress Catalog Card Number: 61-9323

13 LKBP 765432

PREFACE

The main objective of a first course in mechanics should be to develop in the engineering student the ability to analyze any problem in a simple and logical manner and to apply to its solution a few, well-understood, basic principles. It is hoped that this text, as well as the preceding volume, *Mechanics for Engineers: Statics*, will help the instructor achieve this goal.†

In this second edition, a greater emphasis has been placed on the vectorial character of mechanics. The concept of vector and the laws governing the addition and the resolution of vectors were discussed at the beginning of the volume on statics. Throughout the text, forces, velocities, accelerations, and other vector quantities have been clearly distinguished from scalar quantities through the use of boldface type. Products and derivatives of vectors, however, are not used in this text.‡

One of the characteristics of the approach used in these volumes is that the mechanics of *particles* has been clearly separated from the mechanics of *rigid bodies*. This approach makes it possible to consider simple practical applications at an early stage and to postpone the introduction of more difficult concepts. In the volume on statics, the statics of particles was treated first, and the principle of equilibrium was immediately applied to practical situations involving only concurrent forces. The statics of rigid bodies was considered later, at which time the principle of transmissibility and the associated concept of moment of a force were introduced. In this volume, the same division is observed. The basic concepts of force, mass, and acceleration, of work and energy, and of impulse and momentum are introduced and first applied to problems involving only

† Both texts are also available in a single volume, *Mechanics for Engineers: Statics and Dynamics*.

‡ In a parallel text, *Vector Mechanics for Engineers: Dynamics*, vector analysis is used throughout the presentation of dynamics, making it possible to analyze more advanced problems in three-dimensional kinematics and kinetics.

particles. Thus the student may familiarize himself with the three basic methods used in dynamics and learn their respective advantages before facing the difficulties associated with the motion of rigid bodies.

Although the authors strongly believe in the advantage of the approach they use, they do not wish to impose their choice on the instructor. Consequently, the various chapters have been written so that they may be taught in alternate sequences. For example, Chap. 15 may be taken immediately after Chap. 11 if the instructor prefers to keep kinematics apart from kinetics, and Chaps. 13 and 14 may be postponed if he wishes to teach the method of work and energy (Chaps. 13 and 17) and the method of impulse and momentum (Chaps. 14 and 18) as single units. Whatever the sequence used, the very fact that distinct chapters are devoted to the dynamics of particles and to the dynamics of rigid bodies should help the student organize his own thoughts.

Since this text is designed for a first course in dynamics, new concepts have been presented in simple terms and every step explained in detail. On the other hand, by discussing the broader aspects of the problems considered and by pointing out the limitations as well as the possible extensions of the results obtained, a definite maturity of approach has been achieved. For example, the concepts of mass and weight are carefully distinguished, and the limitations of the methods used to analyze plane motion are indicated, so that the student will not be tempted to apply them to cases in which they are not valid.

A number of optional sections have been included. These sections are indicated by asterisks and may thus easily be distinguished from those which form the core of the basic dynamics course. They may be omitted without prejudice to the understanding of the rest of the text. The topics covered in these additional sections include the motion of a particle under a central force with applications to space mechanics, the deflection of fluid streams, problems involving jet and rocket propulsion, Coriolis acceleration, damped mechanical vibrations, and electrical analogues. These topics will be found of particular interest when dynamics is taught in the junior year.

The fact that mechanics is essentially a *deductive* science based on a few fundamental principles has been stressed. Derivations have been presented in their logical sequence and with all the rigor warranted at this level. However, the learning process being largely *inductive*, simple applications have been considered first. Thus the dynamics of particles precedes the dynamics of rigid bodies, and, in the latter, translation and centroidal rotation are considered first and used to establish a general method of analysis that may be applied to all types of plane motion.

Free-body diagrams were introduced early in statics. They were used not only to solve equilibrium problems but also to express the equivalence of two systems of forces or, more generally, of two systems of vectors. The advantage of this approach becomes apparent in the study of the dynamics of rigid bodies. By placing the emphasis on "free-body-diagram equations" rather than on the standard algebraic equations of motion, a more intuitive and more complete understanding of D'Alembert's principle and of the principle of impulse and momentum may be achieved.

The material presented in this text and the large majority of the problems require no mathematical knowledge beyond algebra, trigonometry, and the differentiation and integration of elementary functions. However, special problems have been included, which make use of a more advanced knowledge of calculus, and certain sections, such as Secs. 19.8 and 19.9 on damped vibrations, should be assigned only if the students possess the proper mathematical background.

The text has been divided into units, each consisting of one or several theory sections, one or several Sample Problems, and a large number of problems to be assigned. Each unit corresponds to a well-defined topic and generally may be covered in one lesson. In a number of cases, however, the instructor will find it desirable to devote more than one lesson to a given topic. The Sample Problems have been set up in much the same form that a student will use in solving the assigned problems. They thus serve the double purpose of amplifying the text and demonstrating the type of neat and orderly work that the student should cultivate in his own solutions. Most of the problems to be assigned are of a practical nature and should appeal to the engineering student. They are primarily designed, however, to illustrate the material presented in the text and to help the student understand the basic principles of mechanics. The problems have been grouped according to the portions of material they illustrate and have been arranged in order of increasing difficulty. Problems requiring special attention have been indicated by asterisks. Answers to all even-numbered problems are given at the end of the book.

The authors wish to acknowledge gratefully the many helpful comments and suggestions offered by the users of the first edition of *Mechanics for Engineers*.

FERDINAND P. BEER
E. RUSSELL JOHNSTON, JR.

CONTENTS

LIST OF SYMBOLS

$\mathbf{a}, a$	Acceleration
a	Constant; radius; distance; semimajor axis of ellipse
$\bar{\mathbf{a}}, \bar{a}$	Acceleration of mass center
$\mathbf{a}_{B/A}$	Relative acceleration of B with respect to A
$\mathbf{a}_c$	Coriolis acceleration
$\mathbf{A}, \mathbf{B}, \mathbf{C}, \ldots$	Reactions at supports and connections
$A, B, C, \ldots$	Points
A	Area
b	Width; distance; semiminor axis of ellipse
c	Constant; coefficient of viscous damping
C	Centroid; instantaneous center of rotation; capacitance
d	Distance
e	Coefficient of restitution; base of natural logarithms
E	Voltage
f	Frequency
$\mathbf{F}$	Force; friction force
g	Acceleration of gravity
G	Center of gravity; mass center; constant of gravitation
h	Height; sag of cable
h_O	Angular momentum about O
i	Current
$I, I_x, \ldots$	Moment of inertia
$\bar{I}$	Centroidal moment of inertia
J	Polar moment of inertia
k	Spring constant
k_x, k_y, k_O	Radius of gyration
$\bar{k}$	Centroidal radius of gyration
l	Length
L	Length; span; inductance
m	Mass
$\mathbf{M}$	Couple
M	Moment; mass of earth

n Normal direction
N Normal component of reaction
O Origin of coordinates
p Pressure; circular frequency
P Force
$P_{xy}, \ldots$ Product of inertia
q Electric charge
Q Force
r Position vector
r Radius; distance; polar coordinate
R Resultant force; reaction
R Radius of earth; resistance
s Displacement
s Position coordinate; distance; length of cable
t Time; thickness; tangential direction
T Tension; kinetic energy
u Velocity
u Rectangular coordinate
U Work
v, v Velocity
v Speed; rectangular coordinate
$\bar{\mathbf{v}}, \bar{v}$ Velocity of mass center
$\mathbf{v}_{B/A}$ Relative velocity of B with respect to A
V Volume; potential energy, shear
w Load per unit length
W Weight, load
x, y, z Rectangular coordinates, distances
$\bar{x}, \bar{y}, \bar{z}$ Rectangular coordinates of centroid, center of gravity, or mass center
$\boldsymbol{\alpha}, \alpha$ Angular acceleration
α, β, γ Angles
γ Specific weight
δ Elongation
$\delta \mathbf{s}$ Virtual displacement
δU Virtual work
ε Eccentricity of conic section or of orbit
η Efficiency
θ Angular coordinate; angle; polar coordinate
μ Coefficient of friction
ρ Density; radius of curvature
τ Period; periodic time
ϕ Angle of friction; phase angle; angle
φ Phase difference
$\boldsymbol{\omega}, \omega$ Angular velocity
ω Circular frequency of forced vibration
Ω Rate of precession

LIST OF SYMBOLS

$\mathbf{a}$, a	Acceleration
a	Constant; radius; distance; semimajor axis of ellipse
$\bar{\mathbf{a}}$, $\bar{a}$	Acceleration of mass center
$\mathbf{a}_{B/A}$	Relative acceleration of B with respect to A
$\mathbf{a}_c$	Coriolis acceleration
$\mathbf{A}, \mathbf{B}, \mathbf{C}, \ldots$	Reactions at supports and connections
$A, B, C, \ldots$	Points
A	Area
b	Width; distance; semiminor axis of ellipse
c	Constant; coefficient of viscous damping
C	Centroid; instantaneous center of rotation; capacitance
d	Distance
e	Coefficient of restitution; base of natural logarithms
E	Voltage
f	Frequency
$\mathbf{F}$	Force; friction force
g	Acceleration of gravity
G	Center of gravity; mass center; constant of gravitation
h	Height; sag of cable
h_O	Angular momentum about O
i	Current
$I, I_x, \ldots$	Moment of inertia
$\bar{I}$	Centroidal moment of inertia
J	Polar moment of inertia
k	Spring constant
k_x, k_y, k_O	Radius of gyration
$\bar{k}$	Centroidal radius of gyration
l	Length
L	Length; span; inductance
m	Mass
$\mathbf{M}$	Couple
M	Moment; mass of earth

n	Normal direction
$\mathbf{N}$	Normal component of reaction
O	Origin of coordinates
p	Pressure; circular frequency
$\mathbf{P}$	Force
$P_{xy}, \ldots$	Product of inertia
q	Electric charge
$\mathbf{Q}$	Force
$\mathbf{r}$	Position vector
r	Radius; distance; polar coordinate
$\mathbf{R}$	Resultant force; reaction
R	Radius of earth; resistance
$\mathbf{s}$	Displacement
s	Position coordinate; distance; length of cable
t	Time; thickness; tangential direction
T	Tension; kinetic energy
$\mathbf{u}$	Velocity
u	Rectangular coordinate
U	Work
$\mathbf{v}, v$	Velocity
v	Speed; rectangular coordinate
$\bar{\mathbf{v}}, \bar{v}$	Velocity of mass center
$\mathbf{v}_{B/A}$	Relative velocity of *B* with respect to *A*
V	Volume; potential energy, shear
w	Load per unit length
W	Weight, load
x, y, z	Rectangular coordinates, distances
$\bar{x}, \bar{y}, \bar{z}$	Rectangular coordinates of centroid, center of gravity, or mass center
$\boldsymbol{\alpha}, \alpha$	Angular acceleration
α, β, γ	Angles
γ	Specific weight
δ	Elongation
$\delta\mathbf{s}$	Virtual displacement
δU	Virtual work
ε	Eccentricity of conic section or of orbit
η	Efficiency
θ	Angular coordinate; angle; polar coordinate
μ	Coefficient of friction
ρ	Density; radius of curvature
τ	Period; periodic time
ϕ	Angle of friction; phase angle; angle
φ	Phase difference
$\boldsymbol{\omega}, \omega$	Angular velocity
ω	Circular frequency of forced vibration
Ω	Rate of precession

MECHANICS FOR ENGINEERS: DYNAMICS

DYNAMICS

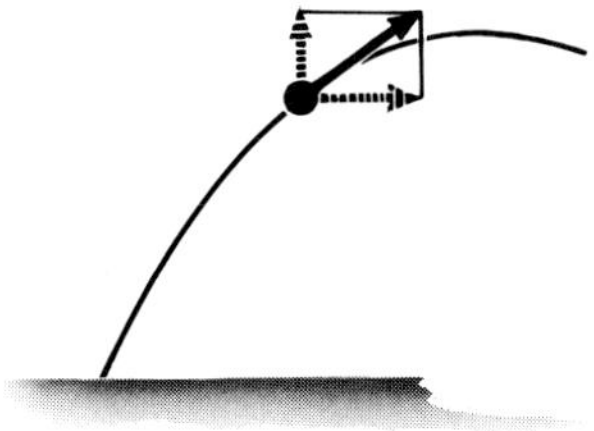

11. KINEMATICS OF PARTICLES

11.1. Introduction to Dynamics. Chapters 1 to 10 were devoted to *statics*, i.e., to the analysis of bodies at rest. We shall now begin the study of *dynamics*, which is the part of mechanics dealing with the analysis of bodies in motion.

While the study of statics goes back to the time of the Greek philosophers, the first significant contribution to dynamics was made by Galileo (1564–1642). His experiments on uniformly accelerated bodies led Newton (1642–1727) to formulate his fundamental laws of motion.

Dynamics is divided into two parts: (1) *Kinematics*, which is the study of the geometry of motion; kinematics is used to relate displacement, velocity, acceleration, and time, without reference to the cause of the motion. (2) *Kinetics*, which is the study of the relation existing between the forces acting on a body, the mass of the body, and the motion of the body; kinetics is used to predict the motion caused by given forces or to determine the forces required to produce a given motion.

Chapters 11 to 14 are devoted to the *dynamics of particles*, and Chap. 11 more particularly to the *kinematics of particles*. The use of the word particles does not imply that we shall restrict our study to that of small corpuscles; it rather indicates that in these first chapters we shall study the motion of bodies—possibly as large as cars, rockets, or airplanes—without regard to their size. By saying that the bodies are analyzed as particles, we mean that only their motion as an entire unit will be considered; any rotation about their own mass center will be neglected. There are cases, however, when such a rotation is not negligible; the bodies, then, may not be considered as particles. The analysis of such motions will be carried out in later chapters dealing with the *dynamics of rigid bodies*.

RECTILINEAR MOTION OF PARTICLES

11.2. Position, Velocity, and Acceleration. A particle moving along a straight line is said to be in *rectilinear motion.* At any given instant t, the particle will occupy a certain position on the straight line. To define the position P of the particle, we choose a fixed origin O on the straight line and a positive direction along the line. We measure the distance s from O to P and record it with a plus or minus sign, according to whether P is reached from O by moving along the line in the positive or the negative direction. The distance s, with the appropriate sign, completely defines the position of the particle; it is called the *position coordinate* of the particle considered. For example, the position coordinate corresponding to P in Fig. 11.1*a* is $s = +5$ ft, while the coordinate corresponding to P' in Fig. 11.1*b* is $s' = -2$ ft.

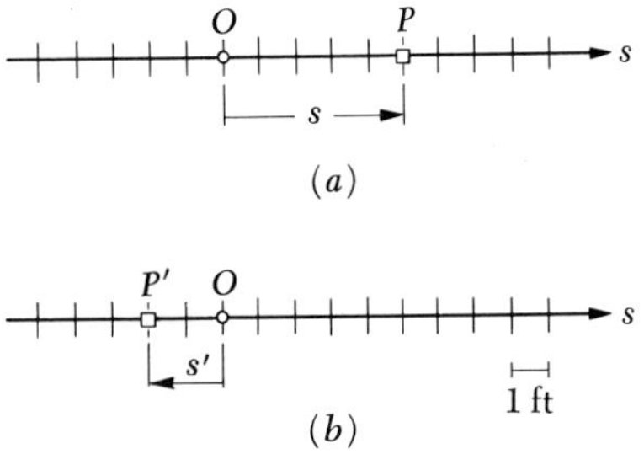

FIG. 11.1

When the position coordinate s of a particle is known for every value of the time t, we say that the motion of the particle is known. The "timetable" of the motion may be given in the form of an equation in s and t, such as $s = 6t^2 - t^3$, or in the form of a graph of s vs. t as shown in Fig. 11.6. The units most generally used to measure s and t are, respectively, feet and seconds.

Consider the position P occupied by the particle at time t and the corresponding coordinate s (Fig. 11.2). Consider also the position P' occupied by the particle at a later time $t + \Delta t$; the position coordinate of P' may be obtained by adding to the coordinate s of P the small displacement Δs, which will be positive or negative according to whether P' is to the right or to the left of P. The *average velocity* of the particle over the time interval Δt is defined as the quotient of the displacement Δs and the time interval Δt,

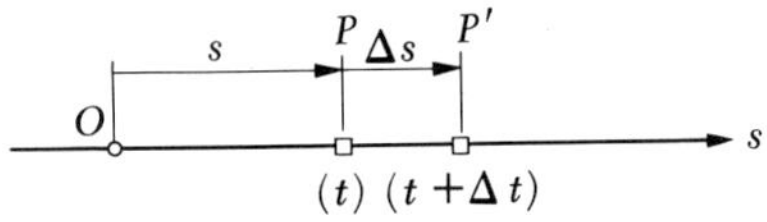

FIG. 11.2

$$\text{Average velocity} = \frac{\Delta s}{\Delta t}$$

If Δs is expressed in feet and Δt in seconds, the average velocity will be expressed in ft/sec.

The *instantaneous velocity* v of the particle at the instant t is obtained from the average velocity by choosing shorter and shorter time intervals Δt and displacements Δs,

$$\text{Instantaneous velocity} = v = \lim_{\Delta t \to 0} \frac{\Delta s}{\Delta t}$$

The instantaneous velocity will also be expressed in ft/sec. Observing that the limit of the quotient is equal, by definition, to the derivative of s with respect to t, we write

$$v = \frac{ds}{dt} \tag{11.1}$$

The velocity v is represented by an algebraic number which may be positive or negative.† A positive value of v indicates that s increases, i.e., that the particle moves in the positive direction (Fig. 11.3*a*); a negative value of v indicates that s decreases, i.e., that the particle moves in the negative direction (Fig. 11.3*b*). The magnitude of v is known as the *speed* of the particle.

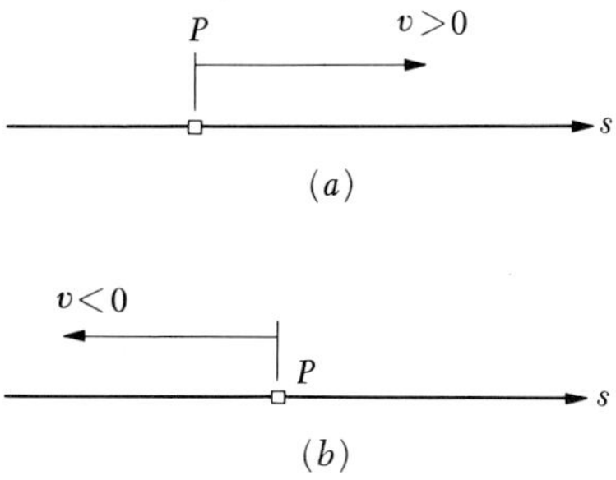

FIG. 11.3

Consider the velocity v of the particle at time t and also its velocity $v + \Delta v$ at a later time $t + \Delta t$ (Fig. 11.4). The *average acceleration* of the particle over the time interval Δt is defined as the quotient of Δv and Δt,

$$\text{Average acceleration} = \frac{\Delta v}{\Delta t}$$

If Δv is expressed in ft/sec and Δt in seconds, the average acceleration will be expressed in ft/sec^2.

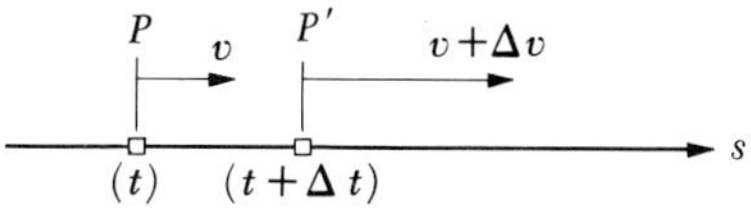

FIG. 11.4

The *instantaneous acceleration* a of the particle at the instant t is obtained from the average acceleration by choosing smaller and smaller values for Δt and Δv,

$$\text{Instantaneous acceleration} = a = \lim_{\Delta t \to 0} \frac{\Delta v}{\Delta t}$$

The instantaneous acceleration will also be expressed in ft/sec^2. The limit of the quotient is by definition the derivative of v with respect to t and measures the rate of change of the velocity. We write

$$a = \frac{dv}{dt} \tag{11.2}$$

or, substituting for v from (11.1),

$$a = \frac{d^2s}{dt^2} \tag{11.3}$$

The acceleration a is represented by an algebraic number which

† As we shall see in Sec. 11.9, the velocity is actually a vector quantity. However, since we are considering here the rectilinear motion of a particle, where the velocity of the particle has a known and fixed direction, we need only specify the sense and magnitude of the velocity; this may be conveniently done by using a scalar quantity with a plus or minus sign. The same remark will apply to the acceleration of a particle in rectilinear motion.

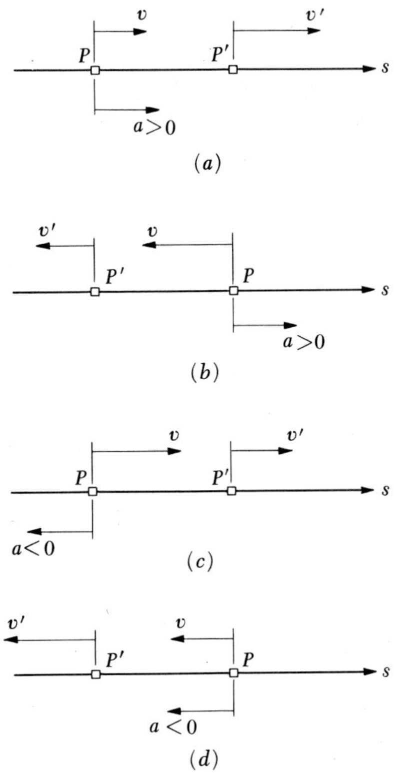

FIG. 11.5

may be positive or negative.† A positive value of a indicates that the velocity (i.e., the algebraic number v) increases. This may mean that the particle is moving faster in the positive direction (Fig. 11.5*a*) or that it is moving more slowly in the negative direction (Fig. 11.5*b*); in both cases, Δv is positive. A negative value of a indicates that the velocity decreases; either the particle is moving more slowly in the positive direction (Fig. 11.5*c*), or it is moving faster in the negative direction (Fig. 11.5*d*).

The term *deceleration* is sometimes used to refer to a when the speed of the particle (i.e., the magnitude of v) decreases; the particle is then moving more slowly. For example, the particle of Fig. 11.5 is decelerated in parts b and c, while it is truly accelerated (i.e., moves faster) in parts a and d.

Another expression may be obtained for the acceleration by eliminating the differential dt in Eqs. (11.1) and (11.2). Solving (11.1) for dt, we obtain $dt = ds/v$; carrying into (11.2), we write

$$a = v\frac{dv}{ds} \tag{11.4}$$

Example. Consider a particle moving in a straight line, and assume that its position is defined by the equation

$$s = 6t^2 - t^3$$

where t is expressed in seconds and s in feet. The velocity v at any time t is obtained by differentiating s with respect to t,

$$v = \frac{ds}{dt} = 12t - 3t^2$$

The acceleration a is obtained by differentiating again with respect to t,

$$a = \frac{dv}{dt} = 12 - 6t$$

The position coordinate, the velocity, and the acceleration have been plotted against t in Fig. 11.6. The curves obtained are known as *motion curves*. It should be kept in mind, however, that the particle does not move along any of these curves; the particle moves in a straight line. Since the derivative of a function measures the slope of the corresponding curve, the slope of the s–t curve at any given time is equal to the value of v at that time and the slope of the v–t curve is equal to the value of a. Since $a = 0$ at $t = 2$ sec, the slope of the v–t curve must be zero at $t = 2$ sec; the velocity reaches a maximum at this in-

† See footnote, page 383.

stant. Also, since $v = 0$ at $t = 0$ and at $t = 4$ sec, the tangent to the s–t curve must be horizontal for both of these values of t.

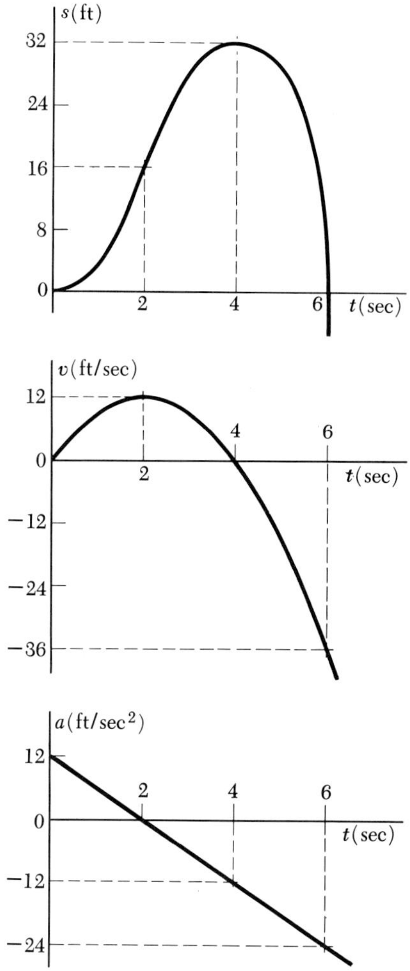

FIG. 11.6

A study of the three motion curves of Fig. 11.6 shows that the motion of the particle from $t = 0$ to $t = \infty$ may be divided into four phases:

1. The particle starts from the origin, $s = 0$, with no velocity but with a positive acceleration. Under this acceleration, the particle gains a positive velocity and moves in the positive direction. From $t = 0$ to $t = 2$ sec, s, v, and a are all positive.

2. At $t = 2$ sec, the acceleration is zero; the velocity has reached its maximum value. From $t = 2$ sec to $t = 4$ sec, v is positive, but a is negative; the particle still moves in the positive direction but more and more slowly; the particle is decelerated.

3. At $t = 4$ sec, the velocity is zero; the position coordinate s has reached its maximum value. From then on, both v and a are negative; the particle is accelerated and moves in the negative direction with increasing speed.

4. At $t = 6$ sec, the particle passes through the origin; its coordinate s is then zero, while the total distance traveled since the beginning of the motion is 64 ft. For values of t larger than 6 sec, s, v, and a will all be negative. The particle keeps moving in the negative direction, away from O, faster and faster.

11.3. Determination of the Motion of a Particle. We saw in the preceding section that the motion of a particle is said to be known if the position of the particle is known for every value of the time t. In practice, however, a motion is seldom defined by a relation between s and t. More often, the conditions of the motion will be specified by the type of acceleration that the particle possesses. For example, a freely falling body will have a constant acceleration, directed downward and equal to 32.2 ft/sec^2; a mass attached to a spring which has been stretched will have an acceleration proportional to the instantaneous elongation of the spring measured from the equilibrium position; etc. In general, the acceleration of the particle may be expressed as a function of one or several of the variables s, v, and t. In order to determine the position coordinate s in terms of t, it will thus be necessary to perform two successive integrations.

We shall consider three common classes of motion:

1. $a = f(t)$. *The Acceleration Is a Given Function of t.* Solving (11.2) for dv and substituting $f(t)$ for a, we write

$$dv = a\,dt$$
$$dv = f(t)\,dt$$

Integrating both members, we obtain the equation

$$\int dv = \int f(t)\,dt$$

which defines v in terms of t. It should be noted, however, that an arbitrary constant will be introduced as a result of the integration. This is due to the fact that there are many motions which correspond to the given acceleration $a = f(t)$. In order to uniquely define the motion of the particle, it is necessary to specify the *initial conditions* of the motion, i.e., the value v_0 of the velocity and the value s_0 of the position coordinate at $t = 0$. Replacing the indefinite integrals by *definite integrals* with lower limits corresponding to the initial conditions $t = 0$ and $v = v_0$ and upper limits corresponding to $t = t$ and $v = v$, we write

$$\int_{v_0}^{v} dv = \int_0^t f(t)\,dt$$

$$v - v_0 = \int_0^t f(t)\,dt$$

which yields v in terms of t.

We shall now solve (11.1) for ds,

$$ds = v\,dt$$

and substitute for v the expression just obtained. Both members are then integrated, the left-hand member with respect to s from $s = s_0$ to $s = s$, and the right-hand member with respect to t from $t = 0$ to $t = t$. The position coordinate s is thus obtained in terms of t; the motion is completely determined.

Two important particular cases will be studied in greater detail in Secs. 11.4 and 11.5, the case when $a = 0$, corresponding to a *uniform motion*, and the case when $a =$ constant, corresponding to a *uniformly accelerated motion.*

2. $a = f(s)$. *The Acceleration Is a Given Function of s.* Rearranging Eq. (11.4) and substituting $f(s)$ for a, we write

$$v\,dv = a\,ds$$
$$v\,dv = f(s)\,ds$$

Since each member contains only one variable, we may integrate the equation. Denoting again by v_0 and s_0, respectively, the initial values of the velocity and of the position coordinate, we obtain

$$\int_{v_0}^{v} v\,dv = \int_{s_0}^{s} f(s)\,ds$$
$$\tfrac{1}{2}v^2 - \tfrac{1}{2}v_0^2 = \int_{s_0}^{s} f(s)\,ds$$

which yields v in terms of s. We now solve (11.1) for dt,

$$dt = \frac{ds}{v}$$

and substitute for v the expression just obtained. Both members may be integrated, and the desired relation between s and t is obtained.

3. $a = f(v)$. *The Acceleration Is a Given Function of v.* We may then substitute $f(v)$ for a either in (11.2) or in (11.4) to obtain either of the following relations:

$$f(v) = \frac{dv}{dt} \qquad\qquad f(v) = v\frac{dv}{ds}$$
$$dt = \frac{dv}{f(v)} \qquad\qquad ds = \frac{v\,dv}{f(v)}$$

Integration of the first equation will yield a relation between v and t; integration of the second equation will yield a relation between v and s. Either of these relations may be used in conjunction with Eq. (11.1) to obtain the relation between s and t which characterizes the motion of the particle.

SAMPLE PROBLEM 11.1

The position of a particle which moves along a straight line is defined by the relation $s = t^3 - 6t^2 - 15t + 40$, where s is expressed in feet and t in seconds. Determine (a) the time at which the velocity will be zero, (b) the position and distance traveled by the particle at that time, (c) the acceleration of the particle at that time, (d) the distance traveled by the particle from $t = 4$ sec to $t = 6$ sec.

Solution. The equations of motion are

$$s = t^3 - 6t^2 - 15t + 40 \tag{1}$$

$$v = \frac{ds}{dt} = 3t^2 - 12t - 15 \tag{2}$$

$$a = \frac{dv}{dt} = 6t - 12 \tag{3}$$

a. **Time at Which $v = 0$.** We make $v = 0$ in (2),

$$3t^2 - 12t - 15 = 0 \qquad t = -1 \text{ sec} \qquad \text{and} \qquad t = +5 \text{ sec} \blacktriangleleft$$

Only the root $t = +5$ sec corresponds to a time after the motion has begun. For $t < 5$ sec, $v < 0$, the particle moves in the negative direction; for $t > 5$ sec, $v > 0$, the particle moves in the positive direction.

b. **Position and Distance Traveled When $v = 0$.** Carrying $t = +5$ sec into (1), we have

$$s_5 = (5)^3 - (6)(5)^2 - (15)(5) + 40 \qquad s_5 = -60 \text{ ft} \blacktriangleleft$$

The initial position at $t = 0$ was $s_0 = +40$ ft. Since $v \neq 0$ during the interval $t = 0$ to $t = 5$ sec, we have

$$\text{Distance traveled} = s_5 - s_0 = -60 \text{ ft} - 40 \text{ ft} = -100 \text{ ft}$$

$$= 100 \text{ ft in the negative direction} \blacktriangleleft$$

c. **Acceleration When $v = 0$.** We carry $t = +5$ sec into (3):

$$a_5 = (6)(5) - 12 \qquad a_5 = +18 \text{ ft/sec}^2 \blacktriangleleft$$

d. **Distance Traveled from $t = 4$ sec to $t = 6$ sec.** Since the particle moves in the negative direction from $t = 4$ sec to $t = 5$ sec and in the positive direction from $t = 5$ sec to $t = 6$ sec, we shall compute separately the distance traveled during each of these time intervals.

From $t = 4$ sec to $t = 5$ sec: $\quad s_5 = -60$ ft

$$s_4 = (4)^3 - (6)(4)^2 - (15)(4) + 40 = -52 \text{ ft}$$

$$\text{Distance traveled} = s_5 - s_4 = -60 \text{ ft} - (-52 \text{ ft}) = -8 \text{ ft}$$

$$= 8 \text{ ft in the negative direction}$$

From $t = 5$ sec to $t = 6$ sec: $\quad s_5 = -60$ ft

$$s_6 = (6)^3 - (6)(6)^2 - (15)(6) + 40 = -50 \text{ ft}$$

$$\text{Distance traveled} = s_6 - s_5 = -50 \text{ ft} - (-60 \text{ ft}) = +10 \text{ ft}$$

$$= 10 \text{ ft in the positive direction}$$

Total distance traveled from $t = 4$ sec to $t = 6$ sec is

$$8 \text{ ft} + 10 \text{ ft} = 18 \text{ ft} \blacktriangleleft$$

SAMPLE PROBLEM 11.2

A ball is thrown from the top of a tower 60 ft high, with a velocity of 40 ft/sec directed vertically upward. Knowing that the acceleration of the ball is constant and equal to 32.2 ft/sec^2 downward, determine (*a*) the velocity and elevation of the ball above the ground at any time t, (*b*) the highest elevation reached by the ball and the corresponding value of t, (*c*) the time when the ball will hit the ground and the corresponding velocity. Draw the v–t and s–t curves.

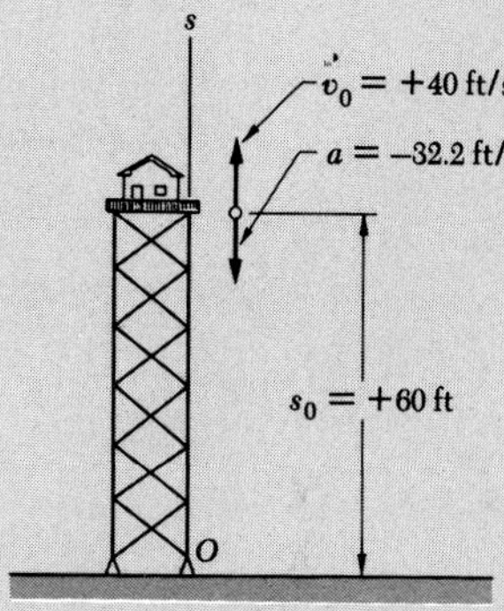

a. **Velocity and Elevation.** The s axis measuring the position coordinate (or elevation) is chosen with its origin O on the ground and its positive sense upward. The value of the acceleration and the initial values of v and s are as indicated. Substituting for a in $a = dv/dt$ and noting that, at $t = 0$, $v_0 = +40$ ft/sec, we have

$$\frac{dv}{dt} = a = -32.2$$

$$\int_{v_0=40}^{v} dv = -\int_0^t 32.2\, dt$$

$$[v]_{40}^{v} = -[32.2t]_0^t$$

$$v - 40 = -32.2t$$

$$v = 40 - 32.2t \quad (1) \blacktriangleleft$$

Substituting for v in $v = ds/dt$ and noting that, at $t = 0$, $s_0 = 60$ ft, we have

$$\frac{ds}{dt} = v = 40 - 32.2t$$

$$\int_{s_0=60}^{s} ds = \int_0^t (40 - 32.2t)\, dt$$

$$[s]_{60}^{s} = [40t - 16.1t^2]_0^t$$

$$s - 60 = 40t - 16.1t^2$$

$$s = 60 + 40t - 16.1t^2 \quad (2) \blacktriangleleft$$

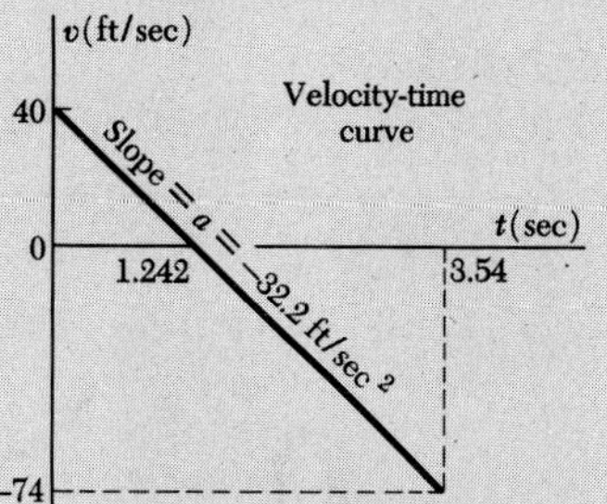

b. **Highest Elevation.** When the ball reaches its highest elevation, we have $v = 0$. Substituting into (1), we obtain

$$40 - 32.2t = 0 \qquad t = 1.242 \text{ sec} \blacktriangleleft$$

Carrying $t = 1.242$ sec into (2), we have

$$s = 60 + (40)(1.242) - (16.1)(1.242)^2 \qquad s = 84.8 \text{ ft} \blacktriangleleft$$

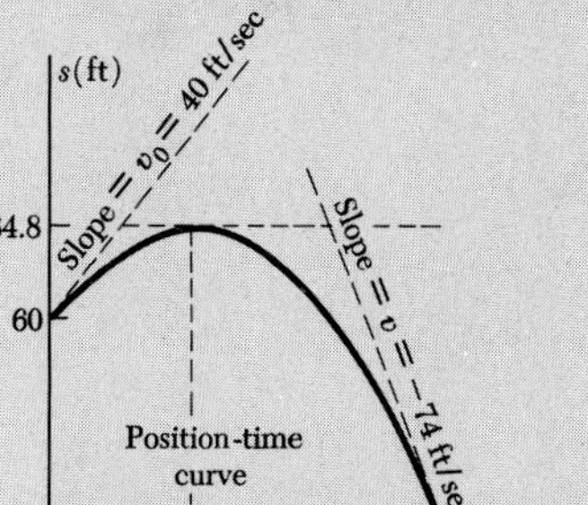

c. **Ball Hits the Ground.** When the ball hits the ground, we have $s = 0$. Substituting into (2), we obtain

$$60 + 40t - 16.1t^2 = 0 \qquad t = -1.06 \text{ sec} \quad \text{and} \quad t = +3.54 \text{ sec} \blacktriangleleft$$

Only the root $t = +3.54$ sec corresponds to a time after the motion has begun. Carrying this value of t into (1), we have

$$v = 40 - (32.2)(3.54) = -74.0 \text{ ft/sec}$$

$$v = 74.0 \text{ ft/sec} \downarrow \blacktriangleleft$$

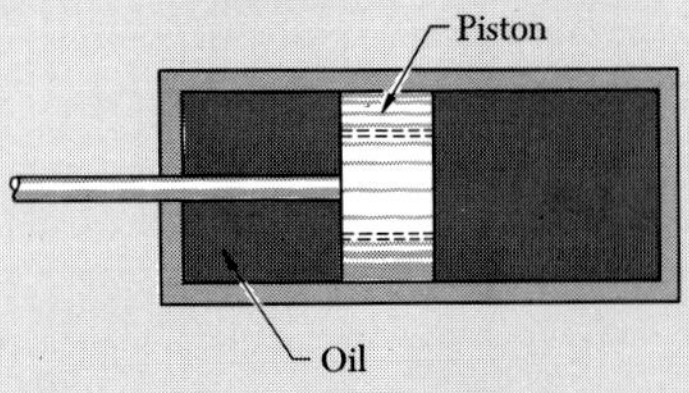

SAMPLE PROBLEM 11.3

The brake mechanism used to reduce recoil in certain types of guns consists essentially of a piston which is attached to the barrel and may move in a fixed cylinder filled with oil. As the barrel recoils with an initial velocity v_0, the piston moves and oil is forced through orifices in the piston, causing the piston and the barrel to decelerate at a rate proportional to their velocity, i.e., $a = -kv$. Express (a) v in terms of t, (b) s in terms of t, (c) v in terms of s. Draw the corresponding motion curves.

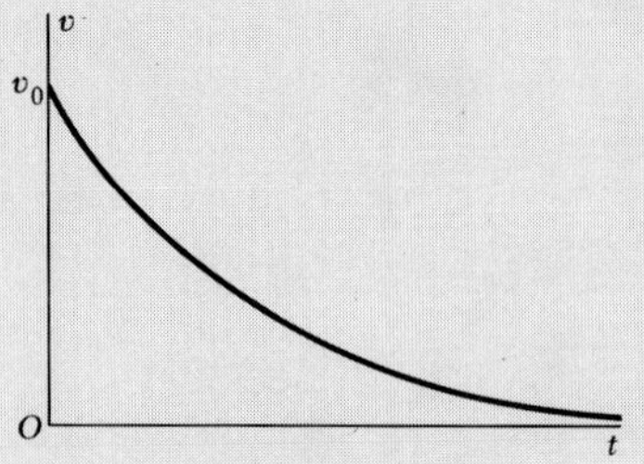

a. v **in Terms of** t. Substituting $-kv$ for a in the fundamental formula defining acceleration, $a = dv/dt$, we write

$$-kv = \frac{dv}{dt} \qquad \frac{dv}{v} = -k\,dt \qquad \int_{v_0}^{v} \frac{dv}{v} = -k \int_0^t dt$$

$$\ln \frac{v}{v_0} = -kt \qquad\qquad v = v_0 e^{-kt} \quad ◄$$

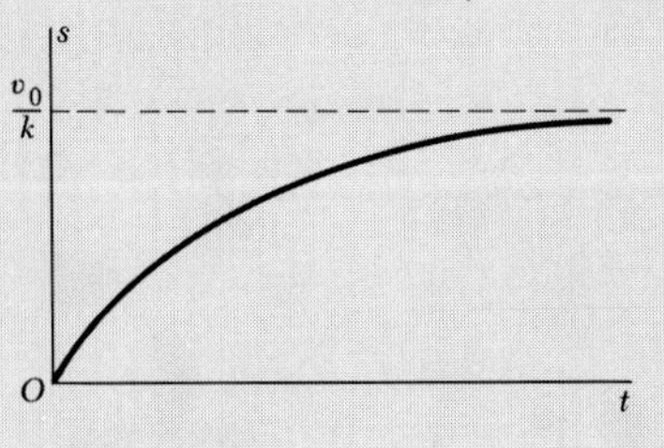

b. s **in Terms of** t. Substituting the expression just obtained for v into $v = ds/dt$, we write

$$v_0 e^{-kt} = \frac{ds}{dt}$$

$$\int_0^s ds = v_0 \int_0^t e^{-kt}\,dt$$

$$s = -\frac{v_0}{k}\left[e^{-kt}\right]_0^t = -\frac{v_0}{k}\left(e^{-kt} - 1\right)$$

$$s = \frac{v_0}{k}\left(1 - e^{-kt}\right) \quad ◄$$

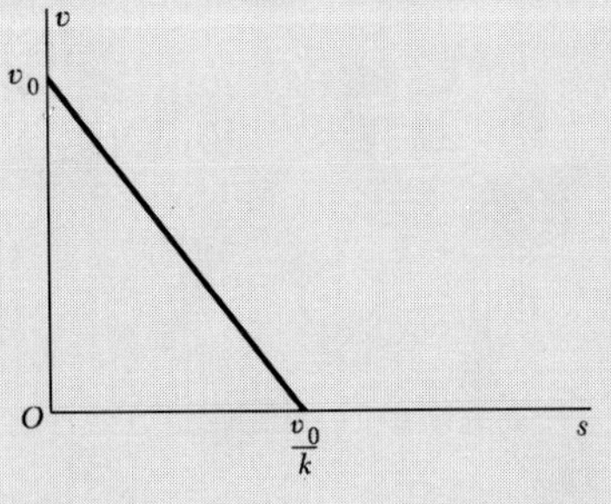

c. v **in Terms of** s. Substituting $-kv$ for a in $a = v\,dv/ds$, we write

$$-kv = v\frac{dv}{ds}$$

$$dv = -k\,ds$$

$$\int_{v_0}^{v} dv = -k\int_0^s ds$$

$$v - v_0 = -ks \qquad\qquad v = v_0 - ks \quad ◄$$

Check. Part *c* could have been solved by eliminating t from the answers obtained for parts a and b. This alternate method may be used as a check. From part a we obtain $e^{-kt} = v/v_0$; substituting in the answer of part b, we obtain

$$s = \frac{v_0}{k}(1 - e^{-kt}) = \frac{v_0}{k}\left(1 - \frac{v}{v_0}\right) \qquad v = v_0 - ks \qquad \text{(checks)}$$

PROBLEMS

11.1. The motion of a particle is defined by the relation $s = 2t^3 - 15t^2 + 36t - 10$, where s is expressed in inches and t in seconds. Determine the position, velocity, and acceleration when $t = 4$ sec.

11.2. The motion of a particle is defined by the relation $s = 2t^3 - 15t^2 + 36t - 27$, where s is expressed in inches and t in seconds. Determine the time, position, and acceleration when $v = 0$.

11.3. The motion of a particle is defined by the relation $s = t^3 - 9t^2 + 15t + 5$, where s is expressed in feet and t in seconds. Determine (*a*) when the velocity is zero, (*b*) the position and the total distance traveled when the acceleration is zero.

11.4. In Prob. 11.3 we have $v = +15$ ft/sec when $t = 0$. Determine the time, position, and total distance traveled when the velocity of the particle is again equal to $+15$ ft/sec.

11.5. The acceleration of a particle is defined by the relation $a = -5$ ft/sec^2. If $v = +20$ ft/sec and $s = 0$ when $t = 0$, determine the velocity, position, and total distance traveled when $t = 6$ sec.

11.6. The acceleration of a particle is directly proportional to the time t. At $t = 0$, the velocity of the particle is $v = -9$ ft/sec. Knowing that both the velocity and the position coordinate are zero when $t = 3$ sec, write the equations of motion for the particle.

11.7. The acceleration of a particle is defined by the relation $a = kt^2$. (*a*) Knowing that $v = -32$ ft/sec when $t = 0$ and that $v = +32$ ft/sec when $t = 4$ sec, determine the constant k. (*b*) Write the equations of motion knowing also that $s = 0$ when $t = 4$ sec.

11.8. The acceleration of a particle is defined by the relation $a = 9 - 3t^2$. The particle starts at $t = 0$ with $v = 0$ and $s = -3$ ft. Determine (*a*) the time when the velocity is again zero, (*b*) the position and velocity when $t = 4$ sec, (*c*) the total distance traveled by the particle from $t = 0$ to $t = 4$ sec.

11.9. The acceleration of an oscillating particle is defined by the relation $a = -ks$. Find the value of k such that $v = 15$ in./sec when $s = 0$ and $s = 3$ in. when $v = 0$.

11.10. The acceleration of a particle is defined by the relation $a = 25 - 3s^2$, where a is expressed in ft/sec^2 and s in feet. The particle starts with no initial velocity at the position $s = 0$. Determine (*a*) the velocity when $s = 2$ ft, (*b*) the position where the velocity is again zero, (*c*) the position where the velocity is maximum.

11.11. The acceleration of a particle moving in a straight line is directed toward a fixed point O and is inversely proportional to the distance of the particle from O. At $t = 0$, the particle is 2 ft to the right of O, has a velocity of 4 ft/sec to the right, and has an acceleration of 3 ft/sec^2 to the left. Determine (*a*) the velocity of the particle when it is 3 ft away from O, (*b*) the position of the particle at which its velocity is zero.

11.12. The acceleration of a particle is defined by the relation $a = -ks^{-2}$. The particle starts with no initial velocity at $s = 10$ in., and it is observed that its velocity is 4 in./sec when $s = 5$ in. Determine (*a*) the value of k, (*b*) the velocity of the particle when $s = 1$ in.

11.13. The acceleration of a particle is defined by the relation $a = -0.002v^2$, where a is the acceleration in ft/sec^2 and v is the velocity in ft/sec. If the particle is given an initial velocity v_0, find the distance it will travel (*a*) before its velocity drops to half the initial value, (*b*) before it comes to rest.

11.14. The acceleration of a particle is defined by the relation $a = -20v$, where a is expressed in ft/sec^2 and v in ft/sec. Knowing that at $t = 0$ the velocity is 200 ft/sec, determine (*a*) the distance the particle will travel before coming to rest, (*b*) the time required for the particle to come to rest, (*c*) the time required for the velocity of the particle to be reduced to 1 per cent of its initial value.

11.15. The acceleration of a particle is defined by the relation $a = -kv^{1.5}$. The particle starts at $t = 0$ and $s = 0$ with an initial velocity v_0. (*a*) Show that the velocity and position coordinate at any time t are related by the equation $s/t = \sqrt{v_0 v}$. (*b*) Determine the value of k, knowing that for $v_0 = 100$ ft/sec the particle comes to rest after traveling 5 ft.

11.16. The acceleration of a particle falling through the atmosphere is defined by the relation $a = g(1 - k^2v^2)$. Knowing that the particle starts at $t = 0$ and $s = 0$ with no initial velocity, (*a*) show that the velocity at any time t is $v = (1/k) \tanh kgt$, (*b*) write an equation defining the velocity for any value of s. (*c*) Why is $v_t = 1/k$ called the terminal velocity?

11.17. The position of an oscillating particle is defined by the relation $s = A \sin (pt + \phi)$. Denoting the velocity and position coordinate when $t = 0$ by v_0 and s_0 respectively, show (*a*) that $\tan \phi = s_0 p/v_0$, (*b*) that the maximum value of the position coordinate is

$$A = \sqrt{s_0^2 + (v_0/p)^2}$$

11.18. The acceleration of a particle is defined by the relation $a = k \sin \pi t/T$. Knowing that both the velocity and the position coordinate of the particle are zero when $t = 0$, determine (*a*) the equations of motion, (*b*) the maximum velocity, (*c*) the position at $t = 2T$, (*d*) the average velocity during the interval $t = 0$ to $t = 2T$.

11.19. The acceleration due to gravity of a particle falling toward the earth is $a = -gR^2/r^2$, where r is the distance from the *center* of the earth to the particle, R is the radius of the earth, and g is the acceleration due to gravity at the surface of the earth. Derive an expression for the *escape velocity*, i.e., for the minimum velocity with which a particle should be projected vertically upward from the surface of the earth if it is not to return to the earth. (*Hint.* $v = 0$ for $r = \infty$.)

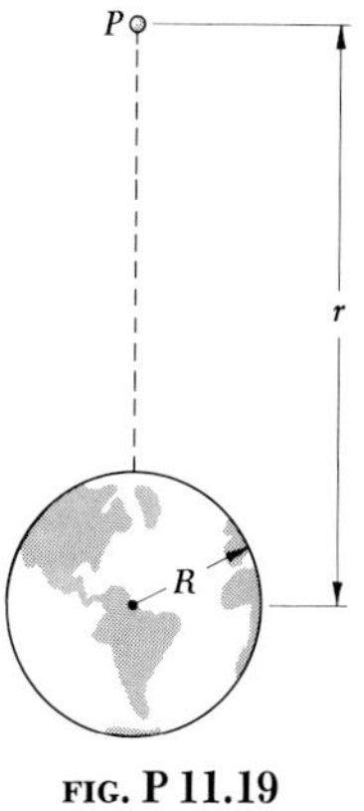

FIG. P 11.19

11.20. A more accurate expression for the acceleration due to gravity is

$$g = \frac{32.2}{\left(1 + \dfrac{y}{20.9 \times 10^6}\right)^2}$$

where g is expressed in ft/sec² and y is the altitude in feet. Using this value of g, compute the height reached by a bullet fired vertically upward with the following initial velocities: (*a*) 1,000 ft/sec, (*b*) 10,000 ft/sec, (*c*) 36,700 ft/sec.

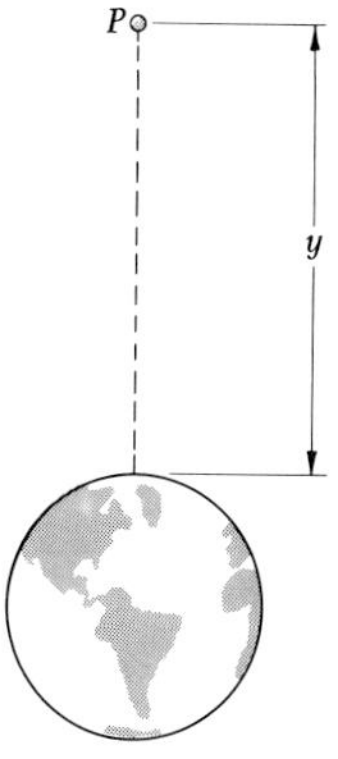

FIG. P 11.20

***11.21.** When a package is dropped on a rigid surface, the acceleration of its cushioned contents may be defined by the relation $a = -k \tan \pi s/2L$, where L is the distance through which the cushioning material can be compressed. Denoting by v_0 the velocity when $s = 0$, show that $v^2 = v_0^2 + (4kL/\pi) \ln \cos \pi s/2L$. If $k = 1{,}000$ ft/sec² and $L = 12$ in., compute the initial velocity v_0 for which the maximum value of the position coordinate s is (*a*) 6 in., (*b*) 12 in.

***11.22.** A particle is released from rest at a distance R above the surface of the earth. Using the expression for the acceleration due to gravity given in Prob. 11.19, determine (*a*) the velocity of the particle as it strikes the earth, (*b*) the time required for it to fall to the surface of the earth. (Radius of earth $= R = 3{,}960$ miles, g = 32.2 ft/sec².)

***11.23.** Using the expression for the acceleration due to gravity given in Prob. 11.19, derive an expression for the time required for a particle to reach the surface of the earth if it is released with no velocity at a distance r_0 from the center of the earth.

11.4. Uniform Rectilinear Motion. This is a type of straight-line motion which is frequently encountered in practical applications. In this motion, the acceleration a of the particle is zero for every value of t. The velocity v is therefore constant, and Eq. (11.1) becomes

$$\frac{ds}{dt} = v = \text{constant}$$

The position coordinate s is obtained by integrating this equation. Denoting by s_0 the initial value of s, we write

$$\int_{s_0}^{s} ds = v\int_0^t dt$$
$$s - s_0 = vt$$
$$s = s_0 + vt \tag{11.5}$$

This equation may be used *only if the velocity of the particle is known to be constant.*

11.5. Uniformly Accelerated Rectilinear Motion. This is another common type of motion. In this motion, the acceleration a of the particle is constant, and Eq. (11.2) becomes

$$\frac{dv}{dt} = a = \text{constant}$$

The velocity v of the particle is obtained by integrating this equation,

$$\int_{v_0}^{v} dv = a\int_0^t dt$$
$$v - v_0 = at$$
$$v = v_0 + at \tag{11.6}$$

where v_0 is the initial velocity. Substituting for v into (11.1), we write

$$\frac{ds}{dt} = v_0 + at$$

Denoting by s_0 the initial value of s and integrating, we have

$$\int_{s_0}^{s} ds = \int_0^t (v_0 + at)\, dt$$
$$s - s_0 = v_0t + \tfrac{1}{2}at^2$$
$$s = s_0 + v_0t + \tfrac{1}{2}at^2 \tag{11.7}$$

We may also use Eq. (11.4) and write

$$v\frac{dv}{ds} = a = \text{constant}$$
$$v\, dv = a\, ds$$

Integrating both sides, we obtain

$$\int_{v_0}^{v} v\, dv = a\int_{s_0}^{s} ds$$
$$\tfrac{1}{2}(v^2 - v_0^2) = a(s - s_0)$$
$$v^2 = v_0^2 + 2a(s - s_0) \tag{11.8}$$

The three equations we have derived provide useful relations between position coordinate, velocity, and time in the case of a uniformly accelerated motion, as soon as appropriate values have been substituted for a, v_0, and s_0. The origin O of the s axis should first be defined and a positive direction chosen along the axis; this direction will be used to determine the signs of a, v_0, and s_0. Equation (11.6) relates v and t and should be used when the value of v corresponding to a given value of t is desired, or inversely. Equation (11.7) relates s and t; Eq. (11.8) relates v and s. An important application of uniformly accelerated motion is the motion of a *freely falling body*. The acceleration of a freely falling body (usually denoted by g) is equal to 32.2 ft/sec^2.

It is important to keep in mind that the three equations above may be used *only when the acceleration of the particle is known to be constant.* If the acceleration of the particle is variable, its motion should be determined from the fundamental equations (11.1) to (11.4), according to the methods outlined in Sec. 11.3.

11.6. Motion of Several Particles. When several particles move independently along the same line, independent equations of motion may be written for each particle. Whenever possible, time should be recorded from the same initial instant for all particles, and displacements should be measured from the same origin and in the same direction. In other words, a single clock and a single measuring tape should be used.

Relative Motion of Two Particles. Consider two particles A and B moving along the same straight line (Fig. 11.7). If the position coordinates s_A and s_B are measured from the same origin, the difference $s_B - s_A$ defines the *relative position coordinate of B with respect to* A and is denoted by $s_{B/A}$. We write

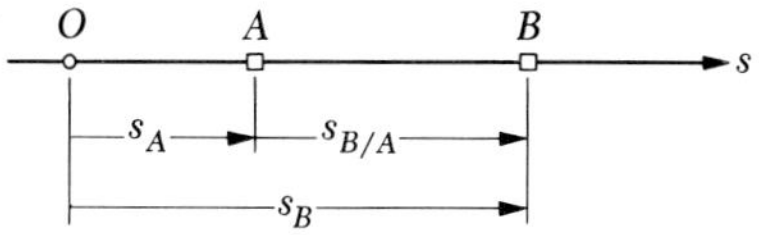

FIG. 11.7

$$s_{B/A} = s_B - s_A \qquad \text{or} \qquad s_B = s_A + s_{B/A} \tag{11.9}$$

A positive sign for $s_{B/A}$ means that B is to the right of A, a negative sign that B is to the left of A, regardless of the position of A and B with respect to the origin.

The rate of change of $s_{B/A}$ is known as the *relative velocity of B with respect to* A and is denoted by $v_{B/A}$. Differentiating (11.9) we write

$$v_{B/A} = v_B - v_A \qquad \text{or} \qquad v_B = v_A + v_{B/A} \tag{11.10}$$

A positive sign for $v_{B/A}$ means that B is *observed from* A to move in the positive direction; a negative sign, that it is observed to move in the negative direction.

The rate of change of $v_{B/A}$ is known as the *relative acceleration of B with respect to A* and is denoted by $a_{B/A}$. Differentiating (11.10), we obtain

$$a_{B/A} = a_B - a_A \qquad \text{or} \qquad a_B = a_A + a_{B/A} \qquad (11.11)$$

Dependent Motions. Sometimes, the position of a particle will depend upon the position of another or of several other particles. The motions are then said to be dependent. For example, the position of block B in Fig. 11.8 depends upon the position of block A. Since the rope $ACDEFG$ is of constant length, and since the lengths of the portions of rope CD and EF wrapped around the pulleys remain constant, it follows that the sum of the lengths of the segments AC, DE, and FG is constant. Observing that the length of the segment AC differs from s_A only by a constant, and that, similarly, the lengths of the segments DE and FG differ from s_B only by a constant, we write

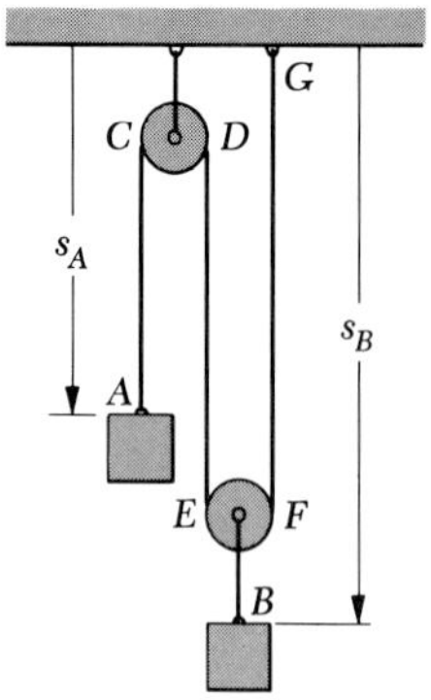

FIG. 11.8

$$s_A + 2s_B = \text{constant}$$

Since only one of the two coordinates s_A and s_B may be chosen arbitrarily, we say that the system shown in Fig. 11.8 has *one degree of freedom.* From the relation between the position coordinates s_A and s_B, it follows that if s_A is given an increment Δs_A, i.e., if block A is lowered by an amount Δs_A, the coordinate s_B will receive an increment $\Delta s_B = -\frac{1}{2}\Delta s_A$, i.e., block B will rise by half the same amount; this may easily be checked directly from Fig. 11.8.

In the case of the three blocks of Fig. 11.9, we may again observe that the length of the rope which passes over the pulleys is constant, and thus that the following relation must be satisfied by the position coordinates of the three blocks:

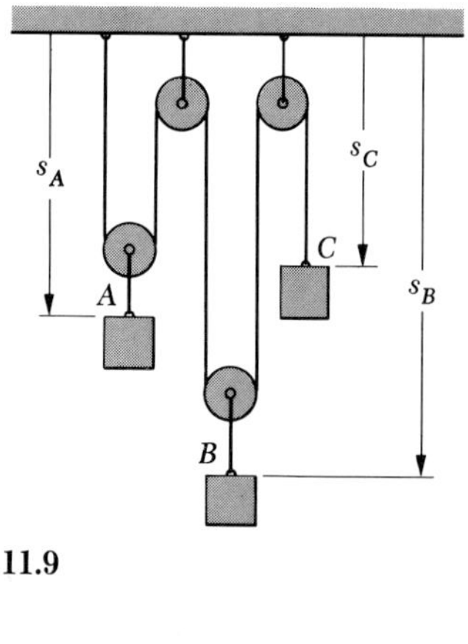

FIG. 11.9

$$2s_A + 2s_B + s_C = \text{constant}$$

Since two of the coordinates may be chosen arbitrarily, we say that the system shown in Fig. 11.9 has *two degrees of freedom.*

When the relation existing between the position coordinates of several particles is *linear,* a similar relation holds between the velocities and between the accelerations of the particles. In the case of the blocks of Fig. 11.9, for instance, we differentiate twice the equation obtained and write

$$2\frac{ds_A}{dt} + 2\frac{ds_B}{dt} + \frac{ds_C}{dt} = 0 \qquad \text{or} \qquad 2v_A + 2v_B + v_C = 0$$

$$2\frac{dv_A}{dt} + 2\frac{dv_B}{dt} + \frac{dv_C}{dt} = 0 \qquad \text{or} \qquad 2a_A + 2a_B + a_C = 0$$

SAMPLE PROBLEM 11.4

A ball is thrown vertically upward from the 40-ft level in an elevator shaft, with an initial velocity of 50 ft/sec. At the same instant an open-platform elevator passes the 10-ft level, moving upward with a constant velocity of 5 ft/sec. Determine (*a*) when and where the ball will hit the elevator, (*b*) the relative velocity of the ball with respect to the elevator when the ball hits the elevator.

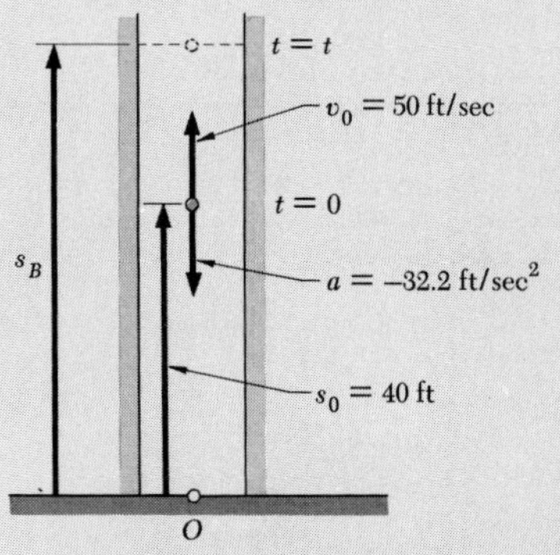

Motion of Ball. Since the ball has a constant acceleration, its motion is *uniformly accelerated.* Placing the origin O at the ground level and choosing arbitrarily the positive direction upward, we find that the initial position is $s_0 = +40$ ft, the initial velocity is $v_0 = +50$ ft/sec, and the acceleration is $a = -32.2$ ft/sec^2. Substituting these values in the equations for uniformly accelerated motion, we write

$$v_B = v_0 + at \qquad v_B = 50 - 32.2t \qquad (1)$$

$$s_B = s_0 + v_0 t + \tfrac{1}{2}at^2 \qquad s_B = 40 + 50t - 16.1t^2 \qquad (2)$$

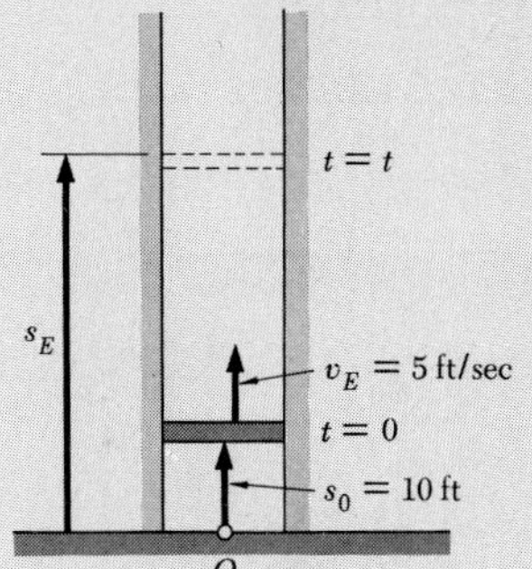

Motion of Elevator. Since the elevator has a constant velocity, its motion is *uniform.* Again placing the origin O at the ground level and choosing the positive direction upward, we note that $s_0 = +10$ ft and write

$$v_E = +5 \text{ ft/sec} \qquad (3)$$

$$s_E = s_0 + v_E t \qquad s_E = 10 + 5t \qquad (4)$$

Ball Hits Elevator. We first note that the same time t and the same origin O were used in writing the equations of motion of both the ball and the elevator. We see from the figure that, when the ball hits the elevator,

$$s_E = s_B \qquad (5)$$

Substituting for s_E and s_B from (2) and (4) into (5), we have

$$10 + 5t = 40 + 50t - 16.1t^2$$

$$t = -0.56 \text{ sec} \quad \text{and} \quad t = +3.35 \text{ sec} \blacktriangleleft$$

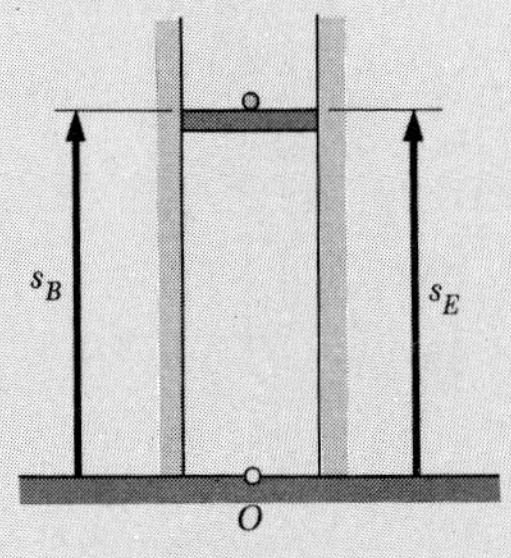

Only the root $t = 3.35$ sec corresponds to a time after the motion has begun. Substituting this value into (4), we have

$$s_E = 10 + (5)(3.35) = 26.7 \text{ ft}$$

$$\text{Elevation from ground} = 26.7 \text{ ft} \blacktriangleleft$$

The relative velocity of the ball with respect to the elevator is

$$v_{B/E} = v_B - v_E = (50 - 32.2t) - 5 = 45 - 32.2t$$

When the ball hits the elevator at time $t = 3.35$ sec, we have

$$v_{B/E} = 45 - (32.2)(3.35) \qquad v_{B/E} = -62.9 \text{ ft/sec} \blacktriangleleft$$

The negative sign means that the ball is observed from the elevator to be moving in the negative sense (downward).

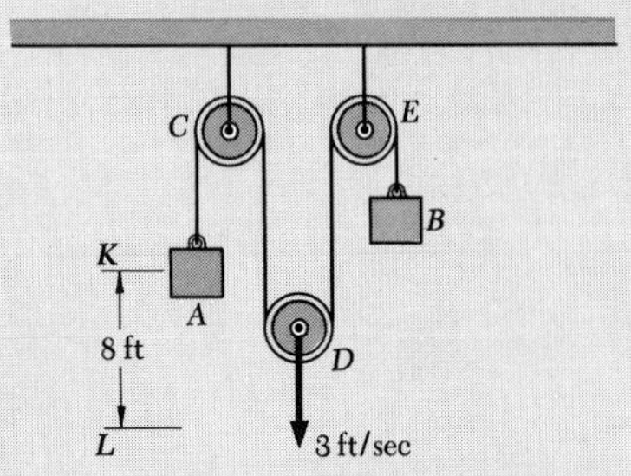

SAMPLE PROBLEM 11.5

Two blocks A and B are connected by a cord passing over three pulleys C, D, and E as shown. Pulleys C and E are fixed, while D is pulled downward with a constant velocity of 3 ft/sec. At $t = 0$, block A starts moving downward from the position K with a constant acceleration and no initial velocity. Knowing that the velocity of block A is 12 ft/sec as it passes through point L, determine the change in elevation, the velocity, and the acceleration of block B when A passes through L.

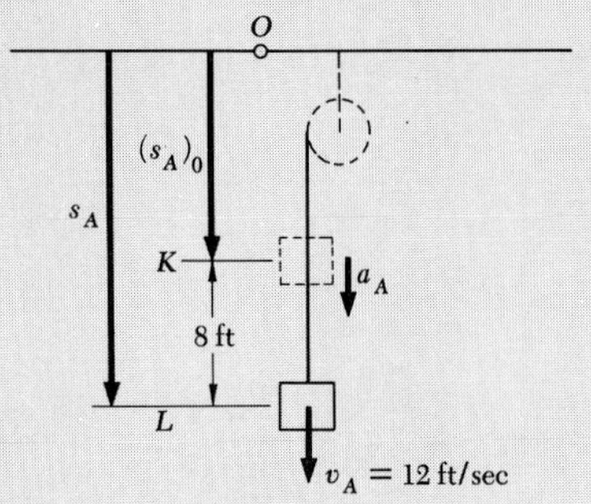

Motion of Block A. We place the origin O at the horizontal surface and choose the positive direction downward. We observe that when $t = 0$, block A is at position K and $(v_A)_0 = 0$. Since $v_A = 12$ ft/sec and $s_A - (s_A)_0 = 8$ ft when the block passes through L, we write

$$v_A^2 = (v_A)_0^2 + 2a_A[s_A - (s_A)_0] \qquad (12)^2 = 0 + 2a_A(8)$$
$$a_A = 9 \text{ ft/sec}^2$$

The time at which block A reaches point L is obtained by writing

$$v_A = (v_A)_0 + a_A t \qquad 12 = 0 + 9t \qquad t = 1.333 \text{ sec}$$

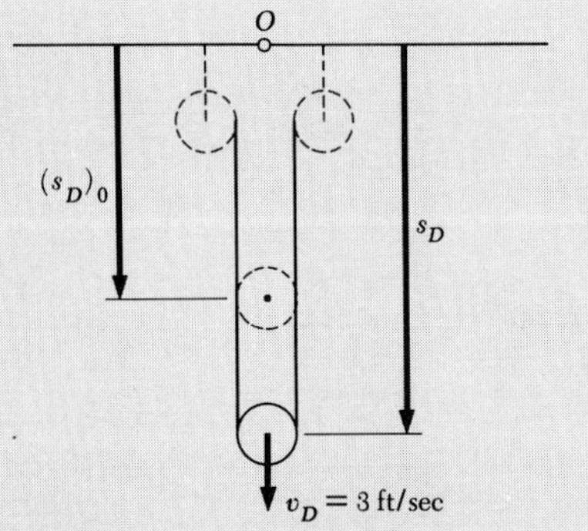

Motion of Pulley D. Recalling that the positive direction is downward, we write

$$a_D = 0 \qquad v_D = 3 \text{ ft/sec} \qquad s_D = (s_D)_0 + v_D t = (s_D)_0 + 3t$$

When block A reaches L, at $t = 1.333$ sec, we have

$$s_D = (s_D)_0 + (3)(1.333) = (s_D)_0 + 4$$

Thus, $\qquad s_D - (s_D)_0 = 4 \text{ ft}$

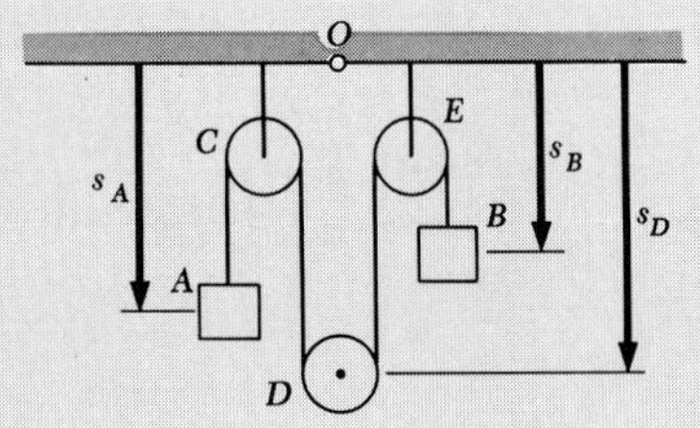

Motion of Block B. We note that the total length of cord $ACDEB$ differs from the quantity $(s_A + 2s_D + s_B)$ only by a constant. Since the cord length is constant during the motion, this quantity must also remain constant. Thus considering the times $t = 0$ and $t = 1.333$ sec, we write

$$s_A + 2s_D + s_B = (s_A)_0 + 2(s_D)_0 + (s_B)_0 \qquad (1)$$
$$[s_A - (s_A)_0] + 2[s_D - (s_D)_0] + [s_B - (s_B)_0] = 0 \qquad (2)$$

But we know that $s_A - (s_A)_0 = 8$ ft and $s_D - (s_D)_0 = 4$ ft; substituting these values in (2), we find

$$8 + 2(4) + [s_B - (s_B)_0] = 0 \qquad s_B - (s_B)_0 = -16 \text{ ft}$$

Thus the change in elevation of B is $\qquad$ 16 ft ↑ ◄

Differentiating (1) twice, we obtain equations relating the velocities and the accelerations of A, B, and D. Substituting for the velocities and accelerations of A and D at $t = 1.333$ sec, we have

$$v_A + 2v_D + v_B = 0: \qquad 12 + 2(3) + v_B = 0$$
$$v_B = -18 \text{ ft/sec} \qquad v_B = 18 \text{ ft/sec} \uparrow \blacktriangleleft$$
$$a_A + 2a_D + a_B = 0: \qquad 9 + 2(0) + a_B = 0$$
$$a_B = -9 \text{ ft/sec}^2 \qquad a_B = 9 \text{ ft/sec}^2 \uparrow \blacktriangleleft$$

PROBLEMS

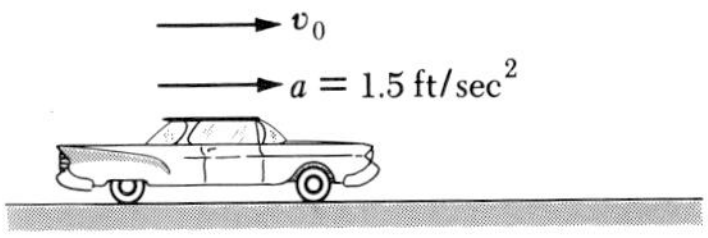

FIG. P 11.24

11.24. An automobile travels 600 ft in 20 sec while being accelerated at a constant rate of 1.5 ft/sec^2. Determine (*a*) its initial velocity, (*b*) its final velocity, (*c*) the distance traveled during the first 10 sec.

11.25. A stone is released from an elevator moving up at a speed of 15 ft/sec and reaches the bottom of the shaft in 3 sec. (*a*) How high was the elevator when the stone was released? (*b*) With what speed does the stone strike the bottom of the shaft?

11.26. A man jumps from a 20-ft cliff with no initial velocity. (*a*) How long does it take him to reach the ground, and with what velocity does he hit the ground? (*b*) If this were to happen on the moon, where $g = 5.31$ ft/sec^2, what would be the values obtained for the time and velocity? (*c*) If a motion picture were taken on the earth, but if the scene were supposed to take place on the moon, how many frames per second should be used so that the scene would appear realistic when projected at the standard speed of 24 frames per second?

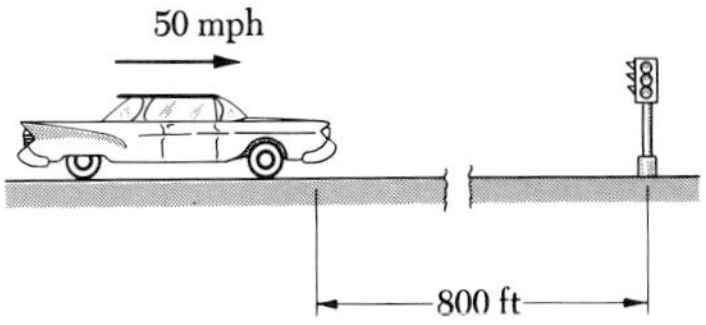

FIG. P 11.27

11.27. A motorist is traveling at 50 mph when he observes that a traffic light 800 ft ahead of him turns red. The traffic light is timed to stay red for 15 sec. If the motorist wishes to pass the light without stopping just as it turns green again, determine (*a*) the required uniform deceleration of the car, (*b*) the speed of the car as it passes the light.

11.28. (*a*) A stone is dropped with no initial velocity into a well. The sound of the stone hitting the water is heard 4.7 sec later. Knowing that the speed of sound is 1,100 ft/sec, determine the vertical distance from the top of the well to the water surface. (*b*) A second stone is thrown downward into the well with an initial velocity v_0. If the sound of the second stone hitting the water is heard in 4.3 sec, determine the initial velocity of the second stone.

11.29. An open-platform elevator is moving down a mine shaft at a constant velocity v_e when the elevator platform hits and dislodges a stone. Assuming that the stone starts falling with no initial velocity, (*a*) show that the stone will hit the platform with a relative velocity of magnitude v_e. (*b*) If $v_e = 15$ ft/sec, determine when and where the stone will hit the elevator platform.

11.30. Two automobiles *A* and *B* traveling in the same direction in adjacent lanes are stopped at a highway traffic signal. As the signal turns green, automobile *A* accelerates at the constant rate of 3 ft/sec^2. Two seconds later automobile *B* starts and accelerates at the constant rate of 4 ft/sec^2. Determine (*a*) when and where *B* will overtake *A*, (*b*) the speed of each automobile at that time.

11.31. Drops of water are observed to drip from a faucet at uniform intervals of time. As any drop *B* begins to fall freely, the preceding drop *A* has already fallen 1 ft. Determine the distance drop *A* will have fallen by the time the distance between *A* and *B* will have increased to 3 ft.

***11.32.** Drops of water fall down a mine shaft at the uniform rate of one drop per second. A mine elevator moving up the shaft at 30 ft/sec is struck by a drop of water when it is 300 ft below ground level. When and where will the next drop of water strike the elevator?

***11.33.** Solve Prob. 11.32 assuming that the elevator is moving *down* the shaft at 30 ft/sec.

11.34. The elevator shown in the figure moves upward at the constant velocity of 12 ft/sec. Determine (*a*) the velocity of the cable *C*, (*b*) the velocity of the counterweight *W*, (*c*) the relative velocity of the cable *C* with respect to the elevator, (*d*) the relative velocity of the counterweight *W* with respect to the elevator.

11.35. The elevator shown starts from rest and moves upward with a constant acceleration. If the counterweight *W* moves through 30 ft in 5 sec, determine (*a*) the accelerations of the elevator and the cable *C*, (*b*) the velocity of the elevator after 5 sec.

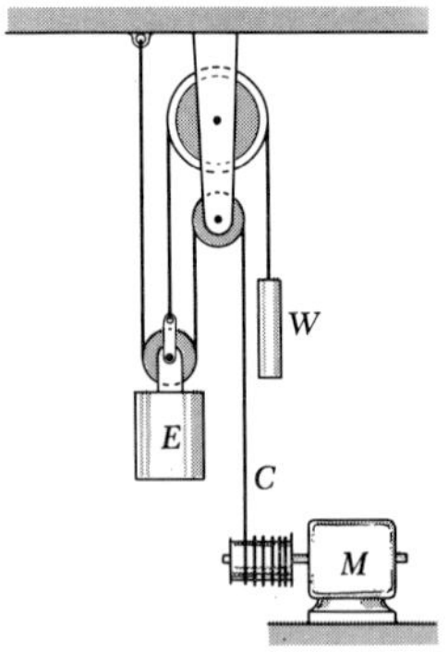

FIG. P 11.34 AND P 11.35

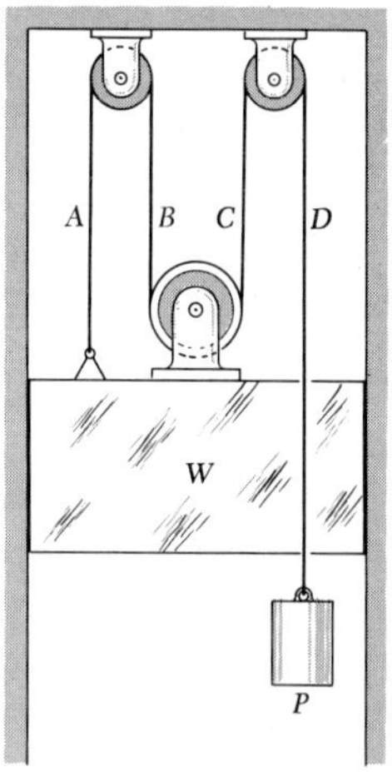

FIG. P 11.36 AND P 11.37

11.36. The slider block *W* moves downward at a constant velocity of 12 in./sec. Find (*a*) the velocities of portions *A*, *B*, *C*, and *D* of the cable, (*b*) the relative velocity of *P* with respect to the weight *W*, (*c*) the relative velocity of portion *B* of the cable with respect to portion *C*.

11.37. The slider block *W* starts from rest and moves downward with a constant acceleration. If after 5 sec the relative velocity of *P* with respect to *W* is 30 in./sec, determine (*a*) the accelerations of *W* and *P*, (*b*) the velocity and position of *W* after 4 sec.

11.38. Blocks A and B start from rest and move to the right with the following accelerations: $a_A = 3$ in./sec^2 and $a_B = 2t$ in./sec^2. Determine (*a*) when the velocity of C will again be zero, (*b*) the corresponding position of each block.

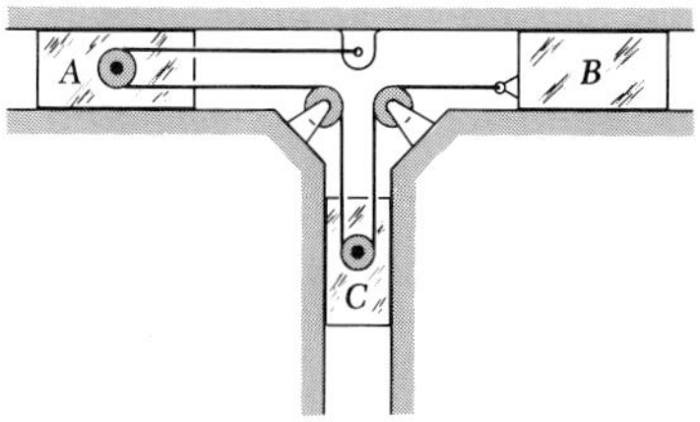

FIG. P 11.38 AND P 11.40

11.39. (*a*) Choosing the positive sense downward for each block, express the velocity of C in terms of the velocities of A and B. (*b*) Knowing that both blocks B and C start from rest and move downward with the respective accelerations $a_B = 4$ in./sec^2 and $a_C = 3$ in./sec^2, determine the position and velocity of A after 2 sec.

11.40. The three blocks shown move with constant velocities. Find the velocities of A and B, knowing that C moves downward with a velocity of 10 in./sec and that B is observed from A to move to the right with a relative velocity of 4 in./sec.

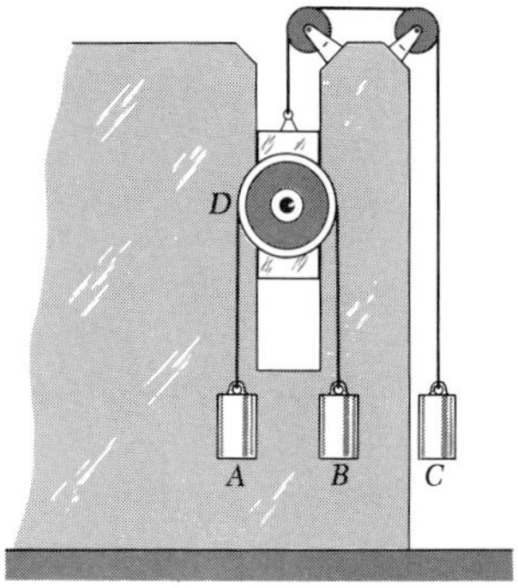

FIG. P 11.39 AND P 11.41

11.41. The three blocks shown move with constant velocities. Find the velocity of each block, knowing that the relative velocity of A with respect to C is 12 in./sec downward and that the relative velocity of B with respect to C is 4 in./sec upward.

11.42. The three blocks of Fig. 11.9 move with constant velocities. Find the velocity of each block, knowing that C is observed from B to move upward with a relative velocity of 7 ft/sec and A is observed from B to move downward with a relative velocity of 6 ft/sec.

11.7. Graphical Solution of Rectilinear-motion Problems. It was observed in Sec. 11.2 that the fundamental formulas

$$v = \frac{ds}{dt} \qquad \text{and} \qquad a = \frac{dv}{dt}$$

have a geometrical significance. The first formula expresses that the velocity at any instant is equal to the slope of the s–t curve at the same instant (Fig. 11.10). The second formula expresses that the acceleration is equal to the slope of the v–t curve. These two properties may be used to derive graphically the v–t and a–t curves of a motion when the s–t curve is known.

Integrating the two fundamental formulas from a time t_1 to a time t_2, we write

$$s_2 - s_1 = \int_{t_1}^{t_2} v\,dt \qquad \text{and} \qquad v_2 - v_1 = \int_{t_1}^{t_2} a\,dt \qquad (11.12)$$

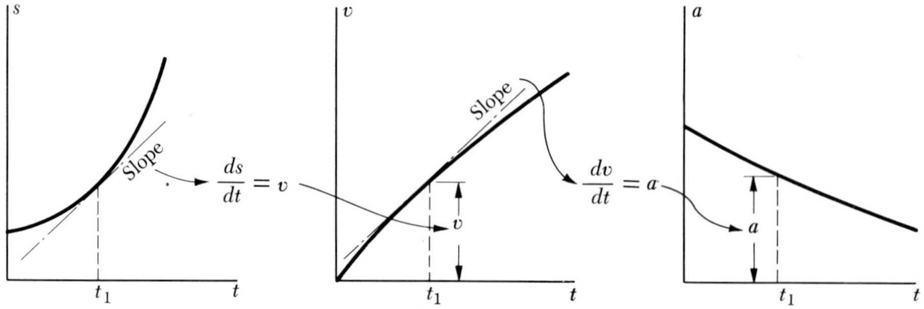

FIG. 11.10

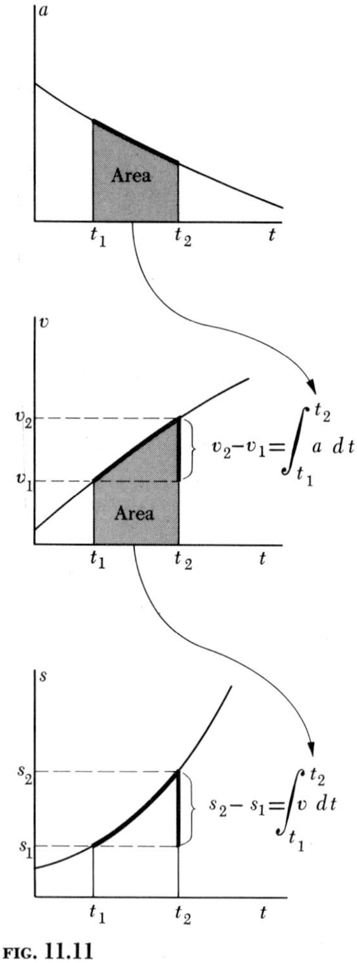

FIG. 11.11

The first formula expresses that the area measured under the v–t curve from t_1 to t_2 is equal to the change in s during that time interval (Fig. 11.11). The second formula expresses similarly that the area measured under the a–t curve from t_1 to t_2 is equal to the change in v during that time interval. These two properties may be used to determine graphically the s–t curve of a motion when its v–t curve or its a–t curve is known (see Sample Prob. 11.6).

Graphical solutions are particularly useful when the motion considered is defined from experimental data and when s, v, and a are not analytical functions of t. They may also be used to advantage when the motion consists of distinct parts and when its analysis requires writing a different equation for each of its parts. When using a graphical solution, however, one should be careful to note (1) that the area under the v-t curve measures the *change in* s, not s itself, and, similarly, that the area under the a-t curve measures the change in v; (2) that, while an area above the t axis corresponds to an increase in s or v, an area located below the t axis measures a decrease in s or v.

It will be useful to remember, in drawing motion curves, that, if the velocity is constant, it will be represented by a horizontal straight line; the position coordinate s will then be a linear function of t and will be represented by an oblique straight line. If the acceleration is constant and different from zero, it will be represented by a horizontal straight line; v will then be a linear function of t, represented by an oblique straight line; and s will be expressed as a second-degree polynomial in t, represented by a parabola. If the acceleration is a linear function of t, the velocity and the position coordinate will be equal, respectively, to second-degree and third-degree polynomials; a is then represented by an oblique straight line, v by a parabola, and s by a cubic. In general, if the acceleration is a polynomial of degree n in t, the velocity will be a polynomial of degree $n + 1$ and the position coordinate a polynomial of degree $n + 2$; these polynomials are represented by motion curves of a corresponding degree.

***11.8. Other Graphical Methods.** An alternate graphical solution may be used to determine directly from the a–t curve the position of a particle at a given instant. Denoting respectively by s_0 and v_0 the values of s and v at $t = 0$, by s_1 and v_1 their values at $t = t_1$, and observing that the area under the v–t curve may be divided into a rectangle of area $v_0 t_1$ and horizontal differential elements of area $(t_1 - t)\,dv$ (Fig. 11.12*a*), we write

$$s_1 - s_0 = \text{area under } v\text{–}t \text{ curve} = v_0 t_1 + \int_{v_0}^{v_1} (t_1 - t)\,dv$$

Substituting $dv = a\,dt$ in the integral, we obtain

$$s_1 - s_0 = v_0 t_1 + \int_0^{t_1} (t_1 - t) a\,dt$$

Referring to Fig. 11.12*b*, we note that the integral represents the first moment of the area under the a–t curve with respect to the line $t = t_1$ bounding the area on the right. This method of solution is known, therefore, as the *moment-area method.* If the abscissa $\bar{t}$ of the centroid C of the area is known, the position coordinate s_1 may be obtained by writing

$$s_1 = s_0 + v_0 t_1 + (\text{area under } a\text{–}t \text{ curve})(t_1 - \bar{t}) \qquad (11.13)$$

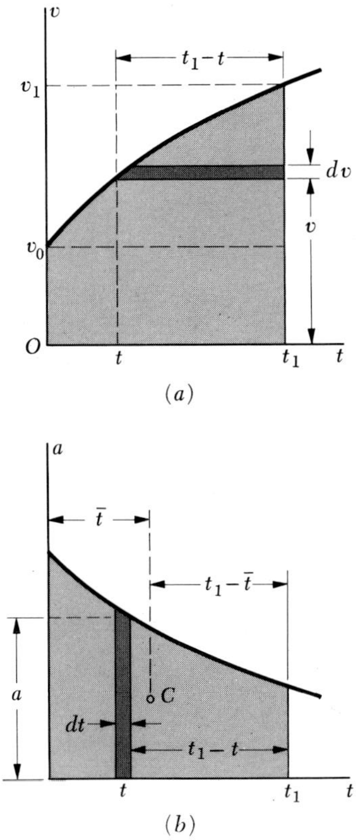

FIG. 11.12

If the area under the a–t curve is a composite area, the last term in (11.13) may be obtained by multiplying each component area by the distance from its centroid to the line $t = t_1$. Areas above the t axis should be considered as positive and areas below the t axis as negative.

Another type of motion curve, the v–s curve, is sometimes used. If such a curve has been plotted (Fig. 11.13), the acceleration a may be obtained at any time by drawing the normal to the curve and *measuring the subnormal BC.* Indeed, observing that the angle between AC and AB is equal to the angle θ between the horizontal and the tangent at A (the slope of which is $\tan\theta = dv/ds$), we write

$$BC = AB \tan\theta = v\frac{dv}{ds}$$

and thus, recalling formula (11.4),

$$BC = a$$

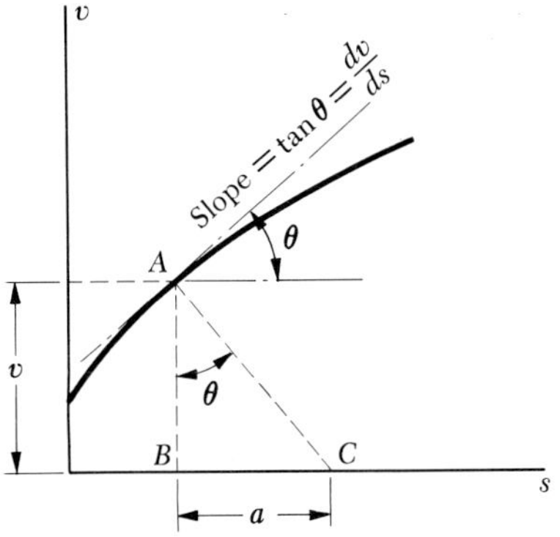

FIG. 11.13

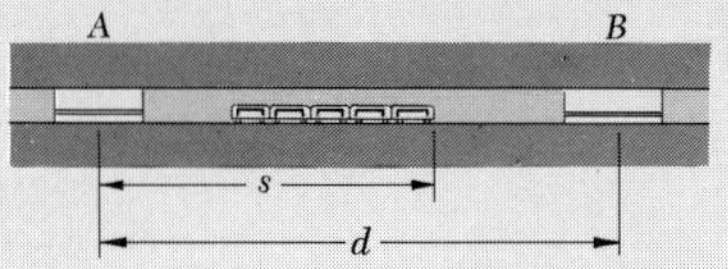

SAMPLE PROBLEM 11.6

A subway train leaves station A; it gains speed at the rate of 4 ft/sec^2 for 6 sec, and then at the rate of 6 ft/sec^2 until it has reached the speed of 48 ft/sec. The train maintains the same speed until it approaches station B; brakes are then applied, giving the train a constant deceleration and bringing it to a stop in 6 sec. The total running time from A to B is 40 sec. Draw the a–t, v–t, and s–t curves, and determine the distance between stations A and B.

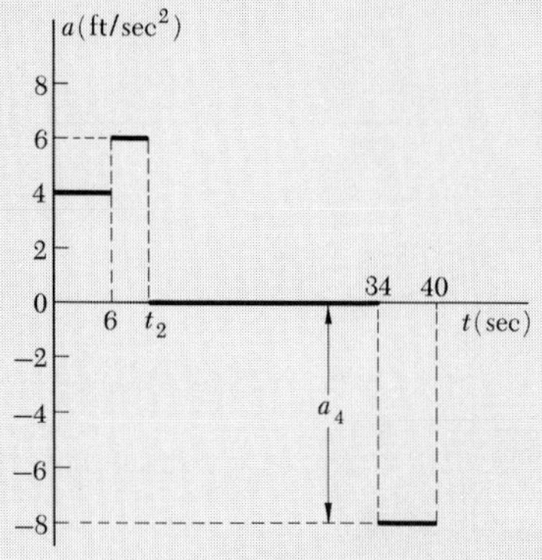

Acceleration-Time Curve. Since the acceleration is either constant or zero, the a–t curve is made of horizontal straight-line segments. The values of t_2 and a_4 are determined as follows:

$0 < t < 6$:

$$\text{Change in } v = \text{area under } a\text{–}t \text{ curve}$$
$$v_6 - 0 = (6 \text{ sec})(4 \text{ ft/sec}^2) = 24 \text{ ft/sec}$$

$6 < t < t_2$: Since the velocity increases from 24 to 48 ft/sec,

$$\text{Change in } v = \text{area under } a\text{–}t \text{ curve}$$
$$48 - 24 = (t_2 - 6)(6 \text{ ft/sec}^2) \qquad t_2 = 10 \text{ sec}$$

$t_2 < t < 34$: Since the velocity is constant, the acceleration is zero.

$34 < t < 40$:

$$\text{Change in } v = \text{area under } a\text{–}t \text{ curve}$$
$$0 - 48 = (6 \text{ sec})a_4 \qquad a_4 = -8 \text{ ft/sec}^2$$

The acceleration being negative, the corresponding area is below the t axis; this area represents a decrease in velocity.

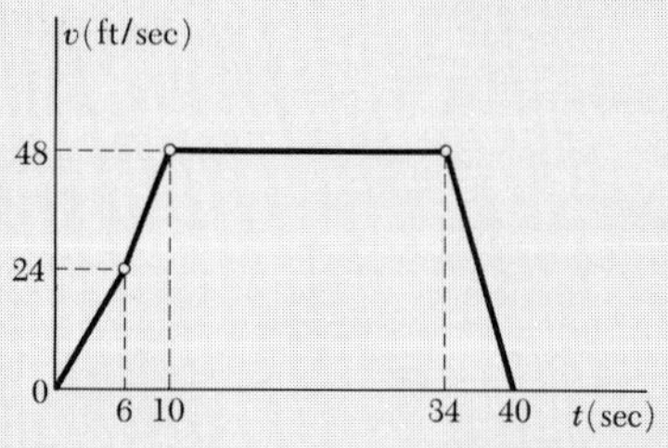

Velocity-Time Curve. Since the acceleration is either constant or zero, the v–t curve is made of segments of straight line connecting the points determined above.

$$\text{Change in } s = \text{area under } v\text{–}t \text{ curve}$$

$0 < t < 6$: $\quad s_6 - 0 = \frac{1}{2}(6)(24) = 72 \text{ ft}$

$6 < t < 10$: $\quad s_{10} - s_6 = \frac{1}{2}(4)(24 + 48) = 144 \text{ ft}$

$10 < t < 34$: $\quad s_{34} - s_{10} = (24)(48) = 1{,}152 \text{ ft}$

$34 < t < 40$: $\quad s_{40} - s_{34} = \frac{1}{2}(6)(48) = 144 \text{ ft}$

Adding the changes in s, we obtain the distance from A to B:

$$d = s_{40} - 0 = 1{,}512 \text{ ft}$$

$$d = 1{,}512 \text{ ft} \quad ◄$$

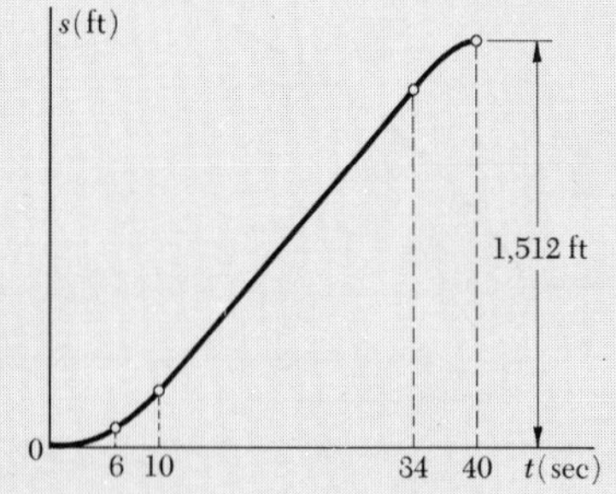

Position-Time Curve. The points determined above should be joined by three arcs of parabola and one segment of straight line. The construction of the s–t curve will be performed more easily and more accurately if we keep in mind that for any value of t the slope of the tangent to the s–t curve is equal to the value of v at that instant.

PROBLEMS

11.43. A particle moves in a straight line with the acceleration shown in the figure. Knowing that it starts from the origin with $v_0 = -24$ ft/sec, (*a*) plot the v–t and s–t curves for $0 < t < 20$ sec, (*b*) determine its velocity, its position, and the total distance traveled after 14 sec.

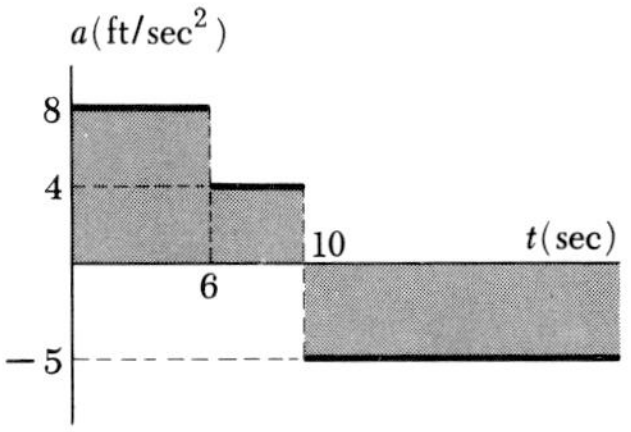

FIG. P 11.43

11.44. For the particle and motion of Prob. 11.43, plot the v–t and s–t curves for $0 < t < 20$ sec and determine (*a*) the maximum value of the velocity of the particle, (*b*) the maximum value of its position coordinate.

11.45. A particle moves in a straight line with the velocity shown in the figure. Knowing $s = -60$ in. at $t = 0$, draw the a–t and s–t curves for $0 < t < 20$ sec and determine (*a*) the total distance traveled by the particle after 16 sec, (*b*) the two values of t at which the particle passes through the origin.

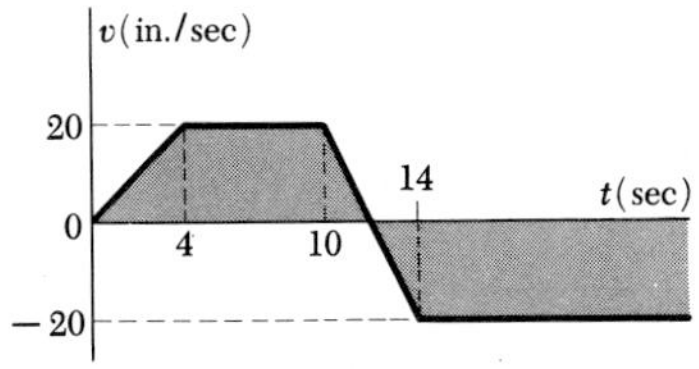

FIG. P 11.45

11.46. For the particle and motion of Prob. 11.45, plot the a–t and s–t curves for $0 < t < 20$ sec and determine (*a*) the maximum value of the position coordinate of the particle, (*b*) the values of t for which the particle is at a distance of 60 in. from the origin.

11.47. The firing of a howitzer causes the barrel to recoil 40 in. before a braking mechanism brings it to rest. From a high-speed photographic record, it is found that the maximum value of the recoil velocity is 270 in./sec and that this is reached 0.02 sec after firing. Assuming that the recoil period consists of two phases during which the acceleration has, respectively, a constant positive value a_1 and a constant negative value a_2, determine (*a*) the values of a_1 and a_2, (*b*) the position of the barrel 0.02 sec after firing, (*c*) the time at which the velocity of the barrel is zero.

11.48. A motorist is traveling at 50 mph when he observes that a traffic signal 800 ft ahead of him turns red. He knows that the signal is timed to stay red for 15 sec. What should he do to pass the signal at 50 mph just as it turns green again? Draw the v–t curve, selecting the solution which calls for the smallest possible deceleration and acceleration, and determine (*a*) the common value of the deceleration and acceleration in ft/sec^2, (*b*) the minimum speed reached in mph.

11.49. A series of city traffic signals are timed so that an automobile traveling at a constant speed of 25 mph will reach each signal just as it turns green. A motorist misses a signal and is stopped at signal *A*. Knowing that the next signal *B* is 600 ft ahead and that the maximum acceleration of his automobile is 5 ft/sec^2, determine what the motorist should do to keep his maximum speed as small as possible, yet reach signal *B* just as it turns green. What is the maximum speed reached?

11.50. During a finishing operation the bed of an industrial planer moves alternately 16 ft to the right and 16 ft to the left. The velocity of the bed is limited to a maximum value of 2 ft/sec to the right and 4 ft/sec to the left; the acceleration is successively equal to 2 ft/sec^2 to the right, zero, 2 ft/sec^2 to the left, zero, etc. Determine the time required for the bed to complete a full cycle, and draw the v–t and s–t curves.

11.51. A policeman on a motorcycle is escorting a motorcade which is traveling at 30 mph. The policeman suddenly decides to take a new position in the motorcade, 200 ft ahead. Assuming that he accelerates and decelerates at the rate of 11 ft/sec^2 and that he does not exceed at any time a speed of 45 mph, draw the a–t and v–t curves for his motion and determine (*a*) the shortest time in which he can occupy his new position in the motorcade, (*b*) the distance he will travel in that time.

11.52. A fighter plane flying horizontally in a straight line at 800 ft/sec is overtaking a bomber flying in the same straight line at 600 ft/sec. The pilot of the fighter plane fires an air-to-air missile at the bomber when his plane is 1,900 ft behind the bomber. The missile accelerates at a constant rate of 1,000 ft/sec^2 for 1 sec and then travels at a constant speed. (*a*) How many seconds after firing will the missile reach the bomber? (*b*) If both planes continue at constant speeds, what will be the distance between the planes when the missile strikes the bomber?

11.53. A car and a truck are both traveling at the constant speed of 35 mph; the car is 30 ft behind the truck. The driver of the car wants to pass the truck, i.e., he wishes to place his car at B, 30 ft in front of the truck, and then resume the speed of 35 mph. The maximum acceleration of the car is 5 ft/sec^2 and the maximum deceleration obtained by applying the brakes is 20 ft/sec^2. What is the shortest time in which the driver of the car can complete the passing operation if he does not at any time exceed the speed limit of 50 mph? Draw the v–t curve.

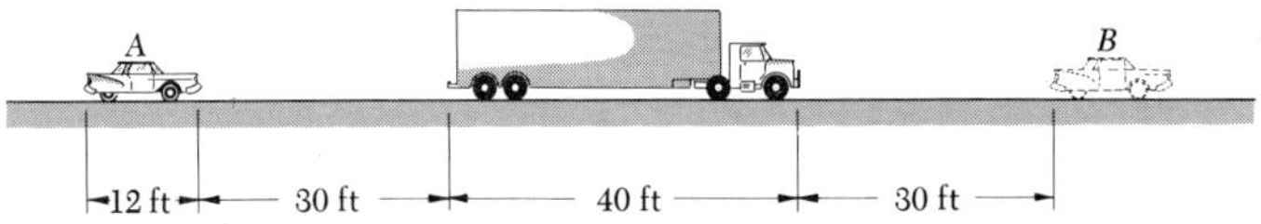

FIG. P 11.53 AND P 11.55

11.54. Solve Prob. 11.53 assuming that the driver of the car does not pay any attention to the speed limit while passing and concentrates on reaching position B and resuming a speed of 35 mph in the shortest possible time. What is the maximum speed reached? Draw the v–t curve.

11.55. A car and a truck are both traveling at the constant speed of 50 mph; the car is 30 ft behind the truck. The truck driver suddenly applies his brakes, causing the truck to decelerate at the constant rate of 9 ft/sec^2. Two seconds later the driver of the car applies his brakes and just manages to avoid a rear-end collision. Determine the constant rate at which the car decelerated.

11.56. Solve Prob. 11.55 assuming that the truck and the car are traveling at 80 mph.

11.57. An express subway train and a train making local stops run on parallel tracks between stations A and E, which are 3,200 ft apart. The local train makes stops of 30-sec duration at each of the stations B, C, and D; the express train proceeds to station E without any intermediate stop. Each train accelerates at a rate of 4 ft/sec^2 until it reaches a speed of 40 ft/sec; it then proceeds at that constant speed. As the train approaches its next stop, the brakes are applied, providing a constant deceleration of 5 ft/sec^2. If the express train leaves station A four minutes after the local train has left A, determine (*a*) which of the two trains will arrive at station E first, (*b*) when the other train will arrive at station E.

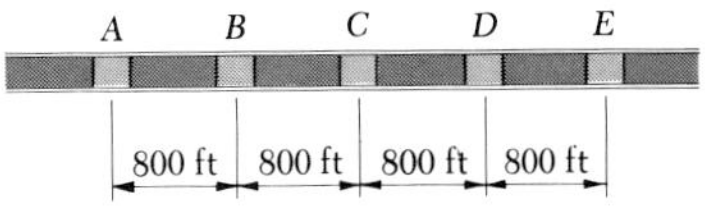

FIG. P 11.57

11.58. A police officer observes a car approaching at the unlawful speed of 60 mph. He gets on his motorcycle and starts chasing the car, just as it passes in front of him. After accelerating for 10 sec at a constant rate, the officer reaches his top speed of 75 mph. How long does it take him to overtake the car from the time he started? Draw the v–t and s–t curves for the car and the motorcycle.

11.59. A train starts at a station and accelerates uniformly at a rate of 1 ft/sec^2 until it reaches a speed of 20 ft/sec; it then proceeds at the constant speed of 20 ft/sec. Determine the time and the distance traveled if its *average* velocity is (*a*) 12 ft/sec, (*b*) 18 ft/sec.

11.60. The acceleration of a particle varies uniformly from $a = 90$ in./sec^2 at $t = 0$, to $a = -90$ in./sec^2 at $t = 6$ sec. Knowing that $s = 0$ and $v = 0$ when $t = 0$, determine (*a*) the maximum velocity of the particle, (*b*) its position at $t = 6$ sec, (*c*) its *average* velocity over the interval $0 < t < 6$ sec. Draw the a–t, v–t, and s–t curves for the motion.

11.61. The rate of change of acceleration is known as the *jerk*; large or abrupt rates of change of acceleration cause discomfort to elevator passengers. If the jerk, or rate of change of the acceleration, of an elevator is limited to ± 1.5 ft/sec^2 per second, determine the shortest time required for an elevator, starting from rest, to rise 24 ft and stop.

11.62. In order to maintain passenger comfort, the acceleration of an elevator is limited to 3 ft/sec^2 and the jerk, or rate of change of acceleration, is limited to ± 1.5 ft/sec^2 per second. If the elevator starts from rest, determine (*a*) the shortest time required for it to attain a constant velocity of 18 ft/sec, (*b*) the distance traveled in that time.

11.63. A training airplane lands on an aircraft carrier and is brought to rest in 3.0 sec by the arresting gear of the carrier. An accelerometer attached to the airplane provides the acceleration record shown. Determine by approximate means (a) the initial velocity of the airplane relative to the deck, (b) the distance the airplane travels along the deck before coming to rest.

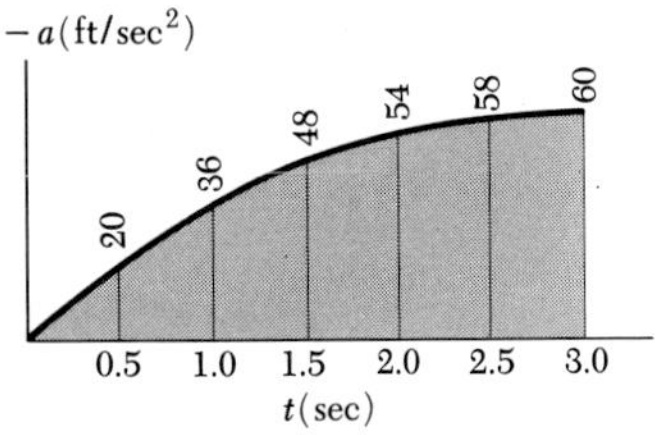

FIG. P 11.63

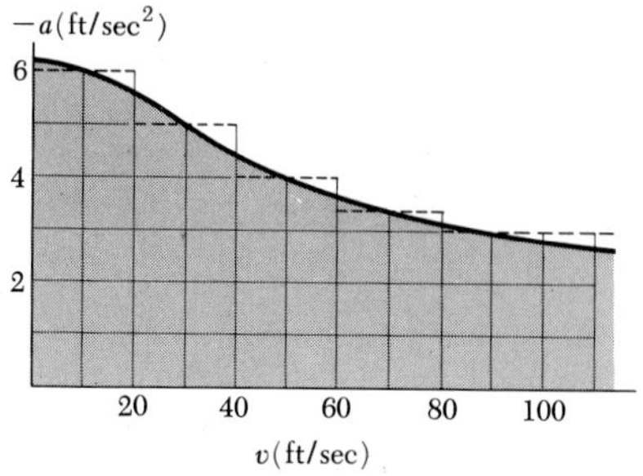

FIG. P 11.64

11.64. The maximum possible deceleration of a freight train under emergency conditions was determined experimentally; the results are shown (solid curve) in the figure. If the brakes are applied when the train is traveling at 40 mph, determine by approximate means (a) the time required for the train to come to rest, (b) the distance traveled in that time.

11.65. Solve Prob. 11.64 assuming that the train is traveling at 70 mph when the brakes are applied.

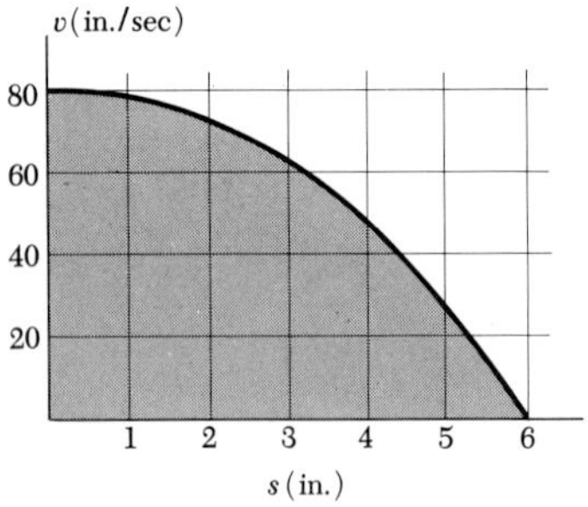

FIG. P 11.66

11.66. The v–s curve shown was obtained experimentally during the recoil of a gun. Determine by approximate means the acceleration (a) when $s = 3$ in., (b) when $v = 40$ in./sec.

***11.67.** Using the method of Sec. 11.8, determine the position of the particle of Prob. 11.43 when $t = 12$ sec.

***11.68.** Using the method of Sec. 11.8, determine the maximum value of the position coordinate of the particle of Prob. 11.43.

***11.69.** For the particle of Prob. 11.45, draw the a–t curve and, using the method of Sec. 11.8, determine the position of the particle when (a) $t = 10$ sec, (b) $t = 14$ sec.

***11.70.** For the particle of Prob. 11.45, draw the a–t curve and, using the method of Sec. 11.8, determine (a) the position of the particle when $t = 8$ sec, (b) the maximum value of its position coordinate.

*11.71. The acceleration of an object subjected to the blast of a large bomb is defined approximately by the curve shown. The object is initially at rest and is again at rest at time t_1. Using the method of Sec. 11.8, determine the distance through which the object is moved by the blast.

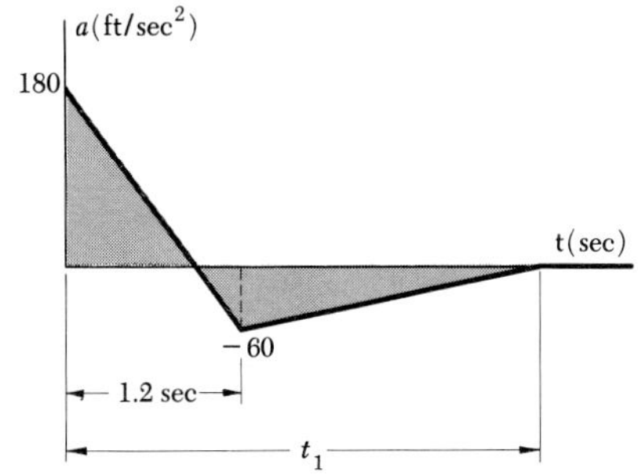

FIG. P 11.71

*11.72. Using the method of Sec. 11.8, derive the formula $s = s_0 + v_0t + \frac{1}{2}at^2$, for the position coordinate of a particle in uniformly accelerated rectilinear motion.

CURVILINEAR MOTION OF PARTICLES

11.9. Rectangular Components. When a particle moves in a plane along a curve other than a straight line, we say that the particle is in *curvilinear motion.* To define the position P occupied by the particle at a given time t, we select a fixed reference system, such as the x and y axes shown in Fig. 11.14*a*, and draw the vector **r** joining the origin O and the point P. Since the vector **r** is characterized by its magnitude r and its direction with respect to the reference axes, it completely defines the position of the particle with respect to those axes; the vector **r** is referred to as the *position vector* of the particle at time t.

Consider now the vector **r′** defining the position P' occupied by the same particle at a later time $t + \Delta t$. The vector Δ**r** joining P and P' represents the change in the position vector during the time interval Δt since, as we may easily check from Fig. 11.14*a*, the vector **r′** is obtained by adding the vectors **r** and Δ**r** according to the triangle rule.† We note that Δ**r** represents a change in *direction* as well as a change in *magnitude* of the position vector **r**. The *average velocity* of the particle over the time interval Δt is defined as the quotient of Δ**r** and Δt. Since Δ**r** is a vector and Δt a scalar, the quotient $\Delta\mathbf{r}/\Delta t$ is a vector attached at P, of the same direction as Δ**r**, and of magnitude equal to the magnitude of Δ**r** divided by Δt (Fig. 11.14*b*).

The *instantaneous velocity* of the particle at time t is obtained by choosing shorter and shorter time intervals Δt and, correspondingly, shorter and shorter vector increments Δ**r**. The instantaneous velocity is thus represented by the vector

$$\mathbf{v} = \lim_{\Delta t \to 0} \frac{\Delta \mathbf{r}}{\Delta t} \qquad (11.14)$$

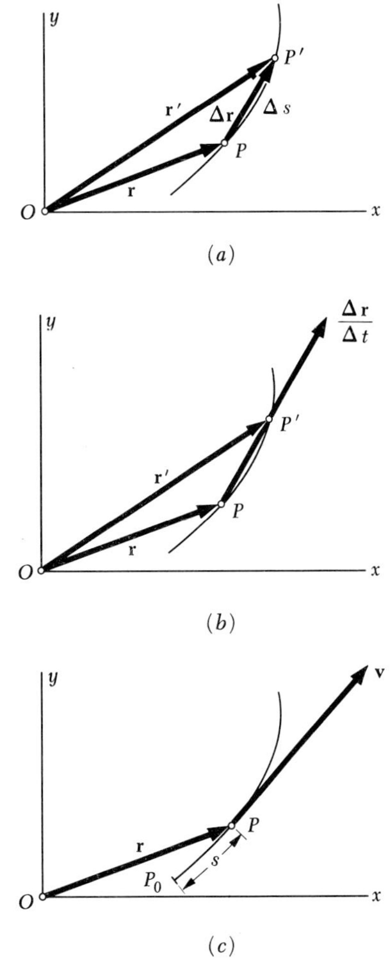

FIG. 11.14

† Since the displacement from O to P' represented by **r′** is clearly equivalent to the two successive displacements represented by **r** and Δ**r**, we verify that displacements satisfy the triangle rule and, therefore, the parallelogram law of addition. Thus, *displacements are truly vectors.*

As Δt and $\Delta\mathbf{r}$ become shorter, the points P and P' get closer; the vector $\mathbf{v}$ obtained at the limit must therefore be tangent to the path of the particle (Fig. 11.14*c*). Its magnitude, denoted by v and called the *speed* of the particle, is obtained by substituting for the vector $\Delta\mathbf{r}$ in formula (11.14) its magnitude represented by the straight-line segment PP'. But the length of the segment PP' approaches the length Δs of the arc PP' as Δt decreases (Fig. 11.14*a*), and we may write

$$v = \lim_{\Delta t\to 0} \frac{PP'}{\Delta t} = \lim_{\Delta t\to 0} \frac{\Delta s}{\Delta t}$$

$$v = \frac{ds}{dt} \tag{11.15}$$

The speed v may thus be obtained by differentiating with respect to t the length s of the arc described by the particle.

It is recalled that in many problems of statics it was found convenient to resolve a force $\mathbf{F}$ into component forces $\mathbf{F}_x$ and $\mathbf{F}_y$. Similarly, we shall often find it convenient in kinematics to resolve the vector $\mathbf{v}$ into rectangular components $\mathbf{v}_x$ and $\mathbf{v}_y$. To obtain these components, we resolve the vector $\Delta\mathbf{r}$ into components $\overrightarrow{PP''}$ and $\overrightarrow{P''P'}$, respectively parallel to the x and y axes (Fig. 11.15*a*), and write

$$\Delta\mathbf{r} = \overrightarrow{PP''} + \overrightarrow{P''P'}$$

where the right-hand member represents a vector sum. Substituting in (11.14) the expression obtained for $\Delta\mathbf{r}$, we write

$$\mathbf{v} = \lim_{\Delta t\to 0} \frac{\overrightarrow{PP''}}{\Delta t} + \lim_{\Delta t\to 0} \frac{\overrightarrow{P''P'}}{\Delta t}$$

Since the first limit represents a vector parallel to the x axis, it must be equal to the component $\mathbf{v}_x$ of the velocity; similarly, the second limit must be equal to its component $\mathbf{v}_y$ (Fig. 11.15*b*). We write

$$\mathbf{v}_x = \lim_{\Delta t\to 0} \frac{\overrightarrow{PP''}}{\Delta t} \qquad \mathbf{v}_y = \lim_{\Delta t\to 0} \frac{\overrightarrow{P''P'}}{\Delta t}$$

The magnitudes v_x and v_y of the components of the velocity may be obtained by observing that the magnitudes of the vectors $\overrightarrow{PP''}$ and $\overrightarrow{P''P'}$ are respectively equal to the increments Δx and Δy of the coordinates x and y of the particle. We write

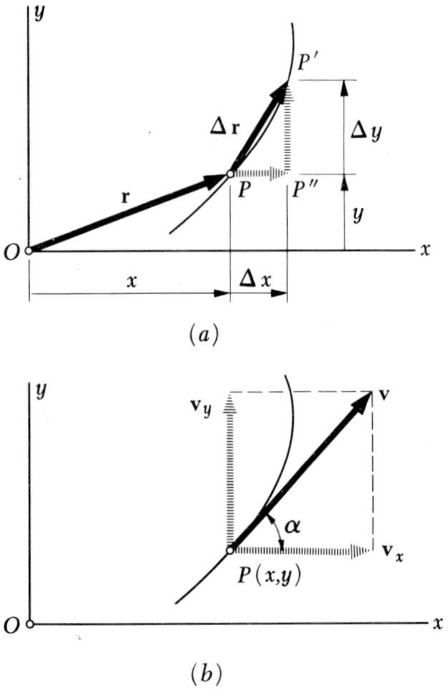

FIG. 11.15

$$v_x = \lim_{\Delta t\to 0} \frac{\Delta x}{\Delta t} \qquad v_y = \lim_{\Delta t\to 0} \frac{\Delta y}{\Delta t}$$

$$v_x = \frac{dx}{dt} \qquad v_y = \frac{dy}{dt} \tag{11.16}$$

The expressions obtained are known as the *scalar components* of the velocity. A positive value for v_x indicates that the vector component $\mathbf{v}_x$ is directed to the right, a negative value that it is directed to the left; similarly, a positive value for v_y indicates that $\mathbf{v}_y$ is directed upward, a negative value that it is directed downward. We verify from Fig. 11.15*b* that the magnitude and direction of the velocity **v** may be obtained from its scalar components v_x and v_y as follows:

$$v^2 = v_x^2 + v_y^2 \qquad \tan \alpha = \frac{v_y}{v_x} \tag{11.17}$$

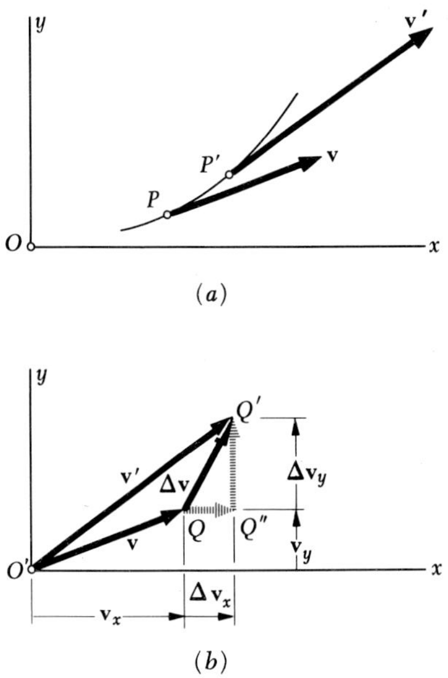

FIG. 11.16

Consider the velocity **v** of the particle at time t and also its velocity **v′** at a later time $t + \Delta t$ (Fig. 11.16*a*). Let us draw both vectors **v** and **v′** from the same origin O' (Fig. 11.16*b*). The vector $\Delta\mathbf{v}$ joining Q and Q' represents the change in the velocity of the particle during the time interval Δt, since the vector **v′** may be obtained by adding the vectors **v** and $\Delta\mathbf{v}$. We should note that $\Delta\mathbf{v}$ represents a change in the *direction* of the velocity as well as a change in *speed.* The *average acceleration* of the particle over the time interval Δt is defined as the quotient of $\Delta\mathbf{v}$ and Δt. Since $\Delta\mathbf{v}$ is a vector and Δt a scalar, the quotient $\Delta\mathbf{v}/\Delta t$ is a vector of the same direction as $\Delta\mathbf{v}$.

The *instantaneous acceleration* of the particle at time t is obtained by choosing smaller and smaller values for Δt and $\Delta\mathbf{v}$. The instantaneous acceleration is thus represented by the vector

$$\mathbf{a} = \lim_{\Delta t \to 0} \frac{\Delta\mathbf{v}}{\Delta t} \tag{11.18}$$

It should be noted that, in general, *the acceleration is not tangent to the path of the particle*; also, in general, the magnitude of the acceleration *does not* represent the rate of change of the speed of the particle.

To obtain the rectangular components $\mathbf{a}_x$ and $\mathbf{a}_y$ of the acceleration, we resolve the vector $\Delta\mathbf{v}$ into components $\overrightarrow{QQ''}$ and $\overrightarrow{Q''Q'}$, respectively parallel to the x and y axes (Fig. 11.16*b*), and write

$$\Delta\mathbf{v} = \overrightarrow{QQ''} + \overrightarrow{Q''Q'}$$

Substituting in (11.18) the expression obtained for $\Delta\mathbf{v}$, we write

$$\mathbf{a} = \lim_{\Delta t \to 0} \frac{\overrightarrow{QQ''}}{\Delta t} + \lim_{\Delta t \to 0} \frac{\overrightarrow{Q''Q'}}{\Delta t}$$

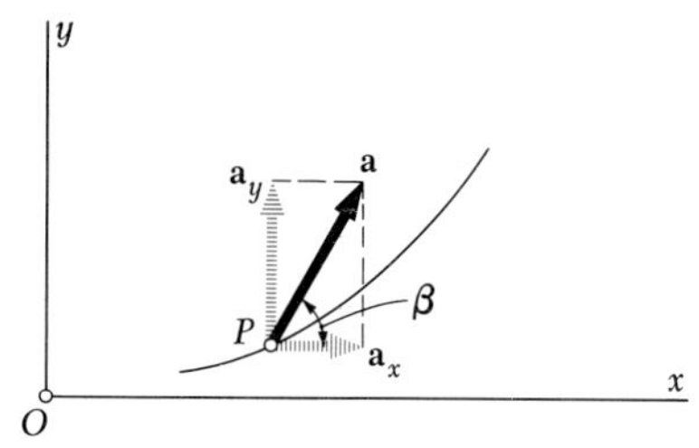

FIG. 11.17

Since the first limit represents a vector parallel to the x axis, it must be equal to the component $\mathbf{a}_x$ of the acceleration; similarly, the second limit must be equal to its component $\mathbf{a}_y$ (Fig. 11.17). We write

$$\mathbf{a}_x = \lim_{\Delta t \to 0} \frac{\overrightarrow{QQ''}}{\Delta t} \qquad \mathbf{a}_y = \lim_{\Delta t \to 0} \frac{\overrightarrow{Q''Q'}}{\Delta t}$$

The magnitudes a_x and a_y of the components of the acceleration, which are known as the scalar components of the acceleration, may be obtained by observing that the magnitudes of the vectors $\overrightarrow{QQ''}$ and $\overrightarrow{Q''Q'}$ are respectively equal to the increments Δv_x and Δv_y of the scalar components v_x and v_y of the velocity of the particle. We write

$$a_x = \lim_{\Delta t \to 0} \frac{\Delta v_x}{\Delta t} \qquad a_y = \lim_{\Delta t \to 0} \frac{\Delta v_y}{\Delta t}$$

$$a_x = \frac{dv_x}{dt} \qquad a_y = \frac{dv_y}{dt} \tag{11.19}$$

or, substituting for v_x and v_y from (11.16),

$$a_x = \frac{d^2x}{dt^2} \qquad a_y = \frac{d^2y}{dt^2} \tag{11.20}$$

The magnitude and direction of the acceleration **a** may be obtained from its scalar components a_x and a_y (Fig. 11.17) by formulas similar to formulas (11.17).

11.10. Component Motions. The use of rectangular components to describe the position, the velocity, and the acceleration of a particle is particularly effective when the component a_x of the acceleration is independent of the coordinate y and of the velocity component v_y and when the component a_y of the acceleration is independent of x and v_x. Equations (11.19) may then be integrated independently, and so may Eqs. (11.16). In other words, the motion of the particle in the x direction and its motion in the y direction may be considered separately.

In the case of the *motion of a projectile*, for example, it may be shown (see Sec. 12.7) that the components of the acceleration are

$$a_x = 0 \qquad a_y = -g = -32.2 \text{ ft/sec}^2$$

if the resistance of the air is neglected. Substituting into Eqs. (11.19), we write

$$\frac{dv_x}{dt} = 0 \qquad\qquad \frac{dv_y}{dt} = -g$$

$$v_x = (v_x)_0 \qquad\qquad v_y = (v_y)_0 - gt$$

where $(v_x)_0$ and $(v_y)_0$ are the components of the initial velocity. Substituting into Eqs. (11.16), and assuming that the projectile is fired from the origin O, we write

$$\frac{dx}{dt} = (v_x)_0 \qquad\qquad \frac{dy}{dt} = (v_y)_0 - gt$$

$$x = (v_x)_0 t \qquad\qquad y = (v_y)_0 t - \tfrac{1}{2}gt^2$$

These equations show that the motion of the projectile in the horizontal direction is uniform, while its motion in the vertical direction is uniformly accelerated. The motion of a projectile may thus be replaced by two independent rectilinear motions, which are easily visualized if we assume that the projectile is fired vertically with an initial velocity $(\mathbf{v}_y)_0$ from a platform moving with a constant horizontal velocity $(\mathbf{v}_x)_0$ (Fig. 11.18). The coordinate x of the projectile is equal at any instant to the distance traveled by the platform, while its coordinate y may be computed as if the projectile were moving along a vertical line.

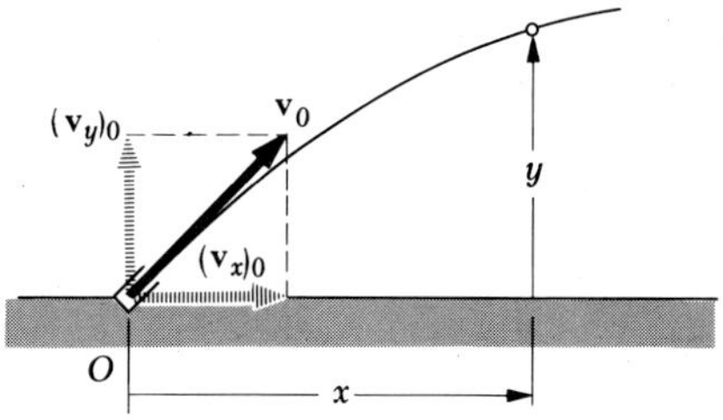

(a) Motion of a projectile

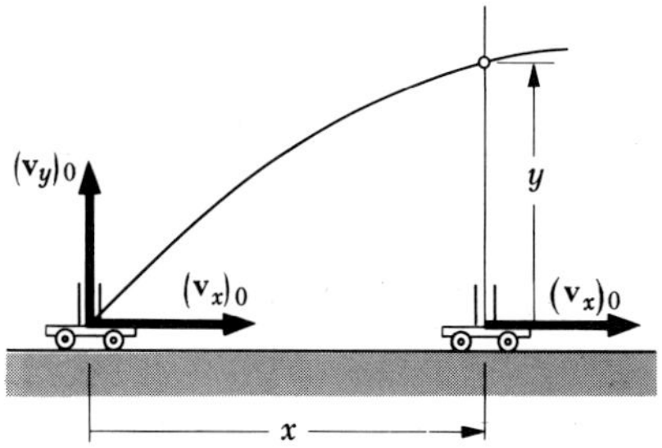

(b) Equivalent rectilinear motions

FIG. 11.18

11.11. Relative Motion. Consider two particles A and B moving in the same plane (Fig. 11.19); the vectors $\mathbf{r}_A$ and $\mathbf{r}_B$ define their position at any given instant with respect to a fixed system of axes xy centered at O. Consider now a system of axes $x'y'$ centered at A and parallel to the x and y axes. While the origin of these axes moves, their orientation remains the same; such a system of axes is said to be in *translation*. The vector $\mathbf{r}_{B/A}$ joining A and B defines the position of the particle B with respect to the moving reference system $x'y'$; it is therefore called the position vector of B relative to the reference system centered at A or, for short, the *position vector of B relative to A*.

We note from Fig. 11.19 that the position vector $\mathbf{r}_B$ of particle B may be obtained by adding by the triangle rule the position vector $\mathbf{r}_A$ of particle A and the position vector $\mathbf{r}_{B/A}$ of B relative to A; we write

$$\mathbf{r}_B = \mathbf{r}_A + \mathbf{r}_{B/A} \tag{11.21}$$

In terms of x and y components, this relation reads

$$x_B = x_A + x_{B/A} \qquad y_B = y_A + y_{B/A} \tag{11.22}$$

where x_B and y_B denote the coordinates of particle B with re-

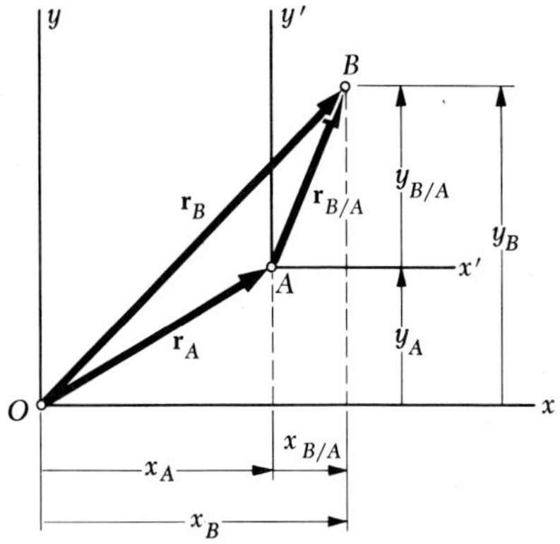

FIG. 11.19

spect to the fixed x and y axes, while $x_{B/A}$ and $y_{B/A}$ represent the coordinates of B with respect to the moving x' and y' axes. Differentiating Eqs. (11.22), we write

$$\frac{dx_B}{dt} = \frac{dx_A}{dt} + \frac{dx_{B/A}}{dt} \qquad \frac{dy_B}{dt} = \frac{dy_A}{dt} + \frac{dy_{B/A}}{dt} \tag{11.23}$$

The derivatives dx_A/dt and dy_A/dt represent the x and y components of the velocity $\mathbf{v}_A$ of particle A, while the derivatives dx_B/dt and dy_B/dt represent the components of the velocity $\mathbf{v}_B$ of particle B. The vector $\mathbf{v}_{B/A}$ of components $dx_{B/A}/dt$ and $dy_{B/A}/dt$ is known as the *relative velocity of B with respect to A* or, more accurately, as the relative velocity of B with respect to a reference system in translation with A. Writing Eqs. (11.23) in vector form, we have

$$\mathbf{v}_B = \mathbf{v}_A + \mathbf{v}_{B/A} \tag{11.24}$$

Differentiating Eqs. (11.23), we write

$$\frac{d^2x_B}{dt^2} = \frac{d^2x_A}{dt^2} + \frac{d^2x_{B/A}}{dt^2} \qquad \frac{d^2y_B}{dt^2} = \frac{d^2y_A}{dt^2} + \frac{d^2y_{B/A}}{dt^2} \tag{11.25}$$

where the first two derivatives in each equation represent the components of the accelerations $\mathbf{a}_B$ and $\mathbf{a}_A$. The vector $\mathbf{a}_{B/A}$ of components $d^2x_{B/A}/dt^2$ and $d^2y_{B/A}/dt^2$ is known as the *relative acceleration of B with respect to A* or, more accurately, as the relative acceleration of B with respect to a reference system in translation with A. Writing Eqs. (11.25) in vector form, we obtain

$$\mathbf{a}_B = \mathbf{a}_A + \mathbf{a}_{B/A} \tag{11.26}$$

The motion of B with respect to the fixed x and y axes is referred to as the *absolute motion of B*, while the motion of B with respect to the x' and y' axes attached at A is referred to as the *relative motion of B with respect to A*. The equations derived in this section show that *the absolute motion of B may be obtained by combining the motion of A and the relative motion of B with respect to A*. Equation (11.24), for example, expresses that the absolute velocity $\mathbf{v}_B$ of particle B may be obtained by adding vectorially the velocity of A and the velocity of B relative to A. Equation (11.26) expresses a similar property in terms of the accelerations. We should keep in mind, however, that the x' and y' axes are in translation, i.e., that, while they move with A, they maintain the same orientation. As we shall see later (Sec. 15.11), different relations must be used when the moving reference axes rotate.

SAMPLE PROBLEM 11.7

A projectile is fired from the edge of a 500-ft cliff with an initial velocity of 600 ft/sec, at an angle of 30° with the horizontal. Neglecting air resistance, find (*a*) the horizontal distance from the gun to the point where the projectile strikes the ground, (*b*) the greatest elevation above the ground reached by the projectile.

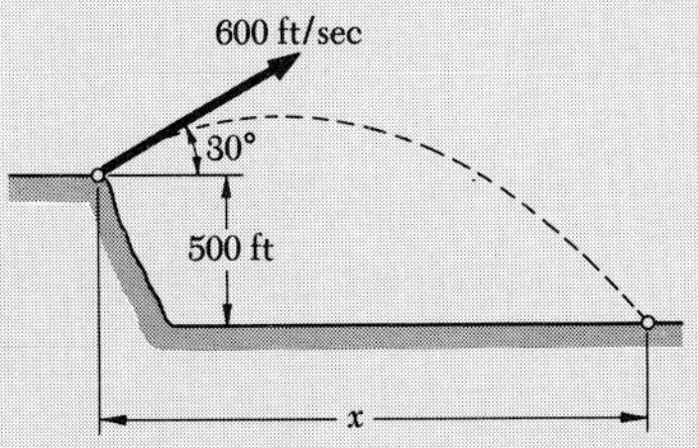

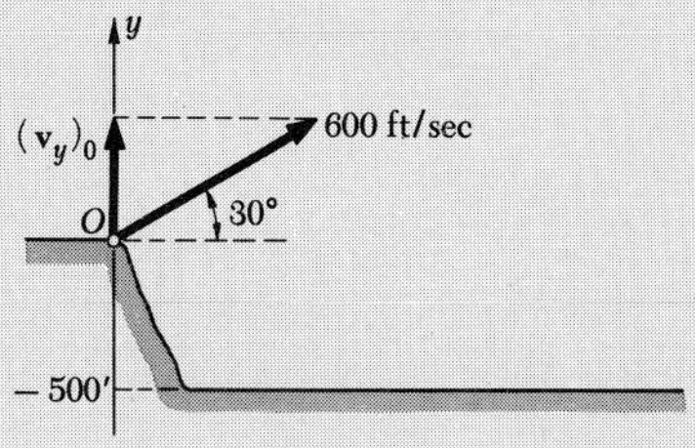

Vertical Motion. Uniformly accelerated motion. Choosing the positive sense of the y axis upward and placing the origin O at the gun, we have

$$(v_y)_0 = 600 \sin 30° = +300 \text{ ft/sec}$$
$$a = -32.2 \text{ ft/sec}^2$$

Substituting into the equations of uniformly accelerated motion, we have

$$v_y = (v_y)_0 + at \qquad v_y = 300 - 32.2t \qquad (1)$$
$$y = (v_y)_0 t + \tfrac{1}{2}at^2 \qquad y = 300t - 16.1t^2 \qquad (2)$$
$$v_y^2 = (v_y)_0^2 + 2ay \qquad v_y^2 = 90{,}000 - 64.4y \qquad (3)$$

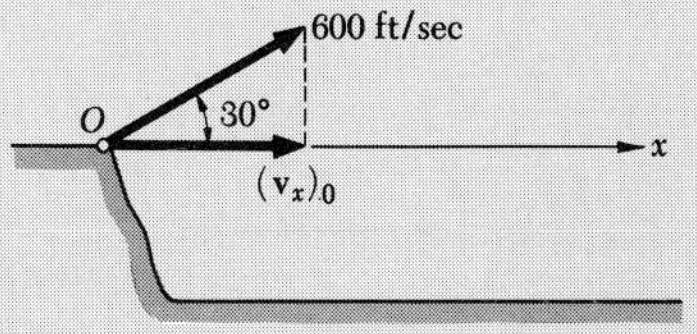

Horizontal Motion. Uniform motion. Choosing the positive sense of the x axis to the right, we have

$$(v_x)_0 = 600 \cos 30° = +520 \text{ ft/sec}$$

Substituting into the equation of uniform motion, we obtain

$$x = (v_x)_0 t \qquad x = 520t \qquad (4)$$

a. **Horizontal Distance.** When the projectile strikes the ground, we have

$$y = -500 \text{ ft}$$

Carrying this value into Eq. (2) for the vertical motion, we write

$$-500 = 300t - 16.1t^2 \qquad t^2 - 18.6t - 31.1 = 0 \qquad t = 20.1 \text{ sec}$$

Carrying $t = 20.1$ sec into Eq. (4) for the horizontal motion, we obtain

$$x = (520)(20.1) \qquad x = 10{,}450 \text{ ft} \quad ◄$$

b. **Greatest Elevation.** When the projectile reaches its greatest elevation, we have $v_y = 0$; carrying this value into Eq. (3) for the vertical motion, we write

$$0 = 90{,}000 - 64.4y \qquad y = 1{,}398 \text{ ft}$$
$$\text{Greatest elevation above ground} = 500 \text{ ft} + 1{,}398 \text{ ft}$$
$$= 1{,}898 \text{ ft} \quad ◄$$

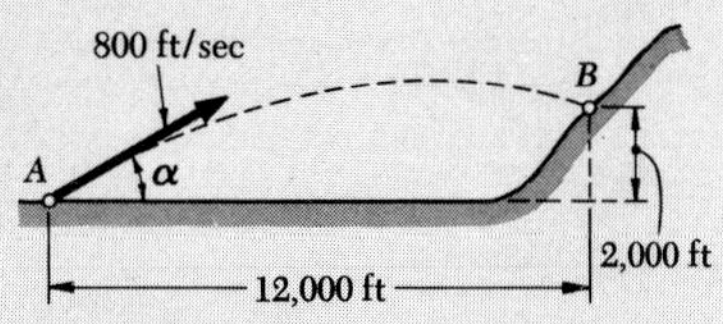

SAMPLE PROBLEM 11.8

A projectile is fired with an initial velocity of 800 ft/sec at a target B located 2,000 ft above the gun A and at a horizontal distance of 12,000 ft. Neglecting air resistance, determine the value of the firing angle α.

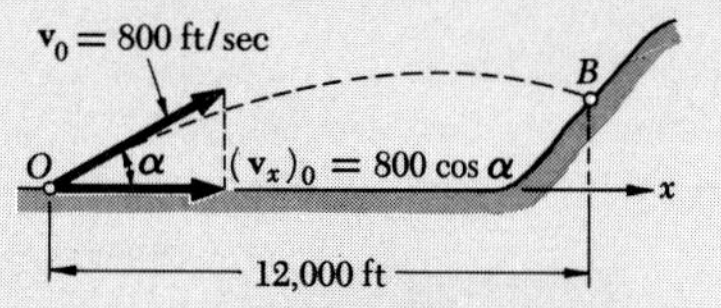

Horizontal Motion. Placing the origin of coordinates at the gun, we have

$$(v_x)_0 = 800 \cos \alpha$$

Substituting into the equation of uniform horizontal motion, we obtain

$$x = (v_x)_0 t \qquad x = (800 \cos \alpha)t$$

The time required for the projectile to move through a horizontal distance of 12,000 ft is obtained by making x equal to 12,000 ft.

$$12{,}000 = (800 \cos \alpha)t$$

$$t = \frac{12{,}000}{800 \cos \alpha} = \frac{15}{\cos \alpha}$$

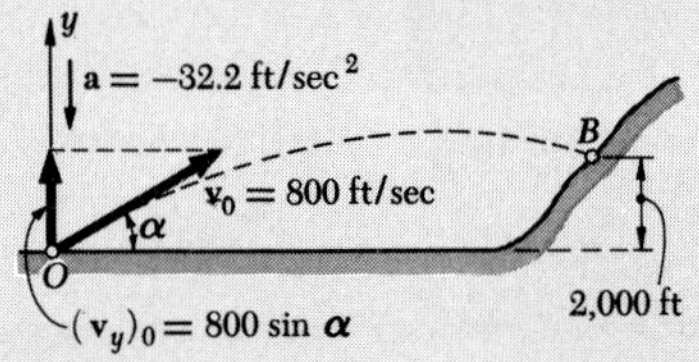

Vertical Motion

$$(v_y)_0 = 800 \sin \alpha \qquad a = -32.2 \text{ ft/sec}^2$$

Substituting into the equation of uniformly accelerated vertical motion, we obtain

$$y = (v_y)_0 t + \tfrac{1}{2}at^2 \qquad y = (800 \sin \alpha)t - 16.1t^2$$

When $x = 12{,}000$ ft, we must have $y = 2{,}000$ ft if the projectile is to hit the target. Substituting for y and making t equal to the value found above, we write

$$2{,}000 = 800 \sin \alpha \frac{15}{\cos \alpha} - 16.1 \left(\frac{15}{\cos \alpha}\right)^2$$

Since $1/\cos^2 \alpha = \sec^2 \alpha = 1 + \tan^2 \alpha$, we have

$$2{,}000 = (800)(15) \tan \alpha - (16.1)(15^2)(1 + \tan^2 \alpha)$$

$$3{,}622 \tan^2 \alpha - 12{,}000 \tan \alpha + 5{,}622 = 0$$

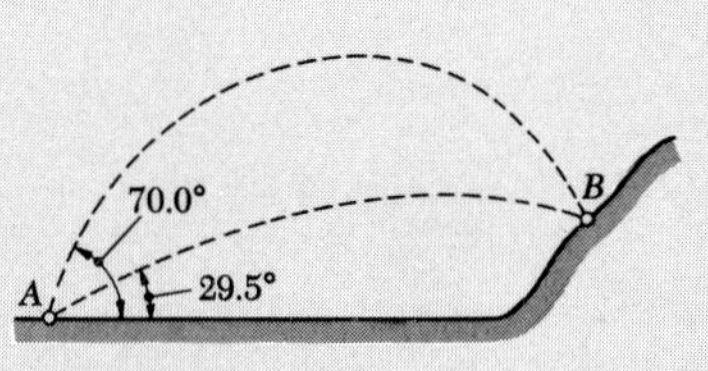

Solving this quadratic equation for $\tan \alpha$, we have

$$\tan \alpha = 0.565 \qquad \text{and} \qquad \tan \alpha = 2.75$$

$$\alpha = 29.5° \qquad \text{and} \qquad \alpha = 70.0° \quad ◀$$

The target will be hit if either of these two firing angles is used (see figure).

SAMPLE PROBLEM 11.9

Automobile A is traveling east at the constant speed of 15 mph. As automobile A crosses the intersection shown, automobile B starts from rest 90 ft north of the intersection and moves south with a constant acceleration of 4 ft/sec². Determine the position, velocity, and acceleration of B relative to A five sec after A crosses the intersection.

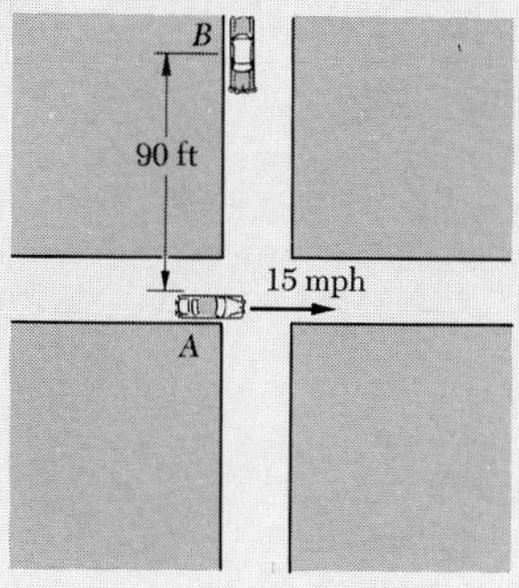

Solution. We choose x and y axes with origin at the intersection of the two streets and with positive senses directed respectively east and north.

Motion of Automobile A. First the speed is expressed in ft/sec.

$$15 \text{ mph} = \left(15 \frac{\text{miles}}{\text{hr}}\right)\left(\frac{5{,}280 \text{ ft}}{1 \text{ mile}}\right)\left(\frac{1 \text{ hr}}{3{,}600 \text{ sec}}\right) = 22 \text{ ft/sec}$$

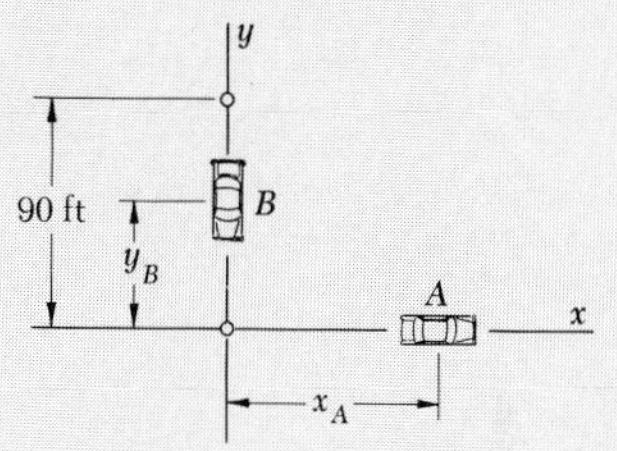

Noting that the motion of A is uniform, we write, for any time t,

$$a_A = 0$$
$$v_A = +22 \text{ ft/sec}$$
$$x_A = (x_A)_0 + v_A t = 0 + 22t$$

For $t = 5$ sec, we have

$$a_A = 0 \qquad \mathbf{a}_A = 0$$
$$v_A = +22 \text{ ft/sec} \qquad \mathbf{v}_A = 22 \text{ ft/sec} \rightarrow$$
$$x_A = +(22)(5) = +110 \text{ ft} \qquad \mathbf{r}_A = 110 \text{ ft} \rightarrow$$

Motion of Automobile B. We note that the motion of B is uniformly accelerated, and write

$$a_B = -4 \text{ ft/sec}^2$$
$$v_B = (v_B)_0 + at = 0 - 4t$$
$$y_B = (y_B)_0 + (v_B)_0 t + \tfrac{1}{2}a_B t^2 = 90 + 0 - \tfrac{1}{2}(4)t^2$$

For $t = 5$ sec, we have

$$a_B = -4 \text{ ft/sec}^2 \qquad \mathbf{a}_B = 4 \text{ ft/sec}^2 \downarrow$$
$$v_B = -(4)(5) = -20 \text{ ft/sec} \qquad \mathbf{v}_B = 20 \text{ ft/sec} \downarrow$$
$$y_B = 90 - \tfrac{1}{2}(4)(5)^2 = +40 \text{ ft} \qquad \mathbf{r}_B = 40 \text{ ft} \uparrow$$

Motion of B Relative to A. We draw the triangle corresponding to the vector equation $\mathbf{r}_B = \mathbf{r}_A + \mathbf{r}_{B/A}$ and obtain the magnitude and direction of the position vector of B relative to A.

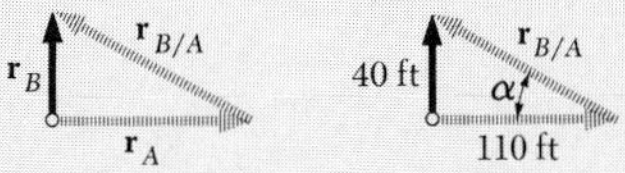

$$r_{B/A} = 117.1 \text{ ft} \qquad \alpha = 20.0°$$
$$\mathbf{r}_{B/A} = 117.1 \text{ ft} \nwarrow 20.0° \quad ◀$$

Proceeding in a similar fashion, we find the velocity and acceleration of B relative to A.

$$\mathbf{v}_B = \mathbf{v}_A + \mathbf{v}_{B/A}$$
$$v_{B/A} = 29.7 \text{ ft/sec} \qquad \beta = 42.3°$$
$$\mathbf{v}_{B/A} = 29.7 \text{ ft/sec} \swarrow 42.3° \quad ◀$$

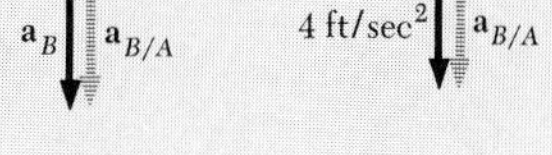

$$\mathbf{a}_B = \mathbf{a}_A + \mathbf{a}_{B/A}$$
$$\mathbf{a}_{B/A} = 4 \text{ ft/sec}^2 \downarrow \quad ◀$$

11.81. A man standing on the edge of a 60-ft cliff throws a stone in a horizontal direction, straight ahead of him. Knowing that the stone hits the ground 80 ft from the bottom of the cliff, determine (*a*) the initial velocity of the stone, (*b*) the distance at which a stone would hit the ground if it were thrown horizontally with the same velocity from a cliff 120 ft high.

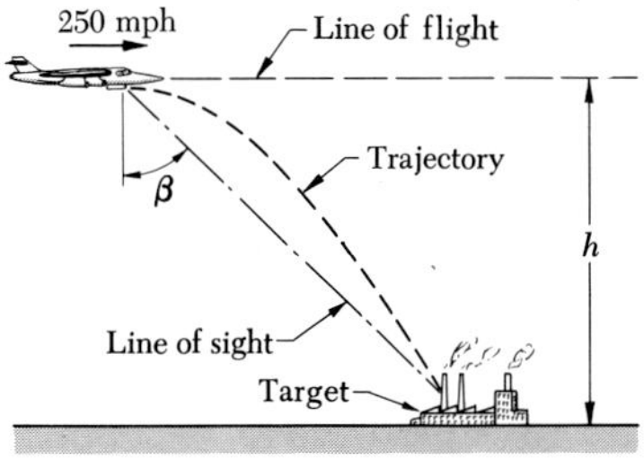

FIG. P 11.82

11.82. A bomber is flying horizontally in a straight line at 250 mph at an altitude $h = 10{,}000$ ft. (*a*) Find the angle β that the line of sight from the bomber to the target should form with the vertical when the bombs are released. (*b*) Where will the bomber be when the bombs strike the target?

11.83. In Prob. 11.82, determine the altitude h for which the angle β is 45°.

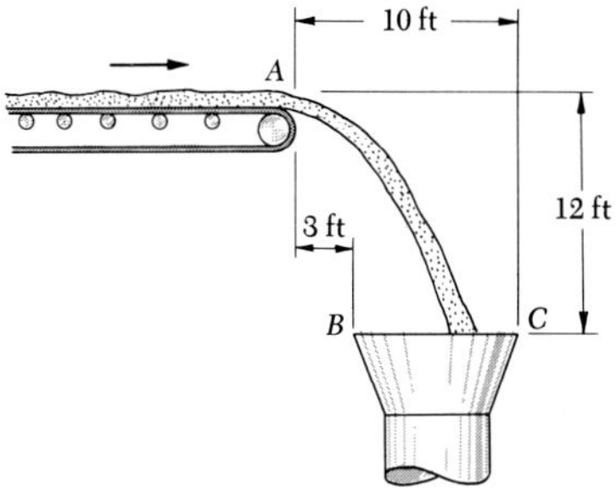

FIG. P 11.84

11.84. Sand is discharged at A from a horizontal conveyor belt into a hopper as shown. For what range of speeds of the belt will the sand enter the hopper BC?

11.85. Standing on the side of a hill, an archer shoots an arrow with an initial velocity of 200 ft/sec at an angle $\alpha = 15°$ with the horizontal. Determine the horizontal distance d traveled by the arrow before it strikes the ground at B.

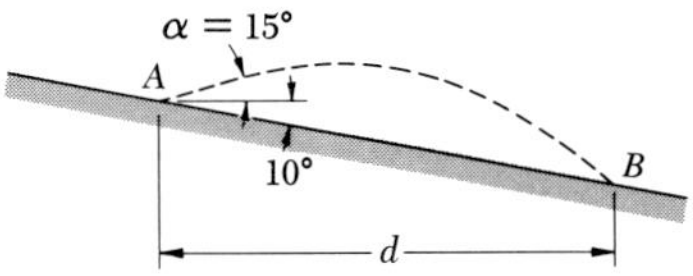

FIG. P 11.85

11.86. A man wants to throw a ball onto the flat roof of a building 37 ft high. Standing 30 ft from the wall, he throws the ball with a velocity of 55.8 ft/sec at an angle of 60° with the horizontal, releasing it 4.8 ft from the ground. How far from the edge of the roof will the ball fall? Check that the ball will clear the edge of the roof.

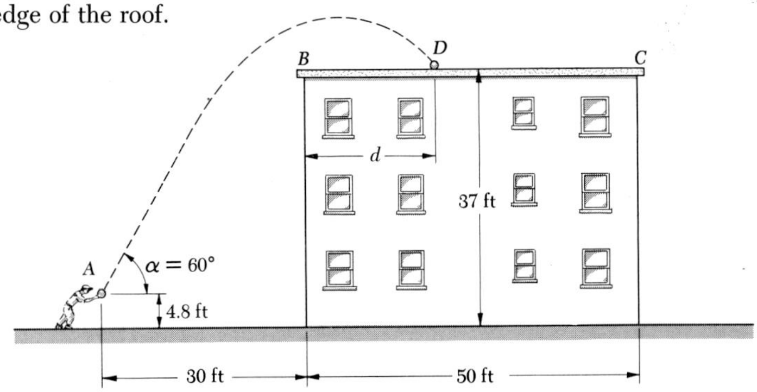

FIG. P 11.86 AND P 11.88

11.87. In Prob. 11.86, determine the largest and smallest values of the initial velocity for which the ball will fall on the roof.

11.88. A man throws a ball from A in the direction shown. Determine the portion of the roof on which the ball cannot land.

11.89. A projectile is fired with an initial velocity of 700 ft/sec. Find the angle at which it should be fired if it is to hit a target located at a distance of 12,000 ft on the same level.

11.90. Solve Sample Prob. 11.8 assuming that the projectile is fired from B and that the target is at A.

11.91. A projectile is fired with an initial velocity $\mathbf{v}_0$ at an angle α with the horizontal. Determine (a) the maximum height h reached by the projectile, (b) the horizontal range R of the projectile.

11.92. Find the maximum horizontal range R of a projectile fired with an initial velocity of magnitude v_0, and determine the corresponding firing angle α.

11.93. A boy can throw a baseball a maximum distance of 90 ft in New York, where $g = 32.2$ ft/sec^2. How far could he throw the baseball (a) in Singapore, where $g = 32.1$ ft/sec^2? (b) on the moon, where $g = 5.31$ ft/sec^2?

11.94. A nozzle discharges a stream of water with an initial velocity $\mathbf{v}_0$ of 40 ft/sec into the end of a horizontal pipe of inside diameter $d = 4$ ft. Determine the largest distance x that the stream can reach.

11.95. If the maximum horizontal range of a given gun is R, determine the firing angle which should be used to hit a target located at a distance $\frac{1}{2}R$ on the same level.

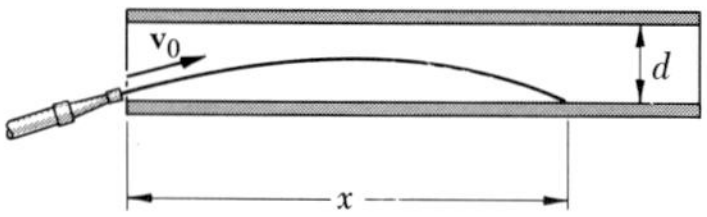

FIG. P 11.94

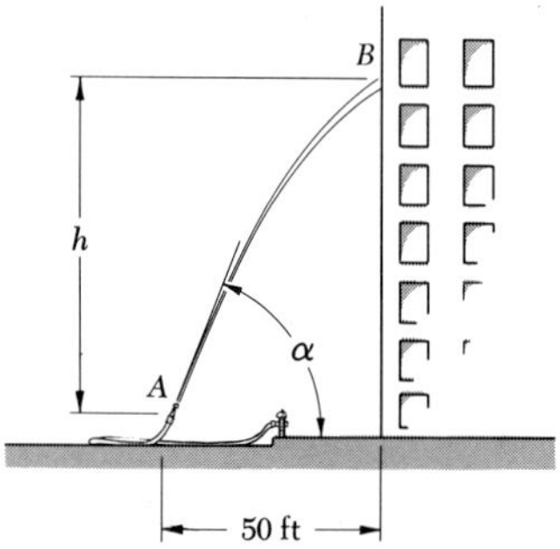

FIG. P 11.96

11.96. A fire nozzle discharges water with an initial velocity $\mathbf{v}_0$ of 80 ft/sec. Knowing that the nozzle is located 50 ft from a building, determine (a) the maximum height h that can be reached by the water, (b) the corresponding angle α.

11.97. Solve Prob. 11.96 assuming that the nozzle is located 100 ft from the building.

11.98. Show that the trajectory of a projectile is a parabola if air resistance is neglected.

11.99. Determine the equation of the path of the projectile of Sample Prob. 11.7 in terms of the coordinates x and y.

***11.100.** A conveyor belt AB of length 20 ft is attached to a hinge at A and may be set at any slope as shown. Sand is discharged by the belt at B and falls freely until it reaches the ground at point C. Knowing that the belt moves with a constant velocity $\mathbf{v}_0$ of 10 ft/sec, determine (*a*) the largest possible distance d between A and C, (*b*) the corresponding angle α.

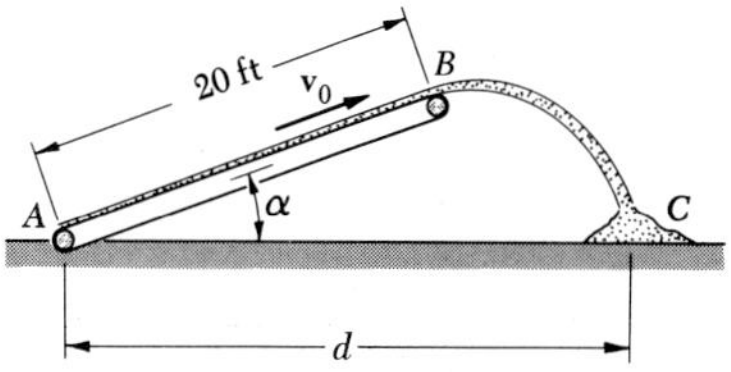

FIG. P 11.100

11.101. Ship A travels due south at 18 knots, while ship B travels toward the southeast at 15 knots. Determine the velocity (*a*) of ship B relative to ship A, (*b*) of ship A relative to ship B.

11.102. As observed from a ship moving due east at 8 mph, the wind appears to blow from the southwest at 12 mph. Determine the magnitude and direction of the true wind velocity.

11.103. Two airplanes A and B are each flying at a constant altitude of 3,000 ft. Plane A is flying due east at a constant speed of 300 mph while plane B is flying southwest at a constant speed of 450 mph. Determine the change in position of plane B relative to plane A which takes place during a 2-min interval.

11.104. The truck A and the automobile B travel at the constant speeds shown. Five seconds after the automobile crosses the overpass, the truck goes under the same overpass. Determine (*a*) the velocity of the automobile relative to the truck, (*b*) the change in position of the automobile relative to the truck during a 10-sec interval, (*c*) the distance between the automobile and the truck 10 sec after the truck has gone under the overpass.

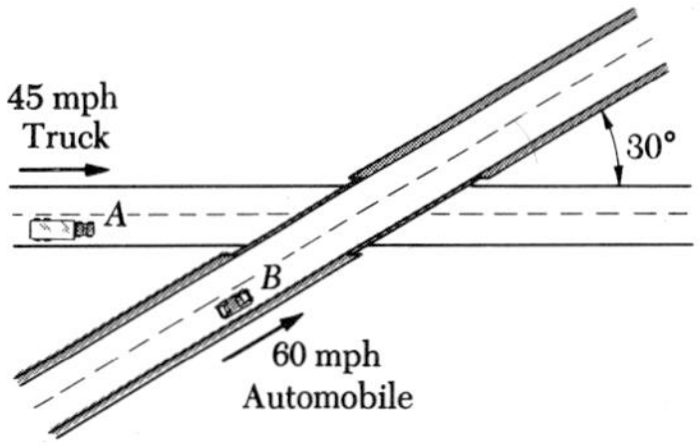

FIG. P 11.104

11.105. As he passes a pole, a man riding in a truck tries to hit the pole by throwing a stone with a horizontal velocity of 75 ft/sec relative to the truck. Knowing that the speed of the truck is 30 mph, determine (*a*) the direction in which he must throw the stone, (*b*) the horizontal velocity of the stone with respect to the ground.

11.106. During a rainstorm the paths of the raindrops appear to form an angle of 30° with the vertical when observed from a side window of a train moving at a speed of 10 mph. A short time later, after the speed of the train has increased to 20 mph, the angle between the vertical and the paths of the drops appears to be 45°. If the train were stopped, at what angle and with what velocity would the drops be observed to fall?

11.107. As the speed of the train of Prob. 11.106 increases, the angle between the vertical and the paths of the drops becomes equal to 60°. Determine the speed of the train at that time.

11.108. An antiaircraft gun fires a shell as a plane passes directly over the position of the gun, at an altitude of 6,000 ft. The muzzle velocity of the shell is 1,500 ft/sec. Knowing that the plane is flying horizontally at 450 mph, determine (*a*) the required firing angle if the shell is to hit the plane, (*b*) the velocity and acceleration of the shell relative to the plane at the time of impact.

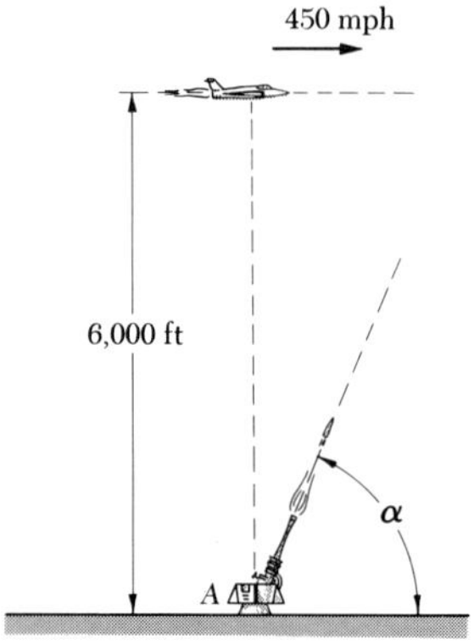

FIG. P 11.108

11.109. The conveyor belt A moves at a constant velocity and discharges sand onto belt B as shown. Knowing that the velocity of belt B is 8 ft/sec, determine the velocity of the sand relative to belt B as it lands on belt B.

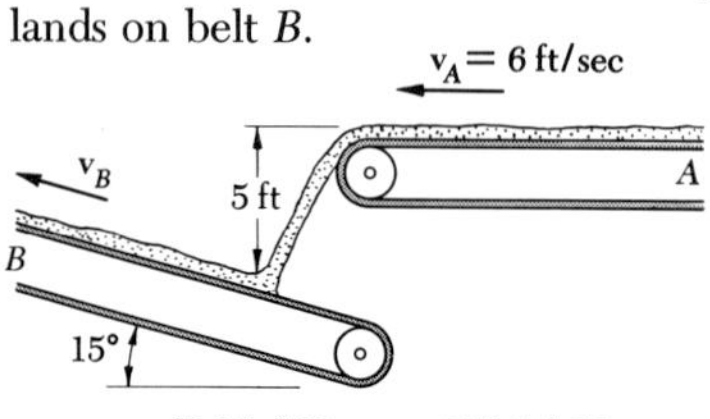

FIG. P 11.109 AND P 11.110

11.110. Determine the required velocity of belt B if the relative velocity with which the sand hits belt B is to be (*a*) vertical, (*b*) as small as possible.

11.12. Tangential and Normal Components. We saw in Sec. 11.9 that the velocity of a particle is a vector tangent to the path of the particle but that, in general, the acceleration is not tangent to the path. It is sometimes convenient to resolve the acceleration into components directed, respectively, along the tangent and the normal to the path of the particle. The positive sense along the tangent is chosen to coincide with the sense of motion of the particle, and the positive sense along the normal is chosen toward the inside of the path (Fig. 11.20).

We consider again, as we did in Sec. 11.9, the velocity $\mathbf{v}$ of the particle at a time t and its velocity $\mathbf{v}'$ at a time $t + \Delta t$ (Fig. 11.20*a*). Drawing both vectors from the same origin O', and joining the points Q and Q', we obtain the small vector $\Delta\mathbf{v}$ representing the difference between the vectors $\mathbf{v}$ and $\mathbf{v}'$ (Fig. 11.20*b*). As we saw earlier, the average acceleration is defined as the quotient of $\Delta\mathbf{v}$ and Δt, and the instantaneous acceleration $\mathbf{a}$ as the limit of this quotient. To obtain the tangential component $\mathbf{a}_t$ and the normal component $\mathbf{a}_n$ of the acceleration, we measure the distance $O'Q'' = O'Q$ along the line $O'Q'$ and resolve the vector $\Delta\mathbf{v}$ into its components $\overrightarrow{QQ''}$ and $\overrightarrow{Q''Q'}$

(Fig. 11.20*b*); we write

$$\Delta \mathbf{v} = \overrightarrow{QQ''} + \overrightarrow{Q''Q'}$$

The component $\overrightarrow{QQ''}$ represents a change in the *direction* of the velocity, while the component $\overrightarrow{Q''Q'}$ represents a change in the *magnitude* of the velocity, i.e., a change in *speed.* Substituting in (11.18) the expression obtained for $\Delta \mathbf{v}$, we write

$$\mathbf{a} = \lim_{\Delta t \to 0} \frac{\Delta \mathbf{v}}{\Delta t} = \lim_{\Delta t \to 0} \frac{\overrightarrow{QQ''}}{\Delta t} + \lim_{\Delta t \to 0} \frac{\overrightarrow{Q''Q'}}{\Delta t}$$

As Δt approaches zero, the vector $\overrightarrow{Q''Q'}$ becomes parallel to the tangent to the path at P and the vector $\overrightarrow{QQ''}$ becomes parallel to the normal. We must have, therefore,

$$\mathbf{a}_t = \lim_{\Delta t \to 0} \frac{\overrightarrow{Q''Q'}}{\Delta t} \qquad \mathbf{a}_n = \lim_{\Delta t \to 0} \frac{\overrightarrow{QQ''}}{\Delta t} \tag{11.27}$$

Considering first the tangential component, we observe that the length of the vector $\overrightarrow{Q''Q'}$ measures the change in speed $v' - v = \Delta v$. The scalar component a_t of the acceleration is therefore

$$a_t = \lim_{\Delta t \to 0} \frac{\Delta v}{\Delta t}$$

$$a_t = \frac{dv}{dt} \tag{11.28}$$

Formula (11.28) expresses that the *tangential component* a_t of the acceleration is equal to the *rate of change of the speed of the particle.*

Considering now the normal component of the acceleration, and denoting by $\Delta\theta$ the angle between the tangents to the path at P and P', we observe that, for small values of $\Delta\theta$, the length of the vector $\overrightarrow{QQ''}$ is equal to $v\Delta\theta$. Since the angle $\Delta\theta$ is equal to the angle between the normals at P and P' (Fig. 11.20*a*), we have $\Delta\theta = \Delta s/\rho$, where Δs is the length of the arc PP' and ρ the radius of curvature of the path at P. It thus follows from the second of the relations (11.27) that the scalar component a_n of the acceleration is

$$a_n = \lim_{\Delta t \to 0} \frac{v\Delta\theta}{\Delta t} = \lim_{\Delta t \to 0} \frac{v}{\rho}\frac{\Delta s}{\Delta t} = \frac{v}{\rho}\frac{ds}{dt}$$

Recalling from (11.15) that $ds/dt = v$, we have

$$a_n = \frac{v^2}{\rho} \tag{11.29}$$

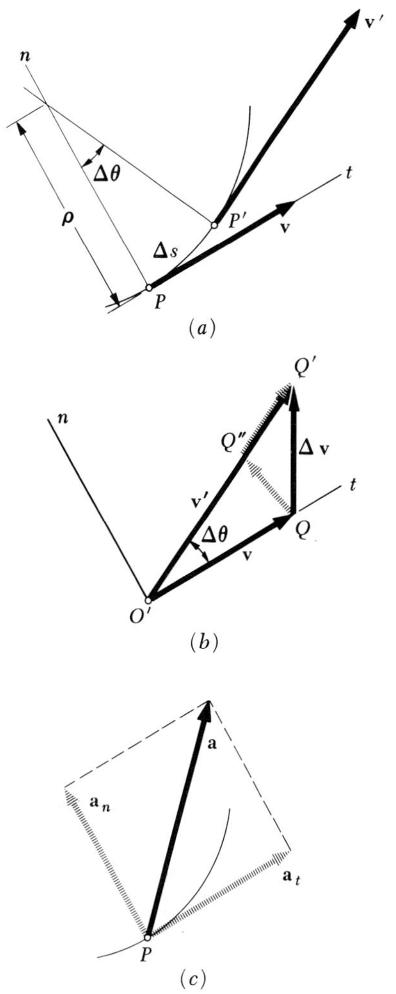

FIG. 11.20

Formula (11.29) expresses that the *normal component* a_n of the acceleration at P is equal to the *square of the speed divided by the radius of curvature of the path at P.* It should be noted that the vector $\mathbf{a}_n$ is always directed *toward the center of curvature of the path* (Fig. 11.20c).

It appears from the above that the tangential component of the acceleration reflects a change in the speed of the particle, while its normal component reflects a change in the direction of motion of the particle. The acceleration of a particle will be zero only if both its components are zero. Thus, the acceleration of a particle moving with constant speed along a curve will not be zero, unless the particle happens to pass through a point of inflection of the curve (where the radius of curvature is infinite) or unless the curve is a straight line.

The fact that the normal component of the acceleration depends upon the radius of curvature of the path followed by the particle is taken into account in the design of structures or mechanisms as widely different as airplane wings, railroad tracks, and cams. In order to avoid sudden changes in the acceleration of the air particles flowing past a wing, wing profiles are designed without any sudden change in curvature. Similar care is taken in designing railroad curves, to avoid sudden changes in the acceleration of the cars (which would be hard on the equipment and unpleasant for the passengers). A straight section of track, for instance, is never directly followed by a circular section. Special transition sections are used, to help pass smoothly from the infinite radius of curvature of the straight section to the finite radius of the circular track. Likewise, in the design of high-speed cams, abrupt changes in acceleration are avoided by using transition curves which produce a continuous change in acceleration.

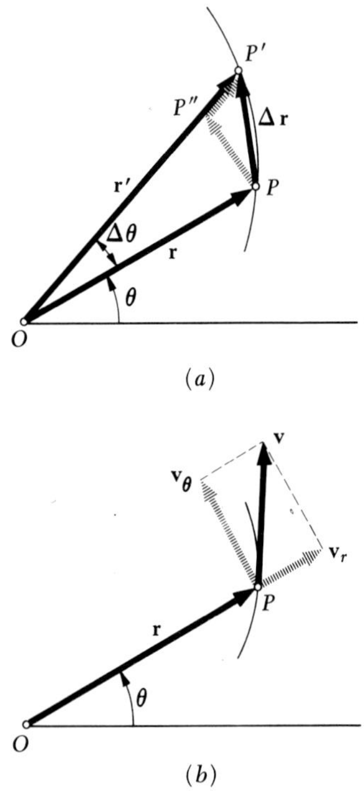

FIG. 11.21

***11.13. Radial and Transverse Components.** In certain problems, the position of a particle is defined by its polar coordinates r and θ. It is then convenient to resolve the velocity and acceleration of the particle into components parallel and perpendicular, respectively, to the position vector $\mathbf{r}$. These components are called *radial* and *transverse components.*

Consider the vectors $\mathbf{r}$ and $\mathbf{r}'$ defining the position of the particle respectively at times t and $t + \Delta t$ (Fig. 11.21*a*). We recall that the velocity of the particle at time t is defined as the limit of the quotient of $\Delta\mathbf{r}$ and Δt, where $\Delta\mathbf{r}$ is the vector joining P and P'. To obtain the radial component $\mathbf{v}_r$ and the transverse component $\mathbf{v}_\theta$ of the velocity, we measure a distance $OP'' = OP$ along the line OP' and resolve the vector $\Delta\mathbf{r}$ into its components $\overrightarrow{PP''}$ and $\overrightarrow{P''P'}$. The velocity $\mathbf{v}$ may thus be expressed as

$$\mathbf{v} = \lim_{\Delta t \to 0} \frac{\Delta \mathbf{r}}{\Delta t} = \lim_{\Delta t \to 0} \frac{\overrightarrow{PP''}}{\Delta t} + \lim_{\Delta t \to 0} \frac{\overrightarrow{P''P'}}{\Delta t}$$

As Δt approaches zero, the vectors $\overrightarrow{P''P'}$ and $\overrightarrow{PP''}$ become parallel and perpendicular, respectively, to $\mathbf{r}$. We must have, therefore,

$$\mathbf{v}_r = \lim_{\Delta t \to 0} \frac{\overrightarrow{P''P'}}{\Delta t} \qquad \mathbf{v}_\theta = \lim_{\Delta t \to 0} \frac{\overrightarrow{PP''}}{\Delta t}$$

We observe that the length of the vector $\overrightarrow{P''P'}$ measures the change in magnitude $r' - r = \Delta r$ of the radius vector. (Note that the change in magnitude Δr should not be confused with the magnitude of the vector $\Delta \mathbf{r}$, which represents a change in direction as well as in magnitude.) On the other hand, the length of the vector $\overrightarrow{PP''}$ is equal to $r\Delta\theta$ for small values of $\Delta\theta$. The scalar components of the velocity are therefore

$$v_r = \lim_{\Delta t \to 0} \frac{\Delta r}{\Delta t} \qquad v_\theta = \lim_{\Delta t \to 0} \frac{r\,\Delta\theta}{\Delta t}$$

$$v_r = \frac{dr}{dt} \qquad v_\theta = r\frac{d\theta}{dt} \tag{11.30}$$

Consider, now, the velocity $\mathbf{v}$ of P at a time t and its velocity $\mathbf{v}'$ at a time $t + \Delta t$ (Fig. 11.22*a*). Drawing the radial and transverse components of $\mathbf{v}$ and $\mathbf{v}'$ from the same origin O', we represent the change in velocity by the two vectors $\overrightarrow{RR'}$ and $\overrightarrow{TT'}$ (Fig. 11.22*b*). The vector $\overrightarrow{RR'}$ represents a change in magnitude and direction for the vector $\mathbf{v}_r$; similarly, the vector $\overrightarrow{TT'}$ represents a change in magnitude and direction for the vector $\mathbf{v}_\theta$. The sum of the vectors $\overrightarrow{RR'}$ and $\overrightarrow{TT'}$ represents the total change in velocity $\Delta\mathbf{v}$. As we saw earlier, the acceleration of the particle is defined as the limit of the quotient of $\Delta\mathbf{v}$ and Δt. To obtain the radial component $\mathbf{a}_r$ and the transverse component $\mathbf{a}_\theta$ of the acceleration, we resolve the vector $\overrightarrow{RR'}$ into its components $\overrightarrow{RR''}$ and $\overrightarrow{R''R'}$ (with $O'R'' = O'R$) and the vector $\overrightarrow{TT'}$ into its components $\overrightarrow{TT''}$ and $\overrightarrow{T''T'}$ (with $O'T'' = O'T$). The acceleration $\mathbf{a}$ of the particle may then be expressed as

$$\mathbf{a} = \lim_{\Delta t \to 0} \frac{\Delta \mathbf{v}}{\Delta t} = \lim_{\Delta t \to 0} \left(\frac{\overrightarrow{RR'}}{\Delta t} + \frac{\overrightarrow{TT'}}{\Delta t} \right)$$
$$= \lim_{\Delta t \to 0} \left(\frac{\overrightarrow{RR''}}{\Delta t} + \frac{\overrightarrow{R''R'}}{\Delta t} + \frac{\overrightarrow{TT''}}{\Delta t} + \frac{\overrightarrow{T''T'}}{\Delta t} \right)$$

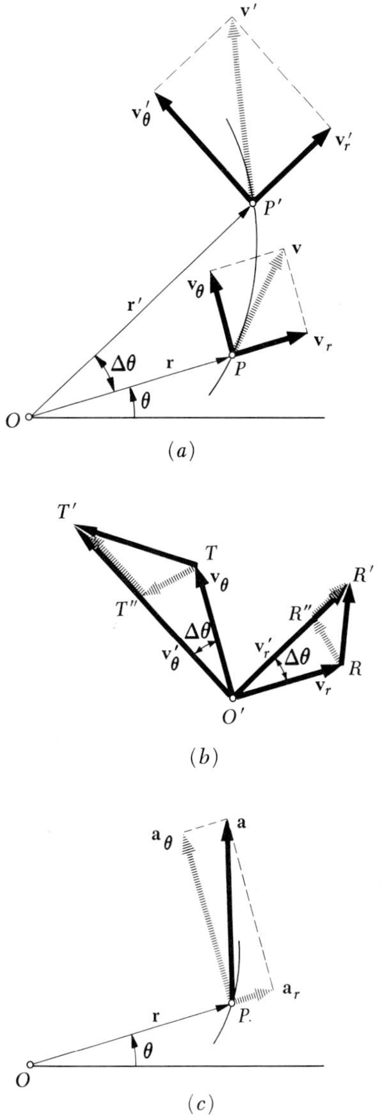

FIG. 11.22

As Δt approaches zero, the vectors $\overrightarrow{R''R'}$ and $\overrightarrow{TT''}$ become parallel to $\mathbf{r}$, while the vectors $\overrightarrow{RR''}$ and $\overrightarrow{T''T'}$ become perpendicular to $\mathbf{r}$. We must have, therefore,

$$\mathbf{a}_r = \lim_{\Delta t \to 0} \left(\frac{\overrightarrow{R''R'}}{\Delta t} + \frac{\overrightarrow{TT''}}{\Delta t} \right) \qquad \mathbf{a}_\theta = \lim_{\Delta t \to 0} \left(\frac{\overrightarrow{T''T'}}{\Delta t} + \frac{\overrightarrow{RR''}}{\Delta t} \right)$$

From Fig. 11.22*b* we observe that, for small values of Δt, the lengths of the various vectors involved are

$$R''R' = \Delta(v_r) \qquad T''T' = \Delta(v_\theta)$$
$$RR'' = v_r \Delta\theta \qquad TT'' = v_\theta \Delta\theta$$

where $\Delta(v_r)$ and $\Delta(v_\theta)$ represent the *change in magnitude* of the vectors $\mathbf{v}_r$ and $\mathbf{v}_\theta$, respectively. Noting also that the vector $\overrightarrow{TT''}$ has a sense opposite to that of $\mathbf{r}$, we obtain the following expressions for the scalar components of the acceleration:

$$a_r = \lim_{\Delta t \to 0} \left[\frac{\Delta(v_r)}{\Delta t} - \frac{v_\theta \, \Delta\theta}{\Delta t} \right] \qquad a_\theta = \lim_{\Delta t \to 0} \left[\frac{\Delta(v_\theta)}{\Delta t} + \frac{v_r \, \Delta\theta}{\Delta t} \right]$$

$$a_r = \frac{d(v_r)}{dt} - v_\theta \frac{d\theta}{dt} \qquad a_\theta = \frac{d(v_\theta)}{dt} + v_r \frac{d\theta}{dt} \qquad (11.31)$$

We should note that, in general, a_r *is not equal to* $d(v_r)/dt$ and a_θ *is not equal to* $d(v_\theta)/dt$. Each of the relations (11.31) contains an extra term which represents the *change in direction* of the vectors $\mathbf{v}_r$ and $\mathbf{v}_\theta$. Differentiating the relations (11.30), we obtain

$$\frac{d(v_r)}{dt} = \frac{d^2r}{dt^2} \qquad \frac{d(v_\theta)}{dt} = \frac{d}{dt}\left(r \frac{d\theta}{dt} \right) = r\frac{d^2\theta}{dt^2} + \frac{dr}{dt}\frac{d\theta}{dt}$$

$$(11.32)$$

Substituting from (11.30) and (11.32) into (11.31), we write

$$a_r = \frac{d^2r}{dt^2} - r\left(\frac{d\theta}{dt}\right)^2 \qquad a_\theta = r\frac{d^2\theta}{dt^2} + 2\,\frac{dr}{dt}\frac{d\theta}{dt} \qquad (11.33)$$

A positive value for a_r indicates that the vector $\mathbf{a}_r$ has the same sense as $\mathbf{r}$; a positive value for a_θ indicates that the vector $\mathbf{a}_\theta$ points toward increasing values of θ.

In the case of a particle moving along a circle of center O, we have r = constant, $dr/dt = d^2r/dt^2 = 0$, and the formulas (11.33) reduce to

$$a_r = -r\left(\frac{d\theta}{dt}\right)^2 \qquad a_\theta = r\frac{d^2\theta}{dt^2} \qquad (11.34)$$

SAMPLE PROBLEM 11.10

A train is traveling on a curved section of track of radius 3,000 ft at the speed of 90 mph. The brakes are suddenly applied, causing the train to slow down at a constant rate; after 6 sec, the speed has been reduced to 60 mph. Determine the acceleration of a car immediately after the brakes have been applied.

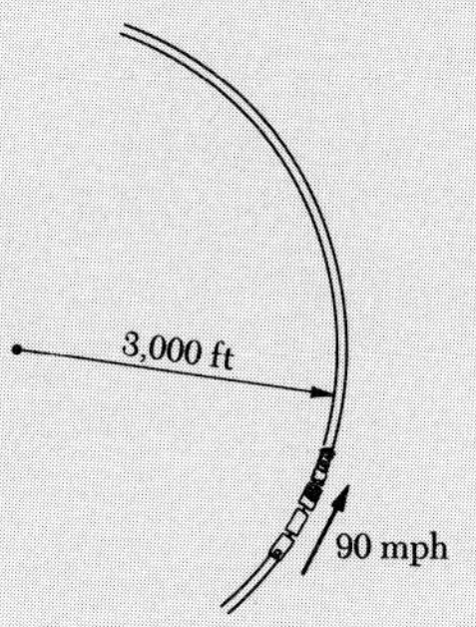

Tangential Component of Acceleration. First the speeds are expressed in ft/sec.

$$90 \text{ mph} = 90 \frac{\text{miles}}{\text{hr}} \frac{5{,}280 \text{ ft}}{1 \text{ mile}} \frac{1 \text{ hr}}{3{,}600 \text{ sec}} = 132 \text{ ft/sec}$$

$$60 \text{ mph} = 88 \text{ ft/sec}$$

Since the train slows down at a constant rate, we have

$$a_t = \text{average } a_t = \frac{\Delta v}{\Delta t} = \frac{88 \text{ ft/sec} - 132 \text{ ft/sec}}{6 \text{ sec}} = -7.33 \text{ ft/sec}^2$$

Normal Component of Acceleration. Immediately after the brakes have been applied, the speed is still 132 ft/sec, and we have

$$a_n = \frac{v^2}{\rho} = \frac{(132 \text{ ft/sec})^2}{3{,}000 \text{ ft}} = 5.81 \text{ ft/sec}^2$$

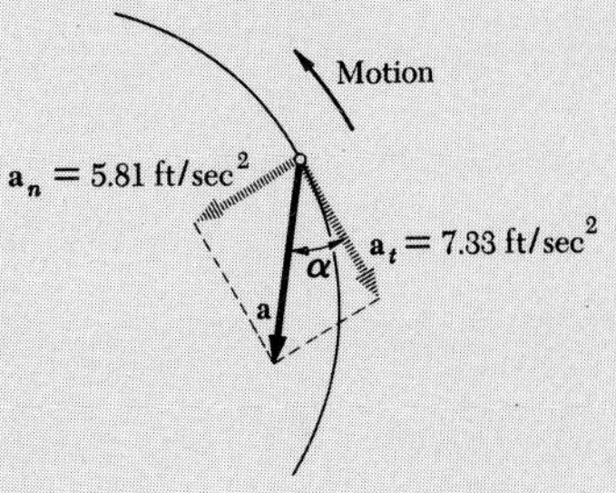

Magnitude and Direction of Acceleration. The magnitude and direction of the resultant **a** of the components $\mathbf{a}_n$ and $\mathbf{a}_t$ are determined as follows:

$$\tan \alpha = \frac{a_n}{a_t} = \frac{5.81 \text{ ft/sec}^2}{7.33 \text{ ft/sec}^2} \qquad \alpha = 38.4° \blacktriangleleft$$

$$a = \frac{a_n}{\sin \alpha} = \frac{5.81 \text{ ft/sec}^2}{\sin 38.4°} \qquad a = 9.35 \text{ ft/sec}^2 \blacktriangleleft$$

SAMPLE PROBLEM 11.11

Determine the minimum radius of curvature of the trajectory described by the projectile considered in Sample Prob. 11.7.

Solution. Since $a_n = v^2/\rho$, we have $\rho = v^2/a_n$. The radius will be small when v is small or when a_n is large. The speed v is minimum at the top of the trajectory, since $v_y = 0$ at that point; a_n is maximum at that same point, since the direction of the vertical coincides with the direction of the normal. Therefore, the minimum radius of curvature occurs at the top of the trajectory. At this point, we have

$$v = v_x = 520 \text{ ft/sec} \qquad a_n = a = 32.2 \text{ ft/sec}^2$$

$$\rho = \frac{v^2}{a_n} = \frac{(520 \text{ ft/sec})^2}{32.2 \text{ ft/sec}^2} \qquad \rho = 8{,}400 \text{ ft} \blacktriangleleft$$

SAMPLE PROBLEM 11.12

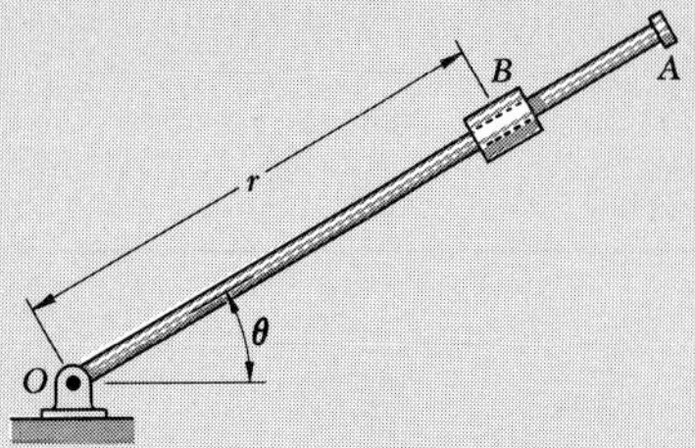

The rotation of the 3-ft arm OA about O is defined by the relation $\theta = 0.15t^2$, where θ is expressed in radians and t in seconds. Block B slides along the arm in such a way that its distance from O is $r = 3 - 0.40t^2$, where r is expressed in feet and t in seconds. Determine the total velocity and the total acceleration of block B after the arm OA has rotated through 30°.

Time When $\theta = 30°$. Substituting $\theta = 30° = 0.524$ radian into the expression for θ, we obtain

$$\theta = 0.15t^2 \qquad 0.524 = 0.15t^2 \qquad t = 1.869 \text{ sec}$$

Equations of Motion. Substituting $t = 1.869$ sec in the expressions for r, θ, and their first and second derivatives, we have

$$r = 3 - 0.40t^2 = 1.603 \text{ ft} \qquad \theta = 0.15t^2 = 0.524 \text{ radian}$$

$$\frac{dr}{dt} = -0.80t = -1.495 \text{ ft/sec} \qquad \frac{d\theta}{dt} = 0.30t = 0.561 \text{ radian/sec}$$

$$\frac{d^2r}{dt^2} = -0.80 = -0.800 \text{ ft/sec}^2 \qquad \frac{d^2\theta}{dt^2} = 0.30 = 0.300 \text{ radian/sec}^2$$

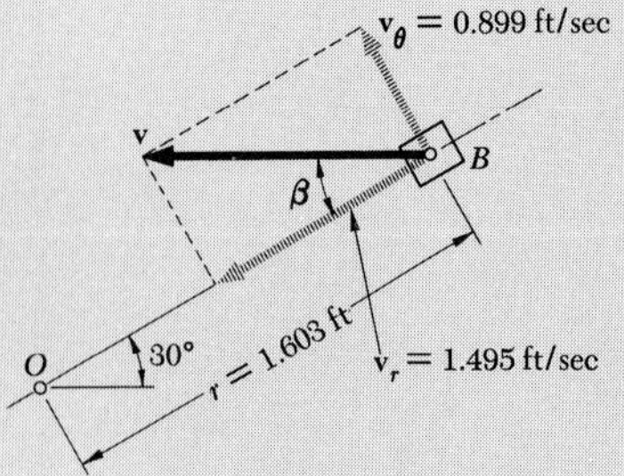

Velocity of B. Using Eqs. (11.30), we obtain the values of v_r and v_θ when $t = 1.869$ sec.

$$v_r = \frac{dr}{dt} = -1.495 \text{ ft/sec}$$

$$v_\theta = r\frac{d\theta}{dt} = (1.603)(0.561) = 0.899 \text{ ft/sec}$$

Solving the right triangle shown, we obtain the magnitude and direction of the velocity,

$$v = 1.745 \text{ ft/sec} \qquad \beta = 31.0° \blacktriangleleft$$

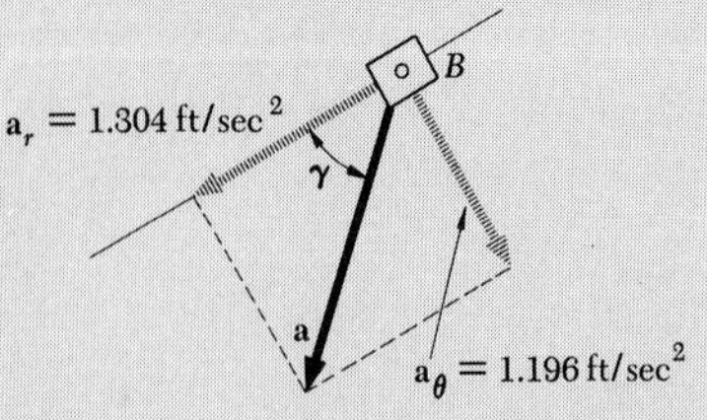

Acceleration of B. Using Eqs. (11.33), we obtain

$$a_r = \frac{d^2r}{dt^2} - r\left(\frac{d\theta}{dt}\right)^2$$

$$= -0.800 - (1.603)(0.561)^2 = -1.304 \text{ ft/sec}^2$$

$$a_\theta = r\frac{d^2\theta}{dt^2} + 2\frac{dr}{dt}\frac{d\theta}{dt}$$

$$= (1.603)(0.300) + (2)(-1.495)(0.561) = -1.196 \text{ ft/sec}^2$$

$$a = 1.770 \text{ ft/sec} \qquad \gamma = 42.5° \blacktriangleleft$$

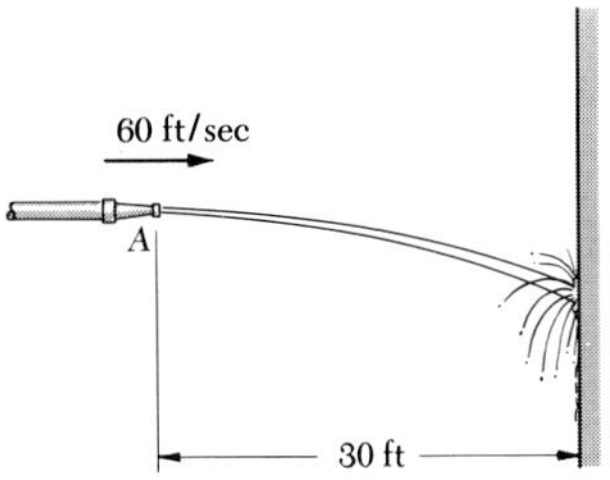

FIG. P 11.121

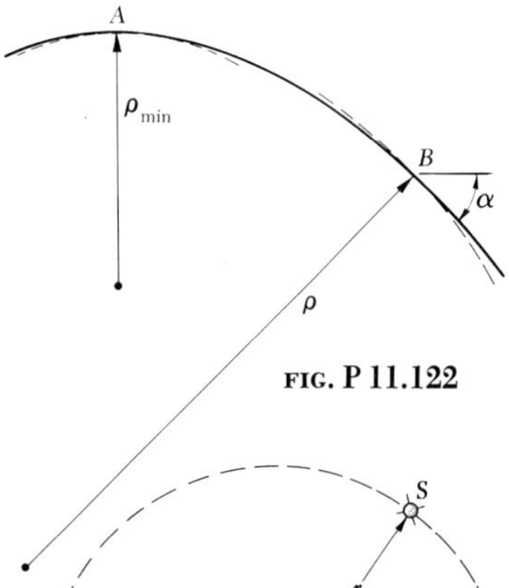

FIG. P 11.122

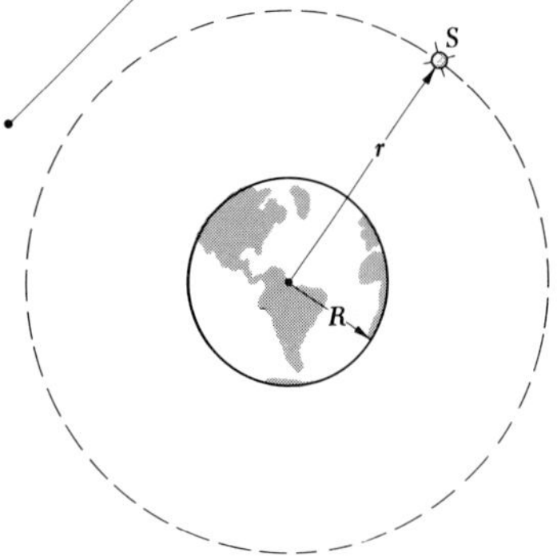

FIG. P 11.123

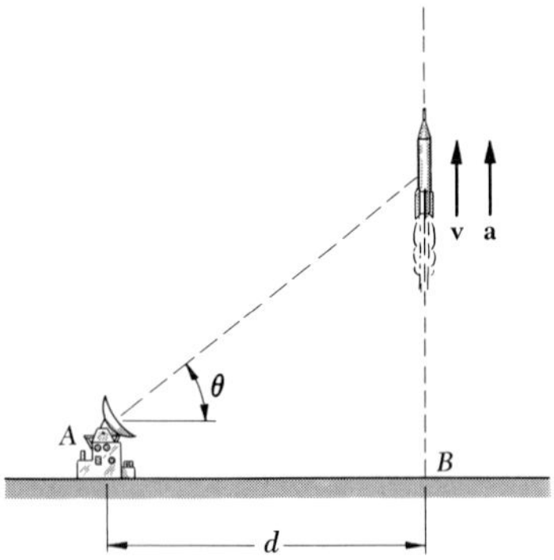

FIG. P 11.131

11.121. A nozzle discharges a stream of water horizontally with an initial velocity of 60 ft/sec. Determine the radius of curvature of the stream (*a*) as it leaves the nozzle, (*b*) as it strikes the wall at *B*.

11.122. (*a*) Show that the radius of curvature of the trajectory of a projectile reaches its minimum value at the highest point *A* of the trajectory. (*b*) Denoting by α the angle formed by the trajectory and the horizontal at a given point *B*, show that the radius of curvature of the trajectory at *B* is $\rho = \rho_{min}/\cos^3\alpha$.

11.123. A satellite will travel indefinitely in a circular orbit around the earth if the normal component of its acceleration is equal to $g(R/r)^2$, where $g = 32.2$ ft/sec², R = radius of the earth = 3,960 miles, and r = distance from the center of the earth to the satellite. Determine the height above the surface of the earth at which a satellite will travel indefinitely around the earth at a speed of 15,000 mph.

11.124. Determine the speed of an earth satellite traveling in a circular orbit 300 miles above the surface of the earth. (See information given in Prob. 11.123.)

11.125. Assuming the orbit of the moon to be a circle of radius 239,000 miles, determine the speed of the moon relative to the earth. (See information given in Prob. 11.123.)

11.126. Show that the speed of an earth satellite traveling in a circular orbit is inversely proportional to the square root of the radius of its orbit. Also, determine the minimum time in which a satellite can circle the earth. (See information given in Prob. 11.123.)

***11.127.** The two-dimensional motion of a particle is defined by the relations $r = t^3 - 2t^2$ and $\theta = t^3 - 4t$, where r is expressed in inches, t in seconds, and θ in radians. Determine the position, velocity, and acceleration of the particle when (*a*) $t = 0$, (*b*) $t = 1$ sec.

***11.128.** The particle of Prob. 11.127 is at the origin at $t = 0$. Determine its velocity and acceleration as it passes again through the origin.

***11.129.** The two-dimensional motion of a particle is defined by the relations $r = 2k \cos t$ and $\theta = t$. Determine (*a*) the path of the particle, (*b*) the velocity and acceleration of the particle at any time t.

***11.130.** The two-dimensional motion of a particle is defined by the relations $r = k(1 + \cos \frac{1}{2}\pi t)$ and $\theta = \frac{1}{2}\pi t$. Determine the velocity and acceleration of the particle when (*a*) $t = 1$, (*b*) $t = 2$.

***11.131.** A rocket is fired vertically from a launching pad at *B*. Its flight is tracked by radar from point *A*. Determine the velocity of the rocket in terms of d, θ, and $d\theta/dt$.

*11.132. Determine the acceleration of the rocket of Prob. 11.131 in terms of d, θ, $d\theta/dt$, and $d^2\theta/dt^2$.

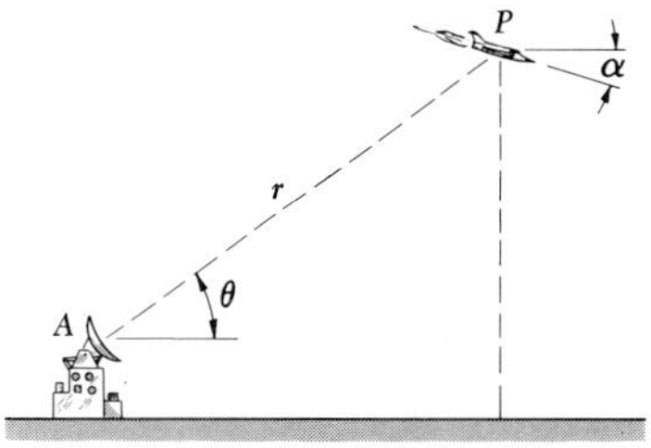

FIG. P 11.133

*11.133. An airplane passes over a radar tracking station at A and continues to fly due east. When the airplane is at P, the distance and angle of elevation of the plane are, respectively, $r = 11{,}200$ ft and $\theta = 26.5°$. Two seconds later the radar station sights the plane at $r = 12{,}300$ ft and $\theta = 23.3°$. Determine approximately the speed and the angle of dive α of the plane during the 2-sec interval.

*11.134 through 11.136. A particle moves along the spiral shown; determine the magnitude of the velocity of the particle in terms of b, θ, and $d\theta/dt$.

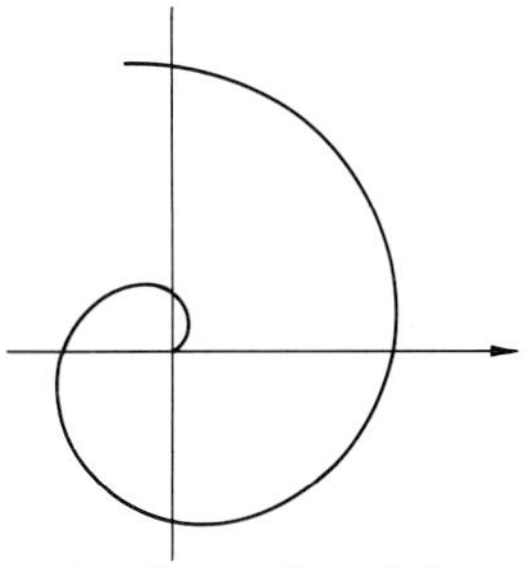

Archimedian spiral $r = b\,\theta$

FIG. P 11.134 AND P 11.137

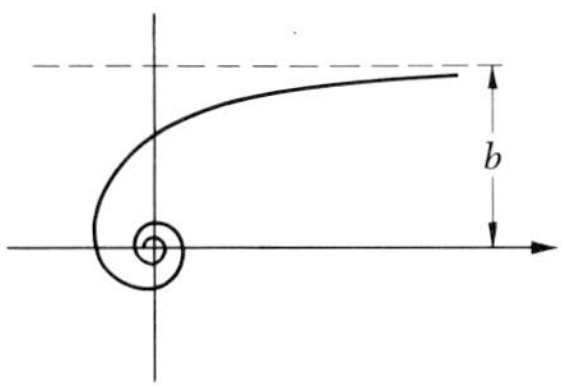

Hyperbolic spiral $r\,\theta = b$

FIG. P 11.135 AND P 11.138

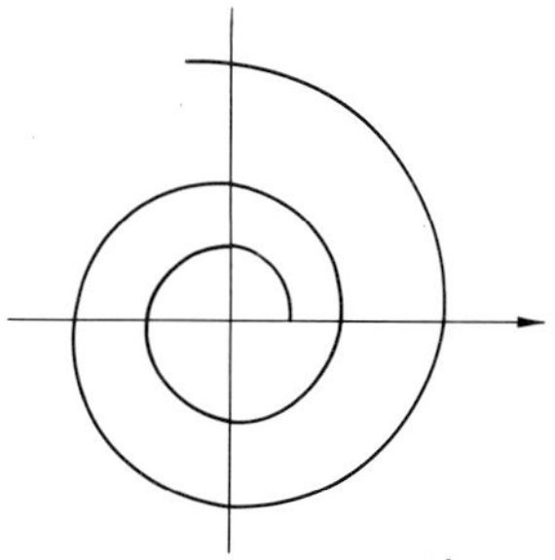

Logarithmic spiral $r = e^{b\theta}$

FIG. P 11.136 AND P 11.139

*11.137 through 11.139. A particle moves along the spiral shown. Knowing that $d\theta/dt$ is constant and denoting this constant by ω, determine the magnitude of the acceleration of the particle in terms of b, θ, and ω.

*11.140. The pin at B is free to slide along the circular slot and along the rotating rod OC. If pin B slides counterclockwise around the circular slot at a constant speed v_0, determine the rate $d\theta/dt$ at which rod OC rotates and the radial component v_r of the velocity of the pin B (a) when $\phi = 0°$, (b) when $\phi = 90°$.

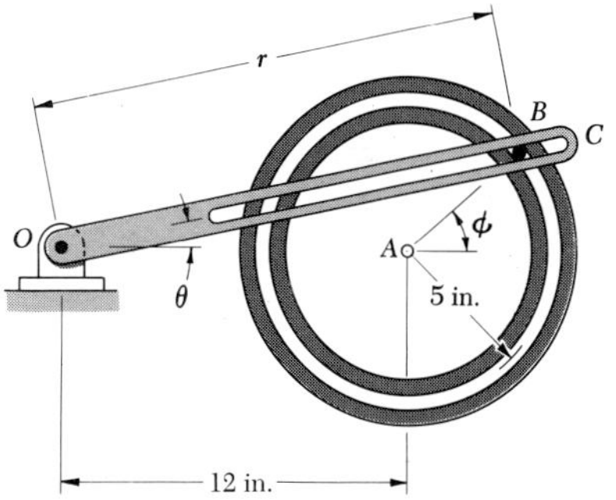

FIG. P 11.140

*11.141. In Prob. 11.140, determine (a) the angle ϕ for which $d\theta/dt$ is zero, (b) the angle ϕ for which $d\theta/dt$ is maximum and the corresponding magnitude of $d\theta/dt$.

REVIEW PROBLEMS

11.142. A ball is dropped vertically onto a 20° incline at A; the direction of rebound forms an angle of 40° with the vertical. Knowing that the ball next strikes the incline at B, determine (a) the velocity of rebound at A, (b) the time required for the ball to travel from A to B.

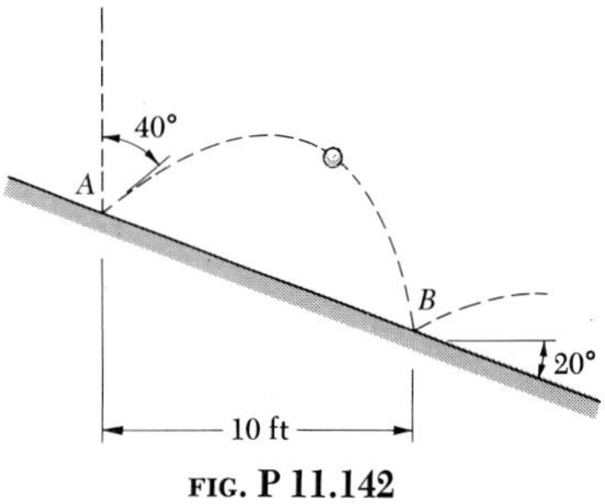

FIG. P 11.142

11.143. A battleship moving at 30 knots fires at a stationary target and hits it. Find the direction in which the guns are aimed, knowing that the muzzle velocity is 2,000 ft/sec, that the firing angle is 20°, and that the target is sighted 25° off the ship's course. (1 knot = 1 nautical mile per hour = 1.152 statute miles per hour.)

11.144. A car starts from rest at point A and accelerates at the rate of 3 ft/sec^2 until it reaches a speed of 45 mph. It then proceeds at 45 mph until the brakes are applied; it comes to a stop at point B, 198 ft beyond the point where the brakes were applied. Knowing that the *average* speed of the car is 30 mph, determine (a) the time required for the car to travel from A to B, (b) the distance from A to B.

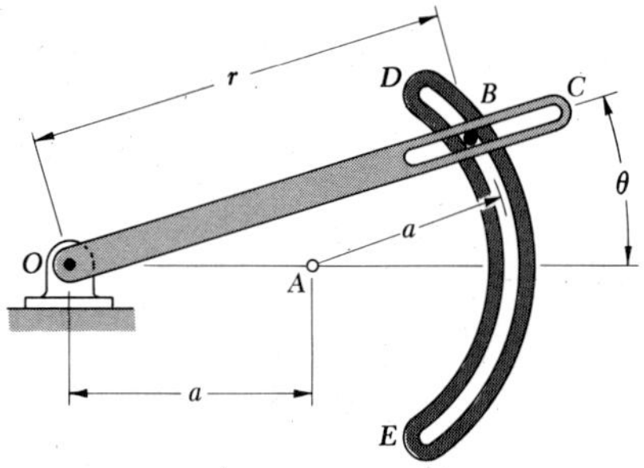

FIG. P 11.145

11.145. The pin at B is free to slide along the circular slot DE and along the rotating rod OC. Assuming that the rod OC rotates at a constant rate $d\theta/dt$, show that the acceleration of pin B is of constant magnitude. Also determine the direction of the acceleration of pin B.

11.146. In Prob. 11.60, the average velocity of the particle during the interval $t = 0$ to $t = t$ varies. Determine (a) the time t when the average velocity is maximum, (b) the magnitude of the maximum average velocity.

11.147. Determine the speed of an earth satellite which travels in a circular orbit at an altitude of 4,000 miles. (See information given in Prob. 11.123.)

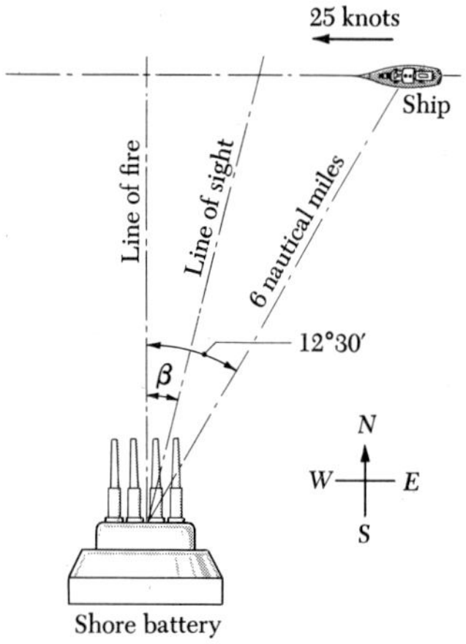

FIG. P 11.148

11.148. An enemy ship is observed from a shore battery 12°30′ east of north, at a distance of 6 nautical miles, steaming due west at a speed of 25 knots. The battery guns are immediately trained 0° north, ready to be fired when the ship crosses the line of sight. Knowing that the battery is located 60 ft above water level and that the muzzle velocity of its guns is 2,400 ft/sec, determine the firing angle α and the direction of the line of sight (angle β). (1 nautical mile = 1.152 statute miles, and 1 knot = 1 nautical mile per hour.)

11.149. An experimental ion-propulsion engine is capable of giving a space vehicle a constant acceleration of 0.01 ft/sec^2. If the engine is placed in operation when the speed of the vehicle is 18,000 mph, determine the time required to bring the speed of the vehicle to 20,000 mph. Assume that the vehicle is moving in a straight line, far from the sun or any planet.

11.150. For each of the two firing angles obtained in Sample Prob. 11.8, determine the radius of curvature of the trajectory described by the projectile as it leaves the gun.

11.151. The magnitude in ft/sec^2 of the deceleration due to air resistance of the nose cone of a small experimental rocket is known to be 0.0002 v^2, where v is expressed in ft/sec. If the nose cone is projected vertically from the ground with an initial velocity of 300 ft/sec, determine the maximum height that it will reach.

11.152. Determine the velocity of the nose cone of Prob. 11.151 when it returns to the ground.

11.153. Determine the time required for the nose cone of Prob. 11.151 to reach its maximum elevation.

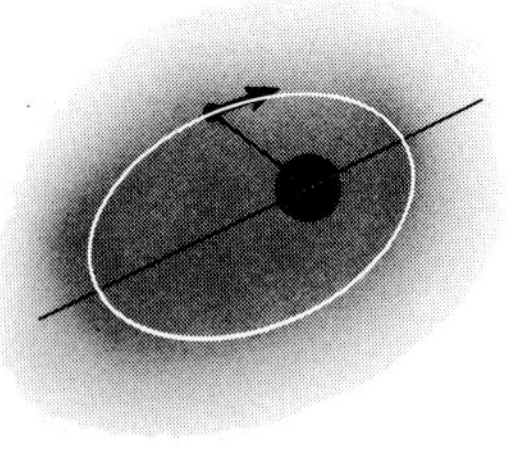

12. KINETICS OF PARTICLES: FORCE, MASS, AND ACCELERATION

12.1. Newton's Second Law of Motion. Newton's first and third laws of motion were used extensively in statics to study bodies at rest and the forces acting upon them. These two laws are also used in dynamics; in fact, they are sufficient for the study of the motion of bodies which have no acceleration. However, when bodies are accelerated, i.e., when the magnitude or the direction of their velocity changes, it is necessary to use the second law of motion in order to relate the motion of the body with the forces acting on it. This law may be stated as follows:

If the resultant force acting on a particle is not zero, the particle will have an acceleration proportional to the magnitude of the resultant and in the direction of this resultant force.

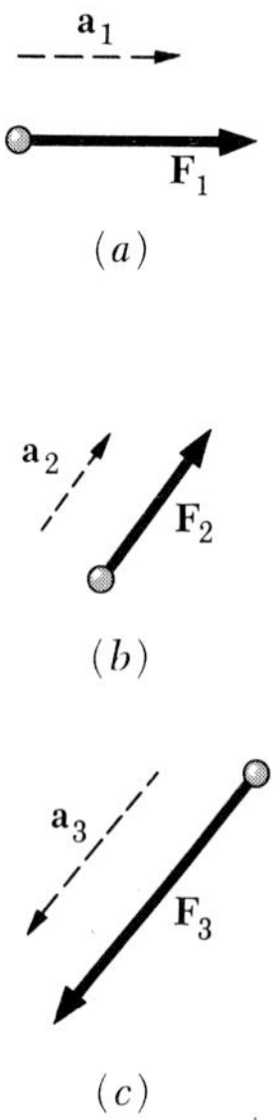

FIG. 12.1

Newton's second law of motion may best be understood if we imagine the following experiment: A particle is subjected to a force $\mathbf{F}_1$ of constant direction and constant magnitude F_1. Under the action of that force, the particle will be observed to move in a straight line and *in the direction of the force* (Fig. 12.1*a*). By determining the position of the particle at various instants, we find that its acceleration has a constant magnitude a_1. If the experiment is repeated with forces $\mathbf{F}_2$, $\mathbf{F}_3$, etc., of different magnitude or direction (Fig. 12.1*b* and *c*), we find each time that the particle moves in the direction of the force acting on it and that the magnitudes a_1, a_2, a_3, etc., of the accelerations are proportional to the magnitudes F_1, F_2, F_3, etc., of the corresponding forces,

$$\frac{F_1}{a_1} = \frac{F_2}{a_2} = \frac{F_3}{a_3} = \cdots = \text{constant}$$

The constant value obtained for the ratio of the magnitudes of the forces and accelerations is a characteristic of the particle under consideration. It is called the *mass* of the particle and is denoted by m. When a particle of mass m is acted upon by a force **F**, the force **F** and the acceleration **a** of the particle must therefore satisfy the relation

$$\mathbf{F} = m\mathbf{a} \tag{12.1}$$

This relation provides a complete formulation of Newton's second law; it expresses not only that the magnitudes of **F** and **a** are proportional, but also (since m is a positive scalar) that the vectors **F** and **a** have the same direction (Fig. 12.2). We should note that, when **F** is not constant but varies with t, the acceleration **a** will also vary with t; however, Eq. (12.1) will still hold at any given instant.

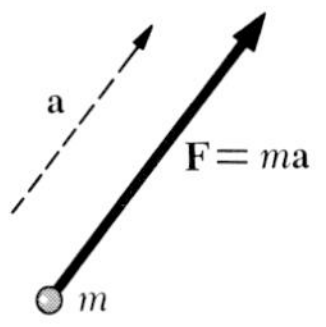

FIG. 12.2

When a particle is subjected simultaneously to several forces, Eq. (12.1) should be replaced by

$$\Sigma\mathbf{F} = m\mathbf{a} \tag{12.2}$$

where $\Sigma\mathbf{F}$ represents the sum, or resultant, of all the forces acting on the particle.

It should be noted that the system of axes with respect to which the acceleration **a** is determined is not arbitrary. These axes must have a constant orientation with respect to the stars, and their origin must either be attached to the sun† or move with a constant velocity with respect to the sun. Such a system of axes is called a *newtonian frame of reference.*‡ A system of axes attached to the earth does *not* constitute a newtonian frame of reference, since the earth rotates with respect to the stars and is accelerated with respect to the sun. However, in most engineering applications, the acceleration **a** may be determined with respect to axes attached to the earth and Eqs. (12.1) and (12.2) used without any appreciable error. On the other hand, these equations do not hold if **a** represents a relative acceleration measured with respect to moving axes, such as axes attached to an accelerated car or to a rotating piece of machinery.

12.2. Systems of Units. In using the fundamental equation $\mathbf{F} = m\mathbf{a}$, the units of force, mass, length, and time cannot be chosen arbitrarily. If they were, the magnitude of the force **F** required to give an acceleration **a** to the mass m would *not* be numerically equal to the product ma; it would only be proportional to this product. Thus, we may choose three of the

† More accurately, to the mass center of the solar system.

‡ Since the stars are not actually fixed, a more rigorous definition of a newtonian frame of reference (also called *inertial system*) is *one with respect to which Eq.* (12.2) *holds.*

four units arbitrarily but must choose the fourth unit so that the equation $\mathbf{F} = m\mathbf{a}$ is satisfied. The units are then said to form a consistent system of kinetic units.

Five consistent systems of kinetic units are shown in Table 12.1. Consider, for instance, the mks system, generally used

TABLE 12.1
Systems of Units

Dimensions	British systems	Metric systems	
	Absolute:	Absolute (mks):	Absolute (cgs):
Length	Foot (ft)	Meter (m)	Centimeter (cm)
Mass	Pound (lb)	Kilogram (kg)	Gram (g)
Time	Second (sec)	Second (sec)	Second (sec)
Force, from $F = ma$	Poundal (lb-ft/sec^2)	Newton (kg-m/sec^2)	Dyne (g-cm/sec^2)
	Gravitational:	Gravitational:	
Length	Foot (ft)	Meter (m)	
Force	Pound (lb)	Kilogram (kg)	
Time	Second (sec)	Second (sec)	
Mass, from $F = ma$	Slug (lb-sec^2/ft)	Kg-sec^2/m	

by physicists. The units of length, mass, and time are, respectively, the *meter* (m), the *kilogram* (kg), and the *second* (sec). All three are arbitrarily defined. The second, which represents the 1/86,400 part of the mean solar day, is officially defined as the 1/31,556,925.9747 part of the tropical year 1900. The meter, originally intended to represent 1 ten-millionth of the distance from the equator to the pole, is now defined as 1,650,763.73 wavelengths of the orange-red line of krypton-86. The kilogram, which is approximately equal to the mass of 0.001 cubic meter of water, is actually defined as the mass of a platinum standard kept at the International Bureau of Weights and Measures at Sèvres, near Paris, France. The unit of force, called the *newton*, is not arbitrary. It is defined as the force which gives an acceleration of 1 m/sec^2 to a mass of 1 kg. From (12.1), we write

$$1 \text{ newton} = (1 \text{ kg})(1 \text{ m/sec}^2)$$

The mks system is said to be an *absolute* system of units. This means that the three fundamental units chosen (meter, kilogram, second) are independent of the location where measurements are made. The meter, the kilogram, and the second may be used anywhere on the earth; they might even be used on another planet. They will always have the same significance.

Other absolute systems of units are the cgs system and the British absolute sytem. In the cgs system, the units of length, mass, and time are, respectively, the *centimeter* (cm), the *gram* (g), and the *second.* The centimeter is defined as 0.01 m and the gram as 0.001 kg. The unit of force is the *dyne,* defined as the force which gives an acceleration of 1 cm/sec² to a mass of 1 g. In the British absolute system, the units of length, mass, and time are, respectively, the *foot,* the *pound,* and the *second.* The foot is equal to 0.304800 m, and the pound is equal to 0.45359243 kg. Both units are represented by standards kept at the National Bureau of Standards in Washington. The unit of force in this system is the *poundal,* defined as the force which gives an acceleration of 1 ft/sec² to a mass of 1 lb.

Engineers do not use absolute systems of units. They prefer to choose as fundamental units the units of *length, force,* and *time.* Such a system of units is called a *gravitational* system of units. In English-speaking countries, engineers use the British gravitational system of units, based on the foot, the pound, and the second. It should be noted that in this system the pound is used, not as a unit of mass, but as a *unit of force.* This force is defined as the *weight* of a mass of 1 lb (i.e., the force exerted by the earth on a mass of 1 lb) at sea level and at the latitude of 45°. Since at such a location the acceleration of freely falling bodies is 32.2 ft/sec², we see that a force of 1 lb gives an acceleration of 32.2 ft/sec² to a mass of 1 lb (Fig. 12.3*a*). The foot, the pound force, the second, and the pound mass, therefore, do not form a consistent system of units. The unit of mass consistent with the foot, the pound force, and the second must be a mass which receives an acceleration of 1 ft/sec² when a force of 1 lb is applied to it (Fig. 12.3*b*). This unit, sometimes called a *slug,* is obtained by solving the equation $F = ma$ for m and substituting 1 lb and 1 ft/sec² for F and a, respectively:

$$m = \frac{F}{a} \qquad 1 \text{ slug} = \frac{1 \text{ lb}}{1 \text{ ft/sec}^2} = 1 \text{ lb-sec}^2\text{/ft}$$

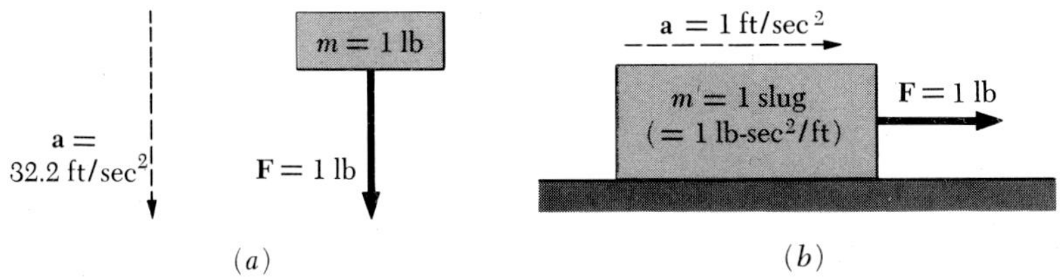

FIG. 12.3

From the definition of the pound force and of the slug (or lb-sec^2/ft), it appears (Fig. 12.3) that

$$1 \text{ slug} = 1 \text{ lb-sec}^2/\text{ft} = 32.2 \text{ lb mass}$$

The mass m (in slugs) of a body whose weight is known to have a magnitude W (in lb) may therefore be expressed as

$$m = \frac{W}{g}$$

where g is the acceleration of gravity ($g = 32.2$ ft/sec^2).

Gravitational units are preferred to absolute units in engineering because forces are more frequently used than masses; it is thus more natural to use the pound as a unit of force than as a unit of mass. These units, however, would present difficulties if very precise measurements were needed (which is usually not the case in engineering) or if experiments were to be conducted on another planet (which engineers have not done yet). Since the force of attraction exerted by the earth on a given object varies with the altitude and latitude of the object,† the weight of the standard kept at the National Bureau of Standards will not be exactly 1 lb at altitudes other than sea level or at latitudes other than 45°, and the weight of the standard pound will obviously be very different if it is measured on the moon, where gravitational forces are much smaller than on the earth. Clearly, the units used by engineers *are not absolute*; and because they depend upon the effects of gravitation, they are said to form a gravitational system of units. However, variations in gravitation may usually be neglected in studying the motion of engineering structures on the surface of the earth.

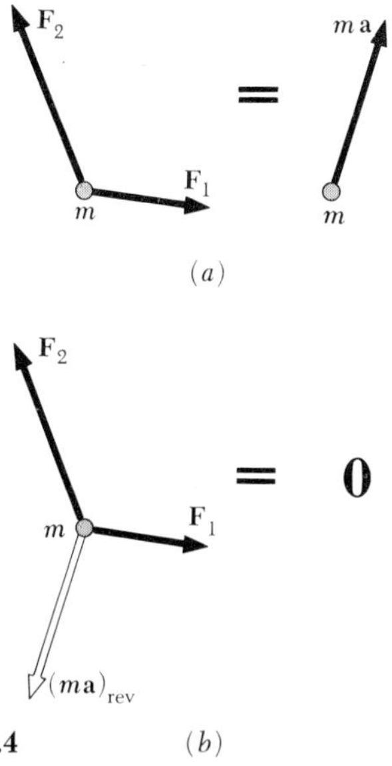

FIG. 12.4

12.3. Equations of Motion. Dynamic Equilibrium. Consider a particle of mass m acted upon by several forces. Newton's second law of motion states that the resultant of these forces must be equal to the vector $m\mathbf{a}$ obtained by multiplying the acceleration $\mathbf{a}$ of the particle by its mass m. The given system of forces must therefore be equivalent to the vector $m\mathbf{a}$ (Fig. 12.4*a*). Using rectangular components, we write the equations of motion,

$$\Sigma F_x = ma_x \qquad \Sigma F_y = ma_y \qquad \Sigma F_z = ma_z \qquad (12.3)$$

Newton's second law may also be expressed by considering a vector of magnitude ma, but of *sense opposite* to that of the

† See Sec. 12.10 and Prob. 12.1.

acceleration. This vector is denoted by $(m\mathbf{a})_{\text{rev}}$, where the subscript indicates that the sense of the acceleration has been reversed, and is called an *inertia vector.* If the inertia vectoı $(m\mathbf{a})_{\text{rev}}$ is added to the forces acting on the particle, *we obtain a system of vectors equivalent to zero* (Fig. 12.4*b*). The particle may thus be considered to be in equilibrium under the given forces and the inertia vector. The particle is said to be in *dynamic equilibrium,* and the problem under consideration may be solved by using the methods developed earlier in statics. We may, for instance, write that the sums of the components of the vectors shown in Fig. 12.4*b, including the inertia vector,* are zero,

$$\Sigma F_x = 0 \quad \Sigma F_y = 0 \quad \Sigma F_z = 0 \quad \text{including inertia vector} \tag{12.4}$$

or if the forces are coplanar, we may draw all vectors tip to tail, including again the inertia vector, to form a closed vector polygon.

The inertia vector measures the resistance the particle offers when we try to set it in motion or when we try to change the conditions of its motion. For this reason, it is often called an *inertia force.* The inertia force, however, is not a force like the forces found in statics, which are either contact forces or gravitational forces (weights). Many people, therefore, object to the use of the word force when referring to the vector $(m\mathbf{a})_{\text{rev}}$ or even avoid altogether the concept of dynamic equilibrium. Others point out that inertia forces and actual forces such as gravitational forces affect our senses in the same way and cannot be distinguished by physical measurements. A man riding in an elevator which is accelerated upward will have the feeling that his weight has suddenly increased; and no measurement made within the elevator could establish whether the elevator is truly accelerated or whether the force of attraction exerted by the earth has suddenly increased.

Our main interest in this text, however, is not the philosophical interpretation of physical concepts but rather the application of these concepts to the solution of engineering problems. From this viewpoint, it makes little difference whether we use Eqs. (12.3) or (12.4) to express the conditions of motion of a particle. In order to distinguish the vector $(m\mathbf{a})_{\text{rev}}$ from actual forces, however, we shall call it an inertia vector throughout this text, rather than an inertia force.

12.4. Systems of Particles. D'Alembert's Principle. When a problem involves the motion of several particles, the equations of motion, (12.3) or (12.4), may be written for each particle considered separately. However, in the case of a system involving a large number of particles, such as a rigid body, it will generally be more convenient to consider the system as a whole. In that case, we should note that the forces acting on a given particle of the system consist (1) of *external forces* exerted by bodies outside the system (such as the weight of the particle, which is exerted by the earth) and (2) of *internal forces* exerted by the other particles of the system. According to Newton's second law, the resultant of the external and internal forces acting on the particle considered is equal to the vector $m\mathbf{a}$ obtained by multiplying the acceleration $\mathbf{a}$ of the particle by its mass m. This vector is generally known as the *effective force* of the particle.

We now consider simultaneously all the particles of the system (Fig. 12.5). Since the relation we have established holds for any particle, it follows that the resultant of all the external and internal forces acting on the particles of the system is equal to the resultant of the effective forces of all the particles. But, according to Newton's third law, the internal forces occur by pairs of equal and opposite forces having the same line of action, and the system of the internal forces therefore reduces to zero. We thus conclude that *the external forces acting on the system of particles are equivalent to the effective forces of the various particles of the system.*

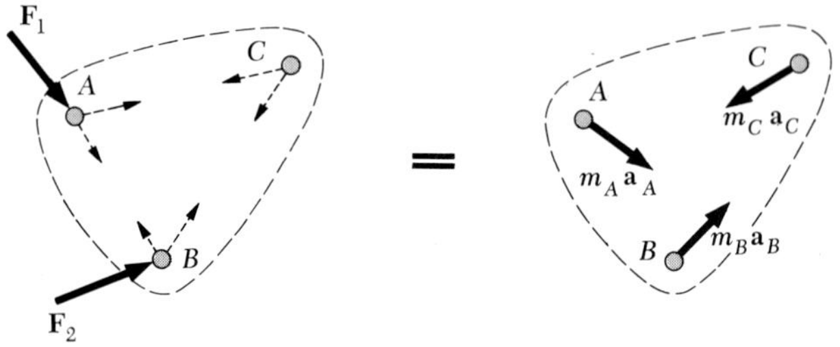

FIG. 12.5

This important statement is known as *D'Alembert's principle,* after the French mathematician Jean le Rond d'Alembert (1717–1783). From this principle it follows that the sum of the components of the external forces in any direction is equal to the sum of the components of the effective forces in the same direction, and that the sum of the moments of the external forces about any axis is equal to the sum of the moments of the effective forces about the same axis. Expressing mathematically the first part of this statement, we write

$$\Sigma(F_x)_{\text{ext}} = \Sigma ma_x \qquad \Sigma(F_y)_{\text{ext}} = \Sigma ma_y \qquad \Sigma(F_z)_{\text{ext}} = \Sigma ma_z \tag{12.5}$$

The result obtained may be presented in an alternate form if we consider the inertia vectors $(m\mathbf{a})_{\text{rev}}$ of sense opposite to the accelerations of the particles. Adding these vectors, also called *reversed effective forces,* to the external forces (Fig. 12.6), we obtain a system equivalent to zero. This alternate presentation will be used extensively in the analysis of the motion of rigid bodies (Chap. 16).

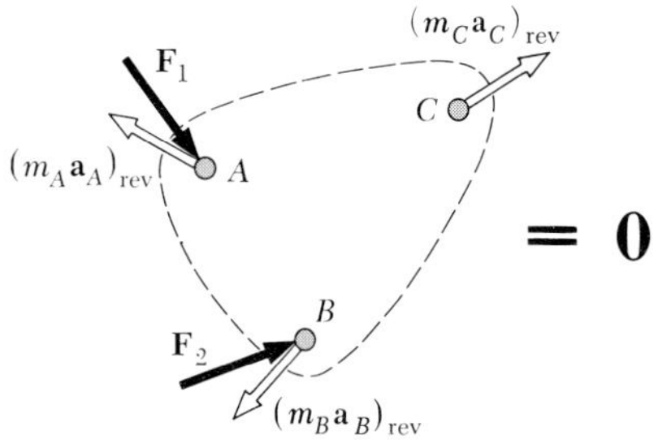

FIG. 12.6

12.5. Motion of the Mass Center of a System of Particles. Equations (12.5) may be written in a modified form if the *mass center* of the system of particles is considered. The mass center of the system is the point G of coordinates $\bar{x}$, $\bar{y}$, $\bar{z}$ defined by the equations

$$(\Sigma m)\bar{x} = \Sigma mx \qquad (\Sigma m)\bar{y} = \Sigma my \qquad (\Sigma m)\bar{z} = \Sigma mz \tag{12.6}$$

Since $W = mg$, we note that G is also the center of gravity of the system. However, in order to avoid any confusion, we shall call G the *mass center* of the system of particles when discussing properties of the system associated with the *mass* of the particles, and we shall refer to it as the *center of gravity* of the system when considering properties associated with the *weight* of the particles. Particles located outside the gravitational field of the earth, for example, have a mass but no weight. We may then properly refer to their mass center, but obviously not to their center of gravity.†

We differentiate twice with respect to t the relations (12.6):

$$\left(\sum m\right)\frac{d^2\bar{x}}{dt^2} = \sum m\frac{d^2x}{dt^2} \qquad \left(\sum m\right)\frac{d^2\bar{y}}{dt^2} = \sum m\frac{d^2y}{dt^2}$$
$$\left(\sum m\right)\frac{d^2\bar{z}}{dt^2} = \sum m\frac{d^2z}{dt^2}$$

Recalling that the second derivatives of the coordinates of a point represent the components of the acceleration of that point, we have

$$(\Sigma m)\bar{a}_x = \Sigma ma_x \qquad (\Sigma m)\bar{a}_y = \Sigma ma_y \qquad (\Sigma m)\bar{a}_z = \Sigma ma_z \tag{12.7}$$

† It may also be pointed out that the mass center and the center of gravity of a system of particles do not exactly coincide, since the weights of the particles are directed toward the center of the earth and thus do not truly form a system of parallel forces.

where $\bar{a}_x$, $\bar{a}_y$, $\bar{a}_z$ represent the components of the acceleration $\bar{\mathbf{a}}$ of the mass center G of the system. Combining the relations (12.5) and (12.7), we write the equations

$$\Sigma(F_x)_{\text{ext}} = (\Sigma m)\bar{a}_x \qquad \Sigma(F_y)_{\text{ext}} = (\Sigma m)\bar{a}_y$$
$$\Sigma(F_z)_{\text{ext}} = (\Sigma m)\bar{a}_z \tag{12.8}$$

which define the motion of the mass center of the system. We note that Eqs. (12.8) are identical with the equations we would obtain for a particle of mass Σm, acted upon by all the external forces. We state therefore: *The mass center of a system of particles moves as if the entire mass of the system and all the external forces were concentrated at that point.*

This principle is best illustrated by the motion of an exploding shell. We know that, if the resistance of the air is neglected, a shell may be assumed to travel along a parabolic path. After the shell has exploded, the mass center G of the fragments of shell will continue to travel along the same path. Indeed, point G must move as if the mass and the weight of all fragments were concentrated at G; it must move, therefore, as if the shell had not exploded.

The principle we have established shows that we may replace a rigid body by a particle of the same mass if we are interested in the motion of the mass center of the body, and not in the motion of the body about its mass center. We should keep in mind, however, that Eqs. (12.7) and (12.8) relate the components, but not the moments of the forces and vectors involved. For example, Eqs. (12.7) *do not express* that the effective forces of the particles of the system are equivalent to a vector $(\Sigma m)\bar{\mathbf{a}}$ attached at the mass center G. As we shall see in Chap. 16, the resultant of the effective forces and, thus, the resultant of the external forces do not in general pass through the mass center of the system of particles.

12.6. Rectilinear Motion of a Particle. Consider a particle of mass m moving in a straight line under the action of coplanar forces $\mathbf{F}_1$, $\mathbf{F}_2$, $\mathbf{F}_3$, etc. The conditions of motion of the particle are expressed by Eq. (12.2). Since the particle moves in a straight line, its acceleration $\mathbf{a}$ must be directed along that line. Choosing the x axis in the same direction and the y axis in the plane of the forces (Fig. 12.7), we have $a_x = a$, $a_y = 0$ and write

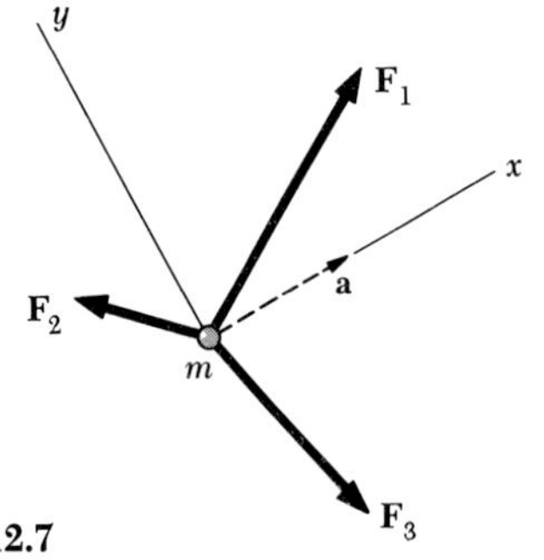

FIG. 12.7

$$\Sigma F_x = ma \qquad \Sigma F_y = 0 \tag{12.9}$$

The equations obtained may be solved for two unknowns.

SAMPLE PROBLEM 12.1

A 200-lb block rests on a horizontal plane. Find the magnitude of the force **P** required to give the block an acceleration of 10 ft/sec² to the right. The coefficient of friction between the block and the plane is $\mu = 0.25$.

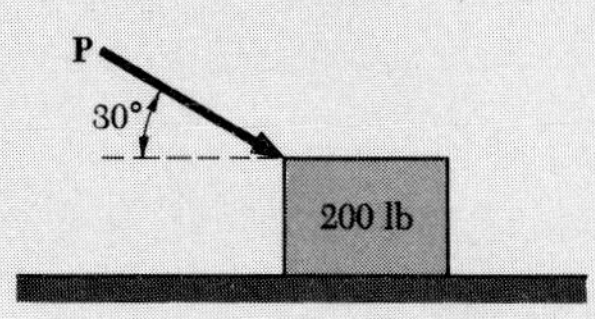

Solution. The mass of the block is

$$m = \frac{W}{g} = \frac{200 \text{ lb}}{32.2 \text{ ft/sec}^2} = 6.21 \text{ lb-sec}^2\text{/ft}$$

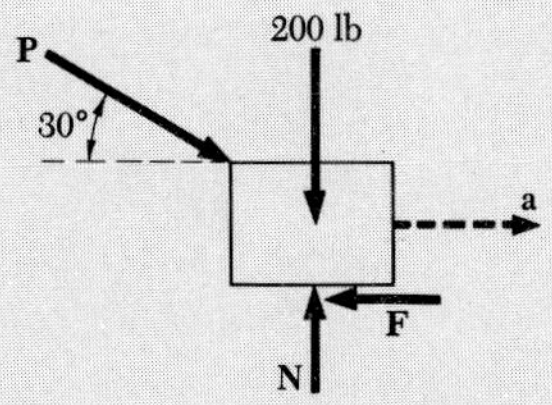

We note that $F = \mu N = 0.25N$ and that $a = 10$ ft/sec². Expressing that the forces acting on the block are equivalent to the vector $m\mathbf{a}$, we write

$$\overset{+}{\rightarrow} \Sigma F_x = ma: \quad P \cos 30° - 0.25N = (6.21)(10) \qquad (1)$$

$$+\uparrow \Sigma F_y = 0: \quad N - P \sin 30° - 200 = 0 \qquad (2)$$

Solving (2) for N and carrying the result into (1), we obtain

$$N = P \sin 30° + 200$$

$$P \cos 30° - 0.25(P \sin 30° + 200) = 62.1$$

$$P = 151 \text{ lb} \quad ◄$$

SAMPLE PROBLEM 12.2

The two blocks shown start from rest; block A moves on a horizontal frictionless plane. Determine the acceleration of block A and the tension in the cord.

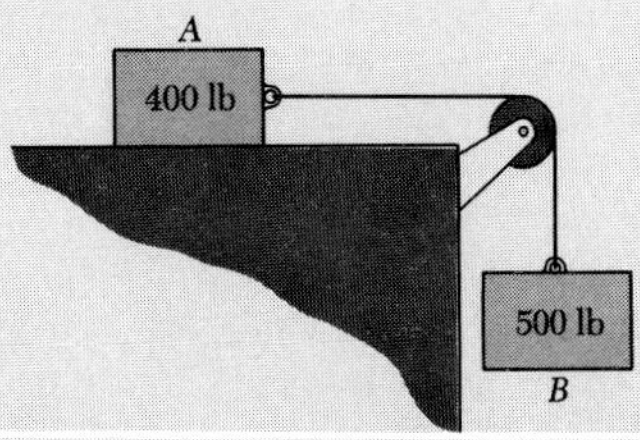

Solution. We note that the accelerations of blocks A and B have the same magnitude a. Applying Newton's second law to each of the blocks, we write the following:

Block A:

$$m_A = \frac{400 \text{ lb}}{32.2 \text{ ft/sec}^2} = 12.42 \text{ lb-sec}^2\text{/ft}$$

$$\overset{+}{\rightarrow} \Sigma F_x = m_A a: \quad T = 12.42a \qquad (1)$$

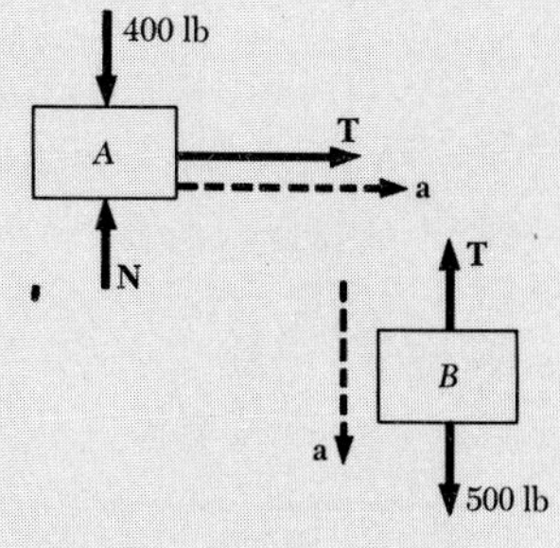

Block B:

$$m_B = \frac{500 \text{ lb}}{32.2 \text{ ft/sec}^2} = 15.53 \text{ lb-sec}^2\text{/ft}$$

$$+\downarrow \Sigma F_y = m_B a: \quad 500 - T = 15.53a \qquad (2)$$

Solving Eqs. (1) and (2) simultaneously, we obtain

$$a = 17.89 \text{ ft/sec}^2 \qquad T = 222 \text{ lb} \quad ◄$$

We should note that the tension in the cord does *not* equal the weight of block B.

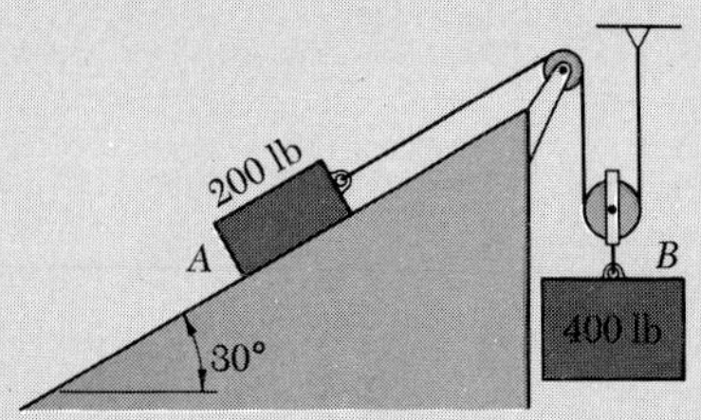

SAMPLE PROBLEM 12.3

The two blocks shown start from rest. The coefficient of friction between block A and the incline is 0.25, and the pulleys are weightless and frictionless. Determine the acceleration of each block and the tension in each cord.

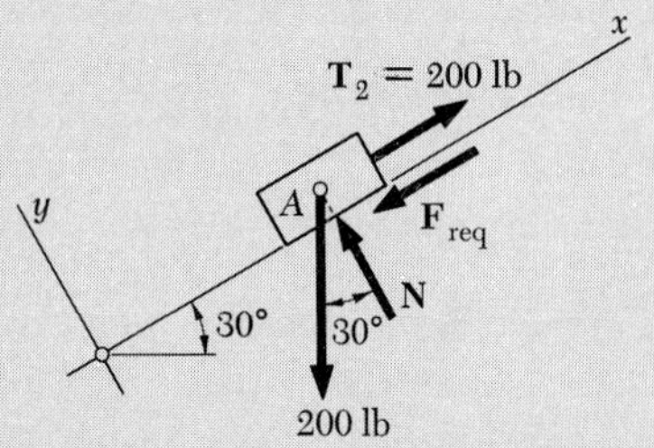

Sense of Motion. When friction is involved, the sense of motion should be determined at the outset by finding what friction force would be *required* to keep the system from moving. This part of the solution may be carried out by the methods of statics with the system at rest and with no acceleration. We first find that the tension in the cable attached to block A is $T_2 = 200$ lb. *Note that this will not be the tension when the blocks are moving.*

$$+\nearrow \Sigma F_x = 0: \qquad 200 - 200 \sin 30° - F_{req} = 0$$

$$F_{req} = +100 \text{ lb} \qquad \mathbf{F}_{req} = 100 \text{ lb} \swarrow$$

$$+\nwarrow \Sigma F_y = 0: \qquad N - 200 \cos 30° = 0 \qquad N = 173 \text{ lb}$$

$$F_m = \mu N \qquad F_m = (0.25)(173) = 43.3 \text{ lb} \qquad \mathbf{F}_m = 43.3 \text{ lb} \swarrow$$

Since the force of friction required to keep the blocks from moving is larger than the maximum friction force $\mathbf{F}_m$ and is directed to the left, block A will *move to the right.*

Accelerations and Tensions. Since the system has only one degree of freedom, the magnitudes of the accelerations of blocks A and B may be expressed in terms of the single unknown a_A.

Block B. The acceleration of B is directed downward and is of magnitude $a_B = \frac{1}{2}a_A$. The mass of B is

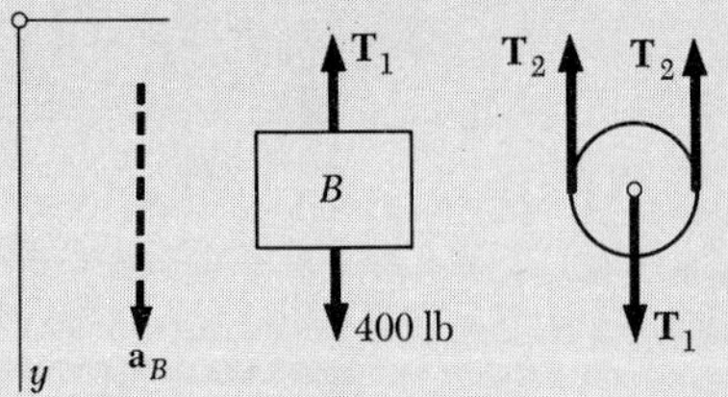

$$m_B = (400 \text{ lb})/(32.2 \text{ ft/sec}^2) = 12.42 \text{ lb-sec}^2/\text{ft}$$

$$+\downarrow \Sigma F_y = m_B a_B: \qquad 400 - T_1 = (12.42)(\tfrac{1}{2}a_A) \qquad (1)$$

Pulley. Since the mass of the pulley is assumed to be zero, we have

$$+\downarrow \Sigma F_y = 0: \qquad T_1 - 2T_2 = 0 \qquad (2)$$

Block A. The mass of block A is

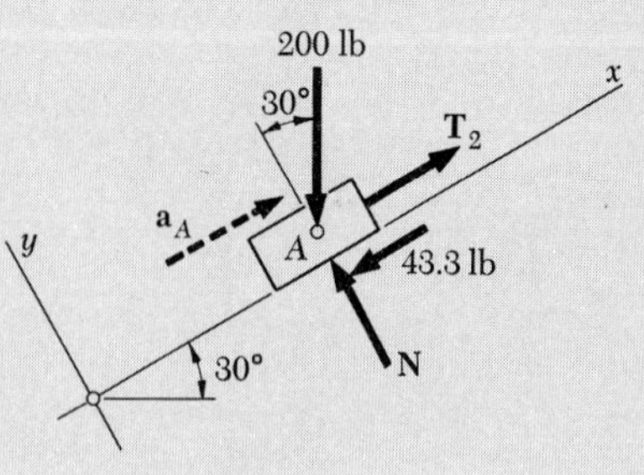

$$m_A = (200 \text{ lb}) / (32.2 \text{ ft/sec}^2) = 6.21 \text{ lb-sec}^2/\text{ft}$$

The friction force was found above:

$$\mathbf{F}_m = 43.3 \text{ lb} \swarrow$$

$$+\nearrow \Sigma F_x = m_A a_A: \qquad T_2 - 200 \sin 30° - 43.3 = 6.21 a_A \qquad (3)$$

Solving Eqs. (1), (2), and (3) simultaneously, we obtain

$$a_A = +6.09 \text{ ft/sec}^2 \qquad \mathbf{a}_A = 6.09 \text{ ft/sec}^2 \nearrow \quad ◀$$

$$T_1 = 362 \text{ lb} \qquad T_2 = 181 \text{ lb} \quad ◀$$

Since $a_B = \frac{1}{2}a_A$,

$$a_B = (\tfrac{1}{2})(6.09) = +3.05 \text{ ft/sec}^2 \qquad \mathbf{a}_B = 3.05 \text{ ft/sec}^2 \downarrow \quad ◀$$

PROBLEMS

12.1. The value of g at any latitude ϕ may be obtained from the formula

$$g = 32.09(1 + 0.0053 \sin^2 \phi) \text{ ft/sec}^2$$

Determine with four significant figures the weight in pounds, the mass in pounds, and the mass in lb-sec²/ft, at the latitudes of 0°, 45°, and 90°, of a silver bar whose mass is officially defined as 100.00 lb.

12.2. The acceleration due to gravity on the moon is 5.31 ft/sec². Determine the weight in pounds, the mass in pounds, and the mass in lb-sec²/ft, on the moon, of a silver bar whose mass is officially defined as 100.00 lb.

12.3. Two boxes are weighed on the scales shown: scale *a* is a lever scale, scale *b* is a spring scale. The scales are attached to the roof of an elevator. When the elevator is at rest, each scale indicates a load of 25 lb. Determine the load which each scale will indicate when the elevator is accelerated upward at the rate of 6.44 ft/sec².

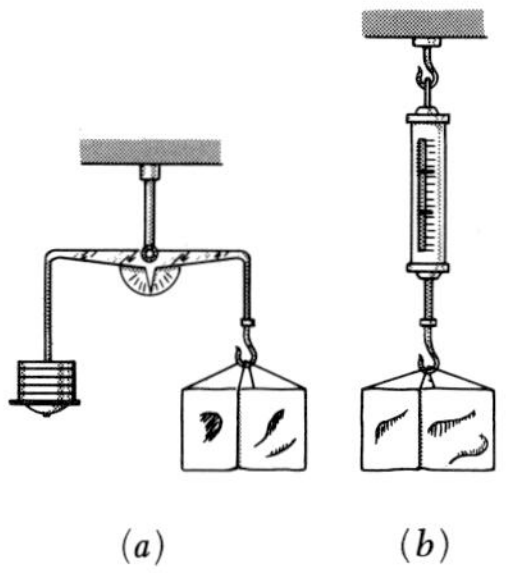

FIG. P 12.3

12.4. If the spring scale of Prob. 12.3 indicates a load of 22 lb, determine the acceleration of the elevator and the load indicated by the lever scale.

12.5. A motorist traveling at a speed of 30 mph suddenly applies his brakes and comes to a stop after skidding 60 ft. Determine (*a*) the time required for the car to stop, (*b*) the coefficient of friction between the tires and the pavement.

12.6. (*a*) Determine the smallest distance in which a car traveling at 60 mph can be stopped on a dry road where the coefficient of friction between the tires and the road is 0.80. (*b*) Determine the maximum allowable speed of a car if it is to stop in the same distance on an icy road where $\mu = 0.08$.

12.7. A truck is proceeding up a long 3 per cent grade at a constant speed of 35 mph. If the driver does not change the setting of his throttle or shift gears, what will be the acceleration of the truck as it starts moving on the level section of the road?

FIG. P 12.7

12.8. A package is projected up a 20° incline with an initial velocity of 25 ft/sec. The package moves up the incline to point *B* and then slides back toward point *A*. Knowing that the distance *d* between *A* and *B* is 20 ft, determine (*a*) the coefficient of friction between the package and the incline, (*b*) the velocity of the package as it returns to point *A*.

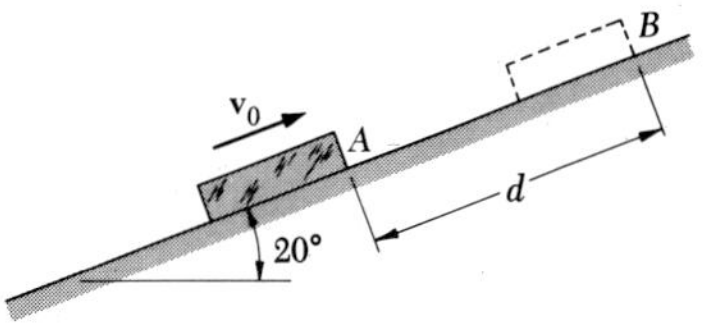

FIG. P 12.8

12.9. A package is projected up a 20° incline with an initial velocity $\mathbf{v}_0$; the package comes to rest at point *B* and then slides back to point *A*. Knowing that the package reaches *B* in 2.4 sec and returns to *A* in an additional 4.5 sec, determine (*a*) the coefficient of friction between the package and the incline, (*b*) the distance *d* from *A* to *B*, (*c*) the initial and final values of the velocity of the package at point *A*.

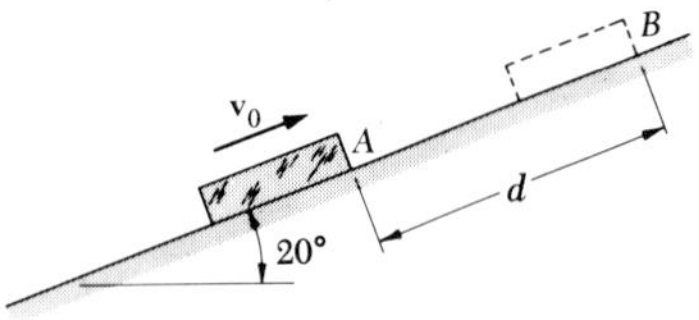

FIG. P 12.9

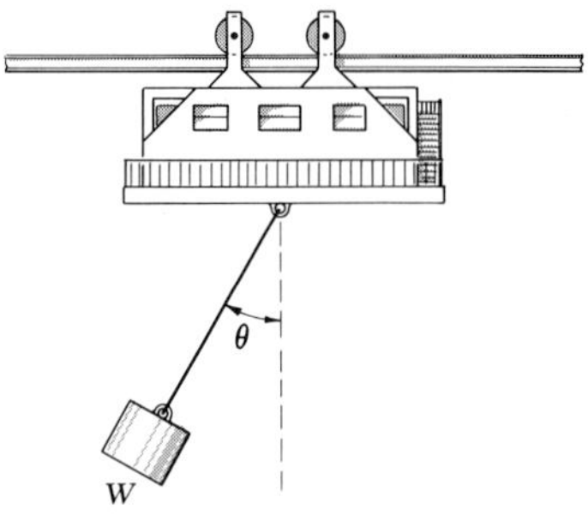

FIG. P 12.10 AND P 12.11

12.10. A load hangs from an overhead crane as shown. Determine the angle θ that the cables supporting the load form with the vertical when the crane moves with an acceleration of 2.5 ft/sec² to the right.

12.11. If the overhead crane shown moves to the left and if the angle θ is equal to 8°, find the acceleration or deceleration of the crane.

FIG. P 12.12

12.12. Each of the 50-lb blocks is initially at rest and is acted upon by a 20-lb force as shown. Assuming the coefficient of friction $\mu = 0.20$, determine for each block (*a*) the acceleration, (*b*) the velocity after 10 sec, (*c*) the velocity after it has moved 50 ft.

12.13. Assuming that block *A* and block *B* of Prob. 12.12 are connected by a horizontal inextensible cable, determine the acceleration of the blocks and the tension in the cable.

12.14. For block *B* of Prob. 12.12 determine (*a*) the angle β for which the acceleration is as large as possible, (*b*) the corresponding value of the acceleration.

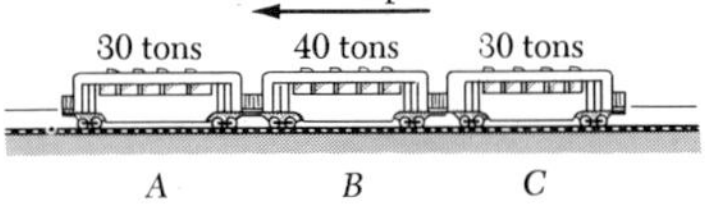

FIG. P 12.15

12.15. The subway train shown travels at a speed of 30 mph. Determine the force in each coupling when the brakes are applied, knowing that the braking force is 5,000 lb on each car.

12.16. Solve Prob. 12.15 assuming that the brakes on car *C* fail to operate.

12.17. Each of the systems shown is initially at rest. Assuming the pulleys to be weightless and neglecting axle friction, determine for each system (*a*) the acceleration of block *A*, (*b*) the velocity of block *A* after 4 sec, (*c*) the velocity of block *A* after it has moved 10 ft.

12.18. How much weight should be added to or taken away from block *A* in each system if the acceleration of block *A* is to be $\frac{1}{4}g$ downward?

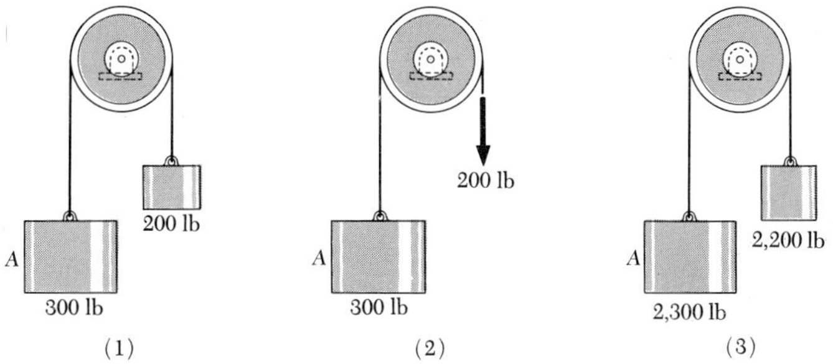

FIG. P 12.17 AND P 12.18

12.19. It is assumed that friction exists between block *A* and the horizontal plane in Sample Prob. 12.2. If block *B* is observed to move 30 ft in 2 sec after starting from rest, determine the coefficient of friction between block *A* and the horizontal plane.

12.20. The Atwood machine sketched was used by physicists to determine the value of *g*. The two weights were released from rest, and their speed v was measured after they had moved through a distance h. Assuming the pulley weightless and frictionless, derive the formula expressing g in terms of m_1, m_2, v, and h.

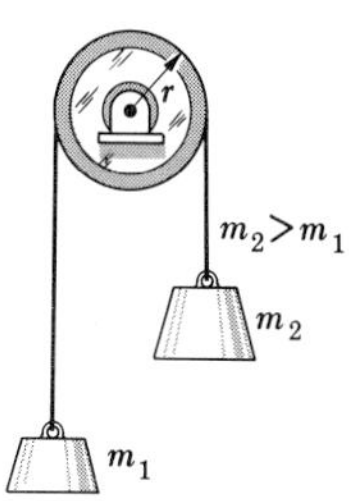

FIG. P 12.20

12.21 and 12.22. The 100-lb slider block *A* is attached to a block *B* of weight 40 lb by the cable arrangement shown. Knowing that the system is released from rest and neglecting friction, determine (*a*) the velocity of block *A* after 5 sec, (*b*) the distance traveled by block *A* when its speed has reached 8 ft/sec.

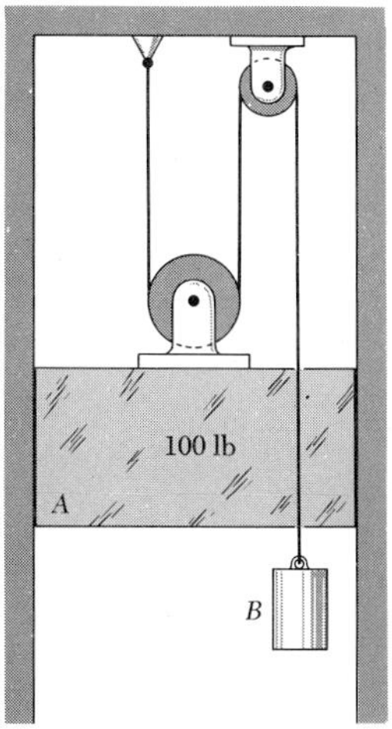

FIG. P 12.21 AND P 12.23

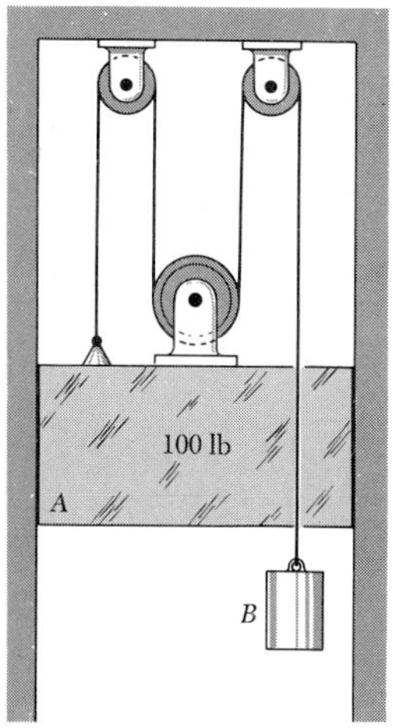

FIG. P 12.22 AND P 12.24

12.23 and 12.24. (*a*) Determine the weight of block *B* knowing that the acceleration of block *A* is 4 ft/sec² directed upward. (*b*) Attempt to solve part *a* assuming the acceleration of *A* to be 18 ft/sec² upward; explain the difficulties encountered.

12.32. A 200-lb crate rests on a 100-lb cart; the coefficient of static friction between the crate and the cart is 0.25. If the crate is not to slip with respect to the cart, determine (*a*) the maximum allowable magnitude of **P**, (*b*) the corresponding acceleration of the cart.

12.33. Solve Prob. 12.32 assuming that the force **P** is applied to the 200-lb crate.

12.34. The coefficients of friction between the 200-lb crate and the 100-lb cart are $\mu_s = 0.25$ and $\mu_k = 0.15$. If a force **P** of magnitude 80 lb is applied to the cart, determine the acceleration (*a*) of the cart, (*b*) of the crate, (*c*) of the cart with respect to the crate.

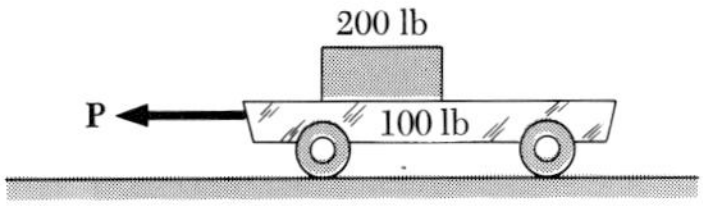

FIG. P 12.32 AND P 12.34

12.35. Solve Prob. 12.34 assuming that the force **P** is applied to the 200-lb crate.

12.36. The force exerted by a magnet on a small steel block varies inversely as the square of the distance between the block and the magnet. When the block is 10 in. from the magnet, the magnetic force is 5 oz. If the block is released from the position shown, determine its velocity when it is 4 in. from the magnet. Assume no friction.

12.37. Solve Prob. 12.36 assuming that the coefficient of friction between the steel block and the horizontal surface is 0.50.

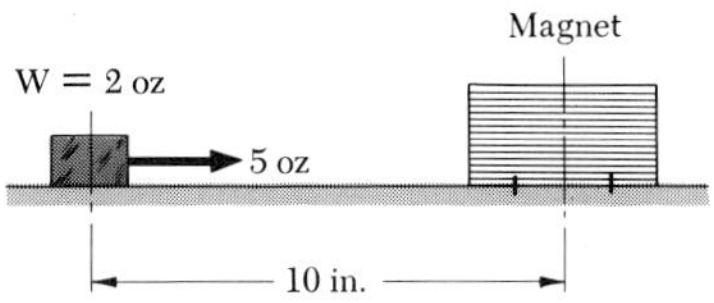

FIG. P 12.36

12.38. The propellers of a ship can produce a propulsive force $\mathbf{F}_0$; they produce a force of the same magnitude but of opposite direction when the engines are reversed. Knowing that the ship was proceeding forward at its maximum speed v_0 when the engines were put into reverse, determine the distance the ship travels before coming to a stop. Assume that the frictional resistance of the water varies directly with the square of the velocity.

12.39. A spring AB of constant k is attached to a support at A and to a collar of weight W. The unstretched length of the spring is l. Neglecting friction between the collar and the horizontal rod, express the acceleration of the collar as a function of the distance x.

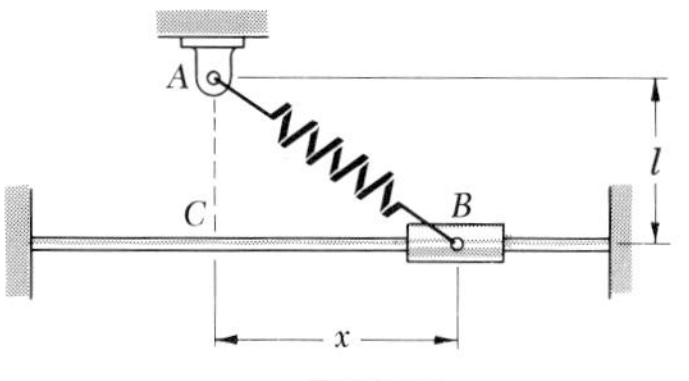

FIG. P 12.39

*__12.40.__ The collar of Prob. 12.39 is released from rest at $x = x_0$. Determine the velocity of the collar as it passes through point C.

12.41. Knowing that blocks B and C strike the ground simultaneously and exactly 1 sec after the system is released from rest, determine W_B and W_C in terms of W_A.

12.42. Determine the acceleration of each block when $W_A = 10$ lb, $W_B = 30$ lb, and $W_C = 20$ lb. Which block strikes the ground first?

12.43. In the system shown, $W_A = 10$ lb and $W_C = 20$ lb. Determine the required weight W_B if block B is not to move when the system is released from rest.

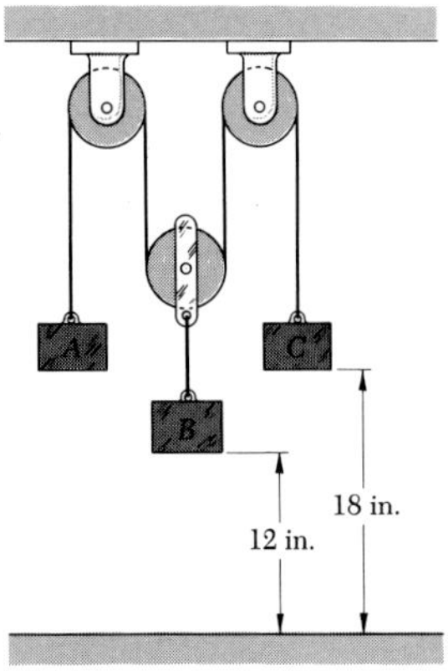

FIG. P 12.41, P 12.42, AND P 12.43

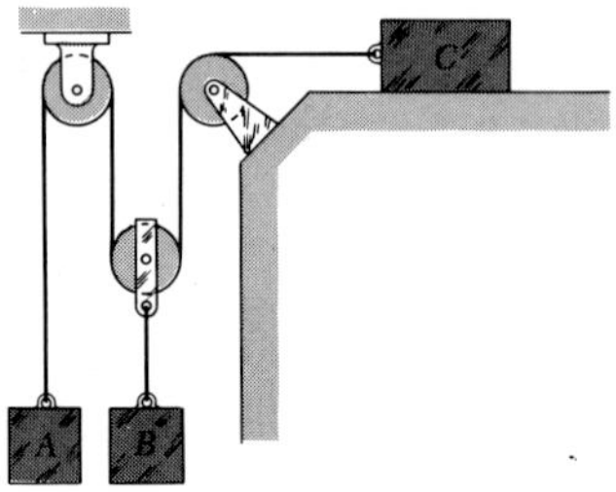

FIG. P 12.44, P 12.45, AND P 12.46

12.44. Knowing that $\mu = 0.30$ and $W_C = 10$ lb, determine W_A and W_B if the acceleration of both A and B is to be $g/5$ directed downward.

12.45. Knowing that $\mu = 0.30$, determine the acceleration of each block when $W_A = W_B = W_C$.

12.46. Knowing that $\mu = 0.50$, determine the acceleration of each block when $W_A = 10$ lb, $W_B = 40$ lb, and $W_C = 30$ lb.

12.7. Curvilinear Motion of a Particle. We saw in Chap. 11 that the acceleration of a particle moving in a plane along a curved path may be represented by its rectangular components $\mathbf{a}_x$ and $\mathbf{a}_y$, by its tangential and normal components $\mathbf{a}_t$ and $\mathbf{a}_n$, or by its radial and transverse components $\mathbf{a}_r$ and $\mathbf{a}_\theta$. We may therefore use any one of these methods of representation to express Newton's second law of motion.

Rectangular Components. Using the rectangular components $\mathbf{a}_x$ and $\mathbf{a}_y$ of the acceleration, and resolving the forces acting on the particle into their components $\mathbf{F}_x$ and $\mathbf{F}_y$, we write

$$\Sigma F_x = ma_x \qquad \Sigma F_y = ma_y \tag{12.10}$$

These equations may be solved for two unknowns.

Consider, as an example, the *motion of a projectile.* If the resistance of the air is neglected, the only force acting on the projectile after it has been fired is its weight $\mathbf{W}$. Substituting $\Sigma F_x = 0$ and $\Sigma F_y = -W$ into Eqs. (12.10), we obtain

$$a_x = 0 \qquad a_y = -\frac{W}{m} = -g$$

where $g = 32.2 \text{ ft/sec}^2$. The equations obtained may be integrated independently, as was shown in Sec. 11.10, to obtain the velocity and displacement of the projectile at any instant.

Tangential and Normal Components. Using the tangential and normal components $\mathbf{a}_t$ and $\mathbf{a}_n$ of the acceleration, and resolving the forces acting on the particle into components $\mathbf{F}_t$ along the tangent to the path (in the direction of motion) and components $\mathbf{F}_n$ along the normal (toward the inside of the path), we write

$$\Sigma F_t = ma_t \qquad \Sigma F_n = ma_n \tag{12.11}$$

Substituting for a_t and a_n from (11.28) and (11.29), we have

$$\Sigma F_t = m\frac{dv}{dt} \qquad \Sigma F_n = m\frac{v^2}{\rho} \tag{12.12}$$

The equations obtained may be solved for two unknowns.

Dynamic Equilibrium. As an alternate method of solution, we may add the inertia vector $(m\mathbf{a})_{rev}$ to the forces acting on the particle and express that the system obtained is balanced. In practice, it is found convenient to resolve the inertia vector into two components. Resolving, for example, the inertia vector into its tangential and normal components, we obtain the system of vectors shown in Fig. 12.8. The tangential component of the inertia vector provides a measure of the resistance the particle offers to a change in speed, while its normal component (also called *centrifugal force*) represents the tendency of the particle to leave its curved path. We should note that either of these two components may be zero under special conditions: (1) if the particle starts from rest, its initial velocity is zero and the normal component of the inertia vector is zero at $t = 0$; (2) if the particle moves at constant speed along its path, the tangential component of the inertia vector is zero and only its normal component needs to be considered.

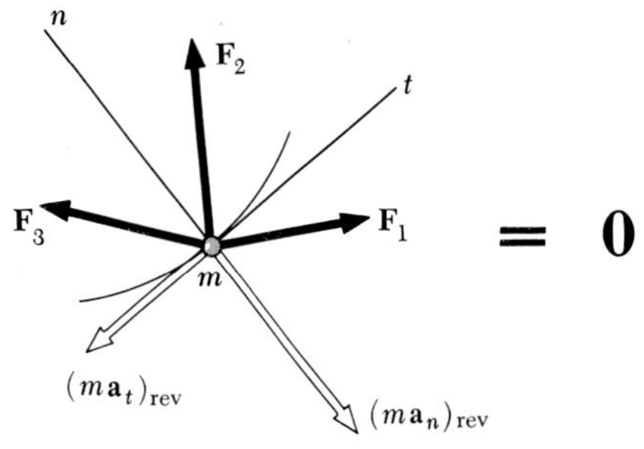

FIG. 12.8

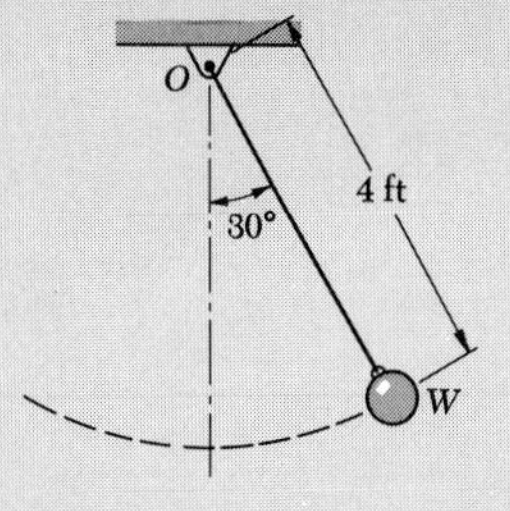

SAMPLE PROBLEM 12.4

The bob of a 4-ft pendulum describes an arc of circle in a vertical plane. If the tension in the cord is 2.5 times the weight of the bob for the position shown, find the velocity and acceleration of the bob in that position.

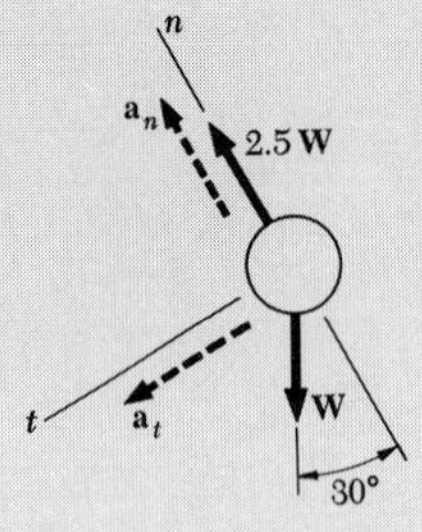

Solution. The mass of the bob is $m = W/g$. Recalling that $\mathbf{a}_n$ is directed toward O and assuming $\mathbf{a}_t$ as shown, we apply Newton's second law and obtain

$$+\swarrow \Sigma F_t = ma_t: \qquad W \sin 30° = \frac{W}{g} a_t$$

$$a_t = g \sin 30° = +16.1 \text{ ft/sec}^2 \qquad \mathbf{a}_t = 16.1 \text{ ft/sec}^2 \swarrow \quad ◄$$

$$+\nwarrow \Sigma F_n = ma_n: \qquad 2.5W - W \cos 30° = \frac{W}{g} a_n$$

$$a_n = (1.633)g = +52.6 \text{ ft/sec}^2 \qquad \mathbf{a}_n = 52.6 \text{ ft/sec}^2 \nwarrow \quad ◄$$

Since $a_n = v^2/\rho$, we write $52.6 = v^2/4$ and obtain

$$v = \pm 14.50 \text{ ft/sec} \qquad \mathbf{v} = 14.50 \text{ ft/sec} \nearrow\!\!\swarrow \text{ (up or down)} \quad ◄$$

SAMPLE PROBLEM 12.5

Determine the rated speed of a highway curve of radius $\rho = 400$ ft banked through an angle $\theta = 18°$. The rated speed of a banked curved road is the speed at which a car should travel if no lateral friction force is to be exerted on its wheels.

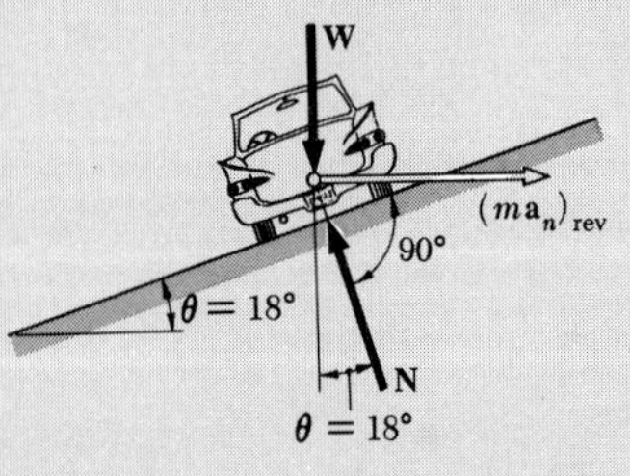

Solution. The car travels in a *horizontal* circular path of radius ρ. The normal component $\mathbf{a}_n$ of the acceleration is directed toward the center of the path; its magnitude is $a_n = v^2/\rho$ where v is the speed of the car in ft/sec. The mass m of the car is W/g, where W is the weight of the car. Since no lateral friction force is to be exerted on the car, the reaction of the road reduces to its normal component **N**.

The car is in *dynamic equilibrium* under the action of **W**, the force **N** exerted by the road, and the inertia vector $(m\mathbf{a}_n)_{\text{rev}}$ directed opposite to $\mathbf{a}_n$, i.e., away from the center of the path. We solve the vector triangle shown for the magnitude of the inertia vector and obtain

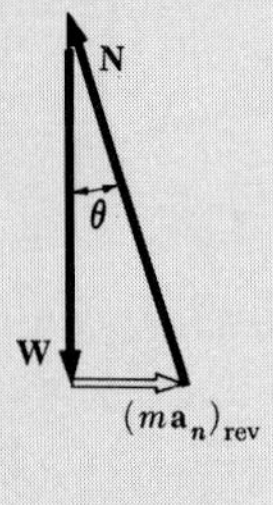

$$ma_n = W \tan \theta \tag{1}$$

Substituting $a_n = v^2/\rho$ into (1), we write

$$\frac{W}{g}\frac{v^2}{\rho} = W \tan \theta \qquad v^2 = g\rho \tan \theta$$

Substituting the given data, $\rho = 400$ ft and $\theta = 18°$, into this equation, we obtain

$$v^2 = (32.2)(400) \tan 18° \qquad v = 64.7 \text{ ft/sec} \qquad v = 44.1 \text{ mph} \quad ◄$$

PROBLEMS

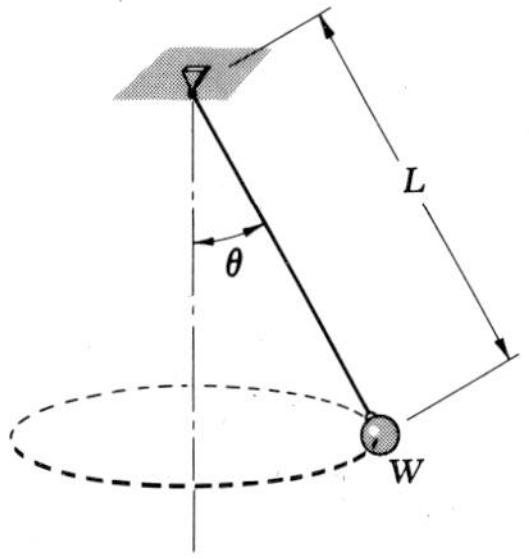

FIG. P 12.47 AND P 12.48

12.47. A small ball of weight $W = 5$ lb is attached to a cord of length $L = 6$ ft and is made to revolve in a horizontal circle at a constant speed v_0. Knowing that the cord forms an angle $\theta = 30°$ with the vertical, determine (*a*) the tension in the cord, (*b*) the speed v_0 of the ball.

12.48. A small ball of weight $W = 5$ lb is made to revolve in a horizontal circle as shown. Knowing that the maximum allowable tension in the cord is 15 lb, determine (*a*) the maximum allowable velocity if $L = 6$ ft, (*b*) the minimum allowable length of the cord if the velocity of the ball is 15 ft/sec.

12.49. Two wires *AC* and *BC* are each tied to a weight at *C*. The weight is made to revolve in a horizontal circle at a constant speed *v*. Determine the range of values of the speed *v* for which *both* wires are taut.

12.50. A single wire *ACB* passes through a small pulley at *C* and is attached to supports at *A* and *B*. A weight *W* is attached to the pulley and is made to revolve in a horizontal circle at a constant speed *v*. Determine the speed *v* for which the wires will form the angles shown with the horizontal and vertical.

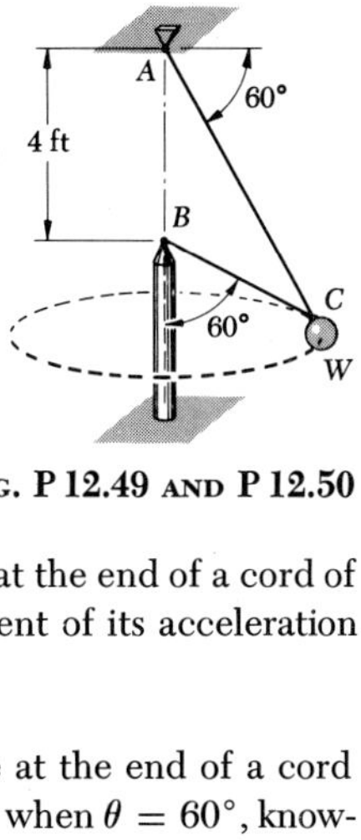

FIG. P 12.49 AND P 12.50

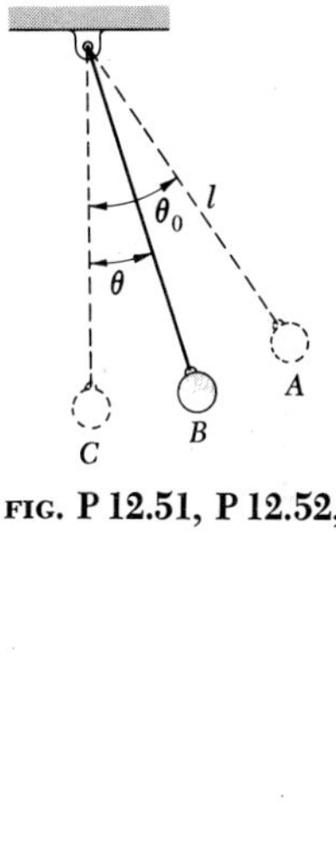

FIG. P 12.51, P 12.52, AND P 12.53

12.51. A 3-lb ball is swung in a vertical circle at the end of a cord of length $l = 18$ in. Find the tangential component of its acceleration when (*a*) $\theta = 90°$, (*b*) $\theta = 30°$, (*c*) $\theta = 0$.

12.52. A 3-lb ball is swung in a vertical circle at the end of a cord of length $l = 18$ in. Find the tension in the cord when $\theta = 60°$, knowing that the velocity is then 6 ft/sec.

12.53. A ball of weight *W* is released with no velocity from position *A* and oscillates in a vertical plane at the end of a cord of length *l*. Determine (*a*) the tangential component of the acceleration in position *B* in terms of the angle θ, (*b*) the velocity in position *B* in terms of θ, θ_0, and *l*, (*c*) the tension in the cord in terms of *W* and θ_0 when the ball passes through its lowest position *C*, (*d*) the value of θ_0 if the tension in the cord is $T = 2W$ when the ball passes through position *C*.

12.54. A small sphere of weight W is attached to the ceiling by means of two wires AB and CD. Wire AB is then cut. Determine (a) the tension in wire CD before AB was cut, (b) the tension in wire CD and the acceleration of the weight just after AB has been cut.

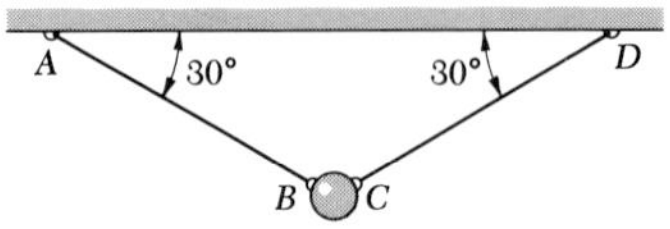

FIG. P 12.54

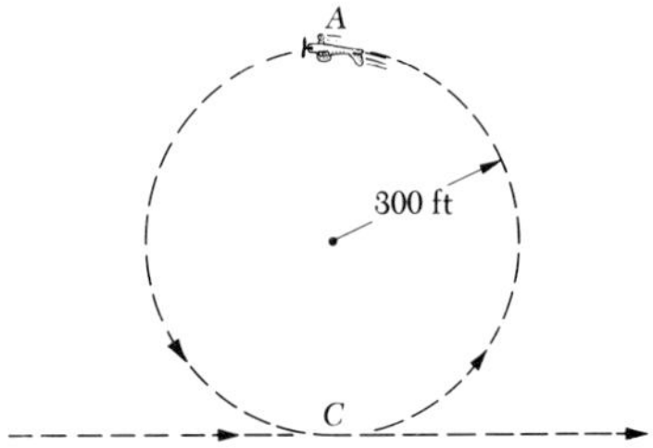

FIG. P 12.55

12.55. A 175-lb pilot flies a small plane in a vertical loop of 300-ft radius. Determine the speed of the plane at points A and C, knowing that at point A the pilot experiences weightlessness and that at point C the pilot's apparent weight is 600 lb.

12.56. At the bottom of a vertical curve, a 175-lb man driving a car seems to weigh 200 lb. (a) If the speed of his car is 45 mph, determine the radius of the curve. (b) What would the man seem to weigh if the speed of his car was 60 mph?

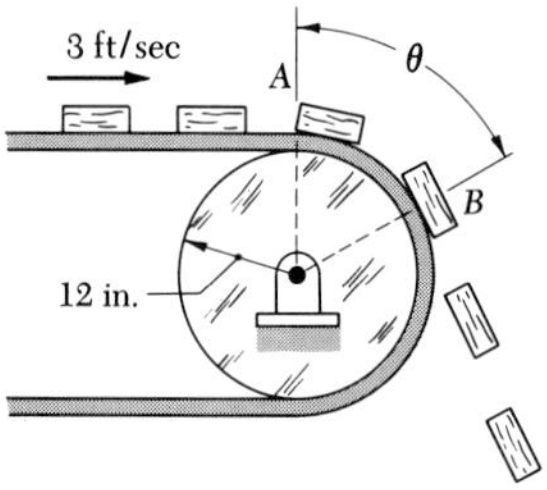

FIG. P 12.57 AND P 12.58

12.57. A series of small packages, each weighing 10 oz, are discharged from a conveyor belt as shown. Determine the force exerted by the belt on a package just after the package has passed point A.

12.58. Knowing that the coefficient of friction between each package and the conveyor belt is 0.50, determine the angle θ defining the point B where the packages first *slip* relative to the belt.

12.59. Express the rated speed of a banked road in terms of the radius r of the curve and the banking angle θ (see Sample Prob. 12.5 for the definition of the rated speed).

12.60. Express the minimum and maximum safe speeds, with respect to skidding, of a car traveling on a banked road, in terms of the radius r of the curve, the banking angle θ, and the friction angle ϕ between the tires and the pavement.

12.61. A man on a motorcycle takes a turn on a flat unbanked road at 45 mph. If the radius of the turn is 100 ft, determine the minimum value of the coefficient of friction between the tires and the road which will ensure no skidding.

12.62. What angle of banking should be given to the road in Prob. 12.61 if the man on the motorcycle is to be able to take the turn at 45 mph with a coefficient of friction $\mu = 0.40$?

12.63. A small ball rolls at a speed v_0 along a horizontal circle inside a bowl as shown. The inside surface of the bowl is a surface of revolution obtained by rotating the curve OA about the y axis. Determine the required equation of the curve OA if the speed v_0 of the ball is to be proportional to the distance x from the y axis to the ball.

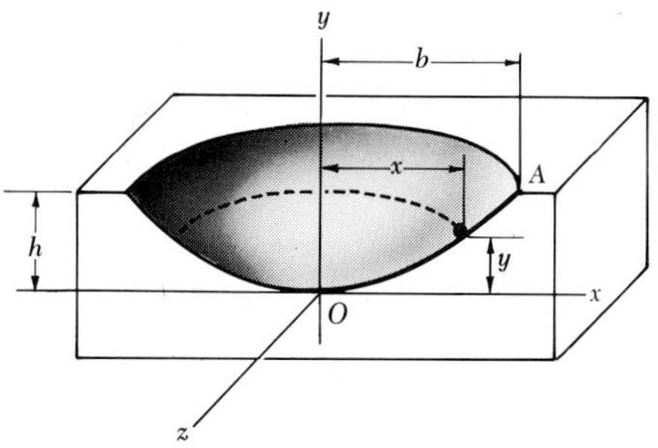

FIG. P 12.63

12.64. Solve Prob. 12.63 assuming that the speed v_0 of the ball is to be proportional to the height y of the ball above the bottom of the bowl.

12.65. A circular curve in an automobile racing track is banked as shown in the cross section. A driver follows a path which is at a constant distance $d = 25$ ft from the inside railing at A. (a) At what speed will the lateral friction force exerted on the wheels be zero? (b) What is the maximum safe speed of the car with respect to skidding if $\mu = 0.60$?

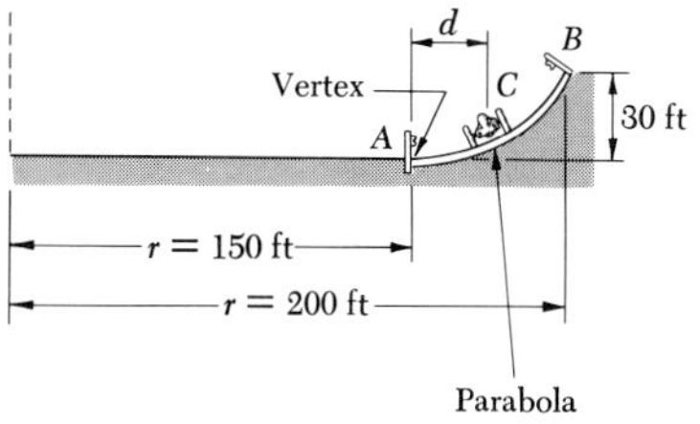

FIG. P 12.65

12.66. Solve Prob. 12.65 assuming that the driver follows the top railing at B, where $d = 50$ ft.

12.67. A bucket is attached to a rope of length $L = 4$ ft and is made to revolve in a horizontal circle. Drops of water leaking from the bucket fall and strike the floor along the perimeter of a circle of radius a. Determine the radius a when $\theta = 30°$.

12.68. Solve Prob. 12.67 assuming that the speed of the bucket is 15 ft/sec. (The angle θ is not 30° in this case.)

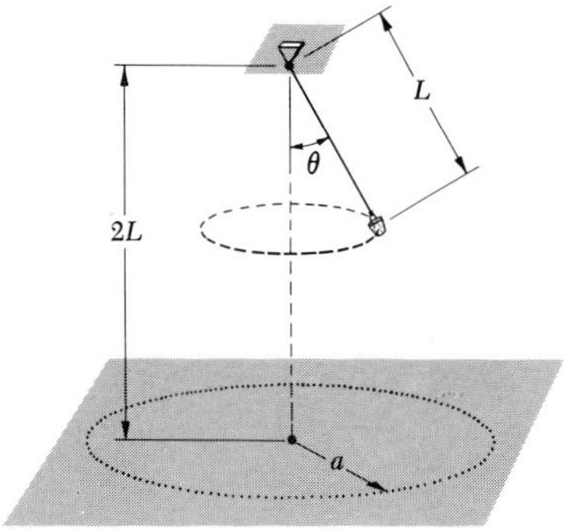

FIG. P 12.67

12.69. In the cathode-ray tube shown, electrons emitted by the cathode and attracted by the anode pass through a small hole in the anode and keep traveling in a straight line with a speed v_0 until they strike the screen at A. However, if a difference of potential V is established between the two parallel plates, each electron will be subjected to a force $\mathbf{F}$ perpendicular to the plates while it travels between the plates and will strike the screen at point B at a distance δ from A. The magnitude of the force $\mathbf{F}$ is $F = eV/d$, where $-e$ is the charge of the electron and d is the distance between the plates. Derive an expression for the deflection δ in terms of V, v_0, the charge $-e$ of the electron, its mass m, and the dimensions d, l, and L.

12.70. A manufacturer wishes to design a new cathode-ray tube which will be only half as long as his current model. If the size of the screen is to remain the same, how should the length l of the plates be modified if all the other characteristics of the circuit are to remain unchanged?

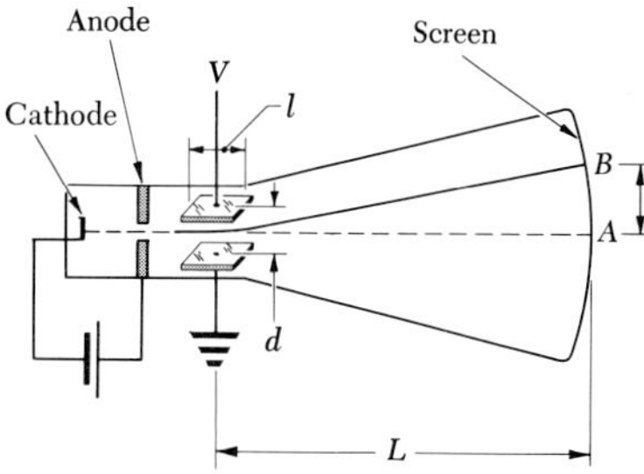

FIG. P 12.69 AND P 12.70

12.71. In Prob. 12.69, determine the smallest allowable value of the ratio d/l in terms of e, m, v_0, and V if the electrons are not to strike the positive plate.

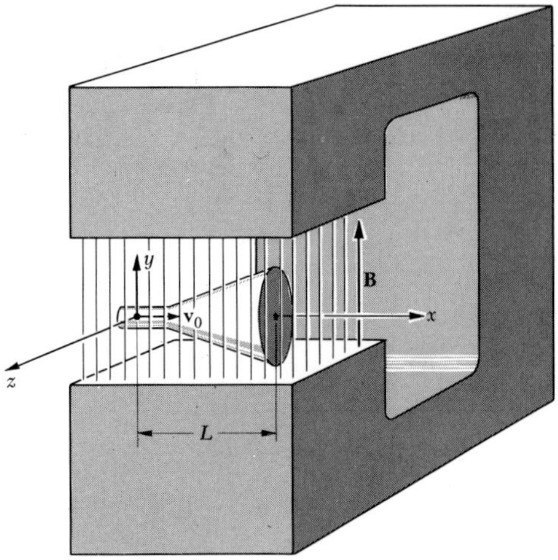

FIG. P 12.72

12.72. A cathode-ray tube emitting electrons with a velocity $\mathbf{v}_0$ is placed as shown between the poles of a large electromagnet which creates a uniform magnetic field of strength **B**. Determine the coordinates of the point where the electron beam strikes the tube screen when no difference of potential exists between the plates. It is known that an electron (mass m and charge $-e$) traveling with a velocity **v** at a right angle to the lines of force of a magnetic field of strength **B** is subjected to a force **F** perpendicular to **B** and **v**, and of magnitude $F = eBv$; the sense of the force is such that **B**, **v**, and **F** form a right-handed triad.

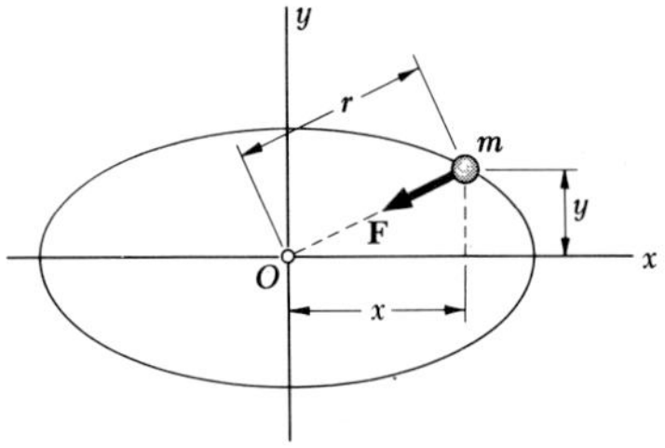

FIG. P 12.73

12.73. A particle of mass m is acted upon by a force **F** of magnitude $F = kr$ directed toward the origin O and proportional to the distance r from O to the particle. If, at $t = 0$, the coordinates of the particle are $x = x_0$, $y = 0$ and the components of its velocity are $v_x = 0$, $v_y = v_0$, show (*a*) that the path of the particle is an ellipse of semiaxes x_0 and $v_0\sqrt{m/k}$, (*b*) that the radius of curvature of the path when $t = 0$ is mv_0^2/kx_0.

*12.8. Curvilinear Motion of a Particle. Radial and Transverse Components.

We shall now use the radial and transverse components $\mathbf{a}_r$ and $\mathbf{a}_\theta$ of the acceleration. Resolving each of the forces acting on the particle into a component $\mathbf{F}_r$ along the line OP joining the origin O to the particle P, and a component $\mathbf{F}_\theta$ in the direction perpendicular to OP (Fig. 12.9), we write

$$\Sigma F_r = ma_r \qquad \Sigma F_\theta = ma_\theta \tag{12.13}$$

Substituting for a_r and a_θ from (11.33), we have

$$\begin{aligned} \Sigma F_r &= m\left[\frac{d^2r}{dt^2} - r\left(\frac{d\theta}{dt}\right)^2\right] \\ \Sigma F_\theta &= m\left(r\frac{d^2\theta}{dt^2} + 2\frac{dr}{dt}\frac{d\theta}{dt}\right) \end{aligned} \tag{12.14}$$

The equations obtained may be solved for two unknowns.

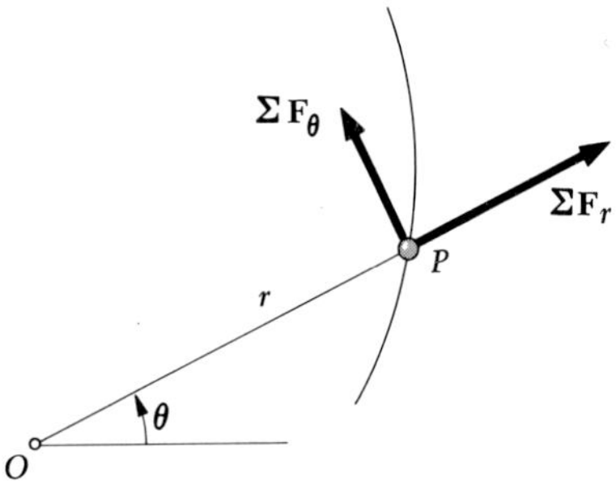

FIG. 12.9

12.9. Motion under a Central Force. When the only force acting on a particle is a force **F** directed toward the origin O or away from the origin O, the particle is said to be moving *under a central force* (Fig. 12.10). Since the transverse component $\mathbf{F}_\theta$ is zero, the second of Eqs. (12.14) yields

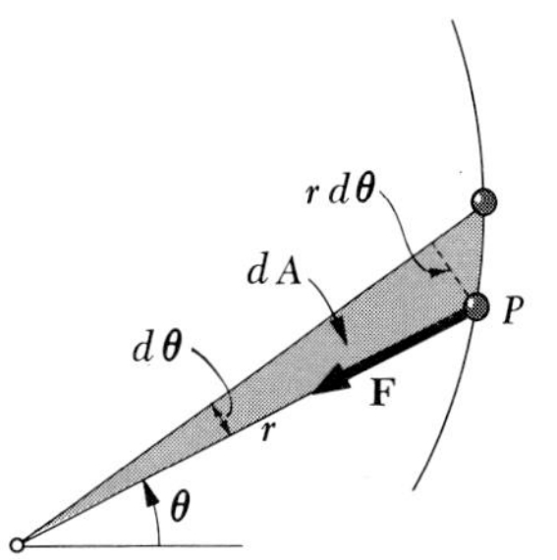

FIG. 12.10

$$r\frac{d^2\theta}{dt^2} + 2\frac{dr}{dt}\frac{d\theta}{dt} = 0 \qquad \text{or} \qquad \frac{1}{r}\frac{d}{dt}\left(r^2\frac{d\theta}{dt}\right) = 0$$

It follows that, for any finite value of r, we must have

$$r^2\frac{d\theta}{dt} = h \tag{12.15}$$

where h is a constant. We may observe from Fig. 12.10 that the radius vector OP sweeps an infinitesimal area $dA = \frac{1}{2}r^2\,d\theta$ as it rotates through an angle $d\theta$. Defining the *areal velocity* of the particle as the quotient dA/dt, we note that the left-hand member of Eq. (12.15) represents twice the areal velocity of the particle. We conclude therefore that, *when a particle moves under a central force, its areal velocity is constant.*

Equation (12.15) may be used to eliminate t from the first of Eqs. (12.14). Noting that $d\theta/dt = h/r^2$, we write

$$\frac{dr}{dt} = \frac{dr}{d\theta}\frac{d\theta}{dt} = \frac{h}{r^2}\frac{dr}{d\theta} = -h\frac{d}{d\theta}\left(\frac{1}{r}\right)$$

$$\frac{d^2r}{dt^2} = \frac{d}{dt}\left(\frac{dr}{dt}\right) = \frac{d}{d\theta}\left(\frac{dr}{dt}\right)\frac{d\theta}{dt}$$

$$= \frac{h}{r^2}\frac{d}{d\theta}\left(\frac{dr}{dt}\right) = \frac{h}{r^2}\frac{d}{d\theta}\left[-h\frac{d}{d\theta}\left(\frac{1}{r}\right)\right]$$

$$\frac{d^2r}{dt^2} = -\frac{h^2}{r^2}\frac{d^2}{d\theta^2}\left(\frac{1}{r}\right) \tag{12.16}$$

Substituting for $d\theta/dt$ and d^2r/dt^2 from (12.15) and (12.16), respectively, into the first of Eqs. (12.14), setting $\Sigma F_r = -F$, and introducing the function $u = 1/r$, we obtain after reductions

$$\frac{d^2u}{d\theta^2} + u = \frac{F}{mh^2u^2} \tag{12.17}$$

In deriving Eq. (12.17), the force **F** was assumed directed toward O. The magnitude F should therefore be positive if **F** is actually directed toward O (attractive force) and negative if **F** is directed away from O (repulsive force). If F is a known function of r and thus of u, Eq. (12.17) is a differential equation in u and θ. This differential equation defines the path followed by the particle under the central force **F**.

12.10. Newton's Law of Gravitation. In his *law of universal gravitation*, Newton states that two particles at distance r from each other and, respectively, of mass M and m, attract each other with equal and opposite forces **F** and **F′** directed along the line joining the particles (Fig. 12.11). The common magnitude F of the two forces is

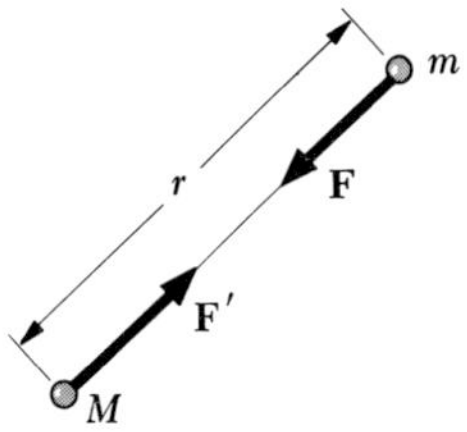

FIG. 12.11

$$F = G\frac{Mm}{r^2} \tag{12.18}$$

where G is a universal constant, called the *constant of gravitation*. Recent experiments show that the value of G is $(6.673 \pm 0.003) \times 10^{-8}$ cm^3/g-sec^2 in the cgs system, or approximately 3.44×10^{-8} ft^4/lb-sec^4 in the British gravitational system of units. While gravitational forces exist between any pair of bodies, their effect is appreciable only when one of the bodies has a very large mass. The effect of gravitational forces is apparent in the case of the motion of a planet about the sun, of satellites orbiting about the earth, or of bodies falling on the surface of the earth.

Since the force exerted by the earth on a body of mass m located on or near its surface is defined as the weight **W** of the body, we may substitute the magnitude $W = mg$ of the weight for F, and the radius R of the earth for r, in Eq. (12.18). We obtain

$$W = mg = \frac{GM}{R^2}m \qquad \text{or} \qquad g = \frac{GM}{R^2} \tag{12.19}$$

where M is the mass of the earth. Since the earth is not truly spherical, the distance R from the center of the earth depends upon the point selected on its surface, and the values of W and g will thus vary with the altitude and latitude of the point considered. Another reason for the variation of W and g with the latitude is that a system of axes attached to the earth does not constitute a newtonian frame of reference (see Sec. 12.1). A more accurate definition of the weight of a body should therefore include a component representing the centrifugal force due to the rotation of the earth. Values of g at sea level vary from 32.09 ft/sec^2 at the equator to 32.26 ft/sec^2 at the poles.†

The discovery of the law of universal gravitation has often

† A formula expressing g in terms of the latitude ϕ was given in Prob. 12.1.

been attributed to the fact that Newton, after observing an apple falling from a tree, had reflected that the earth must attract an apple and the moon in much the same way. While it is doubtful that this incident actually took place, it may be said that Newton would not have formulated his law if he had not first perceived that the acceleration of a falling body must have the same cause as the acceleration which keeps the moon in its orbit. This basic concept of continuity of the gravitational attraction is more easily understood now, when the gap between the apple and the moon is being filled with long-range ballistic missiles and artificial earth satellites.

***12.11. Application to Space Mechanics.** After the last stage of their launching rockets has burned out, earth satellites and other space vehicles are subjected only to the gravitational pull of the earth. Their motion may therefore be determined from Eqs. (12.15) and (12.17), which govern the motion of a body under a central force, after F has been replaced by the expression obtained for the force of gravitational attraction.† Setting in Eq. (12.17)

$$F = \frac{GMm}{r^2} = GMmu^2$$

where M = mass of the earth
m = mass of the space vehicle
r = distance from center of the earth to vehicle
u = 1/r

we obtain the differential equation

$$\frac{d^2u}{d\theta^2} + u = \frac{GM}{h^2} \tag{12.20}$$

where the right-hand member is observed to be a constant.

The solution of the differential equation (12.20) is obtained by adding the particular solution $u = GM/h^2$ to the general solution $u = C\cos(\theta - \theta_0)$ of the corresponding homogeneous equation (i.e., the equation obtained by setting the right-hand member equal to zero). Choosing the polar axis so that $\theta_0 = 0$, we write

$$\frac{1}{r} = u = \frac{GM}{h^2} + C\cos\theta \tag{12.21}$$

† It is assumed that the space vehicles considered here are attracted only by the earth, and that their mass is negligible compared to the mass of the earth. If a vehicle moves very far from the earth, its path may be affected by the attraction of the sun, the moon, or another planet.

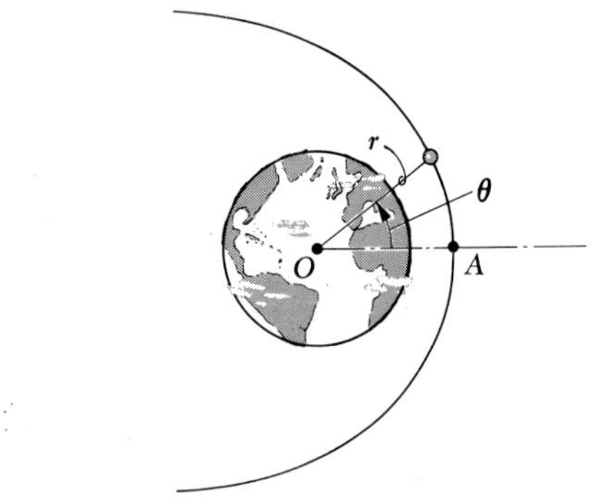

FIG. 12.12

Equation (12.21) is the equation of a *conic section* (ellipse, parabola, or hyperbola) in the polar coordinates r and θ. The origin O of the coordinates, which is located at the center of the earth, is a *focus* of this conic section, and the polar axis is one of its axes of symmetry (Fig. 12.12).

The ratio of the constants C and GM/h^2 defines the *eccentricity* ε of the conic section; we write

$$\varepsilon = \frac{C}{GM/h^2} = \frac{Ch^2}{GM} \qquad (12.22)$$

Three cases may be distinguished:

1. $\varepsilon > 1$, or $C > GM/h^2$: There are two values θ_1 and $-\theta_1$ of the polar angle, defined by $\cos\theta_1 = -GM/Ch^2$, for which the right-hand member of Eq. (12.21) becomes zero. For both of these values, the radius vector r becomes infinite; the conic section is a *hyperbola* (Fig. 12.13).
2. $\varepsilon = 1$, or $C = GM/h^2$: The radius vector becomes infinite for $\theta = 180°$; the conic section is a *parabola*.
3. $\varepsilon < 1$, or $C < GM/h^2$: The radius vector remains finite for every value of θ; the conic section is an *ellipse*. In the particular case when $\varepsilon = C = 0$, the length of the radius vector is constant; the conic section is a circle.

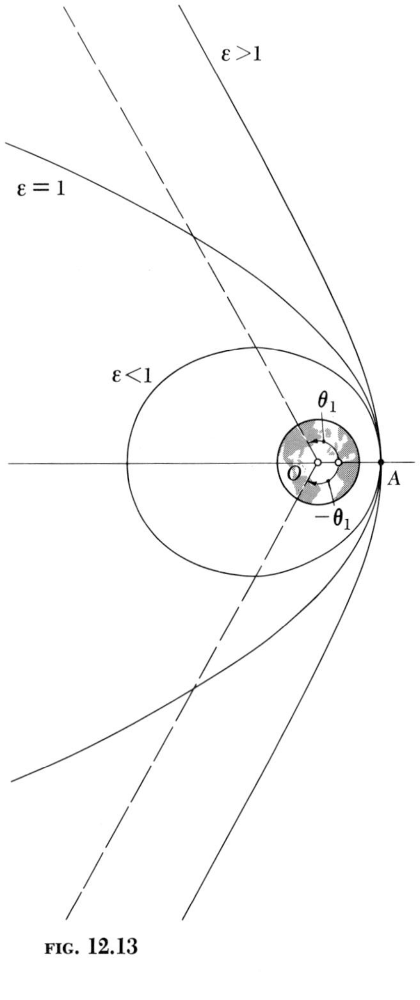

FIG. 12.13

We shall see now how the constants C and GM/h^2 which characterize the trajectory of a space vehicle may be determined from the position and the velocity of the space vehicle at the beginning of its free flight. We shall assume, as it is generally the case, that the powered phase of its flight has been programmed in such a way that, as the last stage of the launching rocket burns out, the vehicle has a velocity parallel to the surface of the earth (Fig. 12.14). In other words, we shall assume that the space vehicle begins its free flight at the vertex A of its trajectory.†

Denoting respectively by r_0 and v_0 the radius vector and speed of the vehicle at the beginning of its free flight, we observe, since the radial component of the velocity is zero, that $v_0 = r_0(d\theta/dt)_0$. Recalling the definition of h given in (12.15), we write

$$h = r_0^2\left(\frac{d\theta}{dt}\right)_0 = r_0 v_0 \qquad (12.23)$$

The value obtained for h may be used to determine the constant GM/h^2. We should also note that the computation of this con-

† Problems involving oblique launchings will be considered in Sec. 14.12.

stant will be simplified if we use the second of the relations (12.19) and write

$$GM = gR^2 \tag{12.24}$$

where R is the radius of the earth (R = 3,960 mi.) and g the acceleration of gravity at the surface of the earth.

The constant C will be determined by setting $\theta = 0$, $r = r_0$ in Eq. (12.21); we obtain

$$C = \frac{1}{r_0} - \frac{GM}{h^2} \tag{12.25}$$

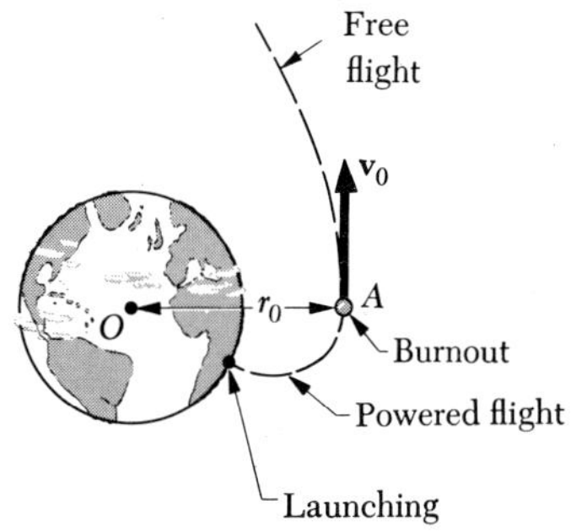

FIG. 12.14

Substituting for h from (12.23), we may then easily express C in terms of r_0 and v_0.

Let us now determine the initial conditions corresponding to each of the three fundamental trajectories indicated above. Considering first the parabolic trajectory, we set C equal to GM/h^2 in Eq. (12.25) and eliminate h between Eqs. (12.23) and (12.25). Solving for v_0, we obtain

$$v_0 = \sqrt{2GM/r_0}$$

We may easily check that a larger value of the initial velocity corresponds to a hyperbolic trajectory, and a smaller value to an elliptic orbit. Since the value of v_0 obtained for the parabolic trajectory is the smallest value for which the space vehicle does not return to its starting point, it is called the *escape velocity*. We write therefore

$$v_{esc} = \sqrt{2GM/r_0} \qquad \text{or} \qquad v_{esc} = \sqrt{2gR^2/r_0} \tag{12.26}$$

if we make use of Eq. (12.24). We note that the trajectory will be (1) hyperbolic if $v_0 > v_{esc}$; (2) parabolic if $v_0 = v_{esc}$; (3) elliptic if $v_0 < v_{esc}$.

Among the various possible elliptic orbits, one is of special interest, the *circular orbit*, which is obtained when $C = 0$. The value of the initial velocity corresponding to a circular orbit is easily found to be

$$v_{circ} = \sqrt{GM/r_0} \qquad \text{or} \qquad v_{circ} = \sqrt{gR^2/r_0} \tag{12.27}$$

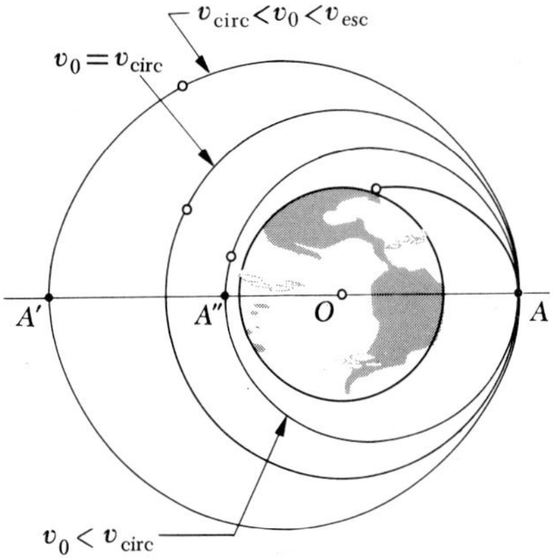

FIG. 12.15

if Eq. (12.24) is taken into account. We may note from Fig. 12.15 that, for values of v_0 comprised between v_{circ} and v_{esc}, point A where free flight begins is the point of the orbit closest to the earth; this point is called the *perigee*, while point A', which is farthest away from the earth, is known as the *apogee*. For values of v_0 smaller than v_{circ}, point A becomes the apogee, while point A'', on the other side of the orbit, becomes the perigee. For values of v_0 much smaller than v_{circ}, the trajectory of the space vehicle intersects the surface of the earth; in such a case, the vehicle does not go into orbit.

Ballistic missiles, which are designed to hit the surface of the earth, also travel along elliptic trajectories. In fact, we should now realize that any object projected in vacuum with an initial velocity v_0 smaller than v_{esc} will move along an elliptic path. It is only when the distances involved are small that the gravitational field of the earth may be assumed uniform, and that the elliptic path may be approximated by a parabolic path, as was done earlier (Sec. 11.10) in the case of conventional projectiles.

Periodic Time. An important characteristic of the motion of an earth satellite is the time required by the satellite to describe its orbit. This time is known as the *periodic time* of the satellite and is denoted by τ. We first observe, in view of the definition of the areal velocity (Sec. 12.9), that τ may be obtained by dividing the area inside the orbit by the areal velocity. Since the area of an ellipse is equal to πab, where a and b denote, respectively, the semimajor and semiminor axes, and since the areal velocity is equal to $h/2$, we write

$$\tau = \frac{2\pi ab}{h} \qquad (12.28)$$

While h may be readily determined from r_0 and v_0 in the case of a satellite launched in a direction parallel to the surface of the earth, the semiaxes a and b are not directly related to the initial conditions. Since, on the other hand, the values r_0 and r_1 of r corresponding to the perigee and apogee of the orbit may easily be determined from Eq. (12.21), we shall express the semiaxes a and b in terms of r_0 and r_1.

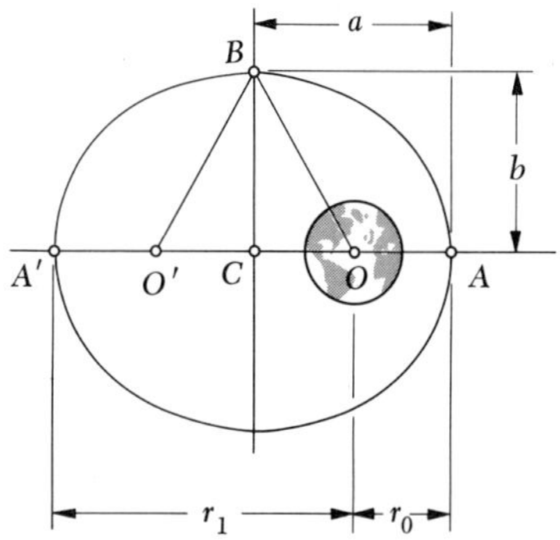

FIG. 12.16

Consider the elliptic orbit shown in Fig. 12.16. The earth's center is located at O and coincides with one of the two foci of the ellipse, while the points A and A' represent, respectively, the perigee and apogee of the orbit. We easily check that

$$r_0 + r_1 = 2a$$

and thus

$$a = \tfrac{1}{2}(r_0 + r_1) \qquad (12.29)$$

Recalling that the sum of the distances from each of the foci to any point of the ellipse is constant, we write

$$O'B + BO = O'A + OA = 2a \qquad \text{or} \qquad BO = a$$

On the other hand, we have $CO = a - r_0$. We may therefore write

$$b^2 = (BC)^2 = (BO)^2 - (CO)^2 = a^2 - (a - r_0)^2$$
$$b^2 = r_0(2a - r_0) = r_0 r_1$$

and thus

$$b = \sqrt{r_0 r_1} \tag{12.30}$$

Formulas (12.29) and (12.30) indicate that the semimajor and semiminor axes of the orbit are respectively equal to the arithmetic and geometric means of the maximum and minimum values of the radius vector. Once r_0 and r_1 have been determined, the lengths of the semiaxes may thus be easily computed and substituted for a and b in formula (12.28).

***12.12. Kepler's Laws of Planetary Motion.** The equations governing the motion of an earth satellite may be used to describe the motion of the moon around the earth. In that case, however, the mass of the moon is not negligible compared to the mass of the earth, and the results obtained are not entirely accurate.

The theory developed in the preceding sections may also be applied to the study of the motion of the planets around the sun. While another error is introduced by neglecting the forces exerted by the planets on each other, the approximation obtained is excellent. Indeed, the properties expressed by Eq. (12.21), where M now represents the mass of the sun, and by Eq. (12.15) had been discovered by the German astronomer Johann Kepler (1571–1630) from astronomical observations of the motion of the planets, even before Newton had formulated his fundamental theory.

Kepler's three *laws of planetary motion* may be stated as follows:

1. Each planet describes an ellipse with the sun located at one of its foci.
2. The radius vector drawn from the sun to a planet sweeps equal areas in equal times.
3. The squares of the periodic times of the planets are proportional to the cubes of the semimajor axes of their orbits.

The first law states a particular case of the result established in Sec. 12.11, while the second law expresses that the areal velocity of each planet is constant (see Sec. 12.9). Kepler's third law may also be derived from the results obtained in Sec. 12.11.†

† See Prob. 12.97.

SAMPLE PROBLEM 12.6

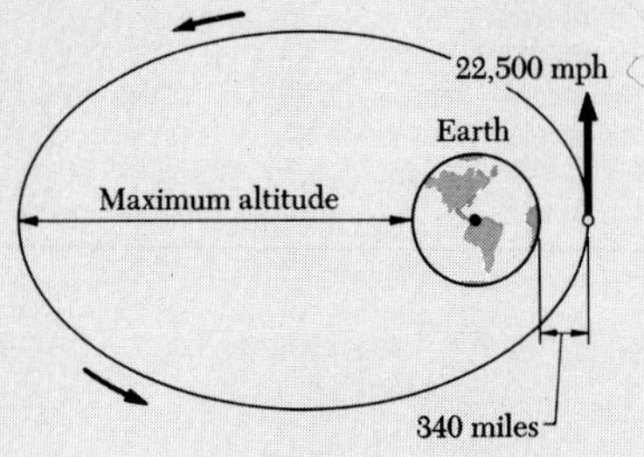

A satellite is launched in a direction parallel to the surface of the earth with a velocity of 22,500 mph from an altitude of 340 miles. Determine (*a*) the maximum altitude reached by the satellite, (*b*) the periodic time of the satellite.

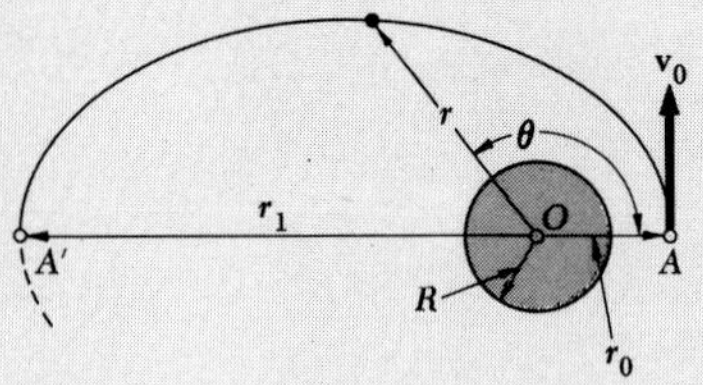

a. **Maximum Altitude.** After launching, the satellite is subjected only to the gravitational attraction of the earth; its motion is thus governed by Eq. (12.21).

$$\frac{1}{r} = \frac{GM}{h^2} + C\cos\theta \qquad (1)$$

Since the radial component of the velocity is zero at the point of launching A, we have $h = r_0 v_0$. Recalling that the radius of the earth is $R = 3{,}960$ miles, we compute

$$r_0 = 3{,}960 + 340 = 4{,}300 \text{ miles} = 22.7 \times 10^6 \text{ ft}$$
$$v_0 = 22{,}500 \text{ mph} = 33{,}000 \text{ ft/sec}$$

$$h = r_0 v_0 = (22.7 \times 10^6)(33{,}000) = 0.7492 \times 10^{12} \text{ ft}^2\text{/sec}$$
$$h^2 = 0.5613 \times 10^{24} \text{ ft}^4\text{/sec}^2$$

Since $GM = gR^2$, where R is the radius of the earth, we have

$$GM = gR^2 = (32.2)(3{,}960 \times 5{,}280)^2 = 1.408 \times 10^{16} \text{ ft}^3\text{/sec}^2$$

$$\frac{GM}{h^2} = \frac{1.408 \times 10^{16}}{0.5613 \times 10^{24}} = 2.508 \times 10^{-8} \text{ ft}^{-1}$$

Substituting this value into (1), we obtain

$$\frac{1}{r} = 2.508 \times 10^{-8} + C\cos\theta \qquad (2)$$

Noting that at point A we have $\theta = 0$ and $r = r_0 = 4{,}300$ miles, we compute the constant C.

$$\frac{1}{(4{,}300)(5{,}280)} = 2.508 \times 10^{-8} + C(\cos 0°) \qquad C = 1.896 \times 10^{-8} \text{ ft}^{-1}$$

At A', the point on the orbit farthest from the earth, we have $\theta = 180°$. Using (2), we compute the corresponding distance r_1.

$$\frac{1}{r_1} = 2.508 \times 10^{-8} + (1.896 \times 10^{-8})(\cos 180°)$$
$$r_1 = 1.634 \times 10^8 \text{ ft} = 30{,}950 \text{ miles}$$
$$\textit{Maximum altitude} = 30{,}950 - 3{,}960 = 26{,}990 \text{ miles} \blacktriangleleft$$

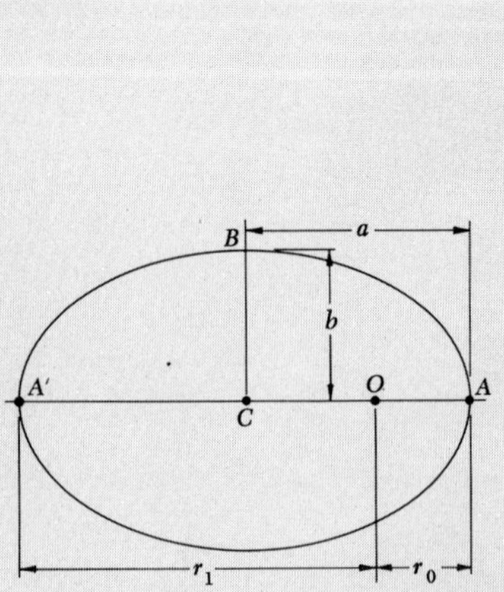

b. **Periodic Time.** Since A and A' are the perigee and apogee, respectively, of the elliptic orbit, we use Eqs. (12.29) and (12.30) and compute the semimajor and semiminor axes of the orbit.

$$a = \tfrac{1}{2}(r_0 + r_1) = \tfrac{1}{2}(22.7 + 163.4)10^6 = 93.05 \times 10^6 \text{ ft}$$
$$b = \sqrt{r_0 r_1} = \sqrt{(22.7)(163.4)}\ 10^6 = 60.9 \times 10^6 \text{ ft}$$
$$\tau = \frac{2\pi ab}{h} = \frac{2\pi(93.05 \times 10^6)(60.9 \times 10^6)}{0.7493 \times 10^{12}}$$
$$\tau = 47{,}500 \text{ sec} = 792 \text{ min} = 13 \text{ hr } 12 \text{ min} \blacktriangleleft$$

PROBLEMS

12.74. The two-dimensional motion of a particle is defined by the relations $r = t^3 - 2t^2$ and $\theta = t^3 - 4t$, where r is expressed in feet, t in seconds, and θ in radians. If the particle weighs 10 lb and moves in a horizontal plane, determine the radial and transverse components of the force acting on the particle when (*a*) $t = 0$, (*b*) $t = 1$ sec.

12.75. For the motion defined in Prob. 12.74, determine the radial and transverse components of the force acting on the 10-lb particle when it passes through the origin at $t = 2$ sec.

12.76. The two-dimensional motion of a particle is defined by the relations $r = 10(1 + \cos \frac{1}{2}\pi t)$ and $\theta = \frac{1}{2}\pi t$, where r is expressed in feet, t in seconds, and θ in radians. If the particle weighs 2 lb and moves in a horizontal plane, determine the radial and transverse components of the force acting on the particle when (*a*) $t = 0$, (*b*) $t = 1$ sec.

12.77. For the motion defined in Sample Prob. 11.12, determine the force exerted by the arm OA on block B and the radial force which must act on the block (*a*) when $\theta = 0°$ and (*b*) when $\theta = 30°$. Assume that block B weighs 2 lb and that the arm rotates in a vertical plane.

12.78. A particle moves under a central force in a path defined by the equation $r = r_0/\cos n\theta$, where n is a positive constant. Using Eq. (12.15), show that the radial and transverse components of the velocity are $v_r = nv_0 \sin n\theta$ and $v_\theta = v_0 \cos n\theta$, where v_0 is the velocity of the particle for $\theta = 0$. What is the motion of the particle when $n = 0$ and when $n = 1$?

12.79. A particle moves under a central force in a circular path of diameter r_0 which passes through the center of force O. Show that its speed is $v = v_0/\cos^2 \theta$, where v_0 is the speed of the particle at point P_0 directly across the circle from O. (*Hint.* Use Eq. (12.15) with $r = r_0 \cos \theta$.)

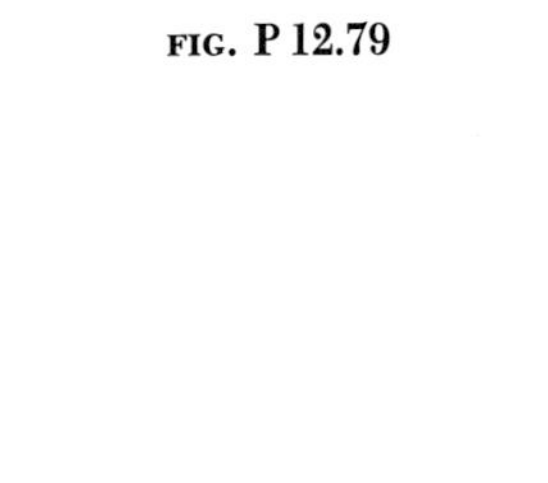

FIG. P 12.79

12.80. Determine the mass of the earth from Newton's law of gravitation, knowing that the radius of the earth is 3,960 miles and that the acceleration of gravity is $g = 32.2$ ft/sec^2 at the surface of the earth.

12.81. Determine the acceleration of gravity at the surface of the planet Mars, knowing that the radius of that planet is 2,110 miles and that its mass is 0.108 times the mass of the earth.

12.82. Determine the acceleration of gravity at the surface of the moon, knowing that the radius of the moon is 1,080 miles and that its mass is 81.3 times smaller than the mass of the earth.

12.83. Show that the radius r of the moon's orbit may be determined from the radius R of the earth, the acceleration of gravity g at the surface of the earth, and the time τ required by the moon to revolve once around the earth. Compute r knowing that $\tau = 27.3$ days.

12.84. A satellite is launched in a direction parallel to the earth's surface from an altitude of 400 miles. (*a*) Determine the required initial velocity if the satellite is to describe a circular orbit. (*b*) What is the allowable percentage of error in the initial velocity if the satellite is not to come closer than 200 miles from the surface of the earth?

12.85. A capsule is to be returned to the earth from a satellite describing a circular orbit at an altitude of 6,000 miles. (*a*) With what absolute velocity $\mathbf{v}_0$, tangential to the orbit, should the capsule leave the satellite if it is to land tangentially to the surface of the earth? (*b*) With what relative velocity does the capsule leave the satellite in part *a*?

12.86. The maximum altitude of an Explorer satellite, as it orbits around the earth, is observed to be 26,000 miles above the earth's surface, and its minimum altitude 400 miles. Determine the maximum and minimum values of its velocity.

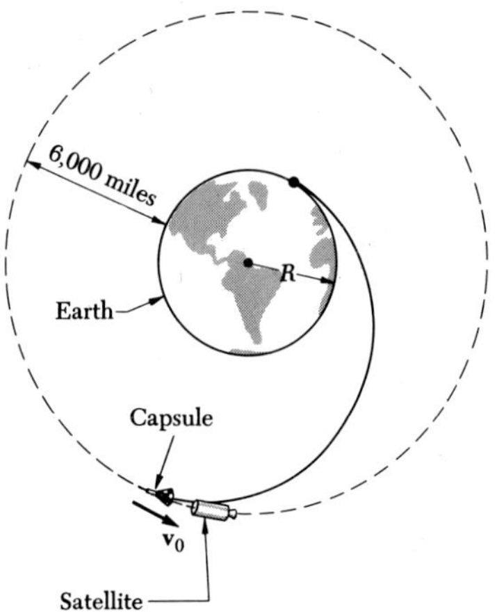

FIG. P 12.85

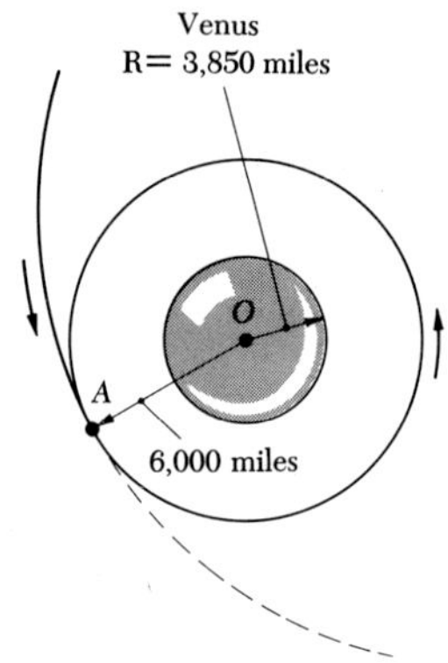

FIG. P 12.87

12.87. A space vehicle approaches the planet Venus along a hyperbolic trajectory of eccentricity $\varepsilon = 2$. As the vehicle reaches point A, which is the point of the trajectory closest to the planet, retrorockets are fired to slow the vehicle and place it in a circular orbit. Knowing that the distance from the center O of the planet to A is 6,000 miles, and that the mass of Venus is 0.82 times the mass of the earth, determine the velocity of the vehicle (*a*) as it approaches A, (*b*) after the retrorockets have been fired.

12.88. A space vehicle approaches the planet Mars along a parabolic trajectory. As the vehicle reaches point A, which is the point of the trajectory closest to the planet, retrorockets are fired to slow the vehicle and place it in an elliptic path which will bring it to a tangential landing at B. Knowing that the distance from the center O of the planet to A is 8,000 miles, that the radius of the planet is 2,110 miles, and that its mass is 0.108 times the mass of the earth, determine the velocity of the vehicle (*a*) as it approaches A, (*b*) after the retrorockets have been fired, (*c*) as it lands at B.

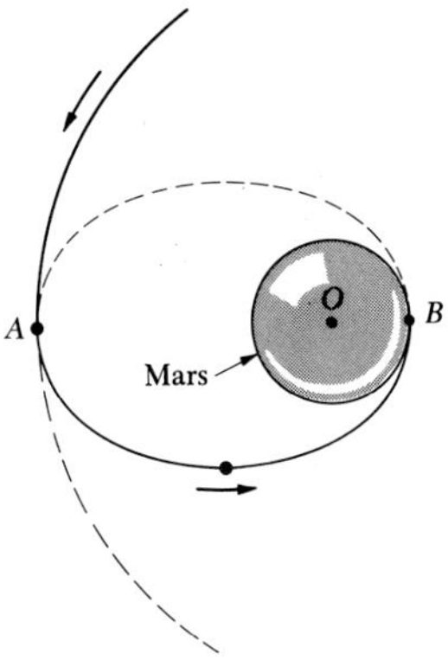

FIG. P 12.88

12.89. In order to place a satellite in a circular orbit of 20,000-mile radius around the earth, the satellite is first projected horizontally from A at an altitude of 300 miles into an elliptic path whose apogee A' is at a distance of 20,000 miles from the center of the earth. Auxiliary rockets are fired as the satellite reaches A' in order to place it in its final orbit. Determine (*a*) the initial velocity of the satellite at A, (*b*) the increase in velocity resulting from the firing of the rockets at A'.

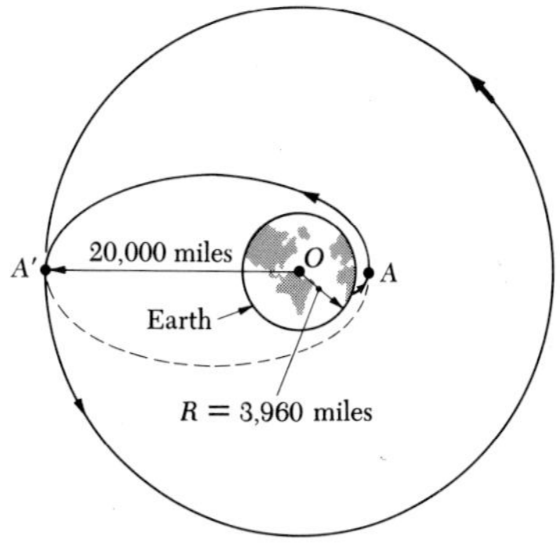

FIG. P 12.89

12.90. Determine the periodic time of the Explorer satellite of Prob. 12.86.

12.91. Determine the periodic time of the space vehicle of Prob. 12.87 after it has been placed in a circular orbit around the planet Venus.

12.92. Determine the time required for the space vehicle of Prob. 12.88 to land on the planet Mars after the retrorockets have been fired.

12.93. Referring to Prob. 12.89, determine the time elapsed between the end of the launching of the satellite at A and the firing of the auxiliary rockets at A' which will place the satellite in its final orbit.

12.94. A satellite is describing a circular orbit of radius r_0 around the earth when auxiliary rockets are fired to increase its velocity by $33\frac{1}{3}$ per cent. Determine (*a*) the maximum distance from the center of the earth reached by the satellite on its new orbit, (*b*) the quotient of the periodic times corresponding respectively to the new and the old orbits of the satellite.

12.95. Two space stations S_1 and S_2 are describing coplanar circular counterclockwise orbits of radius r_0 and $8r_0$, respectively, around the earth. It is desired to send a vehicle from S_1 to S_2. The vehicle is to be launched in a direction tangent to the orbit of S_1 and is to reach S_2 with a velocity tangent to the orbit of S_2. After a short powered phase, the vehicle will travel in free flight from S_1 to S_2. (*a*) Determine the launching velocity (velocity of the vehicle relative to S_1) in terms of the velocity $\mathbf{v}_0$ of S_1. (*b*) Briefly describe the landing operation on S_2. (*c*) Determine the angle θ defining the required position of S_2 relative to S_1 at the time of the launching.

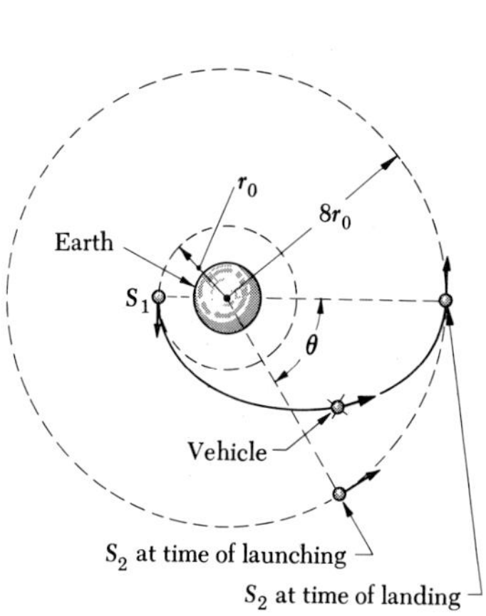

FIG. P 12.95

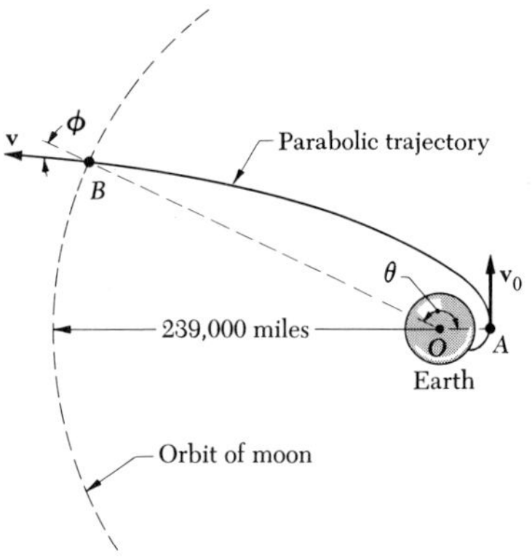

FIG. P 12.96

*12.96. A space vehicle is launched in a direction parallel to the earth's surface from point A at an altitude of 340 miles. Knowing that the trajectory of the space vehicle is parabolic, determine (*a*) the launching velocity $\mathbf{v}_0$ of the vehicle, (*b*) the angle θ described by the vehicle as it crosses the orbit of the moon at point B, 239,000 miles away from the center of the earth, (*c*) the velocity of the vehicle at B (magnitude and angle ϕ), (*d*) the time elapsed as the vehicle travels from A to B.

12.97. Derive Kepler's third law of planetary motion from Eqs. (12.21) and (12.28).

REVIEW PROBLEMS

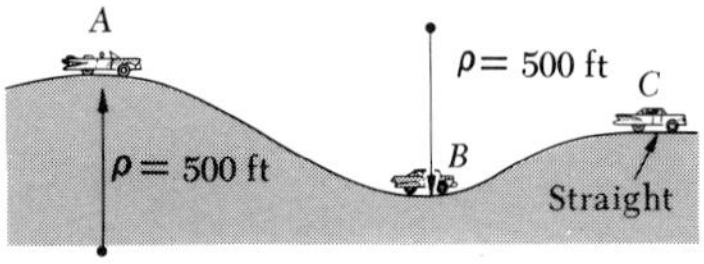

FIG. P 12.98

12.98. Three automobiles are proceeding at a speed of 50 mph along the road shown. Knowing that the coefficient of friction between the tires and the road is 0.60, determine the tangential deceleration of each automobile if its brakes are suddenly applied and the wheels skid.

12.99. A man swings a bucket full of water in a vertical plane in a circle of radius 3 ft. What is the smallest velocity that the bucket should have at the top of the circle if no water is to be spilled?

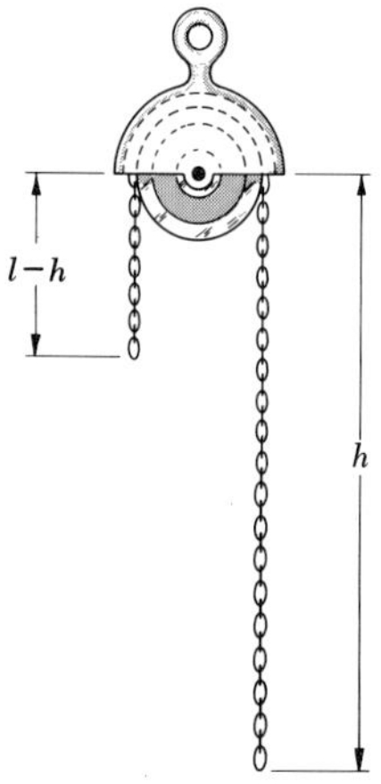

FIG. P 12.100

12.100. A chain weighing w lb/ft and of length l ft rests over a small pulley of negligible mass. If the chain is released in the position shown $(h > \frac{1}{2}l)$, determine the velocity of the chain when the end of the chain leaves the pulley. Also determine the maximum possible final velocity by letting h approach $\frac{1}{2}l$.

12.101. A bomber flying horizontally in a straight line at a constant speed v_0 releases a powered missile which will fly ahead of the bomber in a parallel horizontal path. The missile engine, which is started at the time of release, provides a constant thrust T, while the atmosphere produces a drag equal to kv^2, where v is the speed of the missile. Neglecting any change in the mass of the missile, express the acceleration of the missile as a function of the distance traveled in free flight. It is assumed that $v_0 < \sqrt{T/k}$.

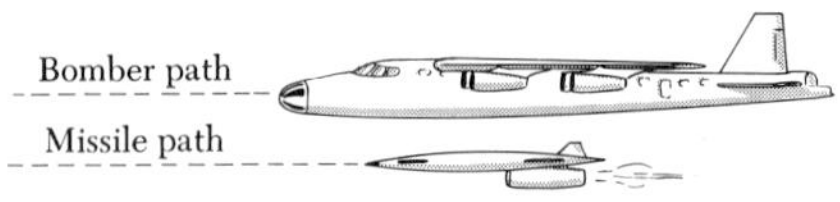

FIG. P 12.101

12.102. In problem 12.101 determine the time t required for the missile to reach a given speed v. Explain why v cannot exceed $\sqrt{T/k}$.

12.103. At what distance from the center of the earth will an object directly in line with the earth and the moon be attracted equally by these two bodies? The mass of the moon is 81.3 times smaller than the mass of the earth, and the distance from the earth to the moon is 239,000 miles.

12.104. A constant force **P** is applied to a piston and rod of total mass m in order to make them move in a cylinder filled with oil. As the piston moves, the oil is forced through orifices in the piston and exerts on the piston an additional force of magnitude kv, proportional to the speed v of the piston and in a direction opposite to its motion. Express the acceleration of the piston as a function of the time t, assuming that the piston starts from rest at time $t = 0$.

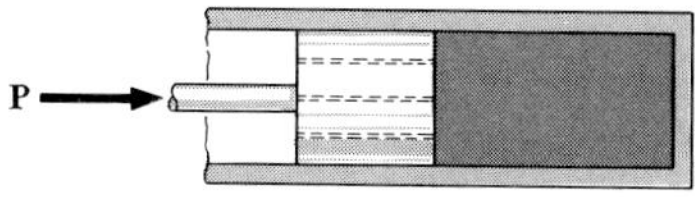

FIG. P 12.104

12.105. What should be the weight of block B of Sample Prob. 12.3 if block A is to move downward with an acceleration of 5 ft/sec^2?

12.106. A daredevil rides a small automobile on the vertical wall of a circular pit of radius 40 ft at a speed of 30 mph. Knowing that this is the lowest speed at which he can perform this stunt, determine the coefficient of friction between the tires and the wall.

12.107. The edge AB of the plate is cut to form a parabola with vertex at A. As the frame and plate are accelerated to the left, the sphere is observed to remain at a distance x from the edge of the frame. Express the horizontal acceleration of the frame in terms of x, L, and h.

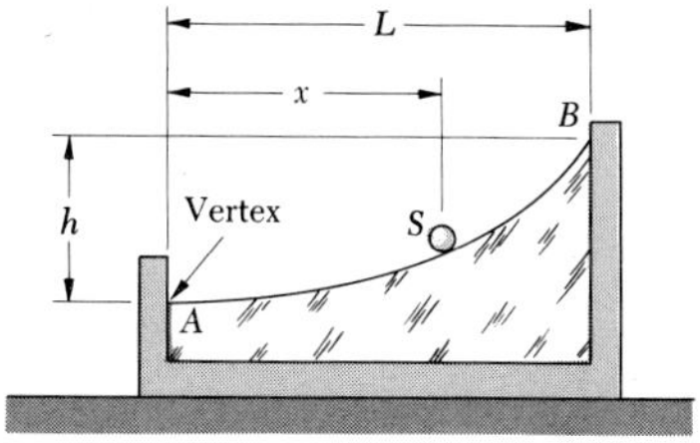

FIG. P 12.107

12.108. A satellite is to be placed in a circular equatorial orbit around the earth. At what distance from the center of the earth should it be placed if it is to remain in the same position relative to the earth?

12.109. A ship of total weight W is anchored in the middle of a river which is flowing with a constant velocity $\mathbf{v}_0$. The horizontal component of the force exerted on the ship by the anchor chain is $\mathbf{T}_0$. If the anchor chain suddenly breaks, determine the time required for the ship to attain a velocity equal to $\frac{1}{2}\mathbf{v}_0$. Assume that the frictional resistance of the water is proportional to the velocity of the ship relative to the water.

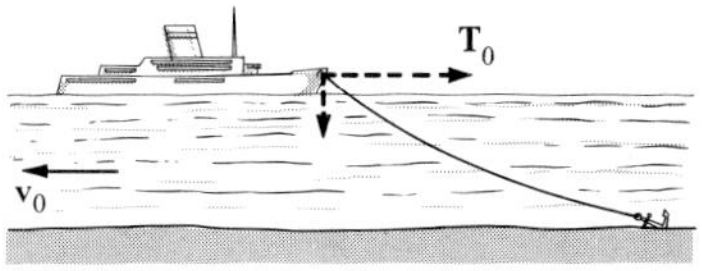

FIG. P 12.109

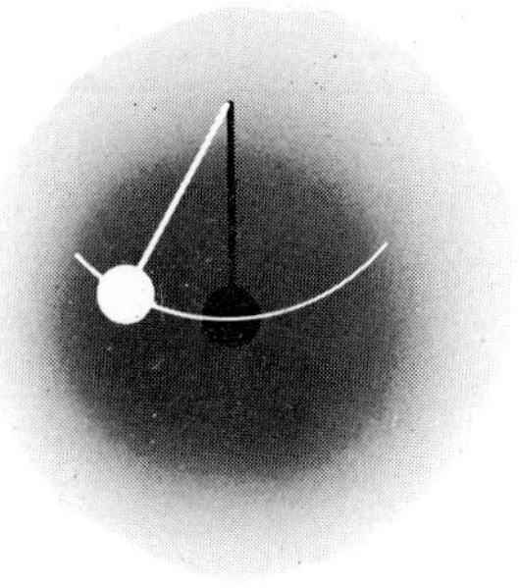

13. KINETICS OF PARTICLES: WORK AND ENERGY

13.1. Introduction. In the preceding chapter, problems dealing with the motion of particles were solved through the use of the fundamental equation of motion $\mathbf{F} = m\mathbf{a}$. Given a particle acted upon by a force $\mathbf{F}$, we could solve this equation for the acceleration $\mathbf{a}$; then, by applying the principles of kinematics, we could determine from $\mathbf{a}$ the velocity and position of the particle at any time.

If the equation $\mathbf{F} = m\mathbf{a}$ and the principles of kinematics are combined, two additional methods of analysis may be obtained, the *method of work and energy* and the *method of impulse and momentum.* The advantage of these methods lies in the fact that they make the determination of the acceleration unnecessary. Indeed, the method of work and energy relates directly force, mass, velocity, and displacement, while the method of impulse and momentum relates force, mass, velocity, and time.

The method of work and energy is treated in the present chapter. It is based on two important concepts, the concept of the *work of a force* and the concept of the *kinetic energy of a particle.* These concepts are defined in the following sections.

13.2. Work of a Force. We shall first define the terms *displacement* and *work* as they are used in mechanics.† Consider a particle which moves from a point A to a neighboring point A' (Fig. 13.1*a*). The small vector which joins A to A' is called the *displacement* of the particle and is denoted by the differential $d\mathbf{r}$, where $\mathbf{r}$ represents the position vector of A. Now, let us assume that a force $\mathbf{F}$, of magnitude F and forming an angle α with $d\mathbf{r}$, is acting on the particle. The *work of the force* $\mathbf{F}$ *during the displacement* $d\mathbf{r}$, of magnitude ds, is de-

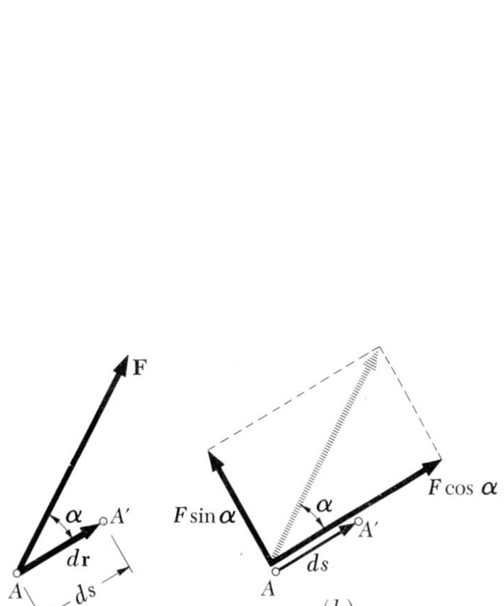

FIG. 13.1

† The definition of work was given in Sec. 10.1, and the basic properties of the work of a force were outlined in Secs. 10.1 and 10.5. For convenience, we repeat here the portions of this material which relate to the kinetics of particles.

fined as the scalar quantity

$$dU = F\,ds\cos\alpha \tag{13.1}$$

Being a *scalar quantity,* work has a magnitude and a sign, but no direction. We also note that work should be expressed in units such as ft-lb or in.-lb, obtained by multiplying units of length by units of force.

It appears from (13.1) that the work dU may be considered as the product of the magnitude ds of the displacement and of the component $F \cos \alpha$ of the force $\mathbf{F}$ in the direction of $d\mathbf{r}$ (Fig. 13.1*b*). If this component and the displacement $d\mathbf{r}$ have the same sense, the work is positive; if they have opposite senses, the work is negative. Three particular cases are of special interest. If the force $\mathbf{F}$ has the same direction as $d\mathbf{r}$, the work dU reduces to $F\,ds$. If $\mathbf{F}$ has a direction opposite to that of $d\mathbf{r}$, the work is $dU = -F\,ds$. Finally, if $\mathbf{F}$ is perpendicular to $d\mathbf{r}$, the work dU is zero.

The work of $\mathbf{F}$ during a *finite* displacement of the particle from A_1 to A_2 (Fig. 13.2*a*) is obtained by integrating Eq. (13.1) from s_1 to s_2. This work, denoted by $U_{1\to2}$, is

$$U_{1\to2} = \int_{s_1}^{s_2} (F\cos\alpha)\,ds \tag{13.2}$$

where the variable of integration s measures the distance traveled by the particle along the path. The work $U_{1\to2}$ is represented by the area under the curve obtained by plotting $F \cos \alpha$ against s (Fig. 13.2*b*).

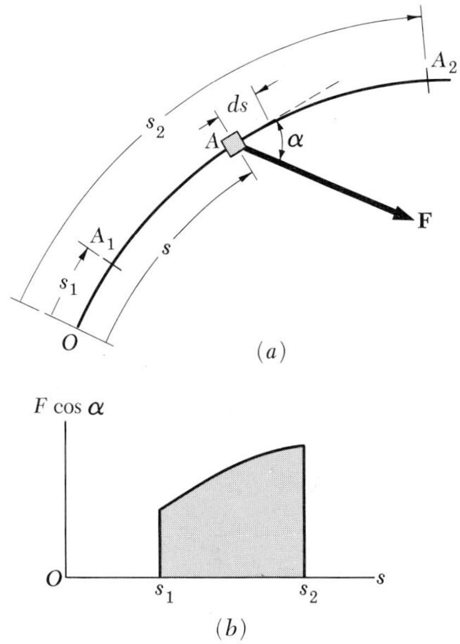

FIG. 13.2

Work of a Constant Force in Rectilinear Motion. When a particle moving in a straight line is acted upon by a force $\mathbf{F}$ of constant magnitude and of constant direction (Fig. 13.3), formula (13.2) yields

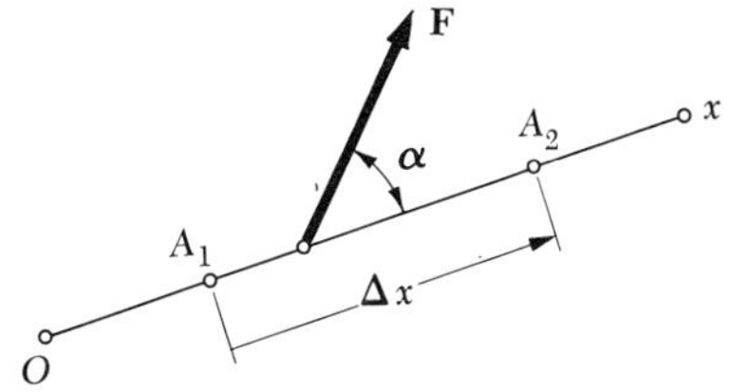

FIG. 13.3

$$U_{1\to2} = (F\cos\alpha)\,\Delta x \tag{13.3}$$

where α = angle the force forms with direction of motion
Δx = displacement from A_1 to A_2

Work of a Weight. The work dU of a force $\mathbf{F}$ during a displacement $d\mathbf{r}$ may also be considered as the product of the magnitude F of the force $\mathbf{F}$ and of the component $ds \cos \alpha$ of the displacement $d\mathbf{r}$ along $\mathbf{F}$. This view is particularly useful in the computation of the work of the weight $\mathbf{W}$ of a body. The work dU of $\mathbf{W}$ is equal to the product of W and of the vertical displacement of the center of gravity G of the body. With the y axis chosen upward, the work of $\mathbf{W}$ during a finite displacement (Fig. 13.4) is obtained by writing

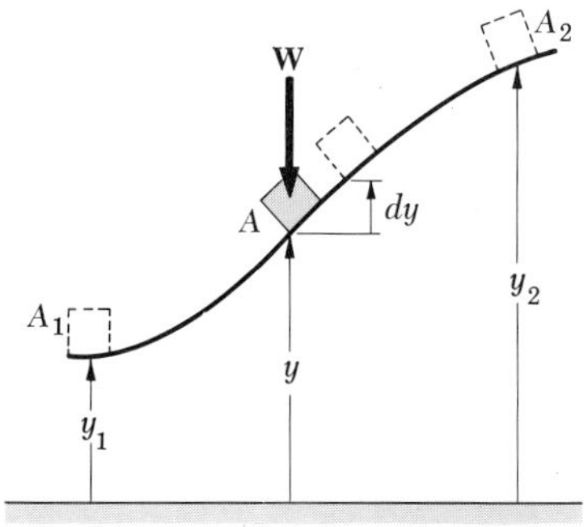

FIG. 13.4

$$dU = -W\,dy$$

$$U_{1\to2} = -\int_{y_1}^{y_2} W\,dy = Wy_1 - Wy_2 \qquad (13.4)$$

or

$$U_{1\to2} = -W(y_2 - y_1) = -W\,\Delta y \qquad (13.4')$$

where Δy is the vertical displacement from A_1 to A_2. The work of the weight **W** is thus equal to *the product of W and of the vertical displacement of the center of gravity of the body.* The work is *positive* when $\Delta y < 0$, that is, *when the body moves down.*

Work of the Force Exerted by a Spring. Consider a body A attached to a fixed point B by a spring; it is assumed that the spring is undeformed when the body is at A_0 (Fig. 13.5*a*). Ex-

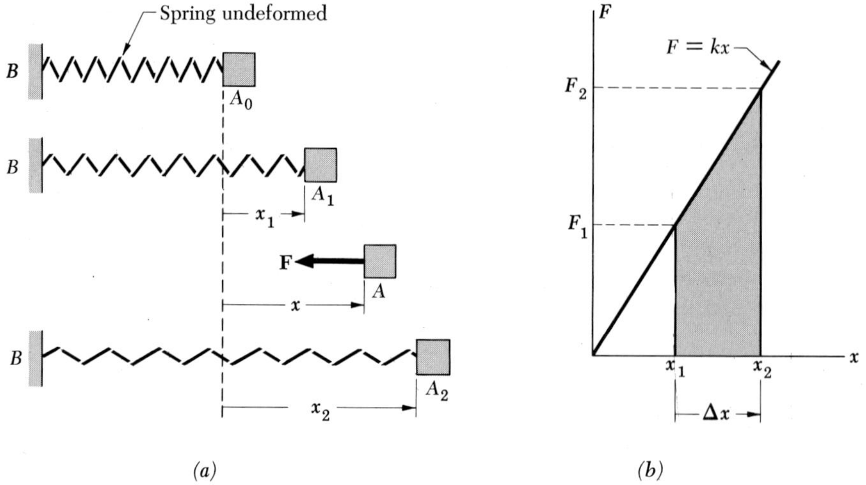

FIG. 13.5

perimental evidence shows that the magnitude of the force **F** exerted by the spring on body A is proportional to the deflection x of the spring measured from the position A_0. We have

$$F = kx \qquad (13.5)$$

where k is the *spring constant,* expressed in lb/ft or lb/in.† The work of the force **F** exerted by the spring during a finite

† The relation $F = kx$ is correct under static conditions only. Under dynamic conditions, formula (13.5) should be modified to take the inertia of the spring into account. However, the error introduced by using the relation $F = kx$ in the solution of kinetics problems is small if the mass of the spring is small compared with the other masses in motion.

displacement of the body from $A_1(x = x_1)$ to $A_2(x = x_2)$ is obtained by writing

$$dU = -F\,dx = -kx\,dx$$

$$U_{1\to 2} = -\int_{x_1}^{x_2} kx\,dx = \tfrac{1}{2}kx_1^2 - \tfrac{1}{2}kx_2^2 \qquad (13.6)$$

Care should be taken to express k and x in consistent units, that is, k in lb/ft and x in feet, or k in lb/in. and x in inches; in the first case, the work is obtained in ft-lb, in the second case, in in.-lb. We note that the work of the force **F** exerted by the spring on the body is *positive* when $x_2 < x_1$, i.e., *when the spring is returning to its undeformed position.*

Since Eq. (13.5) is the equation of a straight line of slope k passing through the origin, the work $U_{1\to 2}$ of **F** during the displacement from A_1 to A_2 may be obtained by evaluating the area of the trapezoid shown in Fig. 13.5*b*. This is done by computing F_1 and F_2 and multiplying the base Δx of the trapezoid by its mean height $\frac{1}{2}(F_1 + F_2)$. Since the work of the force **F** exerted by the spring is positive for a negative value of Δx, we write

$$U_{1\to 2} = -\tfrac{1}{2}(F_1 + F_2)\,\Delta x \qquad (13.6')$$

Formula (13.6′) is usually more convenient to use than (13.6) and affords fewer chances of confusing the units involved.

Work of a Gravitational Force. We saw in Sec. 12.10 that two particles at distance r from each other and, respectively, of mass M and m, attract each other with equal and opposite forces **F** and **F′** directed along the line joining the particles, and of magnitude

$$F = G\frac{Mm}{r^2}$$

Let us assume that the particle M occupies a fixed position O while the particle m moves along the path shown in Fig. 13.6. The work of the force **F** exerted on the particle m during an infinitesimal displacement of the particle from A to A' may be obtained by multiplying the magnitude F of the force by the radial component dr of the displacement. Since **F** is directed toward O, the work is negative and we write

$$dU = -F dr = -G\frac{Mm}{r^2}dr$$

The work of the gravitational force **F** during a finite displacement from $A_1(r = r_1)$ to $A_2(r = r_2)$ is therefore

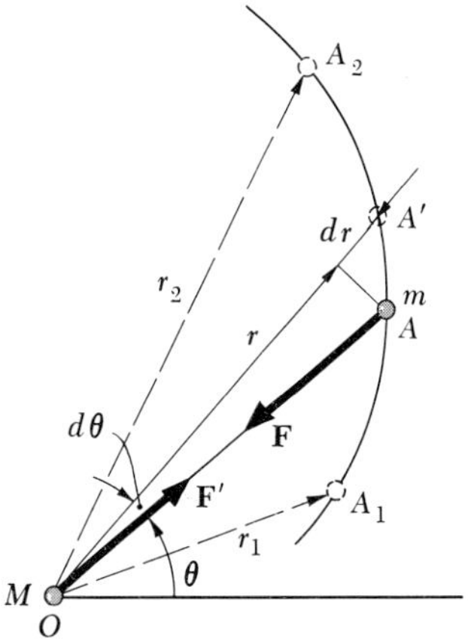

FIG. 13.6

$$U_{1\to 2} = -\int_{r_1}^{r_2} \frac{GMm}{r^2}\,dr = \frac{GMm}{r_2} - \frac{GMm}{r_1} \qquad (13.7)$$

The formula obtained may be used to determine the work of the force exerted by the earth on a body of mass m at a distance r from the center of the earth, when r is larger than the radius R of the earth. The letter M represents then the mass of the earth; recalling the first of the relations (12.19), we may thus replace the product GMm in Eq. (13.7) by WR^2, where R is the radius of the earth ($R = 3{,}960$ miles) and W the value of the weight of the body at the surface of the earth.

A number of forces frequently encountered in problems of kinetics *do no work.* They are forces applied to fixed points ($ds = 0$) or acting in a direction perpendicular to the displacement ($\cos\alpha = 0$). Among the forces which do no work are the following: the reaction at a smooth pin when the body supported rotates about the pin, the reaction at a smooth frictionless surface when the body in contact moves along the surface, the reaction at a roller moving along its track, and the weight of a body when its center of gravity moves horizontally.

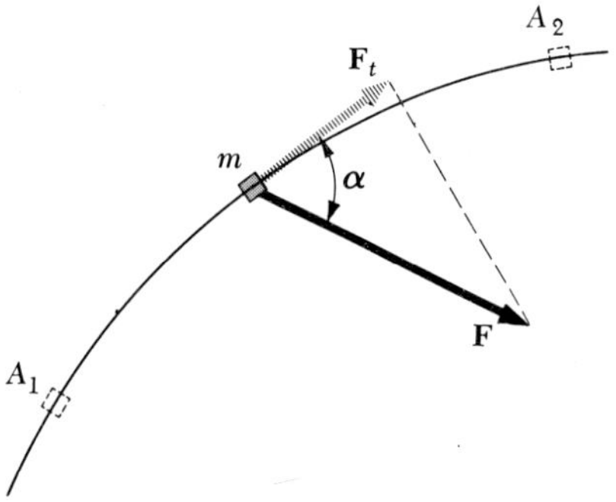

FIG. 13.7

13.3. Kinetic Energy of a Particle. Principle of Work and Energy. Consider a particle of mass m acted upon by a force **F** and moving along a path which is either rectilinear or curved (Fig. 13.7). Expressing Newton's second law in terms of the tangential components of the force and of the acceleration (see Sec. 12.7), we write

$$F_t = ma_t \qquad \text{or} \qquad F\cos\alpha = m\frac{dv}{dt} \qquad (13.8)$$

where α = angle the force forms with direction of motion
v = speed of particle

The speed was shown in Sec. 11.9 to be equal to the rate of change of the distance s traveled by the particle along its path; we write $v = ds/dt$. Solving for dt and substituting into (13.8), we obtain

$$F\cos\alpha = m\frac{dv}{ds}v \qquad (13.9)$$

$$(F\cos\alpha)\,ds = mv\,dv$$

Integrating from A_1, where $s = s_1$ and $v = v_1$, to A_2, where $s = s_2$ and $v = v_2$, we write

$$\int_{s_1}^{s_2} (F\cos\alpha)\,ds = m\int_{v_1}^{v_2} v\,dv = \tfrac{1}{2}mv_2^2 - \tfrac{1}{2}mv_1^2 \qquad (13.10)$$

The left-hand member of Eq. (13.10) represents the work $U_{1\to 2}$ of the force **F** exerted on the particle during the displacement from A_1 to A_2; as indicated in Sec. 13.2, the work $U_{1\to2}$ is a scalar quantity. The expression $\frac{1}{2}mv^2$ is also a scalar quantity; it is defined as the kinetic energy of the particle and is denoted by T. We write

$$T = \tfrac{1}{2}mv^2 \tag{13.11}$$

Substituting into (13.10), we have

$$U_{1\to2} = T_2 - T_1 \tag{13.12}$$

which expresses that, when a particle moves from A_1 to A_2 under the action of a force **F**, *the work of the force* **F** *is equal to the change in kinetic energy of the particle.* This is known as the *principle of work and energy.* Rearranging the terms in (13.12), we write

$$T_1 + U_{1\to2} = T_2 \tag{13.13}$$

Thus, *the kinetic energy of the particle at* A_2 *may be obtained by adding to its kinetic energy at* A_1 *the work done during the displacement from* A_1 *to* A_2 *by the force* **F** *exerted on the particle.* Since both work and kinetic energy are scalar quantities, their sum may be computed as an ordinary algebraic sum, the work $U_{1\to2}$ being considered as positive or negative according to the direction of **F**. When several forces act on the particle, the expression $U_{1\to2}$ represents the total work of the forces acting on the particle; it is obtained by adding algebraically the work of the various forces.

As noted above, the kinetic energy of a particle is a scalar quantity. It further appears from the definition $T = \frac{1}{2}mv^2$ that the kinetic energy is always positive, regardless of the direction of motion of the particle. Considering the particular case when $v_1 = 0$, $v_2 = v$, and substituting $T_1 = 0$, $T_2 = T$ into (13.12), we observe that the work done by the forces acting on the particle is equal to T. Thus, the kinetic energy of a particle moving with a speed v represents the work which must be done to bring the particle from rest to the speed v. Substituting $T_1 = T$ and $T_2 = 0$ into (13.12), we also note that, when a particle moving with a speed v is brought to rest, the work done by the forces acting on the particle is $-T$. Assuming that no energy is dissipated into heat, we conclude that the work done by the forces exerted *by the particle* on the bodies which cause it to come to rest is equal to T. Thus, the kinetic energy of a particle also represents *the capacity to do work associated with the speed of the particle.*

The kinetic energy is measured in the same units as work.

For example, if length, force, and time are measured, respectively, in feet, pounds, and seconds, the kinetic energy should be expressed in ft-lb. We check from formula (13.11) that

$$T = \tfrac{1}{2}mv^2 = \frac{\text{lb-sec}^2}{\text{ft}}\frac{\text{ft}^2}{\text{sec}^2} = \text{ft-lb}$$

13.4. Applications of the Principle of Work and Energy. The application of the principle of work and energy greatly simplifies the solution of many problems involving forces, displacements, and velocities. Consider, for example, a pendulum consisting of a bob of weight W attached to a cord of length l (Fig. 13.8*a*). The pendulum is released with no initial velocity from a horizontal position OA_1 and allowed to swing in a vertical plane. We wish to determine the speed of the bob as it passes through A_2, directly under O.

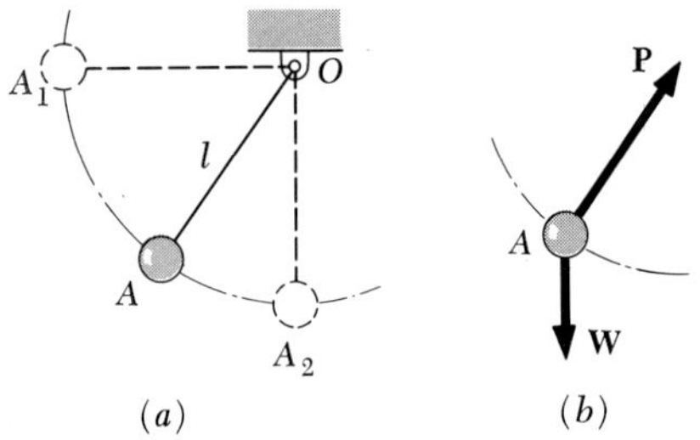

FIG. 13.8

We first determine the work done during the displacement from A_1 to A_2 by the forces acting on the bob. We draw a free-body diagram of the bob, showing all the *actual* forces acting on it, i.e., the weight **W** and the force **P** exerted by the cord (Fig. 13.8*b*). The inertia vector is not an actual force and *should not* be included in the free-body diagram. We note that the force **P** does no work, since it is normal to the path; the only force which does work is thus the weight **W**. The work of **W** is obtained by multiplying its magnitude W by the vertical displacement l (Sec. 13.2); since the displacement is downward, the work is positive. We write therefore $U_{1\to 2} = Wl$.

Considering, now, the kinetic energy of the bob, we find $T_1 = 0$ at A_1 and $T_2 = \frac{1}{2}(W/g)v_2^2$ at A_2. We may now apply the principle of work and energy; recalling formula (13.13), we write

$$T_1 + U_{1\to 2} = T_2 \qquad 0 + Wl = \frac{1}{2}\frac{W}{g}v_2^2$$

Solving for v_2, we find $v_2 = \sqrt{2gl}$. We note that the speed obtained is that of a body falling freely from a height l.

The example we have considered illustrates the following advantages of the method of work and energy:

1. In order to find the speed at A_2, there is no need to determine the acceleration in an intermediate position A and to integrate the expression obtained from A_1 to A_2.
2. All quantities involved are scalars and may be added directly, without using x and y components.
3. Forces which do no work are eliminated from the solution of the problem.

What is an advantage in one problem, however, may become a disadvantage in another. It is evident, for instance, that the method of work and energy cannot be used to determine directly an acceleration. We also note that it should be supplemented by the direct application of Newton's second law in order to determine a force which is normal to the path of the particles, since such a force does no work. Suppose, for example, that we wish to determine the tension in the cord of the pendulum of Fig. 13.8*a* as the bob passes through A_2. We draw a free-body diagram of the bob in that position (Fig. 13.9) and express Newton's second law in terms of tangential and normal components.† The equations $\Sigma F_t = ma_t$ and $\Sigma F_n = ma_n$ yield, respectively, $a_t = 0$ and

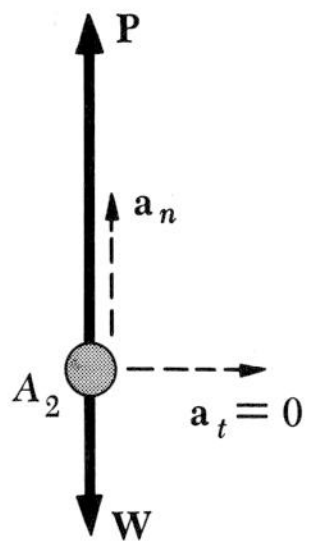

FIG. 13.9

$$P = W + \frac{W}{g} a_n = W + \frac{W}{g} \frac{v^2}{l}$$

But the speed at A_2 was determined earlier by the method of work and energy. Substituting $v^2 = 2gl$, we write

$$P = W + \frac{W}{g} \frac{2gl}{l} = 3W$$

13.5. Systems of Particles. When a problem involves several particles, each particle may be considered separately and the principle of work and energy may be applied to each particle. Adding the kinetic energies of all the particles, and considering the work of all the forces involved, we may also write the equation of work and energy for the entire system. We have

$$T_1 + U_{1\to2} = T_2 \tag{13.13}$$

where T represents the arithmetic sum of the kinetic energies of the particles forming the system (all terms are positive) and $U_{1\to2}$ the work of all the forces acting on the various particles, whether these forces are *internal* or *external* from the point of view of the system as a whole.

The method of work and energy is particularly useful in solving problems involving a system of bodies connected by *inextensible cords or links.* In this case, the internal forces occur by pairs of equal and opposite forces, and the points of application of the forces in each pair *move through equal distances.* As a result, the work of the internal forces is zero and $U_{1\to2}$ reduces to the work of the *external forces only* (see Sample Prob. 13.2).

† We may also use the method of dynamic equilibrium.

SAMPLE PROBLEM 13.1

A railroad car weighing 80,000 lb is initially at rest on a 2° incline. A force of constant magnitude 4,000 lb is then applied as shown. Neglecting friction, determine how far the car will have moved when its velocity is 10 mph.

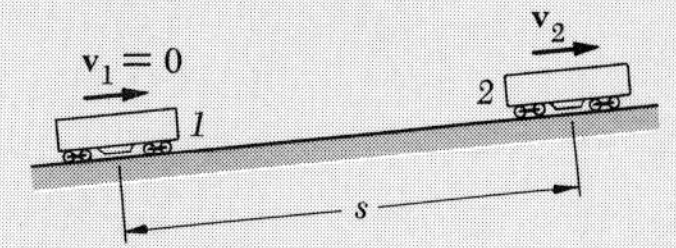

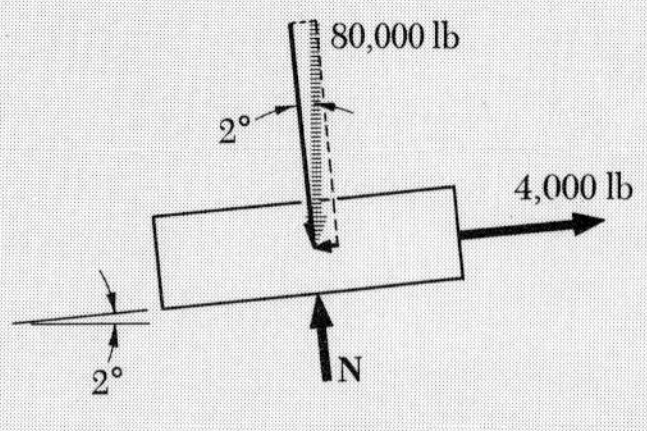

Solution. *Kinetic Energy*

Position *1*: $v_1 = 0 \qquad T_1 = 0$

Position 2: $v_2 = 10 \dfrac{\text{miles}}{\text{hr}} \dfrac{5{,}280 \text{ ft}}{1 \text{ mile}} \dfrac{1 \text{ hr}}{3{,}600 \text{ sec}} = 14.67 \text{ ft/sec}$

$$T_2 = \tfrac{1}{2}mv_2^2 = \frac{1}{2}\frac{80{,}000}{32.2}(14.67)^2 = 267{,}000 \text{ ft-lb}$$

Work

$$U_{1\to2} = 4{,}000s - (80{,}000 \sin 2°)s$$
$$= 4{,}000s - 2{,}790s = 1{,}210s$$

Principle of Work and Energy

$$T_1 + U_{1\to2} = T_2$$
$$0 + 1{,}210s = 267{,}000 \qquad s = 221 \text{ ft} \blacktriangleleft$$

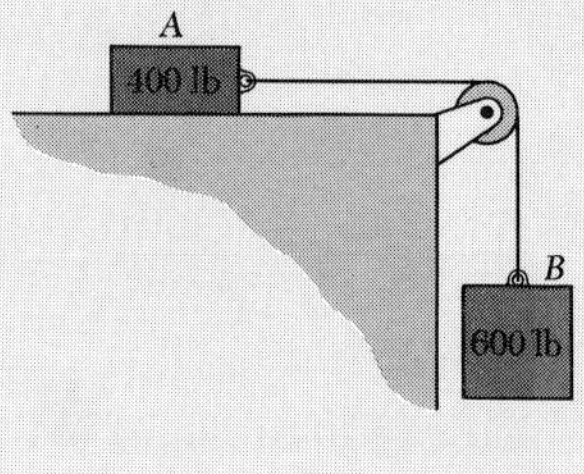

SAMPLE PROBLEM 13.2

Two blocks are joined by an inextensible cable as shown. If the system is released from rest, determine the velocity of block *A* after it has moved 5 ft. Assume that μ equals 0.25 between block *A* and the plane and that the pulley is weightless and frictionless.

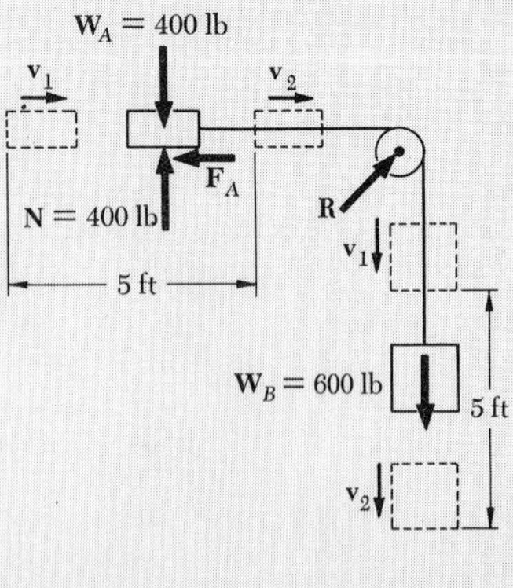

Solution. Since the cable is inextensible, the work done by the forces exerted by the cable will cancel if we consider the two blocks as a single system.

Kinetic Energy

Position *1*: $v_1 = 0 \qquad T_1 = 0$

Position 2: $v_2 = v \qquad T_2 = \tfrac{1}{2}m_Av^2 + \tfrac{1}{2}m_Bv^2$

$$T_2 = \frac{1}{2}\frac{400}{g}v^2 + \frac{1}{2}\frac{600}{g}v^2 = \frac{500}{g}v^2$$

Work. During the motion, only $\mathbf{W}_B$ and $\mathbf{F}_A$ do work. Since $W_B =$ 600 lb and $F_A = \mu N_A$, we have

$$U_{1\to2} = W_B(5 \text{ ft}) - F_A(5 \text{ ft})$$
$$= (600)(5) - (0.25)(400)(5) = 2{,}500 \text{ ft-lb}$$

Principle of Work and Energy

$$T_1 + U_{1\to2} = T_2$$
$$0 + 2{,}500 = \frac{500}{g}v^2 \qquad v = 12.69 \text{ ft/sec} \blacktriangleleft$$

SAMPLE PROBLEM 13.3

A spring is used to stop a 150-lb package which is moving down a 20° incline. The spring has a constant $k = 150$ lb/in. and is held by cables so that it is initially compressed 4 in. If the velocity of the package is 20 ft/sec when it is 30 ft from the spring, determine the maximum additional deformation of the spring in bringing the package to rest. Assume $\mu = 0.20$.

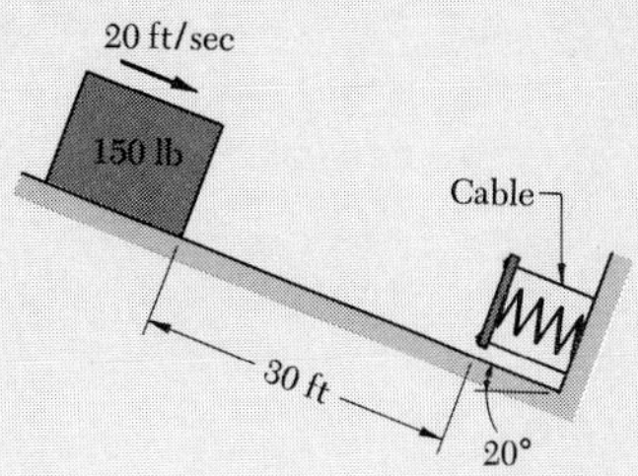

Kinetic Energy

Position *1:*

$$v_1 = 20 \text{ ft/sec}$$

$$T_1 = \tfrac{1}{2}mv_1^2 = \frac{1}{2}\frac{150}{32.2}(20)^2 = 932 \text{ ft-lb}$$

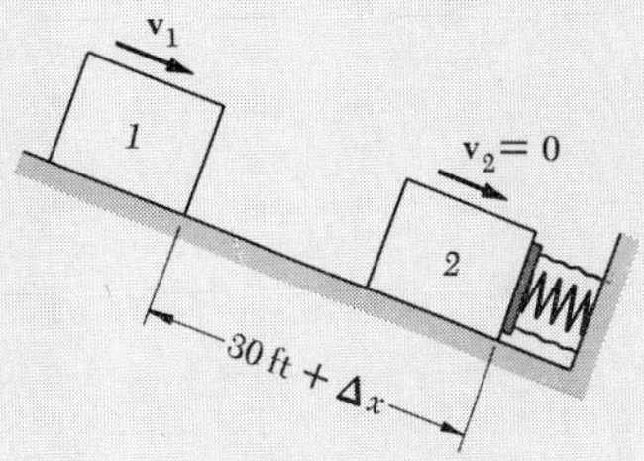

Position 2 (maximum spring deformation):

$$v_2 = 0 \qquad T_2 = 0$$

Work. We assume that when the package is brought to rest the additional deflection of the spring is Δx. The component of the weight parallel to the plane and the friction force act through the entire displacement, i.e., through 30 ft + Δx. The work done by these forces is

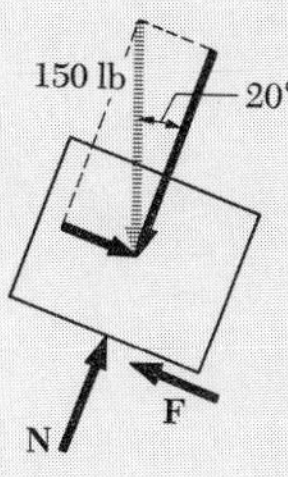

$$\begin{aligned} U_{1\to 2} &= W_t(30 + \Delta x) - F(30 + \Delta x) \\ &= (150 \sin 20°)(30 + \Delta x) - 0.20(150 \cos 20°)(30 + \Delta x) \\ &= 23.1(30 + \Delta x) \end{aligned}$$

In addition, during the compression of the spring, the variable force **P** exerted by the spring does an amount of negative work equal to the area under the force-deflection curve of the spring force.

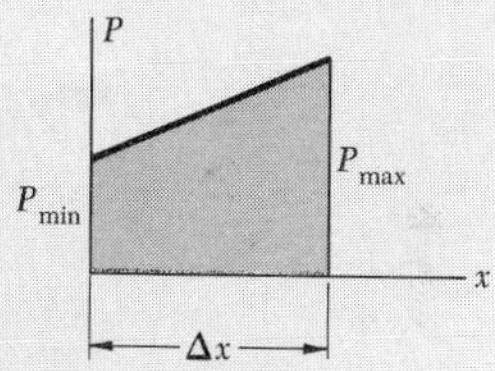

$$\begin{aligned} P_{min} &= (4 \text{ in.})(150 \text{ lb/in.}) = 600 \text{ lb} \\ P_{max} &= 600 + k\,\Delta x \\ &= 600 + (150 \text{ lb/in.})(12 \text{ in./ft})\,\Delta x \\ &= 600 + 1{,}800\,\Delta x \\ U_{1\to 2} &= -\tfrac{1}{2}(P_{min} + P_{max})\,\Delta x = -600\,\Delta x - 900(\Delta x)^2 \end{aligned}$$

The total work is thus

$$U_{1\to 2} = 23.1(30 + \Delta x) - 600\,\Delta x - 900(\Delta x)^2$$

Principle of Work and Energy

$$T_1 + U_{1\to 2} = T_2$$

$$932 + 23.1(30 + \Delta x) - 600\,\Delta x - 900(\Delta x)^2 = 0$$

$$\Delta x = 1.06 \text{ ft} \quad ◄$$

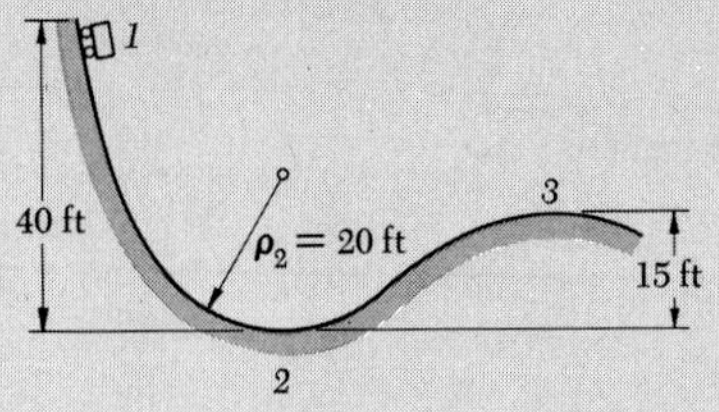

SAMPLE PROBLEM 13.4

A 2,000-lb car starts from rest at point *1* and moves without friction down the track shown. (*a*) Determine the force exerted by the track on the car at point 2, where the radius of curvature of the track is 20 ft. (*b*) Determine the minimum safe value of the radius of curvature at point *3*.

a. **Force Exerted by the Track at Point** *2*. The principle of work and energy is used to determine the velocity of the car as it passes through point 2.

Kinetic Energy

$$T_1 = 0 \qquad T_2 = \tfrac{1}{2}mv_2^2 = \frac{1}{2}\frac{W}{g}v_2^2$$

Work. The only force which does work is the weight **W**. Since the vertical displacement from point *1* to point 2 is 40 ft downward, the work of the weight is

$$U_{1\rightarrow 2} = +W(40\text{ ft})$$

Principle of Work and Energy

$$T_1 + U_{1\rightarrow 2} = T_2 \qquad 0 + W(40) = \frac{1}{2}\frac{W}{g}v_2^2$$

$$v_2^2 = 80g \qquad v_2 = 50.8\text{ ft/sec}$$

Dynamic Equilibrium at Point 2. The acceleration $\mathbf{a}_n$ of the car at point 2 has a magnitude $a_n = v_2^2/\rho$ and is directed upward; the car is in dynamic equilibrium under the action of **W**, **N**, and the inertia vector $(m\mathbf{a}_n)_{\text{rev}}$.

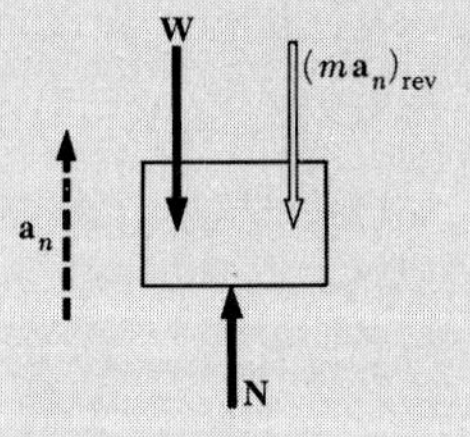

$$+\uparrow \Sigma F_y = 0: \qquad -W + N - ma_n = 0$$

$$-W + N - \frac{W}{g}\frac{v_2^2}{\rho} = 0$$

$$-W + N - \frac{W}{g}\frac{80g}{20} = 0$$

$$N = 5W \qquad \mathbf{N} = 10{,}000\text{ lb}\uparrow$$ ◄

b. **Minimum Value of** ρ **at Point** *3*. *Principle of Work and Energy.* Applying the principle of work and energy between point *1* and point *3*, we obtain

$$T_1 + U_{1\rightarrow 3} = T_3 \qquad 0 + W(25) = \frac{1}{2}\frac{W}{g}v_3^2$$

$$v_3^2 = 50g \qquad v_3 = 40.1\text{ ft/sec}$$

Dynamic Equilibrium at Point 3. The minimum safe value of ρ occurs when $\mathbf{N} = 0$. In this case, the acceleration $\mathbf{a}_n$, of magnitude $a_n = v_3^2/\rho$, is directed downward, and we obtain

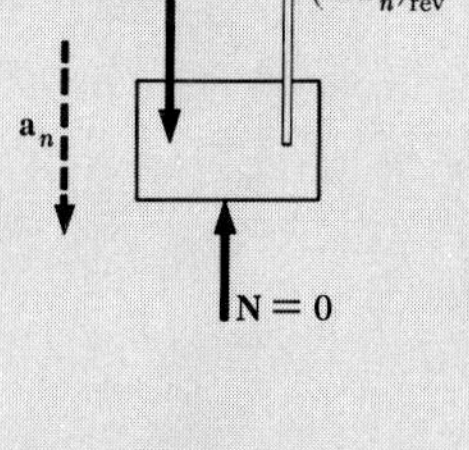

$$+\uparrow \Sigma F_y = 0: \qquad -W + \frac{W}{g}\frac{v_3^2}{\rho} = 0$$

$$-W + \frac{W}{g}\frac{50g}{\rho} = 0 \qquad \rho = 50\text{ ft}$$ ◄

PROBLEMS

13.1. A stone which weighs 5 lb is dropped from a height h and strikes the ground with a velocity of 90 ft/sec. (*a*) Find the kinetic energy of the stone as it strikes the ground and the height h from which it was dropped. (*b*) Solve part *a* assuming that the same stone is dropped on the moon. (Acceleration of gravity on the moon = 5.31 ft/sec^2.)

13.2. A 50-lb satellite was placed in a circular orbit 1,548 miles above the surface of the earth. At this elevation the acceleration of gravity is 16.7 ft/sec^2. Determine the kinetic energy of the satellite, knowing that its orbital speed is 15,000 mph.

13.3. Knowing that the coefficient of friction between rubber tires and concrete is approximately 0.80, determine the length of skid marks which would indicate that an automobile was traveling at 60 mph or faster when the brakes were applied. Assume that all wheels of the car produce skid marks.

13.4. A railroad car weighing 40 tons rolls 500 ft down a 2 per cent incline and then rolls 333 ft up a 2 per cent incline before coming to a stop. Determine the average rolling resistance of the car.

13.5. Using the method of work and energy, solve Prob. 12.8.

13.6. Using the method of work and energy, solve Prob. 12.6.

13.7. Packages are thrown down a chute at A with a velocity of 4 ft/sec. Knowing that $\mu = 0.25$, determine the distance d if the packages are to arrive at point C with a velocity of 8 ft/sec.

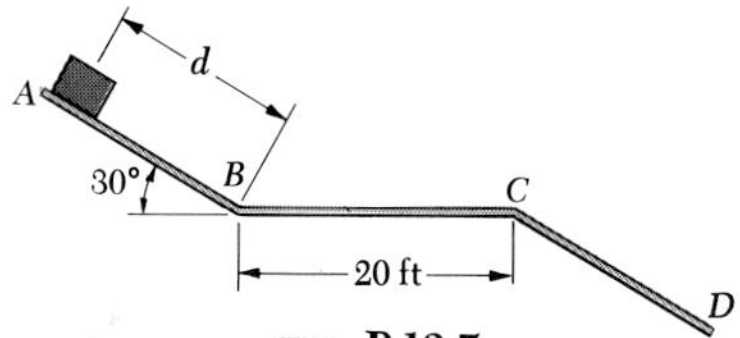

FIG. P 13.7

13.8. Using the method of work and energy, solve Prob. 12.12*c*.

13.9. The subway train shown travels at a speed of 30 mph. Knowing that $\mu = 0.30$, determine the distance required to stop the train and the force in each coupling if the brakes are fully applied on car A but are not applied on cars B and C.

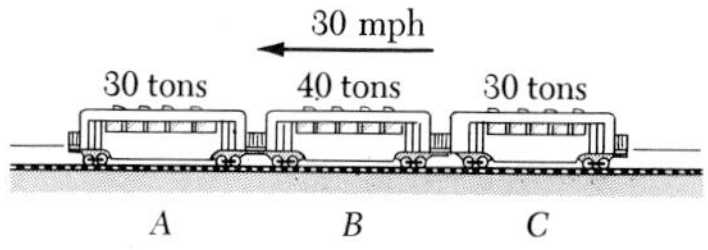

FIG. P 13.9

13.10. Solve Prob. 13.9 assuming that the brakes are fully applied on cars B and C but are not applied on car A.

13.11. The system shown is released from rest. Determine the velocity of the block A after it has moved 6 ft.

13.12. The system shown is released from rest. After moving a distance d, block B strikes the ground and the cable becomes slack. Determine the required distance d if block A is to come to rest after moving a total distance of 10 ft.

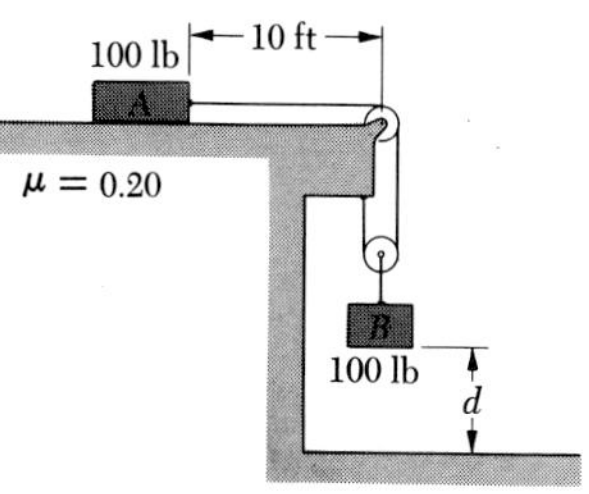

FIG. P 13.11 AND P 13.12

13.13. Four packages weighing 125 lb each are placed as shown on a conveyor belt which is disengaged from its drive motor. Package *1* is just to the left of the horizontal portion of the belt. If the system is released from rest, determine the velocity of package *1* as it falls off the belt at point *A*. Assume that the weight of the belt and rollers is small compared to the weight of the packages.

13.14. In Prob. 13.13, determine the velocity of package 2 as it falls from the belt at *A*.

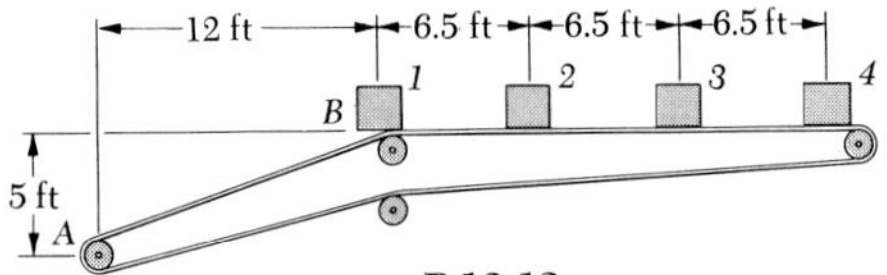

FIG. P 13.13

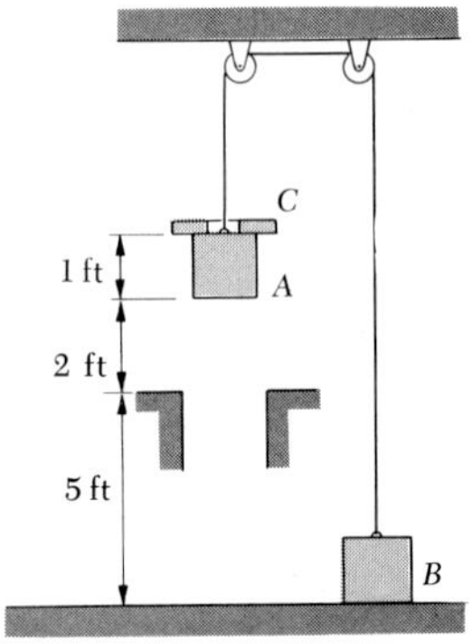

FIG. P 13.15

13.15. Two blocks *A* and *B*, weighing 9 lb and 10 lb, respectively, are connected by a cord which passes over pulleys as shown. A collar *C* is placed on block *A* and the system is released from rest. After the blocks have moved 3 ft, the collar *C* is removed and the blocks continue to move. Knowing that collar *C* weighs 5 lb, determine the speed of block *A* just before it strikes the ground.

13.16. In Prob. 13.15, determine the smallest weight of the collar *C* for which block *A* will reach the ground.

13.17. Using the method of work and energy, solve Prob. 12.17*c*.

13.18. Using the method of work and energy, solve Prob. 12.20.

13.19. Using the method of work and energy, solve Prob. 12.21*b*.

13.20. Using the method of work and energy, solve Prob. 12.22*b*.

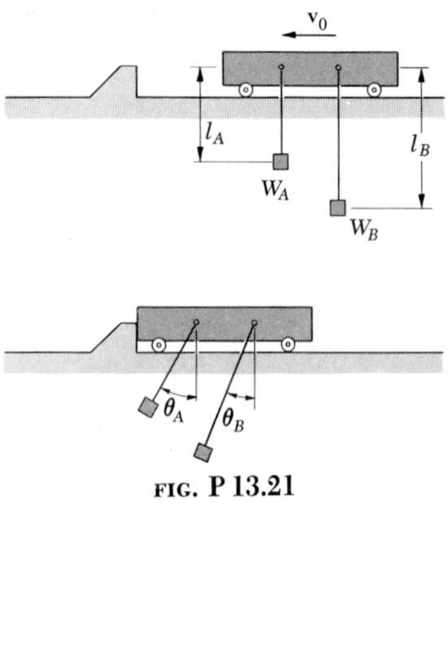

FIG. P 13.21

13.21. The load W_A is suspended from the car by a cable of length l_A. Initially, the car and load are moving at a constant velocity v_0. After the car is stopped by the bumper, the load swings forward. (*a*) What is the maximum angle θ_A through which the load will swing? (*b*) If the maximum angle through which the load swings is 30°, what was the initial velocity of the car, assuming $l_A = 10$ ft?

13.22. When the car of Prob. 13.21 is stopped by the bumper, the maximum angle through which the load W_A swings is observed to be $\theta_A = 30°$. Knowing that $l_A = 10$ ft and $l_B = 20$ ft, determine the maximum angle θ_B through which the load W_B will swing.

13.23. An airplane weighing 12,000 lb lands on an aircraft carrier and is caught by an arresting cable which is characterized by the force-deflection diagram shown. Knowing that the landing speed of the plane is 100 mph, determine (*a*) the distance required for the plane to come to rest, (*b*) the maximum rate of deceleration of the plane.

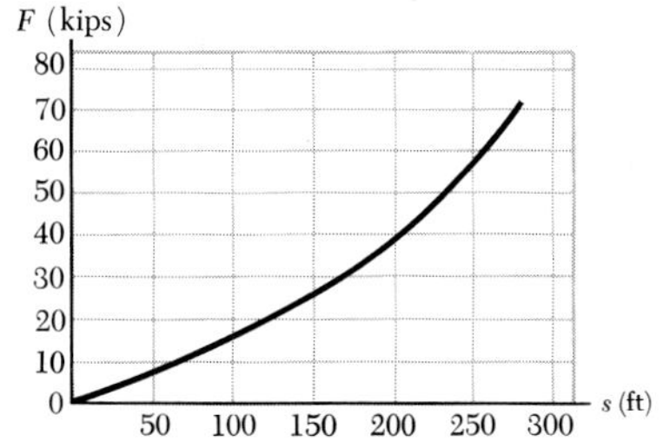

FIG. P 13.23

13.24. In Prob. 13.23, determine the landing speed of an 18,000-lb airplane if it is brought to rest by the arresting cable in 200 ft.

13.25. Two types of energy-absorbing fenders designed to be used on a pier are statically loaded. The force-deflection curve for each type of fender is given in the graph. Determine the maximum deflection of each fender when a 100-ton ship moving at 1 mph strikes the fender and is brought to rest.

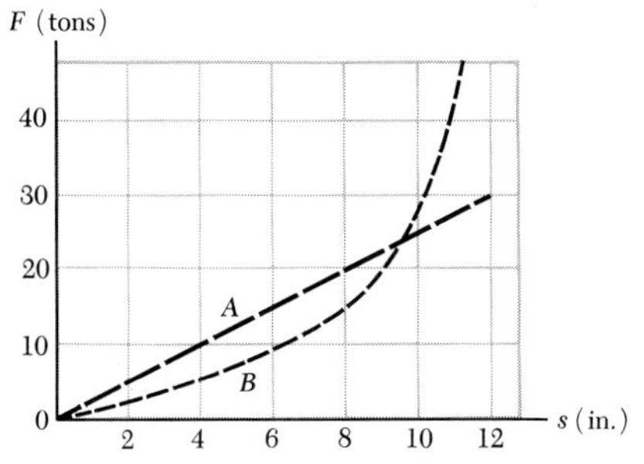

FIG. P 13.25

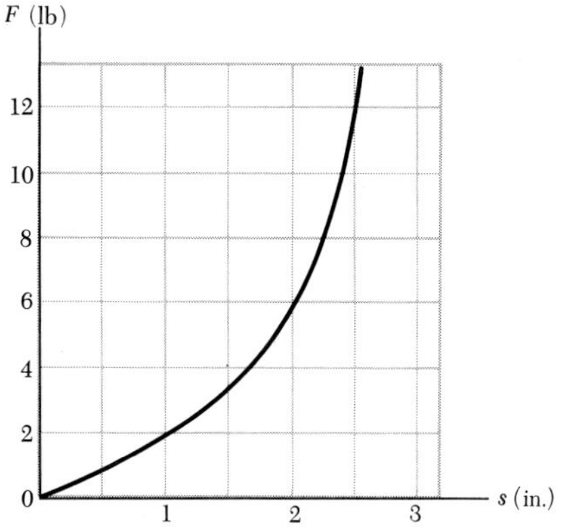

FIG. P 13.26

13.26. In order to protect it during shipping, a delicate instrument weighing 4 oz is packed in excelsior. From the static test of similar excelsior, the force-deflection curve shown was obtained. Determine the maximum height from which the package may be dropped if the force exerted on the instrument is not to exceed 12 lb.

13.27. A railroad car weighing 50,000 lb starts from rest and coasts down a 1 per cent incline for a distance of 50 ft. It is stopped by a bumper having a spring constant of 8,000 lb/in. (*a*) What is the velocity of the car at the bottom of the incline? (*b*) How many inches will the spring be compressed?

13.28. The bumper shown is used to stop the railroad car of Prob. 13.27. Knowing that $k_A = k_B = 4{,}000$ lb/in., determine the required value of k_C if the maximum deflection of the bumper is to be 8 in.

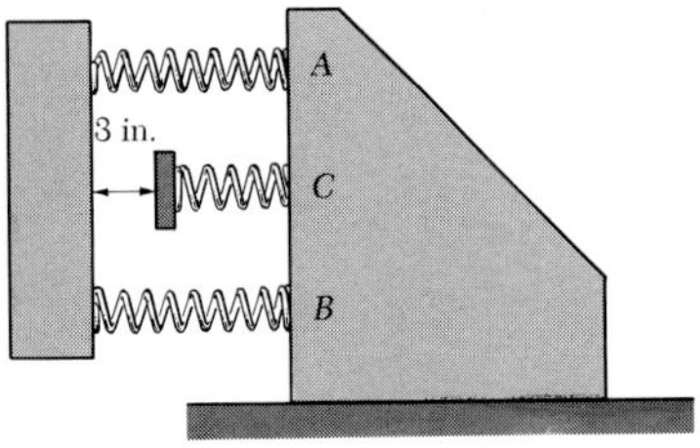

FIG. P 13.28

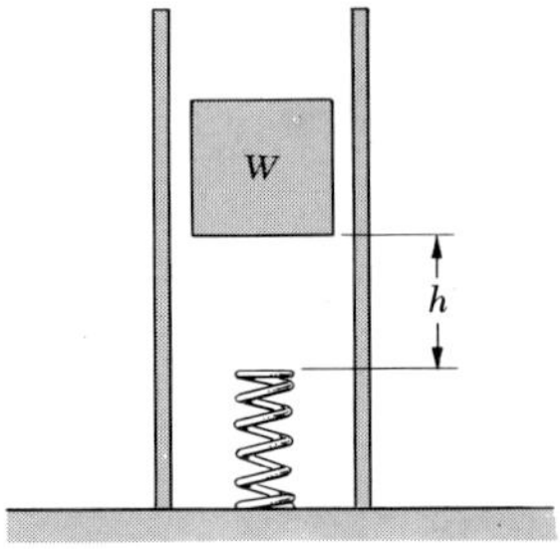

FIG. P 13.29 AND P 13.30

13.29. A weight W is dropped from a height h onto a spring of constant k. Determine (*a*) the maximum deflection of the spring, (*b*) the maximum velocity attained by the weight. (*c*) Solve parts *a* and *b* for $h = 0$.

13.30. A 10-lb weight is released from rest at a distance h above the top of an undeformed spring of constant $k = 5$ lb/in. Determine h if the maximum force exerted on the weight by the spring is to be (*a*) 40 lb, (*b*) 20 lb, (*c*) 15 lb.

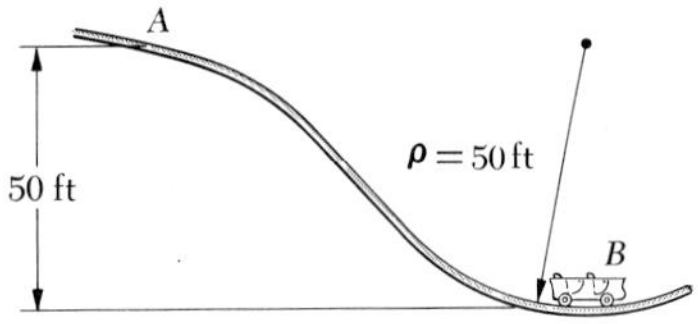

FIG. P 13.31

13.31. A roller coaster is released with no velocity at A and rolls down the track shown. The brakes are suddenly applied as the car passes through point B, causing the wheels of the car to slide on the track ($\mu = 1/3$). Assuming no energy loss between A and B and knowing that the radius of curvature of the track at B is 50 ft, determine the normal and tangential components of the acceleration of the car just after the brakes have been applied.

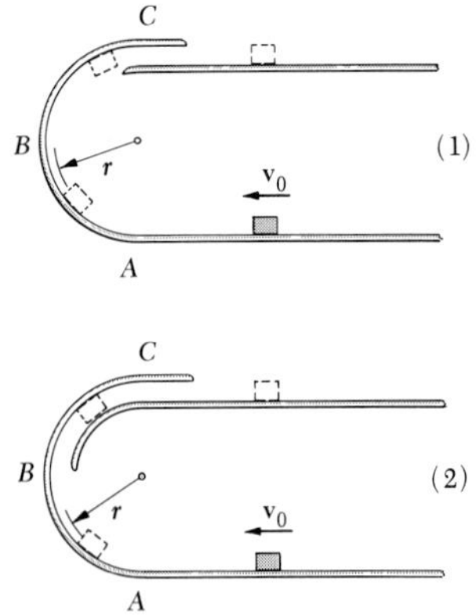

FIG. P 13.32

13.32. A small package of weight W is projected into a vertical return loop at A with a velocity $\mathbf{v}_0$. The package travels without friction along a circle of radius r and is deposited on a horizontal surface at C. For each of the two loops shown, determine (*a*) the smallest velocity $\mathbf{v}_0$ for which the package will reach the horizontal surface at C, (*b*) the corresponding force exerted by the loop on the package as it passes point B.

13.33. In Prob. 13.32, it is desired to have the package deposited on the horizontal surface at C with a speed of 6 ft/sec. Knowing that $r = 24$ in., (*a*) show that this requirement cannot be fulfilled by the first loop, (*b*) determine the required initial velocity $\mathbf{v}_0$ when the second loop is used.

13.34. Using the method of work and energy, solve Prob. 12.36.

13.35. A 6-in.-diameter piston weighing 8 lb slides without friction in a cylinder. When the piston is at a distance $x = 10$ in. from the end of the cylinder, the pressure in the cylinder is atmospheric ($p_a = 14.7$ lb/in.^{2}). If the pressure varies inversely as the volume, find the work done in moving the piston until $x = 4$ in.

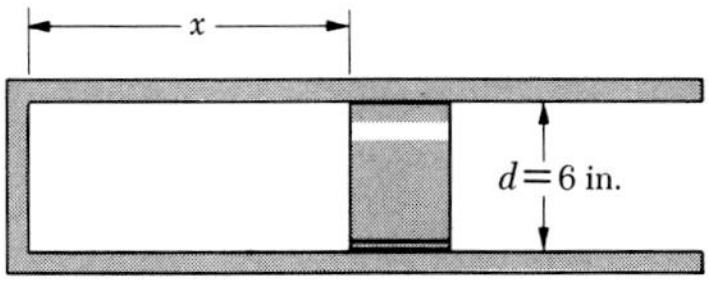

FIG. P 13.35

13.36. The piston of Prob. 13.35 is moved to the left and released with no velocity when $x = 4$ in. Neglecting friction, determine (*a*) the maximum velocity attained by the piston, (*b*) the maximum value of the coordinate x.

13.37. An object is released with no initial velocity at a very great distance from the earth. With what velocity will it strike the earth? (Neglect air resistance.)

13.38. An object is dropped with no initial velocity from an altitude of 400 miles. (*a*) With what velocity does it strike the earth? (Neglect air resistance.) (*b*) What relative error is introduced by assuming a uniform gravitational field?

13.39. A rocket is fired vertically from the ground. Knowing that at burnout the rocket is 40 miles above the ground and has a velocity of 15,000 ft/sec, determine the highest altitude it will reach.

13.40. A rocket is fired vertically from the ground. What should be its velocity $\mathbf{v}_B$ at burnout, 40 miles above the ground, if it is to reach an altitude of 600 miles?

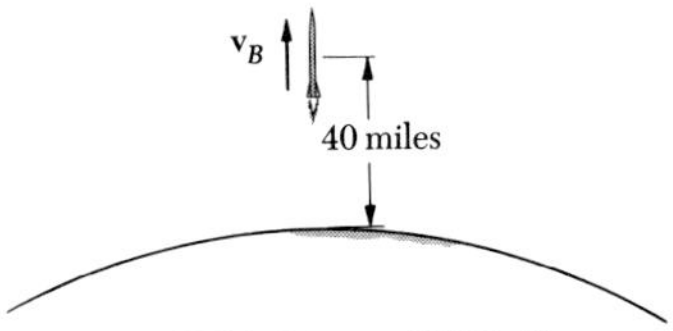

FIG. P 13.39 AND P 13.40

13.6. Potential Energy.†

Let us consider again a body of weight $\mathbf{W}$ which moves along a curved path from a point A_1 of elevation y_1 to a point A_2 of elevation y_2 (Fig. 13.4). We recall from Sec. 13.2 that the work of the weight $\mathbf{W}$ during this displacement is

$$U_{1\rightarrow 2} = Wy_1 - Wy_2 \tag{13.4}$$

The work of $\mathbf{W}$ may thus be obtained by subtracting the value of the function Wy corresponding to the second position of the body from its value corresponding to the first position. The work of $\mathbf{W}$ is independent of the actual path followed; it depends only upon the initial and final values of the function

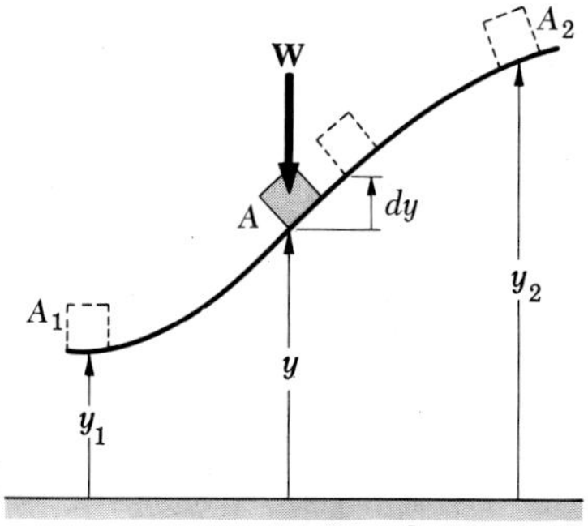

FIG. 13.4 (*repeated*)

† Most of the material in this section has already been considered in Sec. 10.6.

Wy. This function is called the *potential energy* of the body with respect to the *force of gravity* **W** and is denoted by V_g. We write

$$U_{1\rightarrow 2} = (V_g)_1 - (V_g)_2 \qquad \text{with } V_g = Wy \tag{13.14}$$

We note that if $(V_g)_2 > (V_g)_1$, i.e., *if the potential energy increases* during the displacement (as in the case considered here), *the work* $U_{1\rightarrow 2}$ *is negative.* If, on the other hand, the work of **W** is positive, the potential energy decreases. Therefore, the potential energy V_g of the body provides a measure of the work which may be done by its weight **W**. Since only the *change* in potential energy, and not the actual value of V_g, is involved in formula (13.14), an arbitrary constant may be added to the expression obtained for V_g. In other words, the level, or datum, from which the elevation y is measured may be chosen arbitrarily. Note that potential energy is expressed in the same units as work, i.e., in ft-lb or in in.-lb.

It should be noted that the expression just obtained for the potential energy of a body with respect to gravity is valid only as long as the weight **W** of the body may be assumed to remain constant, i.e., as long as the displacements of the body are small compared to the radius of the earth. In the case of a space vehicle, however, we should take into consideration the variation of the force of gravity with the distance r from the center of the earth. Using the expression obtained in Sec. 13.2 for the work of a gravitational force, we write (Fig. 13.6)

$$U_{1\rightarrow 2} = \frac{GMm}{r_2} - \frac{GMm}{r_1} \tag{13.7}$$

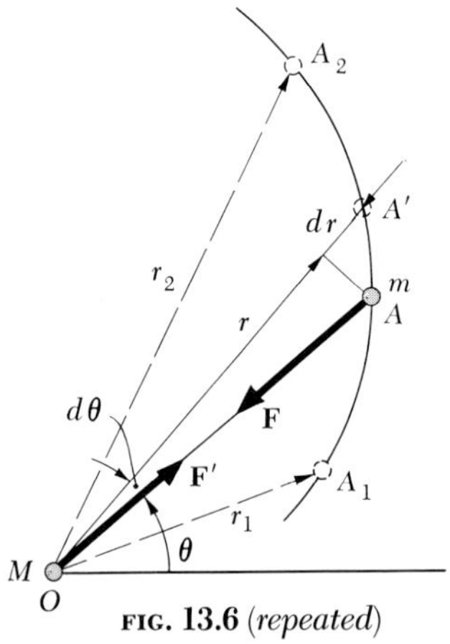

FIG. 13.6 *(repeated)*

The work of the force of gravity may therefore be obtained by subtracting the value of the function $-GMm/r$ corresponding to the second position of the body from its value corresponding to the first position. Thus, the expression which should be used for the potential energy V_g when the variation in the force of gravity cannot be neglected is

$$V_g = -\frac{GMm}{r} \tag{13.15}$$

Taking the first of the relations (12.19) into account, we write V_g in the alternate form

$$V_g = -\frac{WR^2}{r} \tag{13.15'}$$

where R is the radius of the earth (R = 3,960 miles) and W

the value of the weight of the body at the surface of the earth. When either of the relations (13.15) and (13.15′) is used to express V_g, the distance r should, of course, be measured from the center of the earth.† Note that V_g is always negative and that it approaches zero for very large values of r.

Consider, now, a body attached to a spring and moving from a position A_1, corresponding to a deflection x_1 of the spring, to a position A_2, corresponding to a deflection x_2 (Fig. 13.5).

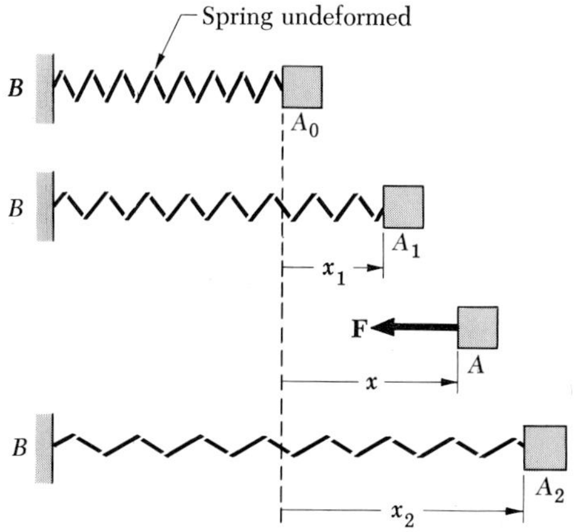

FIG. 13.5 *(repeated)*

We recall from Sec. 13.2 that the work of the force **F** exerted by the spring on the body is

$$U_{1\to2} = \tfrac{1}{2}kx_1^2 - \tfrac{1}{2}kx_2^2 \qquad (13.6)$$

The work of the elastic force is thus obtained by subtracting the value of the function $\frac{1}{2}kx^2$ corresponding to the second position of the body from its value corresponding to the first position. This function is denoted by V_e and is called the *potential energy* of the body with respect to the *elastic force* **F**. We write

$$U_{1\to2} = (V_e)_1 - (V_e)_2 \qquad \text{with } V_e = \tfrac{1}{2}kx^2 \qquad (13.16)$$

and observe that, during the displacement considered, the work of the force **F** exerted by the spring on the body is negative and the potential energy V_e increases. We should note that

† The expressions given for V_g in (13.15) and (13.15′) are valid only when $r \geqq R$, i.e., when the body considered is above the surface of the earth.

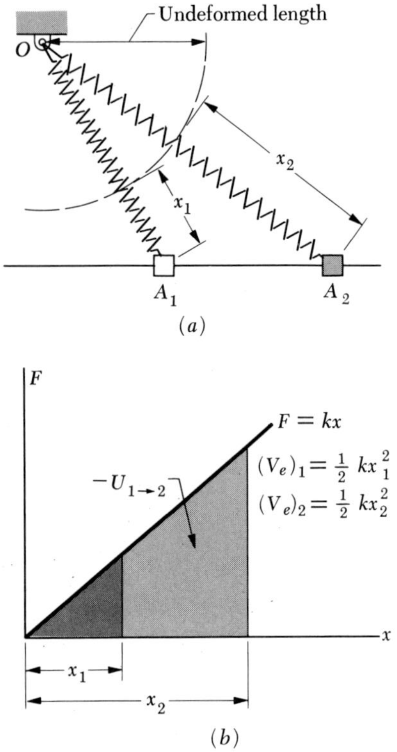

FIG. 13.10

the expression obtained for V_e is valid only if the deflection of the spring is measured from its undeformed position. On the other hand, formula (13.16) may be used even when the spring is rotated about its fixed end (Fig. 13.10*a*). The work of the elastic force depends only upon the initial and final deflections of the spring (Fig. 13.10*b*).

The concept of potential energy may be used when forces other than gravity forces and elastic forces are involved. It remains valid as long as the elementary work dU of the force considered is an *exact differential.* It is then possible to find a function V, called potential energy, such that

$$dU = -dV$$

Integrating over a finite displacement, we obtain the general relationship

$$U_{1\to 2} = V_1 - V_2 \qquad (13.17)$$

which expresses that *the work of the force is independent of the path followed and is equal to minus the change in potential energy.* A force which satisfies Eq. (13.17) is said to be a *conservative force.*

13.7. Conservation of Energy. We saw in the preceding section that the work of a conservative force, such as the weight of a particle or the force exerted by a spring, may be expressed as a change in potential energy. When a particle, or a system of particles, moves under the action of conservative forces, the principle of work and energy stated in Sec. 13.3 may be expressed in a modified form. Substituting for $U_{1\to 2}$ from (13.17) into (13.12), we write

$$V_1 - V_2 = T_2 - T_1$$
$$T_1 + V_1 = T_2 + V_2 \qquad (13.18)$$

Formula (13.18) indicates that, when a system of particles moves under the action of conservative forces, *the sum of the kinetic energy and of the potential energy of the system remains constant.*† The sum $T + V$ is called the *total mechanical energy* of the system and is denoted by E.

Consider, for example, the pendulum analyzed in Sec. 13.4, which is released with no velocity from A_1 and allowed to swing in a vertical plane (Fig. 13.11). Measuring the potential energy from the level of A_2, we have, at A_1,

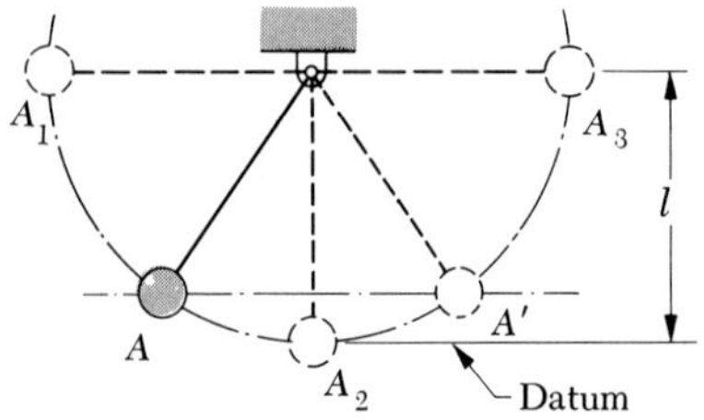

FIG. 13.11

† When the particles of a system move with respect to each other under the action of internal forces, the potential energy of the system must include the potential energy corresponding to the internal forces.

$$T_1 = 0 \qquad V_1 = Wl \qquad T_1 + V_1 = Wl$$

Recalling that, at A_2, the speed of the pendulum is $v_2 = \sqrt{2gl}$, we have

$$T_2 = \frac{1}{2}\frac{W}{g}v_2^2 = Wl \qquad V_2 = 0 \qquad T_2 + V_2 = Wl$$

We thus check that the total mechanical energy $E = T + V$ of the pendulum is the same at A_1 and A_2. While the energy is entirely potential at A_1, it becomes entirely kinetic at A_2 and, as the pendulum keeps swinging to the right, the kinetic energy is transformed back into potential energy. At A_3, we shall have $T_3 = 0$ and $V_3 = Wl$.

Since the total mechanical energy of the pendulum remains constant and since its potential energy depends only upon its elevation, the kinetic energy of the pendulum will have the same value at any two points located on the same level. Thus, the speed of the pendulum is the same at A and at A' (Fig. 13.11). This result may be extended to the case of a particle moving along any given path, regardless of the shape of the path, as long as the only forces acting on the particle are its weight and the normal reaction of the path. The particle of Fig. 13.12, for example, which slides in a vertical plane along a frictionless track, will have the same speed at A, A', and A''.

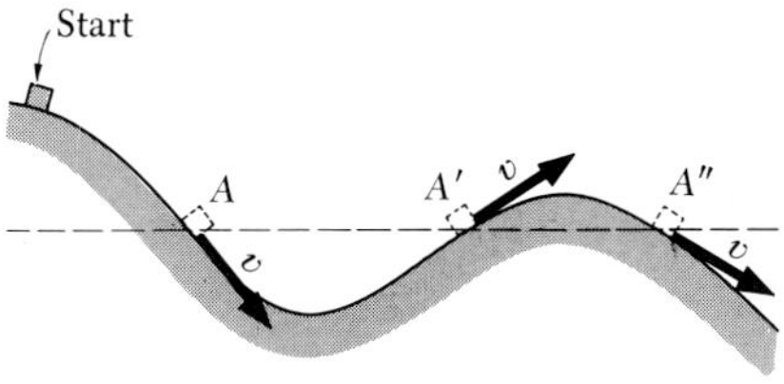

FIG. 13.12

While the weight of a particle and the force exerted by a spring are conservative forces, *friction forces are nonconservative forces.* In other words, *the work of a friction force cannot be expressed as a change in potential energy.* The work of a friction force depends upon the path followed by its point of application; and while the work $U_{1\to2}$ defined by (13.17) is positive or negative according to the sense of motion, *the work of a friction force is always negative.* It follows that, when a system involves friction, its total mechanical energy does not remain constant but decreases. The mechanical energy of the system, however, is not lost; it is transformed into heat, and the sum of the *mechanical energy* and of the *thermal energy* of the system remains constant.

Other forms of energy may also be involved in a system. For instance, a generator converts mechanical energy into *electrical energy*; a gasoline engine converts *chemical energy* into mechanical energy; a nuclear reactor converts *mass* into thermal energy. If all forms of energy are considered, the energy of any system may be considered as constant and the principle of conservation of energy remains valid under all conditions.

SAMPLE PROBLEM 13.5

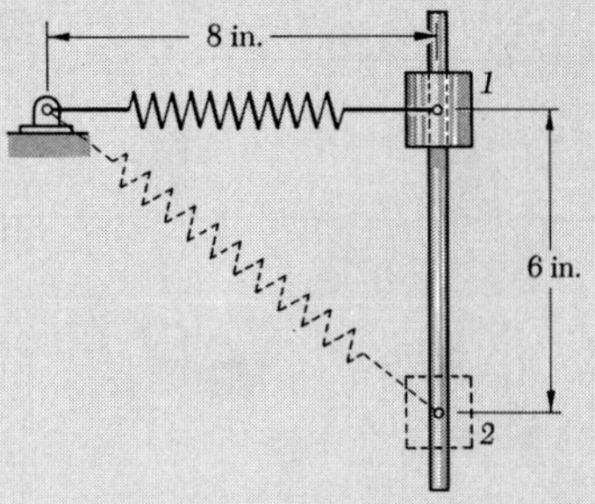

A 20-lb collar slides without friction along a vertical rod as shown. The spring attached to the collar has an undeformed length of 4 in. and a constant of 3 lb/in. If the collar is released from rest in position *1*, determine its velocity after it has moved 6 in. to position 2.

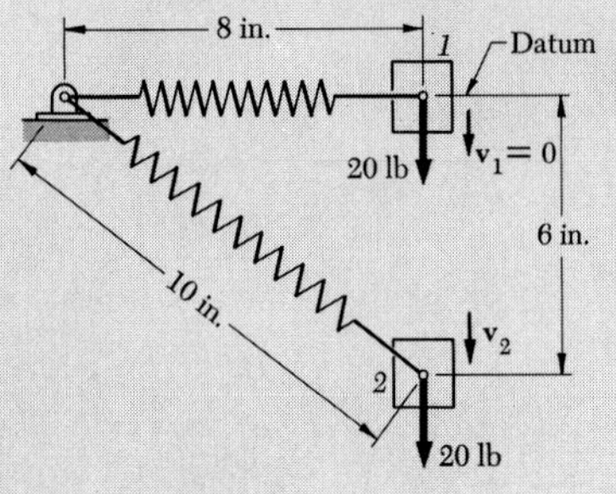

Position *1*. *Potential Energy.* The elongation of the spring is $x_1 = 8 \text{ in.} - 4 \text{ in.} = 4 \text{ in.}$, and we have

$$V_e = \tfrac{1}{2}kx_1^2 = \tfrac{1}{2}(3 \text{ lb/in.})(4 \text{ in.})^2 = 24 \text{ in.-lb}$$

Choosing the datum as shown, we have $V_g = 0$. Therefore,

$$V_1 = V_e + V_g = 24 \text{ in.-lb} = 2 \text{ ft-lb}$$

Kinetic Energy. Since the velocity in position *1* is zero, $T_1 = 0$.

Position 2. *Potential Energy.* The elongation of the spring is $x_2 = 10 \text{ in.} - 4 \text{ in.} = 6 \text{ in.}$, and we have

$$V_e = \tfrac{1}{2}kx_2^2 = \tfrac{1}{2}(3 \text{ lb/in.})(6 \text{ in.})^2 = 54 \text{ in.-lb}$$
$$V_g = Wy = (20 \text{ lb})(-6 \text{ in.}) = -120 \text{ in.-lb}$$

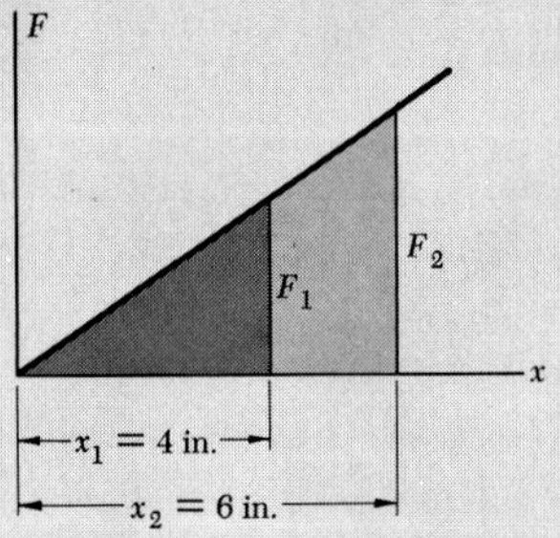

Therefore,

$$V_2 = V_e + V_g = 54 - 120 = -66 \text{ in.-lb}$$
$$= -5.5 \text{ ft-lb}$$

Kinetic Energy

$$T_2 = \tfrac{1}{2}mv_2^2 = \frac{1}{2}\frac{20}{32.2}v_2^2 = 0.311v_2^2$$

Conservation of Energy. Applying the principle of conservation of energy between positions *1* and 2, we write

$$T_1 + V_1 = T_2 + V_2$$
$$0 + 2 \text{ ft-lb} = 0.311v_2^2 - 5.5 \text{ ft-lb}$$

$$v_2 = \pm 4.92 \text{ ft/sec} \qquad \mathbf{v}_2 = 4.92 \text{ ft/sec} \downarrow$$ ◄

SAMPLE PROBLEM 13.6

The $\frac{1}{2}$-lb pellet is released from rest at A when the spring is compressed 3 in. and travels around the loop $ABCDE$. Determine the smallest value of the spring constant for which the pellet will travel around the loop and will at all times remain in contact with the loop.

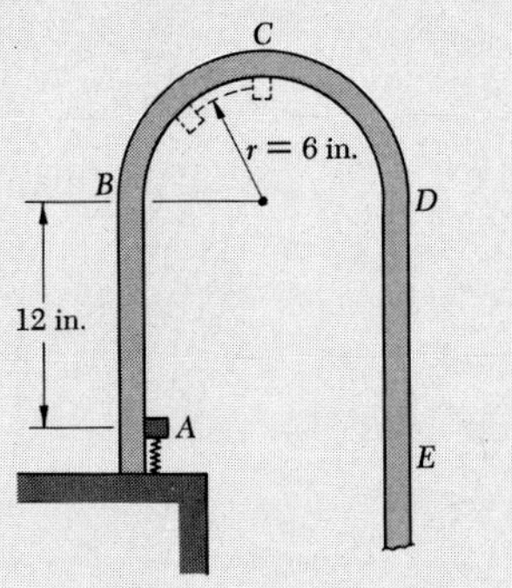

Required Speed at Point C. As the pellet passes through the highest point C, its potential energy with respect to gravity is maximum; thus, at the same point its kinetic energy and its speed are minimum. Since the pellet must remain in contact with the loop, the force $\mathbf{N}$ exerted on the pellet by the loop must be equal to, or greater than, zero. Setting $\mathbf{N} = 0$, we compute the smallest possible speed v_C.

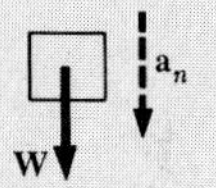

$$+\downarrow \Sigma F_n = ma_n: \qquad W = \frac{W}{g} a_n = \frac{W}{g}\frac{v_C^2}{r}$$

$$v_C^2 = gr = g(\tfrac{6}{12}\text{ ft}) = \tfrac{1}{2}g$$

Position *1*. *Potential Energy*. Since the spring is compressed 3 in. from its undeformed position, we have

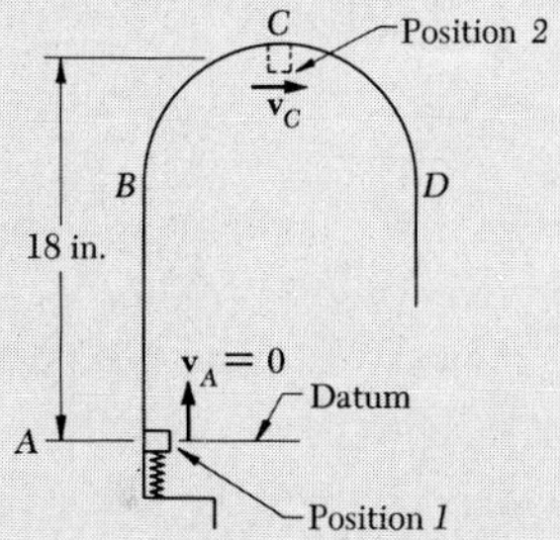

$$V_e = \tfrac{1}{2}kx^2 = \tfrac{1}{2}k(\tfrac{3}{12}\text{ ft})^2 = \tfrac{1}{32}k$$

Choosing the datum at A, we have $V_g = 0$; therefore,

$$V_1 = V_e + V_g = \tfrac{1}{32}k$$

Kinetic Energy. Since the pellet is released from rest, $v_A = 0$ and we have $T_1 = 0$.

Position *2*. *Potential Energy*. The spring is now undeformed; thus $V_e = 0$. Since the pellet is 18 in. above the datum,

$$V_g = Wy = (\tfrac{1}{2}\text{ lb})(\tfrac{18}{12}\text{ ft}) = 0.75\text{ ft-lb}$$
$$V_2 = V_e + V_g = 0.75\text{ ft-lb}$$

Kinetic Energy. Using the value of v_C^2 obtained above, we write

$$T_2 = \frac{1}{2}\frac{W}{g}v_C^2 = \frac{1}{2}\frac{0.50}{g}(\tfrac{1}{2}g) = 0.125\text{ ft-lb}$$

Conservation of Energy. Applying the principle of conservation of energy between positions *1* and *2*, we write

$$T_1 + V_1 = T_2 + V_2$$
$$0 + \tfrac{1}{32}k = 0.125 + 0.75$$
$$k = (0.875)(32) = 28\text{ lb/ft}$$

The required minimum value of k is therefore

$$k = 28\text{ lb/ft} = 2.33\text{ lb/in.} \blacktriangleleft$$

PROBLEMS

13.41. Knowing that the relation between the force and deflection of a given nonlinear spring is $F = kx(1 + cx^2)$, (*a*) derive an expression for the potential energy of the spring, (*b*) compute the values of k and c, if $F = 11$ lb when $x = 1$ in., and $F = 28$ lb when $x = 2$ in.

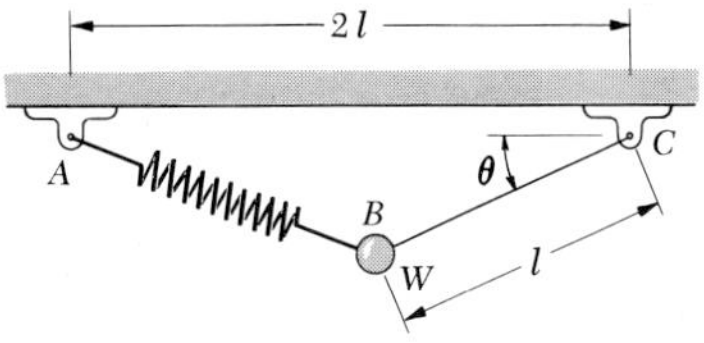

FIG. P 13.42

13.42. A ball of weight W is attached to the spring AB and to the rod BC. The spring has a constant k and is undeformed when $\theta = 0$. Express the potential energy of the ball with respect (*a*) to the spring, (*b*) to gravity (place datum at C).

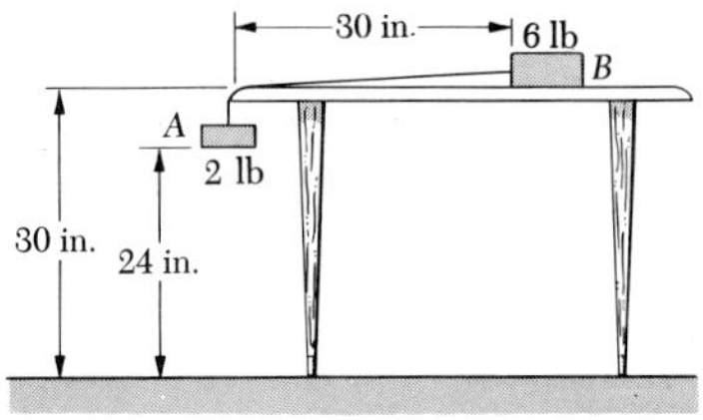

FIG. P 13.43

13.43. Two blocks A and B connected by a cord are released from rest in the position shown. Neglecting the effect of friction, determine the maximum velocity attained by block B.

13.44. In Prob. 13.43, determine the position of block A when the velocity of block B is 4 ft/sec to the left.

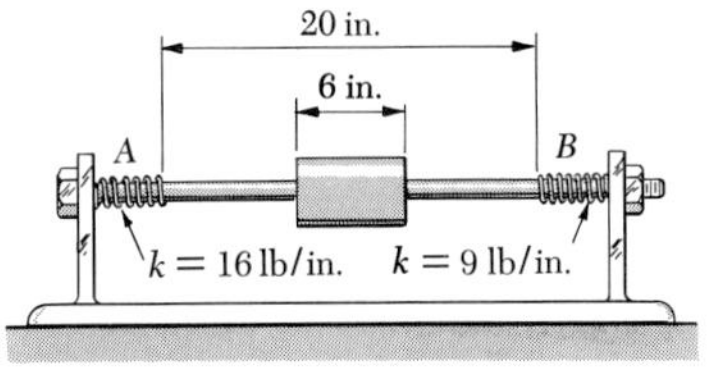

FIG. P 13.45

13.45. A collar of weight W slides without friction between two springs. If the collar is pushed until spring A is compressed 3 in. and released, determine the distance the collar will travel before coming to rest (*a*) if $W = 2$ lb, (*b*) if $W = 5$ lb.

13.46. Solve Prob. 13.45 assuming that the frame is placed in a vertical position with spring B at the top.

13.47. Using the principle of conservation of energy, solve Prob. 12.21*b*.

13.48. Using the principle of conservation of energy, solve Prob. 12.22*b*.

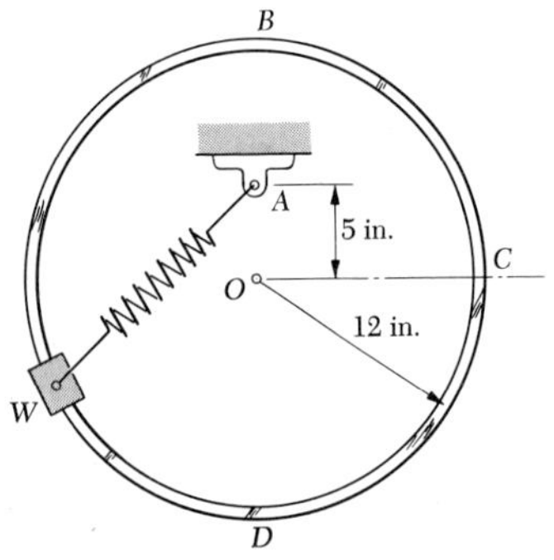

FIG. P 13.49

13.49. A collar of weight $W = 2$ lb is attached to a spring and slides without friction along a circular rod which lies in a *horizontal* plane. The spring has a constant $k = 3$ lb/in. and is undeformed when the collar is at B. If the collar is released from rest at C, determine the speed of the collar as it passes through point B.

13.50. It is possible for the collar of Prob. 13.49 to have a continuous, although nonuniform, motion along the rod. If the speed of the collar at B is to be twice the speed of the collar at D, determine (*a*) the required speed at D, (*b*) the corresponding speed at C.

13.51. Assuming that the circular rod of Prob. 13.49 lies in a *vertical* plane with point B directly above point D, determine (*a*) the value of the spring constant k for which the speed at B and at D is 8 ft/sec, (*b*) the corresponding speed at C.

13.52. A slingshot is made of a rubber band stretched between two arms A and B which are 6 in. apart. When stretched directly between A and B, the tension in the rubber band is 6 lb. Find the velocity which is imparted to a 2-oz pellet with this slingshot by pulling the pellet 4 in. back and releasing it. The spring constant for the entire length of the rubber band is 3 lb/in.

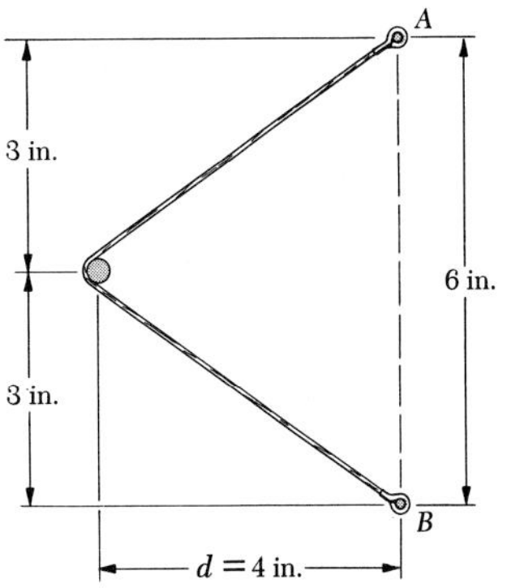

FIG. P 13.52

13.53. In using the slingshot of Prob. 13.52, the pellet is drawn back until the tension in the rubber band is 24 lb, and then is released. Determine the velocity imparted to the pellet.

13.54. The 2-lb collar slides without friction along the horizontal rod. Knowing that the spring has a constant $k = 3$ lb/in. and is unstretched in the position shown, determine the required speed v_0 if it is to reach point C.

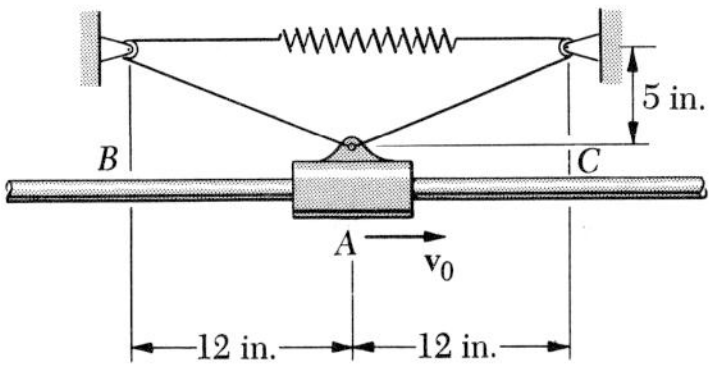

FIG. P 13.54 AND P 13.55

13.55. The 2-lb collar slides without friction along the horizontal rod. Knowing that the constant of the spring is 3 lb/in. and that $v_0 = 12$ ft/sec, determine the required spring tension in the position shown if the speed of the collar is to be 8 ft/sec at point C.

13.56. As the 6-lb slider shown moves horizontally to the right, pin A follows the groove BCD and moves upward in the vertical slot of the slider. Knowing that the tension in the spring is 3 lb when the slider is at B, and neglecting the effect of friction, determine the smallest speed v_0 for which the slider will reach point D.

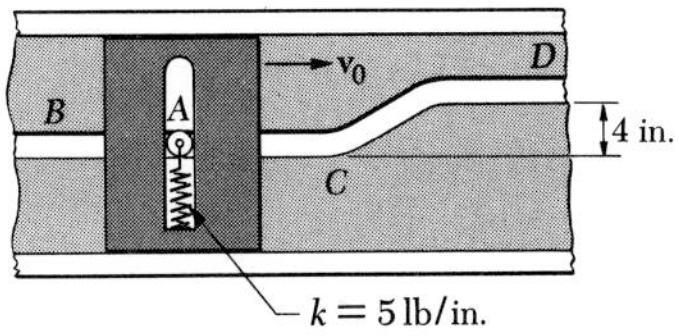

FIG. P 13.56

13.57. Determine the required speed v_0 of the slider of Prob. 13.56 if the speed at D (*a*) is to be $\frac{9}{10}v_0$, (*b*) is to be 2 ft/sec less than v_0.

13.58. The ball of Prob. 13.42 is released from rest when $\theta = 0$. If $W = kl$, determine the velocity of the ball when $\theta = 45°$.

13.59. A particle is released from rest at A on the surface of a smooth circular cylinder of radius r. The particle slides to a point B where it leaves the surface of the cylinder. Derive an expression relating the angles θ_0 and θ_1.

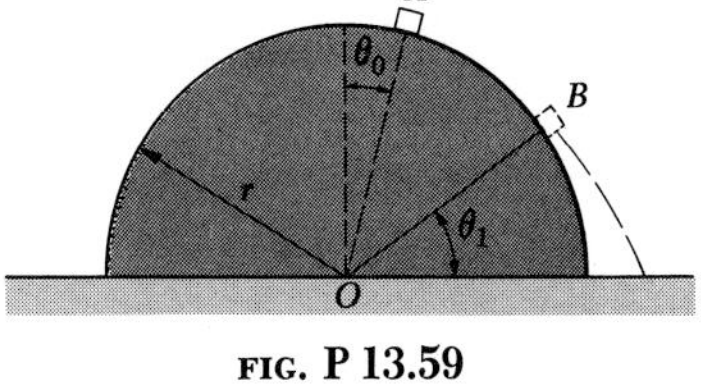

FIG. P 13.59

13.60. The particle of Prob. 13.59 is released from the position $\theta_0 = 0$. Determine (*a*) the value of θ_1 defining the point B where the particle leaves the cylinder, (*b*) the distance from the center of the cylinder O to the point where the particle strikes the floor, knowing that $r = 3$ ft.

13.61. In Prob. 13.49, determine the force exerted on the collar as it passes through point B.

13.62. The collar of Prob. 13.49 is released from rest at point D. Determine the horizontal component of the force exerted by the rod on the collar as the collar passes through point C. Show that the force is independent of the weight of the collar.

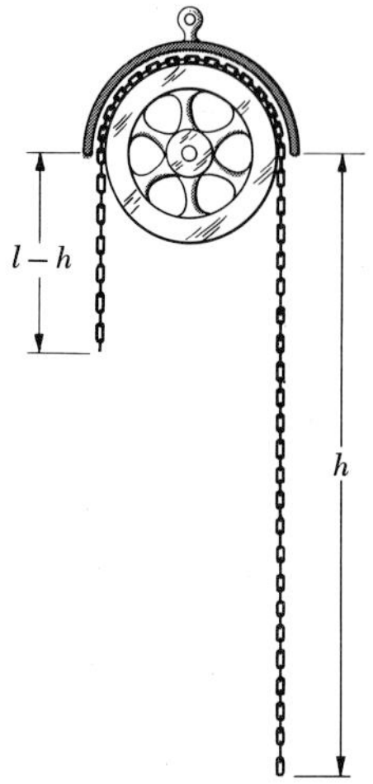

FIG. P 13.63

13.63. A chain weighing w lb/ft and of length l ft rests over a small pulley of negligible mass. If the chain is released in the position shown $(h > \frac{1}{2}l)$, determine the velocity of the chain when the end of the chain leaves the pulley. Also determine the maximum possible final velocity by letting h approach $\frac{1}{2}l$.

13.64. A delicate instrument weighing 8 lb is placed on a spring of length l so that its base is just touching the undeformed spring. The instrument is then inadvertently released from that position. Determine the maximum deflection x of the spring and the maximum force exerted by the spring if the constant of the spring is $k = 10$ lb/in.

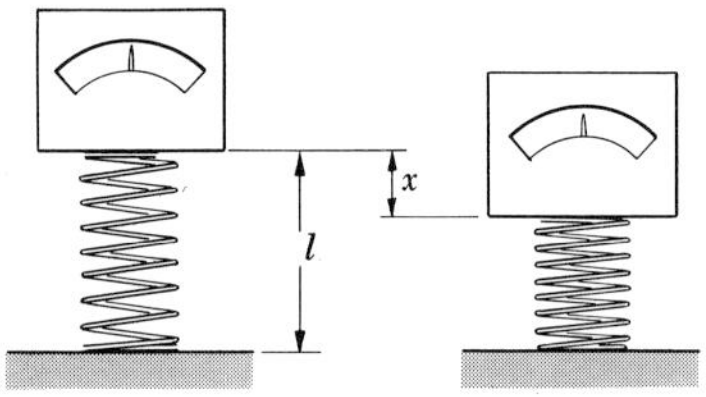

FIG. P 13.64

13.65. Nonlinear springs are classified as hard or soft, depending upon the curvature of their force-deflection curves (see figure). Solve Prob. 13.64 assuming (*a*) that a hard spring is used, for which $F = 10x(1 + 0.1x^2)$, (*b*) that a soft spring is used, for which $F = 10x(1 - 0.1x^2)$.

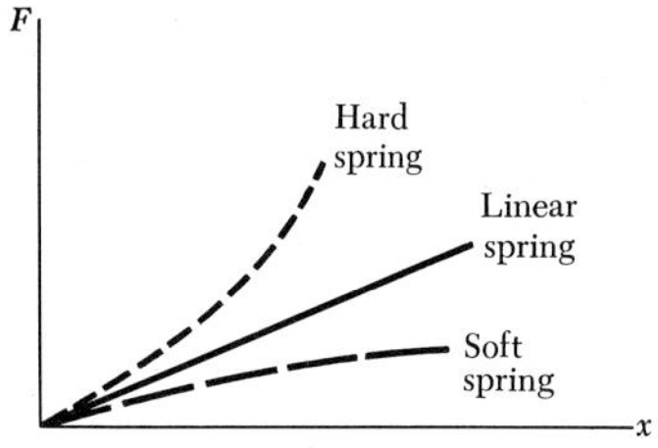

FIG. P 13.65

13.66. A chain of length L is suspended from a strip of rubber, of natural length h, and is in equilibrium in the position shown. The chain is then cut at point A. Determine the length x, knowing that the remaining portion of the chain will rise sufficiently (*a*) to allow the rubber strip to become slack, (*b*) to touch the ceiling.

13.67. Show, by setting $r = R + y$ in formula (13.15′) and expanding in a power series in y/R, that the expression obtained in (13.14) for the potential energy V_g due to gravity is a first-order approximation for the expression given in (13.15′). Using the same expansion, derive a second-order approximation for V_g.

13.68. Determine the escape velocity of a missile, i.e., the velocity with which it should be fired from the surface of the earth if it is to reach an infinite distance from the earth. Show that the result obtained is independent of the firing angle.

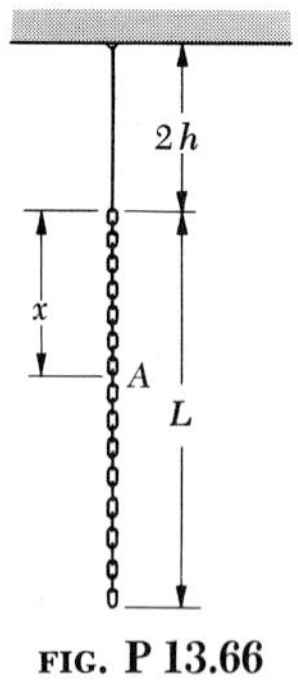

FIG. P 13.66

13.69. How much energy should be imparted to a 5-ton satellite in order to place it in a circular orbit at an altitude of (*a*) 300 miles, (*b*) 3,000 miles?

13.70. Determine the minimum amount of energy which should be imparted to a space vehicle of mass m (*a*) to place it in a low-level circular orbit around the earth, (*b*) to send it to another planet. Why would it be more convenient to originate space trips from a station circling the earth?

13.71. A satellite of mass m describes a circular orbit around the earth. Express (*a*) its potential energy, (*b*) its kinetic energy, and (*c*) its total energy as a function of the radius r of the orbit, assuming that both its potential and its kinetic energies had a value equal to zero when the satellite was on its launching pad. Plot the kinetic, potential, and total energies against r.

***13.72.** Knowing that the satellite of Prob. 12.89 weighs 500 lb, determine (*a*) the energy imparted to the satellite during the original launching operation, (*b*) the additional energy imparted to the satellite in placing it in its final circular orbit.

13.73. Show that the ratio of the potential and kinetic energies of an electron, as it enters the plates of the cathode-ray tube of Prob. 12.69, is equal to $d\delta/lL$. (Place the datum at the surface of the positive plate.)

13.8. Power and Efficiency. *Power* is defined as the time rate at which work is done. In the selection of a motor or engine, power is a much more important criterion than the actual amount of work to be performed. A small motor or a large power plant may both be used to do a given amount of work; but the small motor may require a month to do the work done by the power plant in a matter of minutes. If ΔU is the work done during the time interval Δt, then the average power during this time interval is

$$\text{Average power} = \frac{\Delta U}{\Delta t}$$

Letting Δt approach zero, we obtain at the limit

$$\text{Power} = \frac{dU}{dt} \tag{13.19}$$

Since $dU = (F \cos \alpha)\, ds$ and $v = ds/dt$, the power may also be expressed as follows:

$$\text{Power} = \frac{dU}{dt} = \frac{(F \cos \alpha)\, ds}{dt} = (F \cos \alpha)v \tag{13.20}$$

where v = magnitude of velocity of point of application of force $\mathbf{F}$

α = angle between $\mathbf{F}$ and velocity $\mathbf{v}$

Several units are used to measure power; mechanical power

is usually measured in *horsepower* (hp) and electrical power in *watts* or *kilowatts* (kw). These units are defined as follows:

$$\begin{aligned} 1\text{ hp} &= 550\text{ ft-lb/sec} = 33{,}000\text{ ft-lb/min} \\ 1\text{ watt} &= 1\text{ joule/sec} = 1\text{ newton-m/sec} \\ 1\text{ kw} &= 1{,}000\text{ watts} \end{aligned}$$

We may check the following relations:

$$\begin{aligned} 1\text{ hp} &= 746\text{ watts} = 0.746\text{ kw} \\ 1\text{ kw} &= 737\text{ ft-lb/sec} \end{aligned}$$

Although many specific formulas exist, from which the horsepower or kilowatt requirements may be computed for given applications, it is advisable to compute the power directly from its definition. For instance, when work is done at a constant rate, we may determine the work done during a given time interval and note that each 550 ft-lb of work done per second is equivalent to 1 hp.

The *mechanical efficiency* of a machine was defined in Sec. 10.4 as the ratio of the output work to the input work:

$$\eta = \frac{\text{output work}}{\text{input work}} \tag{13.21}$$

This definition is based on the assumption that work is done at a constant rate. The ratio of the output to the input work is therefore equal to the ratio of the rates at which output and input work are done, and we have

$$\eta = \frac{\text{power output}}{\text{power input}} \tag{13.22}$$

Because of energy losses due to friction, the output work is always smaller than the input work, and, consequently, the power output is always smaller than the power input. The mechanical efficiency of a machine, therefore, is always less than 1.

When a machine is used to transform mechanical energy into electrical energy, or thermal energy into mechanical energy, its *over-all efficiency* may be obtained from formula (13.22). The over-all efficiency of a machine is always less than 1; it provides a measure of all the various energy losses involved (losses of electrical or thermal energy as well as frictional losses). We should note that it is necessary, before using formula (13.22), to express the power output and the power input in the same units.

SAMPLE PROBLEM 13.7

A train of total weight 800 tons starts from rest and accelerates uniformly to a speed of 30 mph in 25 sec. After reaching this speed, the train travels with constant velocity. During the entire motion the train is traveling up a 3 per cent grade, and the rolling resistance is 15 lb/ton. Determine the horsepower required as a function of time.

Solution. The two types of motion will be treated separately; for $t < 25$ sec, uniformly accelerated motion; for $t > 25$ sec, uniform motion.

Uniformly Accelerated Motion ($t < 25$ sec). *Velocity.* Since the velocity is known, we write, at $t = 0$, $v_0 = 0$; at $t = 25$ sec, $v = 30$ mph $= 44$ ft/sec.

$$v = v_0 + at \qquad 44 \text{ ft/sec} = 0 + a(25 \text{ sec}) \qquad a = 1.76 \text{ ft/sec}^2$$
$$v = +1.76t$$

Engine Force. The magnitude of the engine force **P** may be calculated by choosing the x axis parallel to the tracks and writing $+\nearrow \Sigma F_x = ma$. The x component of the weight is

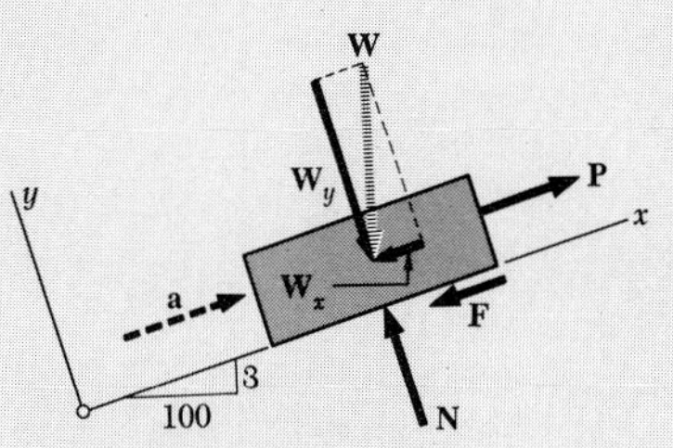

$$\mathbf{W}_x \approx \tfrac{3}{100}(800 \text{ tons})\frac{2{,}000 \text{ lb}}{1 \text{ ton}} = 48{,}000 \text{ lb} \swarrow$$

The friction force due to rolling resistance is

$$\mathbf{F} = (15 \text{ lb/ton})(800 \text{ tons}) = 12{,}000 \text{ lb} \swarrow$$

$$+\nearrow \Sigma F_x = ma: \qquad P - W_x - F = ma$$

$$P - 48{,}000 - 12{,}000 = \frac{(800)(2{,}000)}{32.2}(1.76)$$

$$P = +147{,}500 \text{ lb}$$

Horsepower. Since the power is equal to the product of the magnitudes of the force and velocity, we write

$$\text{Power} = Pv = (147{,}500)(1.76t)$$

$$\text{Horsepower} = \frac{Pv}{550} = \frac{(147{,}500)(1.76t)}{550} = 472t$$

Uniform Motion ($t > 25$ sec). *Velocity.* We have $v = 30$ mph $=$ 44 ft/sec.

Engine Force. Since v is constant, we have $a = 0$ and write

$$+\nearrow \Sigma F_x = 0: \qquad P - W_x - F = 0$$
$$P - 48{,}000 - 12{,}000 = 0 \qquad P = +60{,}000 \text{ lb}$$

$$\textit{Horsepower} = \frac{Pv}{550} = \frac{(60{,}000 \text{ lb})(44 \text{ ft/sec})}{550} = 4{,}800$$

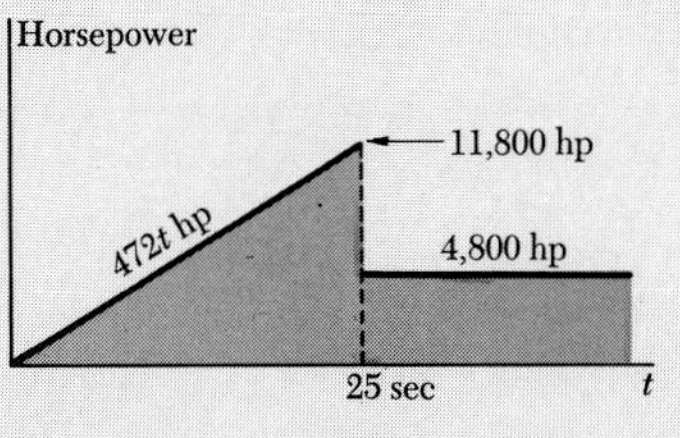

Horsepower Required vs. Time. For $t < 25$ sec, the horsepower required increases linearly with t, reaching, at $t = 25$ sec, a maximum value.

For $t > 25$ sec, the train is no longer accelerated, and the horsepower required is constant.

PROBLEMS

13.74. A 150-lb man and a 175-lb man run up a flight of stairs in 4 sec. If the flight of stairs is 12 ft high, determine the average horsepower required by each man.

13.75. A utility hoist can lift its maximum allowable load of 7,000 lb at the rate of 65 ft/min. Knowing that the hoist is run by a 20-hp engine, determine the over-all efficiency of the hoist.

13.76. Starting from rest, a 3,000-lb automobile is accelerated at a constant rate of 4 ft/sec^2 until it reaches a speed of 40 mph and then travels at a constant speed. During the entire motion, the automobile is traveling on a horizontal road, and the rolling resistance is equal to 1.8 per cent of the weight of the automobile. Determine the power required as a function of time.

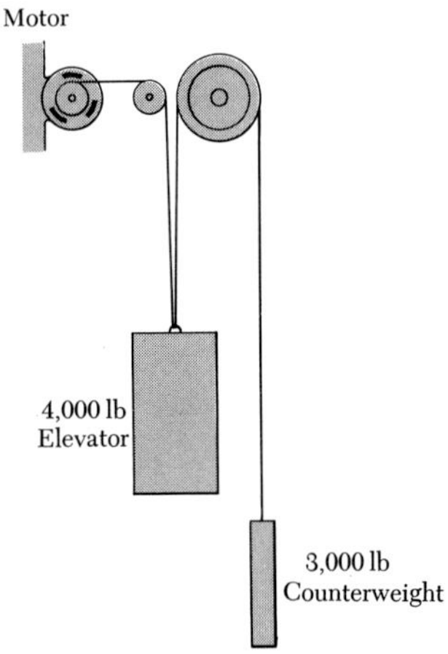

FIG. P 13.78

13.77. Solve Prob. 13.76 assuming that the automobile travels down a 2 per cent grade.

13.78. Determine the power required when the elevator shown (*a*) is moving upward at a constant speed of 20 ft/sec, (*b*) has an instantaneous velocity of 20 ft/sec upward and an upward acceleration of 3 ft/sec^2.

13.79. Solve Prob. 13.78 assuming that the weight of the elevator and the counterweight have both been increased by 1,000 lb.

13.80. The escalator shown is designed to transport 8,000 persons per hour at a constant speed of 90 ft/min. Assuming an average weight of 150 lb per person, determine (*a*) the average power required, (*b*) the required capacity of the motor if the mechanical efficiency is 85 per cent and if a 300 per cent overload is to be allowed.

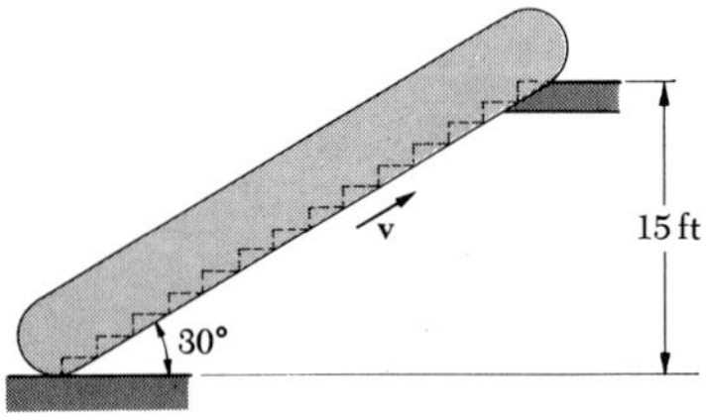

FIG. P 13.80

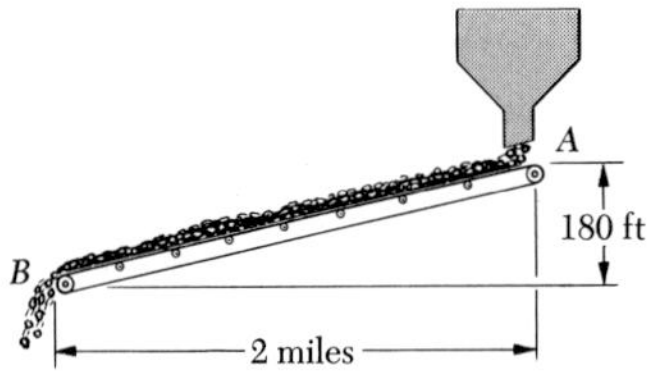

FIG. P 13.81

13.81. Crushed stone is moved from a quarry at *A* to a construction site at *B* at the rate of 4,000 tons per 8-hour period. An electric generator is attached to the system in order to maintain a constant belt speed. Knowing that the efficiency of the belt-generator system is 0.65, determine the average power developed by the generator (*a*) if the belt speed is 5 ft/sec, (*b*) if the belt speed is 8 ft/sec.

13.82. The engine of the rocket shown provides a constant vertical thrust of 60,000 lb. The rocket and fuel weigh 20,000 lb at the time of firing, and the rocket has attained a speed of 4,500 mph when the engine is cut off, after burning 12,000 lb of fuel. Determine the horsepower actually used to propel the rocket (*a*) just after firing, (*b*) just before the engine is cut off.

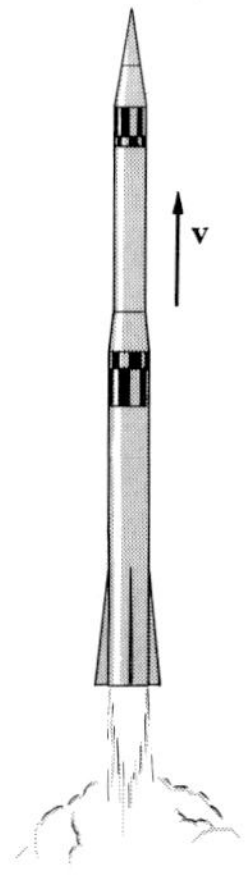

FIG. P 13.82

***13.83.** The fluid transmission of a truck of weight W permits the engine to deliver an essentially constant power P to the driving wheels. Determine the time elapsed and the distance traveled as the speed is increased from v_0 to v_1.

***13.84.** The fluid transmission of a 15-ton truck permits the engine to deliver an essentially constant power of 75 hp to the driving wheels. Determine the time required and the distance traveled as the speed of the truck is increased from 30 mph to 45 mph.

***13.85.** Determine the time required for the truck of Prob. 13.84 to increase its speed from 30 to 45 mph assuming that the truck has a rolling resistance of 20 lb/ton.

***13.86.** The frictional resistance F of a ship of weight W is known to vary as the square of the speed v of the ship and is expressed as $F = kv^2$. (*a*) Show that the power P_0 required to maintain a constant speed v_0 is $P_0 = kv_0^3$. (*b*) If the power delivered by the engine is suddenly increased to P_2 and then held constant, determine the distance that the ship will travel before reaching a given speed v_1. (The speed v_1 is chosen smaller than the constant speed v_2 which can be maintained with the power P_2.)

13.87. A $\frac{1}{2}$-oz bullet leaves a fixed rifle barrel 0.002 sec after it is fired. Knowing that the muzzle velocity is 2,800 ft/sec, determine the average power developed by the rifle. Neglect the effect of friction.

REVIEW PROBLEMS

13.88. An elevator travels upward at a constant speed of 5 ft/sec. A boy riding the elevator throws a 2-lb stone upward with a speed of 10 ft/sec *relative* to the elevator. Determine (*a*) the work done by the boy in throwing the stone, (*b*) the difference in the values of the kinetic energy of the stone before and after it was thrown. (*c*) Why are the values obtained in parts *a* and *b* not the same?

13.89. The weight C and the block A are both moving to the left with a velocity $\mathbf{v}_0$ when the block is suddenly stopped by the wall. Determine the smallest velocity $\mathbf{v}_0$ for which the weight C will swing in a full circle about the pivot B (*a*) if BC is a slender rod of negligible weight, (*b*) if BC is a cord.

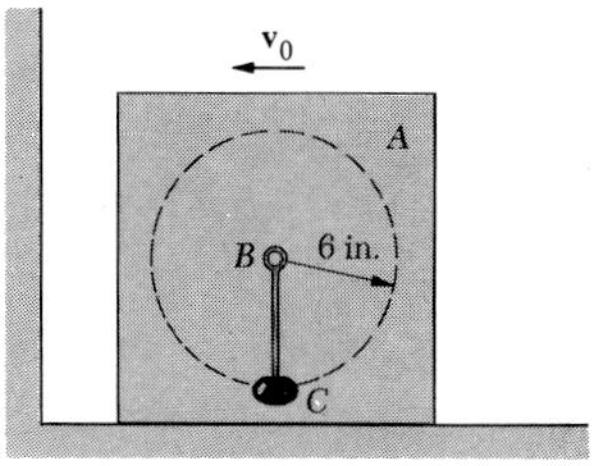

FIG. P 13.89

13.90. The frictional resistance of a ship is known to vary directly as the 1.8 power of the speed v of the ship. A single tugboat can tow the ship at a constant speed of 4 mph by exerting a constant force of 50,000 lb. (*a*) Determine the horsepower delivered by the single tugboat. (*b*) Three tugboats are then used to tow the same ship. If each tugboat exerts a towing force of 50,000 lb, determine the resulting speed and the horsepower delivered by each tugboat. (*c*) If each of the three tugboats can deliver only the horsepower delivered by the single tugboat of part *a*, determine the resulting speed and the force exerted by each tugboat.

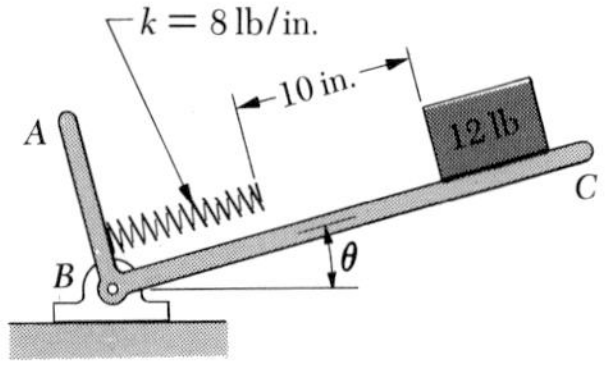

FIG. P 13.91

13.91. As the bracket ABC is slowly rotated, the 12-lb block starts to slide toward the spring when $\theta = 15°$. The maximum deflection of the spring is observed to be 2 in. Determine the values of the coefficients of static and kinetic friction.

13.92. Using the methods of Chap. 13, solve Prob. 12.40.

13.93. Two weights are attached to a rope which passes over a fixed pipe as shown. The coefficient of friction between the rope and the pipe is 0.30. Knowing that the system is released from rest in the position shown, determine the velocity of the 100-lb weight as it strikes the floor.

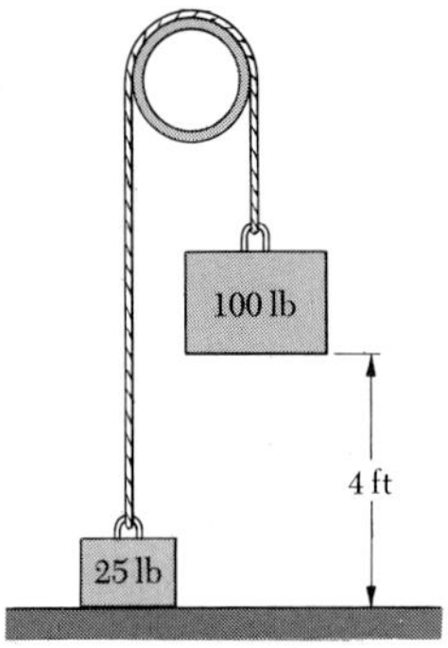

FIG. P 13.93

13.94. Determine the energy which must be imparted to a missile of mass m (*a*) to shoot it vertically to a height equal to the radius R of the earth, (*b*) to place it in a circular orbit of radius $2R$.

13.95. Determine the maximum power utilized in each of the five forward gears of the truck of Prob. 12.28.

13.96. Two portions AB and BC of the same elastic cord are connected as shown. The portion of cord BC supports a load W while, initially, the portion AB is under no tension. Determine the maximum tension which will develop in the entire cord after the stick DE suddenly breaks. (Assume that the tensions in AB and BC are instantaneously equalized after the stick breaks and that the elongation of the cord is small compared to L.)

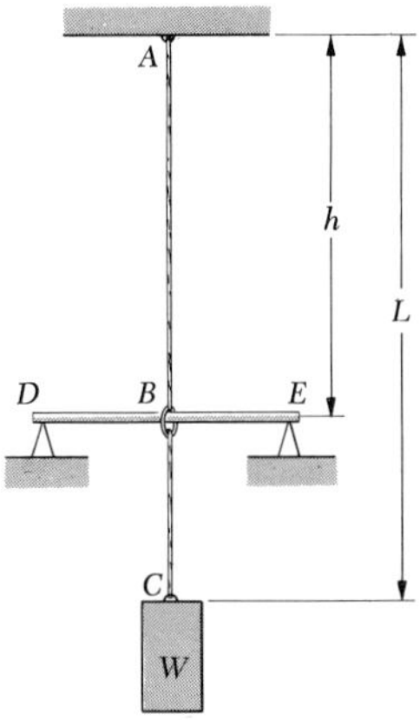

FIG. P 13.96

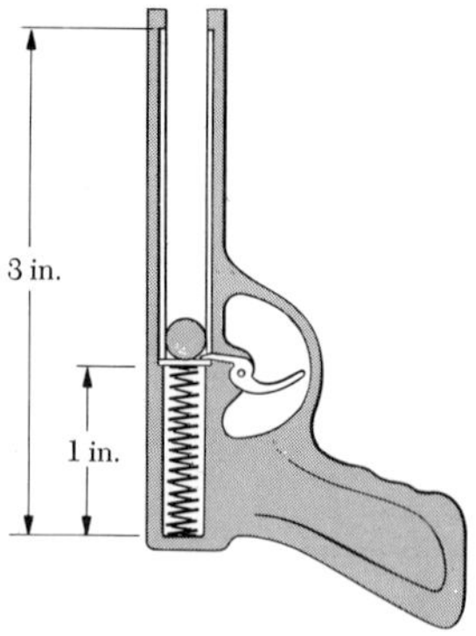

FIG. P 13.97

13.97. A toy spring gun is used to shoot 1-oz bullets vertically upward. The undeformed length of the spring is 5 in.; it is compressed to a length of 1 in. when the gun is ready to be shot and expands to a length of 3 in. as the bullet leaves the gun. A force of 8 lb is required to maintain the spring in firing position when the length of the spring is 1 in. Determine (*a*) the velocity of the bullet as it leaves the gun, (*b*) the maximum height reached by the bullet.

13.98. A 45-lb package is projected up a 15° incline with an initial speed of 40 ft/sec. Knowing that the package returns to its original position with a speed of 20 ft/sec, determine (*a*) the distance the package moved up the incline, (*b*) the coefficient of friction between the package and the incline.

13.99. A package of weight W is released from rest at A and swings in a vertical plane at the end of a 12-ft rope. The rope will break when the tension in the rope is equal to twice the weight of the package. (*a*) Determine the difference in elevation h between point A and point B where the rope will break. (*b*) How far from the vertical wall will the package strike the floor?

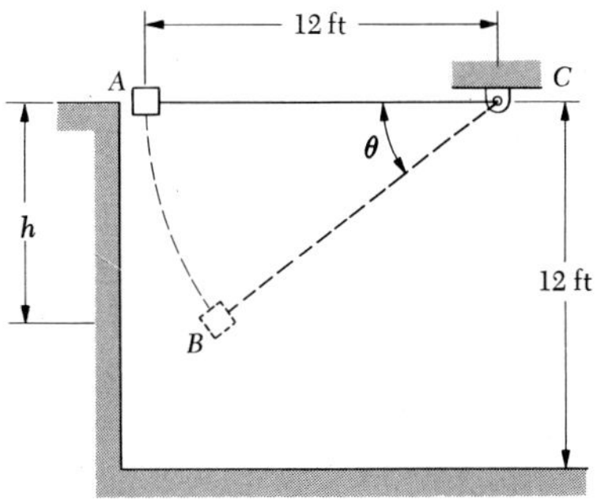

FIG. P 13.99

14. KINETICS OF PARTICLES: IMPULSE AND MOMENTUM

14.1. Principle of Impulse and Momentum. A third basic method for the solution of problems dealing with the motion of particles will be considered in this chapter. This method is based on the principle of impulse and momentum and is of particular interest in problems involving force, mass, velocity, and time.

Consider a particle of mass m acted upon by a force $\mathbf{F}$. Expressing Newton's second law $\mathbf{F} = m\mathbf{a}$ in terms of the x and y components of the force and of the acceleration, we write

$$F_x = ma_x \qquad F_y = ma_y$$

$$F_x = m\frac{dv_x}{dt} \qquad F_y = m\frac{dv_y}{dt}$$

Since the mass m of the particle is constant, we have

$$F_x = \frac{d}{dt}(mv_x) \qquad F_y = \frac{d}{dt}(mv_y) \tag{14.1}$$

or, in vector form,

$$\mathbf{F} = \frac{d}{dt}(m\mathbf{v}) \tag{14.2}$$

The vector $m\mathbf{v}$ is called the *linear momentum*, or simply the *momentum*, of the particle. It has the same direction as the velocity of the particle and its magnitude is expressed in lb-sec; we check that

$$mv = \frac{\text{lb-sec}^2}{\text{ft}}\,\frac{\text{ft}}{\text{sec}} = \text{lb-sec}$$

Equation (14.2) expresses that *the force* $\mathbf{F}$ *acting on the particle is equal to the rate of change of the momentum of the particle.* It is in this form that the second law of motion was originally stated by Newton.

Multiplying both sides of Eqs. (14.1) by dt and integrating from a time t_1 to a time t_2, we write

$$F_x\,dt = d(mv_x) \qquad F_y\,dt = d(mv_y)$$

$$\int_{t_1}^{t_2} F_x\,dt = (mv_x)_2 - (mv_x)_1 \qquad \int_{t_1}^{t_2} F_y\,dt = (mv_y)_2 - (mv_y)_1$$

$$(mv_x)_1 + \int_{t_1}^{t_2} F_x\,dt = (mv_x)_2 \qquad (mv_y)_1 + \int_{t_1}^{t_2} F_y\,dt = (mv_y)_2 \tag{14.3}$$

or, in vector form,

$$m\mathbf{v}_1 + \int_{t_1}^{t_2} \mathbf{F}\,dt = m\mathbf{v}_2 \tag{14.4}$$

The integral in Eq. (14.4) is a vector known as the *linear impulse*, or simply the *impulse*, of the force **F** during the interval of time considered. From Eqs. (14.3), we note that the components of the impulse of the force **F** are equal, respectively, to the areas under the curves obtained by plotting the components F_x and F_y against t (Fig. 14.1). In the case of a force **F** of constant magnitude and direction, the impulse is represented by the vector $\mathbf{F}(t_2 - t_1)$, which has the same direction as **F**. We easily check that the magnitude of the impulse of a force is expressed in lb-sec.

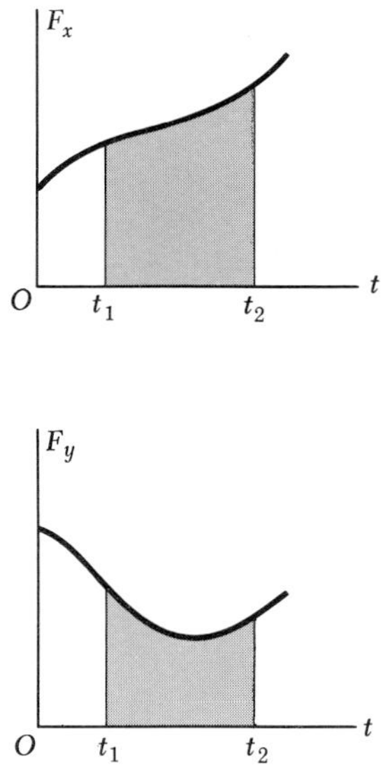

FIG. 14.1

Equation (14.4) expresses that, when a particle is acted upon by a force **F** during a given time interval, *the final momentum* $m\mathbf{v}_2$ *of the particle may be obtained by adding vectorially its initial momentum* $m\mathbf{v}_1$ *and the impulse of the force* **F** *during the time interval considered* (Fig. 14.2). We write

$$m\mathbf{v}_1 + \mathbf{Imp}_{1\rightarrow 2} = m\mathbf{v}_2 \tag{14.5}$$

We note that, while kinetic energy and work are scalar quantities, momentum and impulse are vector quantities. To obtain an analytic solution, it is thus necessary to replace Eq. (14.5) by the two corresponding component equations (14.3).

When several forces act on a particle, the impulse of each of the forces must be considered. We have

$$m\mathbf{v}_1 + \Sigma\,\mathbf{Imp}_{1\rightarrow 2} = m\mathbf{v}_2 \tag{14.6}$$

Again, the equation obtained represents a relation between vector quantities; in the actual solution of a problem, it should be replaced by the two corresponding component equations.

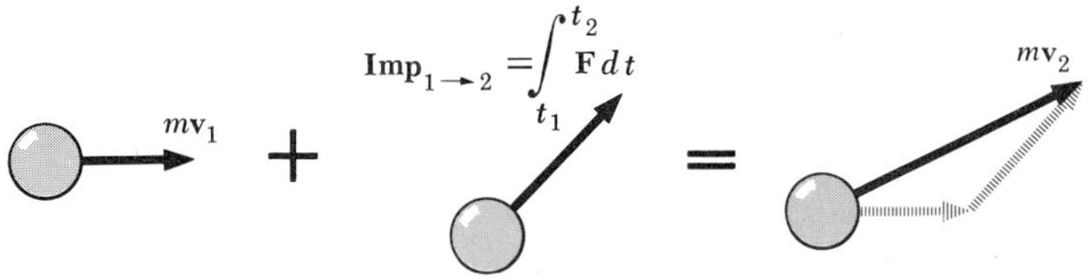

FIG. 14.2

14.2. Systems of Particles. When a problem involves the motion of several particles, each particle may be considered separately and Eq. (14.6) may be written for each particle. We may also add vectorially the momenta of all the particles and the impulses of all the forces involved. We write then

$$\Sigma m\mathbf{v}_1 + \Sigma\, \mathbf{Imp}_{1\to 2} = \Sigma m\mathbf{v}_2 \tag{14.7}$$

But since the internal forces occur by pairs of equal and opposite forces having the same line of action, their sum is zero and we need consider only the impulses of the external forces. We have

$$\Sigma m\mathbf{v}_1 + \Sigma\, \mathbf{Ext\ Imp}_{1\to 2} = \Sigma m\mathbf{v}_2 \tag{14.8}$$

Formula (14.8) may be written in a modified form if the mass center of the system of particles is considered. From Sec. 12.5, we recall that the mass center of the system is the point G of coordinates $\bar{x}$ and $\bar{y}$ defined by the equations

$$(\Sigma m)\bar{x} = \Sigma mx \qquad (\Sigma m)\bar{y} = \Sigma my \tag{14.9}$$

Differentiating (14.9) with respect to t, we have

$$(\Sigma m)\bar{v}_x = \Sigma mv_x \qquad (\Sigma m)\bar{v}_y = \Sigma mv_y \tag{14.10}$$

Writing (14.8) in terms of x and y components, and substituting for Σmv_x and Σmv_y from (14.10), we obtain

$$\begin{aligned} (\Sigma m)(\bar{v}_x)_1 + \Sigma \int_{t_1}^{t_2} (F_x)_{\text{ext}}\, dt &= \Sigma m(\bar{v}_x)_2 \\ (\Sigma m)(\bar{v}_y)_1 + \Sigma \int_{t_1}^{t_2} (F_y)_{\text{ext}}\, dt &= \Sigma m(\bar{v}_y)_2 \end{aligned} \tag{14.11}$$

We note that Eqs. (14.11) are identical with the equations we would obtain for a particle of mass Σm acted upon by all the external forces. We thus check that the mass center of a system of particles moves as if the entire mass of the system and all the external forces were concentrated at that point. We should keep in mind, however, that Eqs. (14.10) and (14.11) relate the components, but not the moments of the impulses and momenta involved. Therefore, Eqs. (14.10) *do not express* that the momenta of the particles of the system are equivalent to a vector $(\Sigma m)\bar{\mathbf{v}}$ attached at the mass center G. Indeed, as we shall see in Chap. 18, the resultant of the momenta of the particles of a system does not in general pass through the mass center of the system.

SAMPLE PROBLEM 14.1

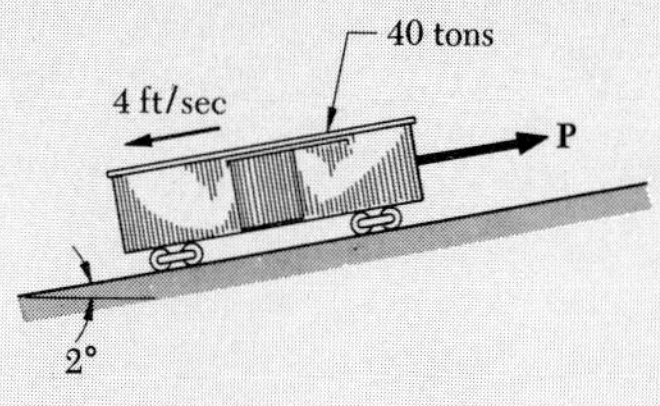

A 40-ton railroad car is moving down a 2° incline with a speed of 4 ft/sec. The rolling resistance of the car is 15 lb/ton. If a force **P** of magnitude 4,000 lb is applied as shown, determine the time required to stop the car.

Solution. The rolling resistance of the car is equivalent to a force **F** of magnitude

$$F = (15\,\text{lb/ton})(40\,\text{tons}) = 600\,\text{lb}$$

The forces acting on the car are its weight **W**, the applied force **P**, the normal reaction **N**, and the rolling resistance **F**. Since the magnitude and direction of each force are constant, the impulse of each force is equal to the product of the force and the time interval t.

Principle of Impulse and Momentum. The momentum at $t_1 = 0$ is shown in the first sketch, the impulses of the forces during the time interval t are shown in the second sketch, and the momentum at $t_2 = t$ is shown in the third sketch.

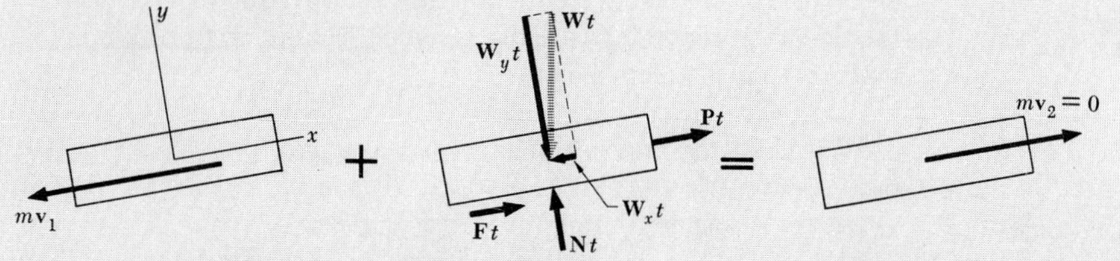

Applying the principle of impulse and momentum, we write

$$m\mathbf{v}_1 + \Sigma\,\mathbf{Imp}_{1\to 2} = m\mathbf{v}_2$$

$+\nearrow$ x components: $\quad -mv_1 - W_x t + Pt + Ft = 0$

$$-\frac{80{,}000}{32.2}(4\,\text{ft/sec}) - 80{,}000\,(\sin 2°)t + 4{,}000t + 600t = 0$$

$$t = 5.50\,\text{sec} \quad ◄$$

PROBLEMS

14.1. A stone weighing 5 lb is dropped from rest and strikes the ground with a velocity of 90 ft/sec. (*a*) Determine the momentum of the stone as it strikes the ground and the time of fall. (*b*) Solve part *a* assuming that the same stone is dropped on the moon. (Acceleration of gravity on the moon $= 5.31$ ft/sec^2.)

14.2. A 50-lb satellite has been placed in a circular orbit 1,548 miles above the surface of the earth. The acceleration of gravity at this elevation is 16.7 ft/sec^2. Determine the momentum of the satellite, knowing that its orbital speed is 15,000 mph.

14.3. A 2,800-lb automobile is moving at a speed of 45 mph when the brakes are fully applied, causing all four wheels to skid. Determine the time required to stop the automobile (*a*) on concrete ($\mu = 0.80$), (*b*) on ice ($\mu = 0.10$).

14.4. A tugboat exerts a constant force of 15 tons on a 50,000-ton ocean liner. Neglecting the frictional resistance of the water, determine the time required to increase the speed of the liner (*a*) from 1 mph to 2 mph, (*b*) from 2 mph to 3 mph.

14.5. Using the principle of impulse and momentum, solve Prob. 12.9, parts *a* and *c*.

14.6. Using the principle of impulse and momentum, solve Prob. 12.12*b*.

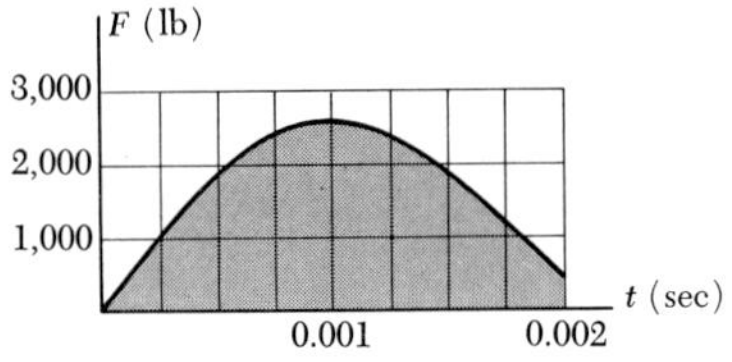

FIG. P 14.7

14.7. A $\frac{3}{4}$-oz bullet is fired from a fixed rifle. The magnitude of the force **F** exerted on the bullet by the expanding gases produced by the burning of the powder charge is shown in the graph. Knowing that the bullet leaves the barrel 0.002 sec after firing, determine the muzzle velocity of the bullet.

14.8. Solve Prob. 14.7 assuming that the barrel of the rifle is shorter and that the bullet leaves the barrel 0.0015 sec after firing.

14.9. A light train made of two cars travels at 60 mph. The first car weighs 15 tons, and the second car weighs 20 tons. When the brakes are applied, a constant braking force of 5,000 lb is applied to each car. Determine (*a*) the time required for the train to stop after the brakes are applied, (*b*) the force in the coupling between the cars while the train is slowing down.

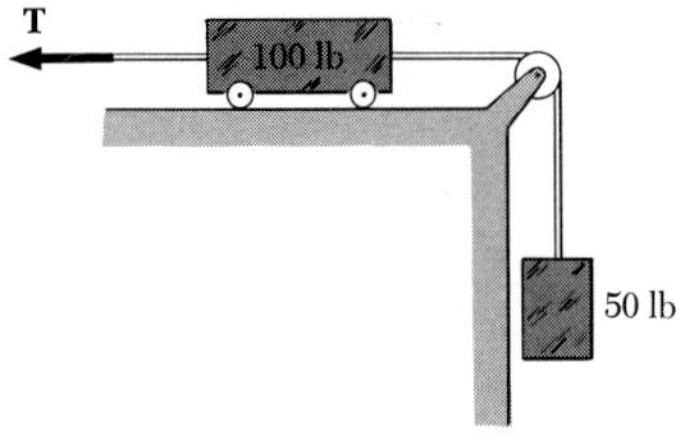

FIG. P 14.10

14.10. At a time $t = 0$ when the velocity of the 50-lb counterweight is 10 ft/sec downward, a force **T** of magnitude 80 lb is applied as shown. Determine the time t at which the 50-lb counterweight has (*a*) no velocity, (*b*) a velocity of 10 ft/sec upward.

14.11. Solve Prob. 14.10 assuming that the wheels of the 100-lb car are locked and skid along the horizontal surface ($\mu = 0.20$).

14.12. Using the principle of impulse and momentum, solve Prob. 12.17*b*.

14.13. Using the principle of impulse and momentum, solve Prob. 12.21*a*.

14.14. Using the principle of impulse and momentum, solve Prob. 12.22*a*.

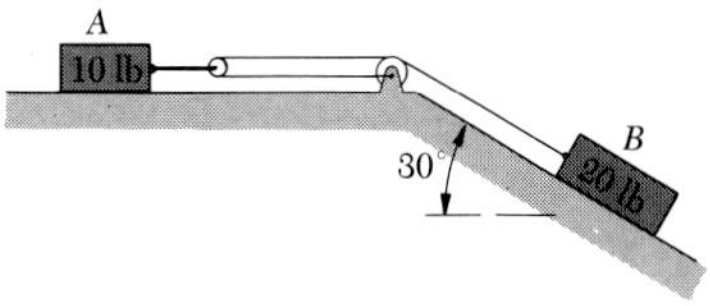

FIG. P 14.15

14.15. Blocks *A* and *B* slide on lubricated surfaces for which μ may be assumed equal to 0.10. Knowing that the system is released from rest, determine the velocity of block *B* after 5 sec.

14.16. Solve Prob. 14.15 assuming that block *A* weighs 20 lb and block *B* weighs 10 lb.

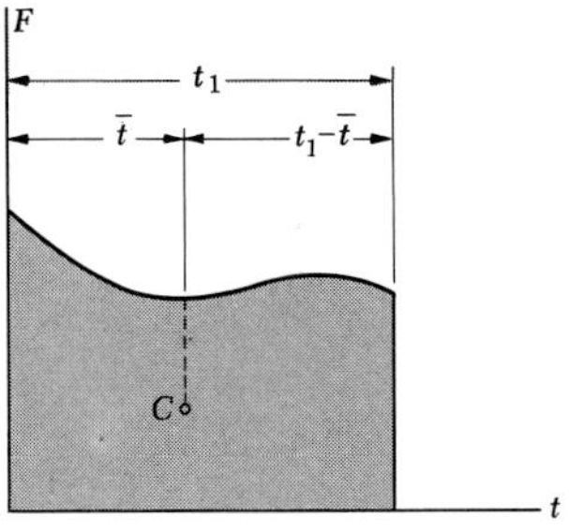

FIG. P 14.18

***14.17.** A grain of sand of mass *m* is released from rest in water. It is acted upon by a constant force of magnitude *Q* (equal to its submerged weight) and by a frictional force of magnitude *kv*, where *k* is a constant and *v* is the speed of the particle. Using the principle of impulse and momentum ($F\,dt = m\,dv$), show that, if at $t = 0$, $v_0 = 0$, the speed at any time *t* is $v = (Q/k)\,(1 - e^{-(k/m)t})$. Further show that the resultant of the forces acting on the grain at any time *t* is $Qe^{-(k/m)t}$.

***14.18.** A particle of mass *m* moves in a straight line under the action of a force of magnitude *F* which varies with respect to the time *t* as shown. Derive the following expressions for the motion of the particle: $v_1 = v_0 + A/m$; $s_1 = s_0 + v_0 t_1 + (t_1 - \bar{t})A/m$, where *A* is the area under the *F–t* curve between $t = 0$ and $t = t_1$ and *C* is the centroid of the same area.

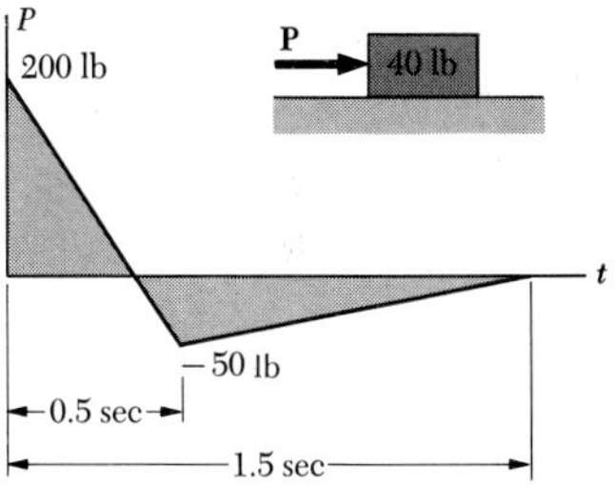

FIG. P 14.19

14.19. A block weighing 40 lb is initially at rest and is subjected to a force **P** which varies as shown. Neglecting the effect of friction, determine (*a*) the maximum speed attained by the block, (*b*) the speed of the block at $t = 1.5$ sec.

14.20. Solve Prob. 14.19 assuming that $\mu = 0.25$ between the block and the surface.

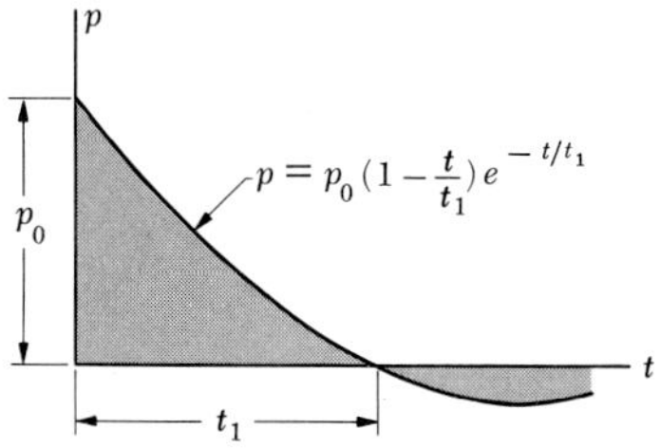

FIG. P 14.21

***14.21.** The explosion of a bomb creates a pressure wave which travels in all directions from the point of explosion. The graph shown represents the pressure-time curve at a large distance from the point of explosion of an atomic bomb. Show that the total positive impulse per unit area is $p_0 t_1/e$ and that the total impulse per unit area from $t = 0$ to $t = \infty$ is zero. (*Hint.* $\lim_{t\to\infty} te^{-t} = 0$.)

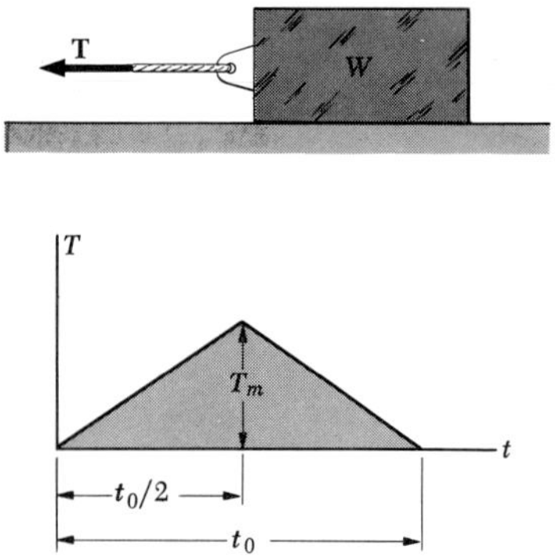

FIG. P 14.23

*14.22. An object of mass m and effective area A, initially at rest, is subjected to the pressure p defined in Prob. 14.21. Show that (a) at $t = t_1$, $v_1 = v_{max} = \frac{p_0 t_1}{e} \frac{A}{m}$, (b) at $t = t_1$, $s_1 = p_0 t_1^2 (1 - 2/e)(A/m)$, (c) the final displacement of the object is $s = p_0 t_1^2 \; (A/m)$.

*14.23. A block of weight W is at rest on a rough surface when a force **T** is applied to the cable. The magnitude T of the force varies with time as shown in the graph. Denoting by μ the coefficient of friction between the block and the surface, determine (a) the value of T_m for which the block will move and will again be at rest when $t = t_0$, (b) the corresponding maximum velocity attained by the block.

14.3. Impulsive Forces. In some problems, a very large force may act during a very short time interval on a particle and produce a definite change in momentum. Such a force is called an *impulsive force.* For example, when a baseball is struck, the contact between bat and ball takes place during a very short time interval Δt. But the average value of the force **F** exerted by the bat on the ball is very large, and the resulting impulse $\mathbf{F}\,\Delta t$ is large enough to change the sense of motion of the ball (Fig. 14.3).

When impulsive forces act on a particle, Eq. (14.6) becomes

$$m\mathbf{v}_1 + \Sigma\mathbf{F}\,\Delta t = m\mathbf{v}_2 \qquad (14.12)$$

Any force which is not an impulsive force may be neglected, since the corresponding impulse $\mathbf{F}\,\Delta t$ is very small. *Nonimpulsive forces* include the weight of the body, the force exerted by a spring, or any other force which is *known* to be small compared with an impulsive force. Unknown reactions may or may not be impulsive; their impulse should therefore be included in Eq. (14.12) as long as it has not been proved negligible. The impulse of the weight of the baseball considered above, for example, may be neglected. If the motion of the bat is analyzed, the impulse of the weight of the bat may also be neglected. The impulses of the reactions of the player's hands on the bat, however, should be included; these impulses will not be negligible if the ball is incorrectly hit.

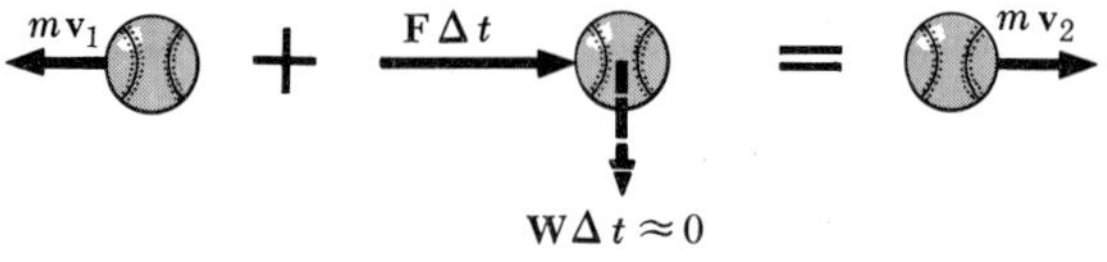

FIG. 14.3

14.4. Conservation of Momentum. We saw in Sec. 14.2 that, when a system of particles moves under the action of various forces, the following relation must hold between the initial momenta of the particles, the final momenta of the particles, and the impulses of the external forces:

$$\Sigma m\mathbf{v}_1 + \Sigma\ \textbf{Ext Imp}_{1\to2} = \Sigma m\mathbf{v}_2 \qquad (14.8)$$

Let us now consider the case when the sum of the impulses of the external forces is zero. Equation (14.8) reduces then to

$$\Sigma m\mathbf{v}_1 = \Sigma m\mathbf{v}_2 \qquad (14.13)$$

Thus, *when the sum of the impulses of the external forces acting on a system of particles is zero, the total momentum of the system remains constant.*

Introducing again the mass center G of the system, and using formulas (14.10), Eq. (14.13) reduces to

$$\overline{\mathbf{v}}_1 = \overline{\mathbf{v}}_2 \qquad (14.14)$$

Thus, when the sum of the impulses of the external forces acting on a system of particles is zero, *the mass center of the system moves with a constant velocity.*

Two distinct cases of conservation of momentum are frequently encountered:

1. *The external forces acting on the system during the interval of time considered are balanced.* No matter how long the time interval is, we have $\Sigma\ \textbf{Ext Imp}_{1\to2} = 0$ and formula (14.13) applies. Consider, for example, two boats, of mass m_A and m_B, initially at rest, which are being pulled together (Fig. 14.4). If the resistance of the water is neglected, the only external forces acting on the boats are their weights and the buoyant forces exerted on them. Since these forces are balanced, we write

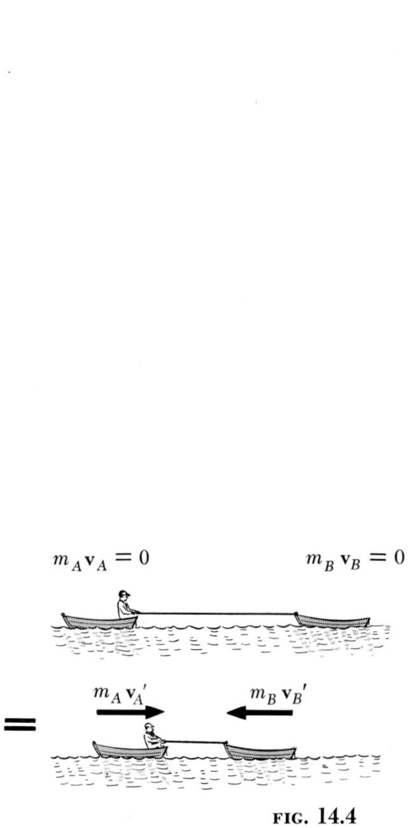

FIG. 14.4

$$\Sigma m\mathbf{v}_1 = \Sigma m\mathbf{v}_2$$
$$0 = m_A\mathbf{v}'_A + m_B\mathbf{v}'_B$$

where $\mathbf{v}'_A$ and $\mathbf{v}'_B$ represent the velocities of the boats after a finite interval of time. The equation obtained indicates that the boats move in opposite directions (toward each other) with velocities inversely proportional to their masses. We also note that the mass center of the two boats, which was initially at rest, remains in the same position.

2. *The interval of time considered is very short, and all the external forces are nonimpulsive.* Again we have $\Sigma\ \textbf{Ext Imp}_{1\to2} = 0$, and formula (14.13) applies. Consider, for

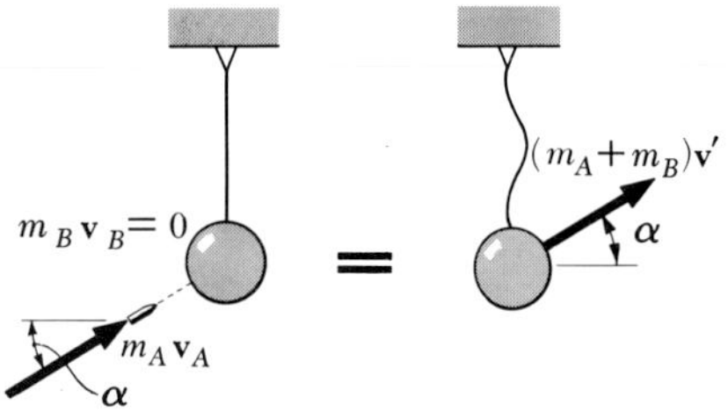

FIG. 14.5

example, a bullet of mass m_A fired with a velocity $\mathbf{v}_A$ into a wooden sphere of mass m_B suspended from an inextensible wire and initially at rest (Fig. 14.5). The bullet penetrates the sphere and imparts to it a velocity $\mathbf{v}'$, which we propose to determine. After the sphere has been hit, the tension in the wire becomes zero and the combined weight of the sphere and bullet is unbalanced. But the impulse of the weight may be neglected since the time interval is very short. We write, therefore,

$$\Sigma m\mathbf{v}_1 = \Sigma m\mathbf{v}_2$$
$$m_A\mathbf{v}_A + 0 = (m_A + m_B)\mathbf{v}'$$

The equation obtained may be solved for $\mathbf{v}'$; we note that $\mathbf{v}'$ will have the same direction as $\mathbf{v}_A$.

Let us now consider the case when the bullet is fired downward into the sphere (Fig. 14.6). Since the wire is inextensi-

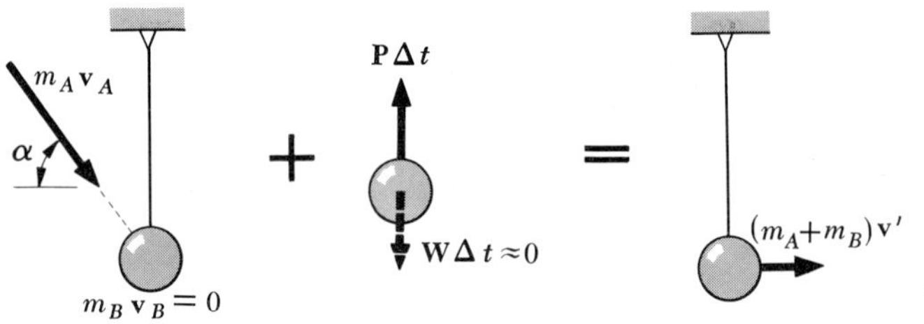

FIG. 14.6

ble, it will prevent any downward motion of the sphere and exert on it a reaction **P**. This reaction is unknown and should therefore be assumed impulsive until proved to the contrary. Writing the general formula (14.8) in terms of horizontal and vertical components, and observing again that the impulse of the weight is negligible, we have

$$\Sigma m\mathbf{v}_1 + \Sigma \text{ Ext Imp}_{1\rightarrow 2} = \Sigma m\mathbf{v}_2$$

$\overset{+}{\rightarrow} x$ components: $\quad m_A v_A \cos\alpha + 0 = (m_A + m_B)v'$

$+\uparrow y$ components: $\quad -m_A v_A \sin\alpha + P\,\Delta t = 0$

The first equation expresses that *the x component of the momentum is conserved*; it may be used to determine v'. The second equation indicates that *the y component of the linear momentum is not conserved*; this equation may be used to determine the magnitude $P\,\Delta t$ of the impulse of the force exerted by the wire. Thus, the momentum of the system considered is not conserved, and Eq. (14.13) does not hold, except in the x direction.

SAMPLE PROBLEM 14.2

An old 4,000-lb gun fires a 20-lb shell with an initial velocity of 2,000 ft/sec at an angle of 30°. The gun rests on a horizontal surface and is free to move horizontally. Assuming that the barrel of the gun is rigidly attached to the frame (no recoil mechanism) and that the shell leaves the barrel 0.006 sec after firing, determine the recoil velocity of the gun and the resultant **R** of the vertical impulsive forces exerted by the ground on the gun.

Solution. We apply the principle of impulse and momentum to the system consisting of the gun and the shell. Since the time interval $\Delta t = 0.006$ sec is very short, we neglect all nonimpulsive forces and consider only the impulse $\mathbf{R}\,\Delta t$.

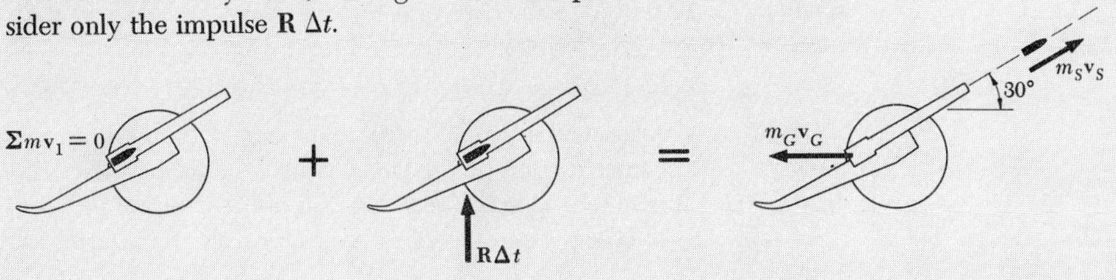

$$\Sigma m\mathbf{v}_1 + \Sigma\ \mathbf{Ext\ Imp}_{1\to 2} = \Sigma m\mathbf{v}_2$$

$\overset{+}{\rightarrow}$ x components:

$$0 + 0 = -m_G v_G + m_S v_S \cos 30°$$

$$0 = -\frac{4{,}000}{32.2} v_G + \frac{20}{32.2}(2{,}000)(0.866)$$

$$v_G = +8.66 \text{ ft/sec}$$

$$\mathbf{v}_G = 8.66 \text{ ft/sec} \leftarrow \blacktriangleleft$$

$+\uparrow$ y components:

$$0 + R\,\Delta t = m_S v_S \sin 30°$$

$$R(0.006) = \frac{20}{32.2}(2{,}000)(0.500)$$

$$R = +103{,}500 \text{ lb}$$

$$\mathbf{R} = 103{,}500 \text{ lb} \uparrow \blacktriangleleft$$

The total force exerted by the ground on the gun during the time interval Δt should include the static reaction due to the weight of the gun as well as the impulsive reaction **R**. Since the gun weighs 4,000 lb, the magnitude of this total force is 103,500 + 4,000 = 107,500 lb.

The high value obtained for the magnitude of **R** clearly indicates the need in modern guns for a recoil mechanism which will allow the barrel to move and will bring it to rest over a period of time substantially longer than Δt. Although the total vertical impulse must remain constant, the longer time interval will result in a smaller value for the magnitude of the reaction **R**.

PROBLEMS

14.24. A 1-oz rifle bullet is fired with an initial velocity of 2,200 ft/sec into a block of wood rigidly attached to the ground. If the bullet is brought to rest in 0.001 sec, determine the average impulsive force exerted by the bullet on the block.

14.25. A 12,000-lb plane lands on the deck of an aircraft carrier at a speed of 120 mph relative to the carrier and is brought to a stop in 3.0 sec. Determine the average impulsive force exerted by the carrier on the plane (*a*) if the carrier is at rest, (*b*) if the carrier is steaming at a speed of 15 knots in the same direction as the airplane. (1 knot = 1.152 mph.)

14.26. A 4-oz baseball is pitched with a velocity of 60 ft/sec toward a batter. After the ball is hit by the bat *B*, it has a velocity of 120 ft/sec in the direction shown. If the bat and ball are in contact 0.03 sec, determine the average impulsive force exerted on the ball during the impact.

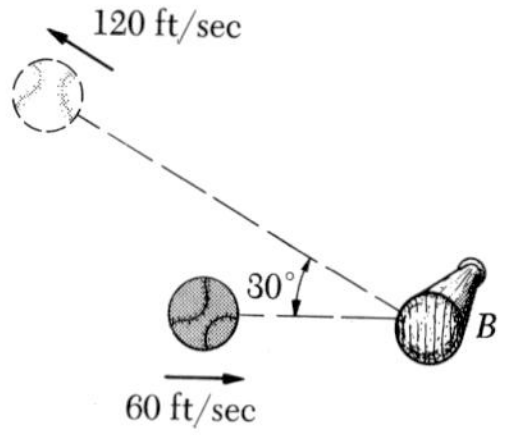

FIG. P 14.26

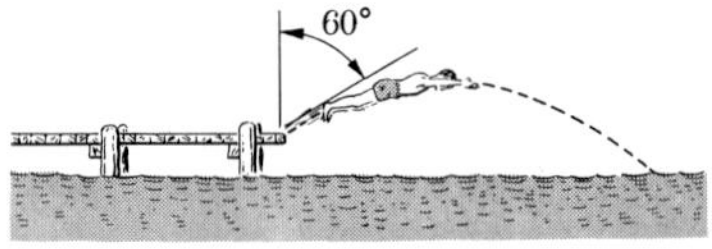

FIG. P 14.27

14.27. A 175-lb man dives off the end of a pier with an initial velocity of 8 ft/sec in the direction shown. Determine the horizontal and vertical components of the force exerted on the pier during the 0.75 sec that the man takes to leave the pier.

14.28. Determine the initial recoil velocity of a 9-lb rifle which fires a $\frac{3}{4}$-oz bullet with a velocity of 2,000 ft/sec.

14.29. A 2-oz bullet is fired horizontally into an 8-lb block which can move freely in the horizontal direction. The horizontal velocity of the block after the bullet has embedded itself is 20 ft/sec. Determine the initial velocity of the bullet.

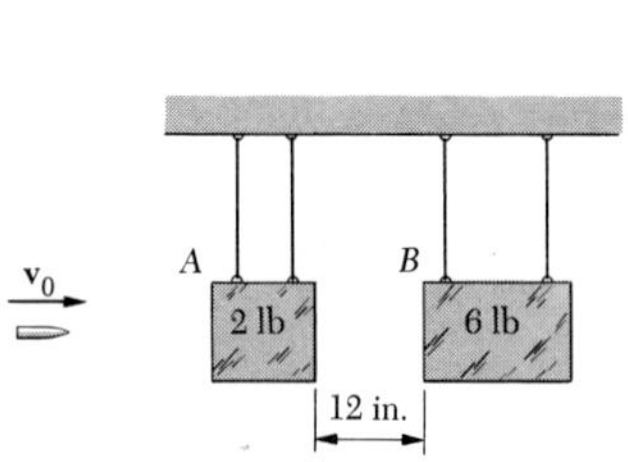

FIG. P 14.30

14.30. A $\frac{3}{4}$-oz bullet is fired in a horizontal direction through block *A* and becomes embedded in block *B*. The bullet causes *A* and *B* to start moving with velocities of 15 ft/sec and 12 ft/sec respectively. Determine (*a*) the initial velocity $\mathbf{v}_0$ of the bullet, (*b*) the velocity of the bullet as it travels from block *A* to block *B*.

14.31. A barge is initially at rest and carries a 1,000-lb crate. The barge weighs 3 tons and is equipped with a winch which is used to move the crate along the deck. Neglecting any friction between the crate and the barge, determine (*a*) the velocity of both the barge and the crate when the winch is drawing in rope at the rate of 9 ft/sec, (*b*) the final position of the barge after 30 ft of rope has been drawn in by the winch. (*c*) Solve parts *a* and *b* assuming that $\mu = 0.25$ between the crate and the barge.

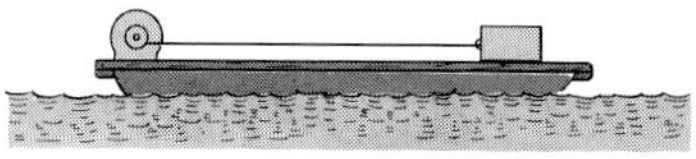

FIG. P 14.31

14.32. A 40-ton railroad car is to be coupled to a second car which weighs 60 tons. If initially the speed of the 40-ton car is 1 mph and the 60-ton car is at rest, determine the final speed of the coupled cars and the average impulsive force acting on each car if the coupling is completed in 0.3 sec.

14.33. Solve Prob. 14.32 assuming that, initially, the 40-ton car is at rest and the 60-ton car has a speed of 1 mph.

14.34. An airline employee tosses a 30-lb suitcase with a horizontal velocity of 10 ft/sec onto a 70-lb baggage carrier. Knowing that the carrier can roll freely and is initially at rest, determine the final velocity of the carrier (*a*) if the suitcase slides to a relative stop on the carrier, (*b*) if the suitcase is stopped by end *A* of the carrier.

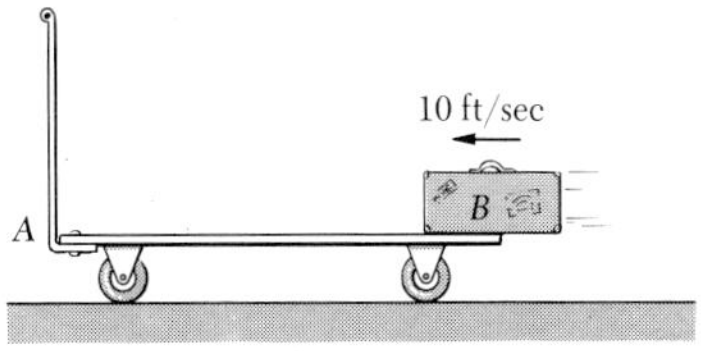

FIG. P 14.34 AND P 14.35

14.35. An employee tosses suitcases with a horizontal velocity of 10 ft/sec relative to the ground onto a carrier. Determine the final velocity of the 70-lb carrier after the employee has tossed (*a*) one 30-lb suitcase, (*b*) two 15-lb suitcases. In the latter case the first 15-lb suitcase comes to a relative stop on the carrier before the second suitcase reaches the carrier.

14.36. A 150-lb man dives horizontally off the end of a 300-lb boat, which is initially at rest. During the dive, the relative horizontal velocity of the man with respect to the boat is 12 ft/sec to the right. (*a*) Determine the resulting velocity of the boat. (*b*) If the man leaves the boat in 0.75 sec, determine the average impulsive force that he exerted on the boat.

14.37. Two men dive horizontally off the end of a 300-lb boat. The boat is initially at rest, and each man weighs 150 lb. If each man dives so that his relative horizontal velocity with respect to the boat is 12 ft/sec to the right, determine (*a*) the velocity of the boat after the men dive simultaneously, (*b*) the velocity of the boat after one man dives and the velocity of the boat after the second man dives.

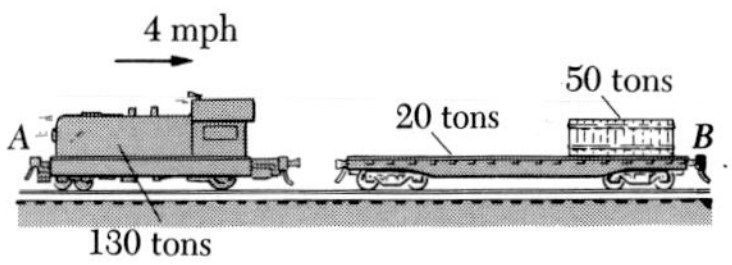

FIG. P 14.38

14.38. A 130-ton engine coasting at 4 mph strikes, and is automatically coupled with, a 20-ton flat car which carries a 50-ton load. The load is *not* securely fastened to the car but may slide along the floor ($\mu = 0.20$). Knowing that the car was at rest with its brakes released, determine the velocity of the engine *immediately* after the coupling, assuming that the coupling takes place (*a*) instantaneously, (*b*) in a period of 0.40 sec. (*c*) Determine the final velocity of the engine after the load has slid to a stop relative to the car.

14.39. A rifle is rigidly attached to a test stand when a $\frac{1}{2}$-oz bullet is fired. Knowing that the muzzle velocity of the bullet is 2,800 ft/sec, determine the total horizontal impulse exerted on the rifle by the stand. A second bullet weighing $\frac{3}{4}$ oz is then fired using the same size of powder charge. Assuming that the kinetic energy of the second bullet is the same as that of the first bullet, determine again the total impulse exerted on the rifle.

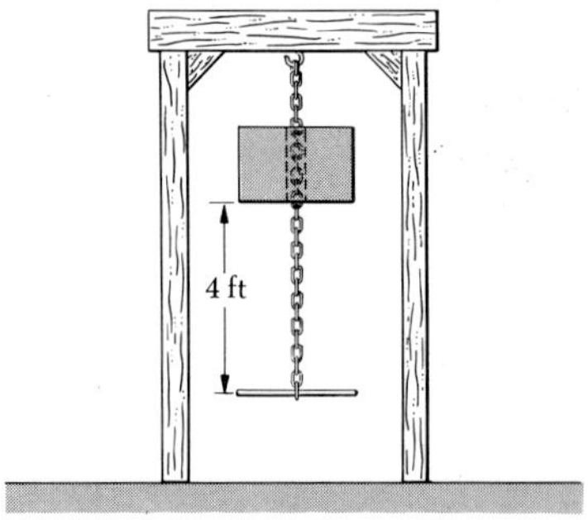

FIG. P 14.40

***14.40.** In order to test the resistance of a chain to impact, the chain is suspended from a 200-lb dead weight supported by two columns. A rod attached to the last link of the chain is then hit by a 50-lb block dropped from a 4-ft height. Determine the initial impulse exerted on the chain, assuming that the chain is inelastic and that the columns supporting the dead weight (*a*) are perfectly rigid, (*b*) are equivalent to two perfectly elastic springs.

***14.41.** A machine part is forged in a small drop forge. The hammer weighs 400 lb and is dropped from a height of 5 ft. Determine the initial impulse exerted on the machine part, assuming that the 1,000-lb anvil (*a*) is resting directly on hard ground, (*b*) is supported by springs.

14.5. Impact. A collision between two bodies which occurs in a very small interval of time, and during which the two bodies exert on each other relatively large forces, is called an *impact*. The common normal to the surfaces in contact during the impact is called the *line of impact*. If the mass centers of the two colliding bodies are located on this line, the impact is a *central impact*. Otherwise, the impact is said to be *eccentric*. We shall limit our present study to that of the central impact of two particles and postpone until later the analysis of the eccentric impact of two rigid bodies (Sec. 18.6).

If the velocities of the two particles are directed along the line of impact, the impact is said to be a *direct impact* (Fig. 14.7*a*). If, on the other hand, either or both particles move along a line other than the line of impact, the impact is said to be an *oblique impact* (Fig. 14.7*b*).

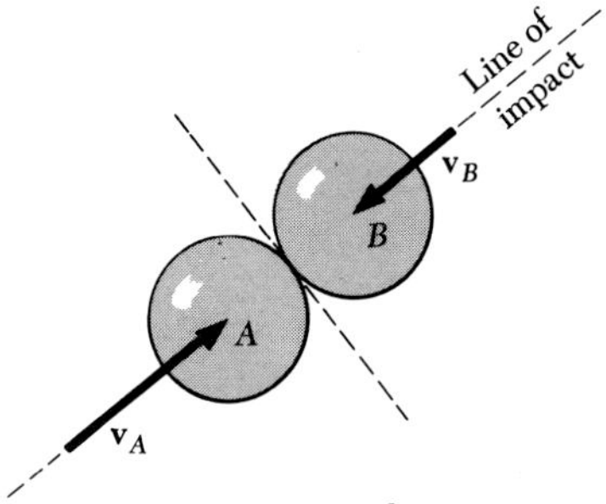

(*a*) Direct central impact

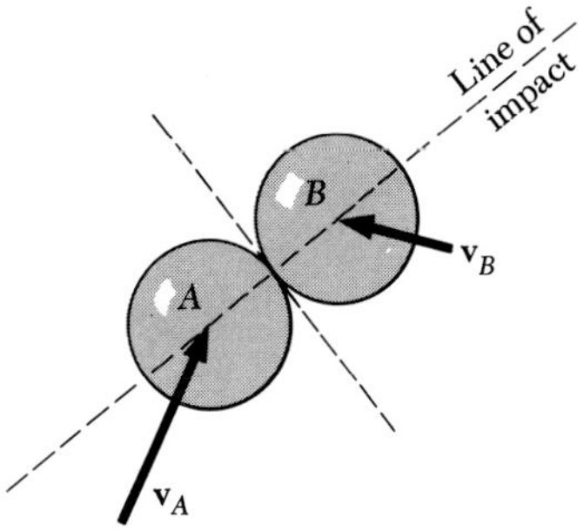

(*b*) Oblique central impact

FIG. 14.7

14.6. Direct Central Impact. Consider two particles *A* and *B*, of mass m_A and m_B, which are moving in the same straight line and to the right with known velocities $\mathbf{v}_A$ and $\mathbf{v}_B$ (Fig. 14.8*a*). If $\mathbf{v}_A$ is larger than $\mathbf{v}_B$, particle *A* will eventually strike particle *B*. Under the impact, the two particles will *deform* and, at the end of the period of deformation, they will have the same velocity $\mathbf{u}$ (Fig. 14.8*b*). A period of *restitution* will then take place, at the end of which, depending upon the magnitude of the impact forces and upon the materials involved, the two particles either will have regained their original shape or will stay permanently deformed. Our purpose here is to determine the velocities $\mathbf{v}'_A$ and $\mathbf{v}'_B$ of the particles at the end of the period of restitution (Fig. 14.8*c*).

Considering first the system of the two particles as a whole, we note that the only impulsive forces acting during the impact are internal forces. Thus, *the momentum of the system is conserved*, and we write

$$m_A\mathbf{v}_A + m_B\mathbf{v}_B = m_A\mathbf{v}'_A + m_B\mathbf{v}'_B$$

Since all the velocities considered are directed along the same axis, we may replace the equation obtained by the following relation involving only scalar components:

$$m_A v_A + m_B v_B = m_A v'_A + m_B v'_B \qquad (14.15)$$

A positive value for any of the scalar quantities v_A, v_B, v'_A, or v'_B means that the corresponding vector is directed to the right; a negative value indicates that the corresponding vector is directed to the left.

To obtain the velocities $\mathbf{v}'_A$ and $\mathbf{v}'_B$, it is necessary to establish a second relation between the scalars v'_A and v'_B. For this purpose, we shall consider now the motion of particle *A* during the period of deformation and apply the principle of im-

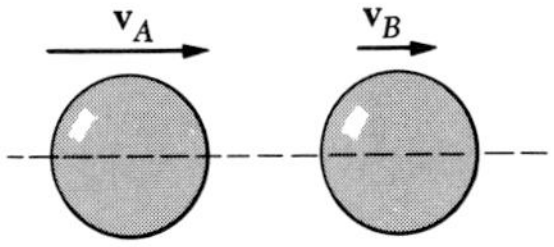

(*a*) Before impact

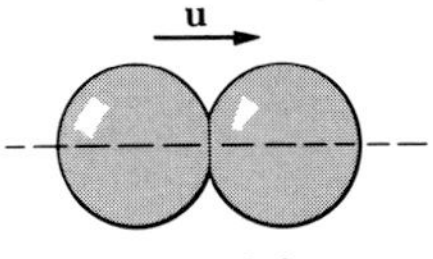

(*b*) At maximum deformation

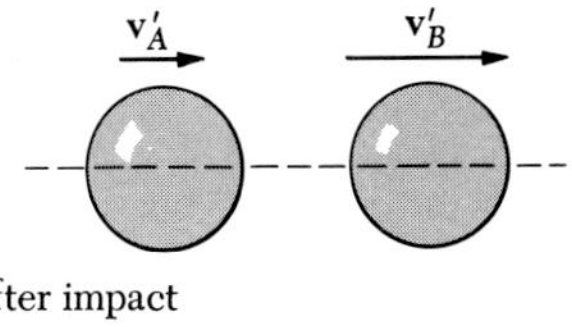

(*c*) After impact

FIG. 14.8

pulse and momentum. Since the only impulsive force acting on A during this period is the force $\mathbf{P}$ exerted by B (Fig. 14.9a), we write, using again scalar components,

$$m_A v_A - \int P\,dt = m_A u \qquad (14.16)$$

where the integral extends over the period of deformation. Considering now the motion of A during the period of restitution, and denoting by $\mathbf{R}$ the force exerted by B on A during this period (Fig. 14.9b), we write

$$m_A u - \int R\,dt = m_A v'_A \qquad (14.17)$$

where the integral extends over the period of restitution.

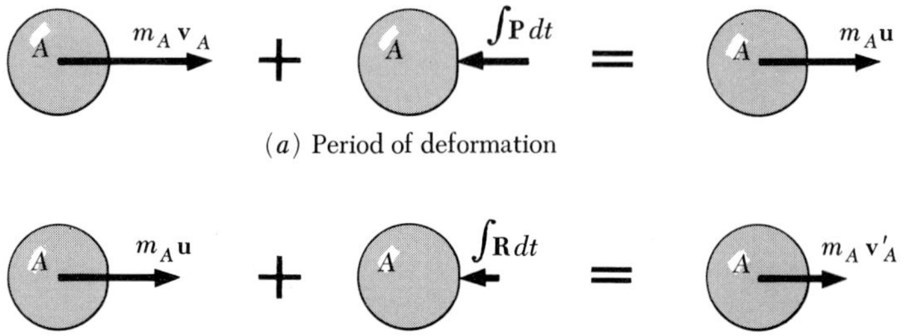

(a) Period of deformation

FIG. 14.9 (b) Period of restitution

In general, the force $\mathbf{R}$ exerted on A during the period of restitution differs from the force $\mathbf{P}$ exerted during the period of deformation, and the magnitude $\int R dt$ of its impulse is smaller than the magnitude $\int P dt$ of the impulse of $\mathbf{P}$. The ratio of the magnitudes of the impulses corresponding respectively to the period of restitution and to the period of deformation is called the *coefficient of restitution* and is denoted by e. We write

$$e = \frac{\int R\,dt}{\int P\,dt} \qquad (14.18)$$

The value of the coefficient e is always between 0 and 1 and depends to a large extent on the two materials involved. However, it also varies considerably with the impact velocity and the shape and size of the two colliding bodies.

Solving Eqs. (14.16) and (14.17) for the two impulses and substituting into (14.18), we write

$$e = \frac{u - v'_A}{v_A - u} \qquad (14.19)$$

A similar analysis of particle B leads to the relation

$$e = \frac{v'_B - u}{u - v_B} \tag{14.20}$$

Since the quotients in (14.19) and (14.20) are equal, they are also equal to the quotient obtained by adding, respectively, their numerators and their denominators. We have, therefore,

$$e = \frac{(u - v'_A) + (v'_B - u)}{(v_A - u) + (u - v_B)} = \frac{v'_B - v'_A}{v_A - v_B}$$

and

$$v'_B - v'_A = e(v_A - v_B) \tag{14.21}$$

Since $v'_B - v'_A$ represents the relative velocity of the two particles after impact and $v_A - v_B$ their relative velocity before impact, formula (14.21) expresses that *the relative velocity of the two particles after impact may be obtained by multiplying their relative velocity before impact by the coefficient of restitution.* This property is used to determine experimentally the value of the coefficient of restitution of two given materials.

The velocities of the two particles after impact may now be obtained by solving Eqs. (14.15) and (14.21) simultaneously for v'_A and v'_B, i.e., by using the principle of conservation of momentum and the concept of coefficient of restitution. It is recalled that the derivation of Eqs. (14.15) and (14.21) was based on the assumption that particle B is located to the right of A, and that both particles are initially moving to the right. If particle B is initially moving to the left, the scalar v_B should be considered negative. The same sign convention holds for the velocities after impact: a positive sign for v'_A will indicate that particle A moves to the right after impact, and a negative sign that it moves to the left.

Two particular cases of impact are of special interest:

1. $e = 0$, *Perfectly Plastic Impact.* When $e = 0$, Eq. (14.21) yields $v'_B = v'_A$. There is no period of restitution, and both particles stay together after impact. Substituting $v'_B = v'_A = v'$ into Eq. (14.15), which expresses that the momentum of the system is conserved, we write

$$m_A v_A + m_B v_B = (m_A + m_B)v' \tag{14.22}$$

This equation may be solved for the common velocity v' of the two particles after impact.

2. $e = 1$, *Perfectly Elastic Impact.* When $e = 1$, Eq. (14.21) reduces to

$$v'_B - v'_A = v_A - v_B \tag{14.23}$$

which expresses that the relative velocities before and after impact are equal. The impulses received by each particle during the period of deformation and during the period of restitution are equal. The particles move away from each other after impact with the same velocity with which they approached each other before impact. The velocities v'_A and v'_B may be obtained by solving Eqs. (14.15) and (14.23) simultaneously.

It is worth noting that, *in the case of a perfectly elastic impact, the energy of the system,* as well as its momentum, *is conserved.* Equations (14.15) and (14.23) may be written as follows:

$$m_A(v_A - v'_A) = m_B(v'_B - v_B) \tag{14.15'}$$

$$v_A + v'_A = v_B + v'_B \tag{14.23'}$$

Multiplying (14.15′) and (14.23′) member by member, we have

$$m_A(v_A - v'_A)(v_A + v'_A) = m_B(v'_B - v_B)(v'_B + v_B)$$
$$m_A v_A^2 - m_A(v'_A)^2 = m_B(v'_B)^2 - m_B v_B^2$$

Rearranging the terms in the equation obtained, and multiplying by $\frac{1}{2}$, we write

$$\tfrac{1}{2}m_A v_A^2 + \tfrac{1}{2}m_B v_B^2 = \tfrac{1}{2}m_A(v'_A)^2 + \tfrac{1}{2}m_B(v'_B)^2$$

which expresses that the kinetic energy of the system is conserved. It should be noted, however, that *in the general case of impact,* i.e., when e is not equal to 1, *the energy of the system is not conserved.* This may be shown in any given case by comparing the kinetic energies before and after impact. The lost kinetic energy is in part transformed into heat and in part spent in generating elastic waves within the two colliding bodies.

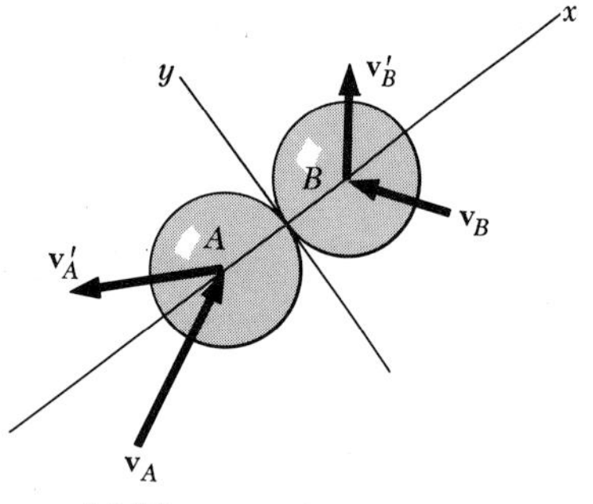

FIG. 14.10

14.7. Oblique Central Impact. Let us now consider the case when the velocities of the two colliding particles are *not* directed along the line of impact (Fig. 14.10). As indicated in Sec. 14.5, the impact is said to be *oblique.* Since the velocities $\mathbf{v}'_A$ and $\mathbf{v}'_B$ of the particles after impact are unknown in direction as well as in magnitude, their determination will require the use of four independent equations.

We choose x and y axes, respectively, along the line of impact and along the common tangent to the surfaces in contact. Assuming that the particles are perfectly *smooth and frictionless,* we observe that the only impulsive forces acting on the particles during the impact are internal forces directed along the x axis. We may therefore express that:

1. The y component of the momentum of particle A is conserved.

2. The y component of the momentum of particle B is conserved.

3. The x component of the total momentum of the system is conserved.

4. The x component of the relative velocity of the two particles after impact is obtained by multiplying the x component of their relative velocity before impact by the coefficient of restitution.

We thus obtain four independent equations which may be solved for the components of the velocities of A and B after impact. This method of solution is illustrated in Sample Prob. 14.5.

14.8. Problems Involving Energy and Momentum. We have now at our disposal three different methods for the solution of kinetics problems: the application of the fundamental equation $\Sigma\mathbf{F} = m\mathbf{a}$, the method of work and energy, and the method of impulse and momentum. To derive the maximum benefit from these three methods, we should be able to choose the method best suited for the solution of a given problem. We should also be prepared to use different methods for solving the various parts of a problem when such a procedure seems advisable.

We have already seen that the method of work and energy is in many cases more expeditious than the direct application of the equation $\Sigma\mathbf{F} = m\mathbf{a}$. As indicated in Sec. 13.4, however, the method of work and energy has limitations, and it must sometimes be supplemented by the use of $\Sigma\mathbf{F} = m\mathbf{a}$. This is the case, for example, when we wish to determine an acceleration or a normal force.

There is generally no great advantage in using the method of impulse and momentum for the solution of problems involving no impulsive forces. It will usually be found that the equation $\Sigma\mathbf{F} = m\mathbf{a}$ yields a solution just as fast and that the method of work and energy, if it applies, is more rapid and more convenient. However, the method of impulse and momentum is the only practicable method in problems of impact. A solution based on the direct application of $\Sigma\mathbf{F} = m\mathbf{a}$ would be unwieldy, and the method of work and energy cannot be used since impact (unless perfectly elastic) involves a loss of mechanical energy.

Many problems involve only conservative forces, except for a short impact phase during which impulsive forces act. The solution of such problems may be divided into several parts. While the part corresponding to the impact phase calls for the application of the method of impulse and momentum and the use of the coefficient of restitution, the other parts may usually be solved by the method of work and energy. The use of the equation $\Sigma \mathbf{F} = m\mathbf{a}$ will be necessary, however, if the problem involves the determination of a normal force.

Consider, for example, a pendulum A, of weight $\mathbf{W}_A$ and length l, which is released with no velocity from a position A_1 (Fig. 14.11*a*). The pendulum swings freely in a vertical plane and hits a second pendulum B, of weight $\mathbf{W}_B$ and same length l, which is initially at rest. Under the impact (with coefficient of restitution e), pendulum B swings through an angle θ that we wish to determine.

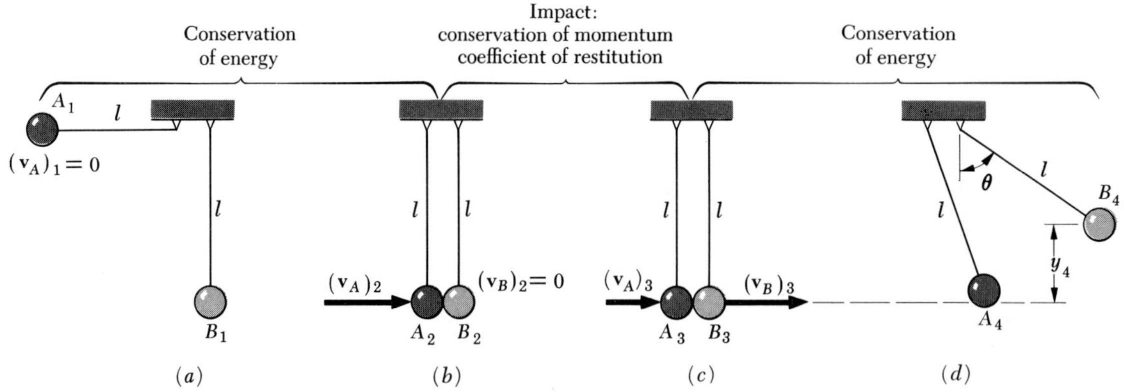

FIG. 14.11

The solution of the problem may be divided into three parts:

1. *Pendulum A Swings from A_1 to A_2.* The principle of conservation of energy may be used to determine the velocity $(\mathbf{v}_A)_2$ of the pendulum at A_2 (Fig. 14.11*b*).

2. *Pendulum A Hits Pendulum B.* Using the principle of conservation of momentum and the coefficient of restitution e, we determine the velocities $(\mathbf{v}_A)_3$ and $(\mathbf{v}_B)_3$ of the two pendulums after impact (Fig. 14.11*c*).

3. *Pendulum B Swings from B_3 to B_4.* Applying the principle of conservation of energy, we determine the maximum elevation y_4 reached by pendulum B (Fig. 14.11*d*). The angle θ may then be determined by trigonometry.

We note that the method of solution just described should be supplemented by the use of $\Sigma \mathbf{F} = m\mathbf{a}$ if the tensions in the cords holding the pendulums are to be determined.

SAMPLE PROBLEM 14.3

A 40,000-lb railroad car moving at a speed of 2 ft/sec to the right collides with a 70,000-lb car which is at rest. If after the collision the 70,000-lb car is observed to move to the right at a speed of 1.2 ft/sec, determine the coefficient of restitution between the two cars.

Solution. We consider the system consisting of the two cars and apply the principle of conservation of momentum.

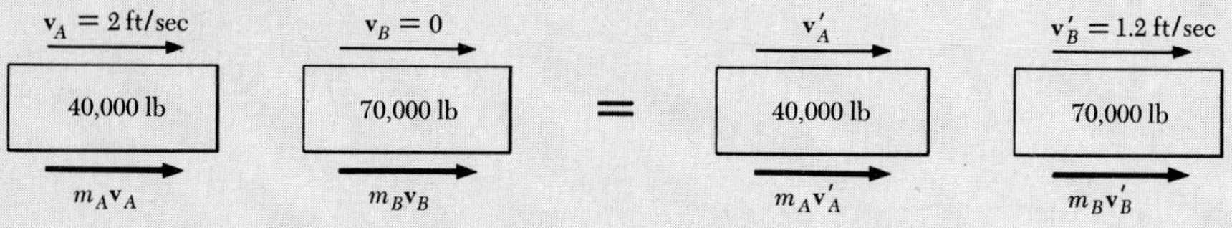

$$m_A\mathbf{v}_A + m_B\mathbf{v}_B = m_A\mathbf{v}'_A + m_B\mathbf{v}'_B$$

$$\frac{40{,}000}{32.2}(+2) + \frac{70{,}000}{32.2}(0) = \frac{40{,}000}{32.2}v'_A + \frac{70{,}000}{32.2}(+1.2)$$

$$v'_A = -0.1 \text{ ft/sec} \qquad \mathbf{v}'_A = 0.1 \text{ ft/sec} \leftarrow$$

The coefficient of restitution is obtained by writing

$$e = \frac{v'_B - v'_A}{v_A - v_B} \qquad e = \frac{+1.2 - (-0.1)}{+2.0 - 0} = \frac{1.3}{2.0} \qquad e = 0.65 \blacktriangleleft$$

SAMPLE PROBLEM 14.4

A ball is thrown against a smooth vertical wall. Immediately before the ball strikes the wall, its velocity has a magnitude v and forms an angle of 30° with the horizontal. Knowing that $e = 0.90$, determine the magnitude and direction of the velocity of the ball as it rebounds from the wall.

Solution. We resolve the initial velocity of the ball into components

$$v_x = v\cos 30° = 0.866v \qquad v_y = v \sin 30° = 0.500v$$

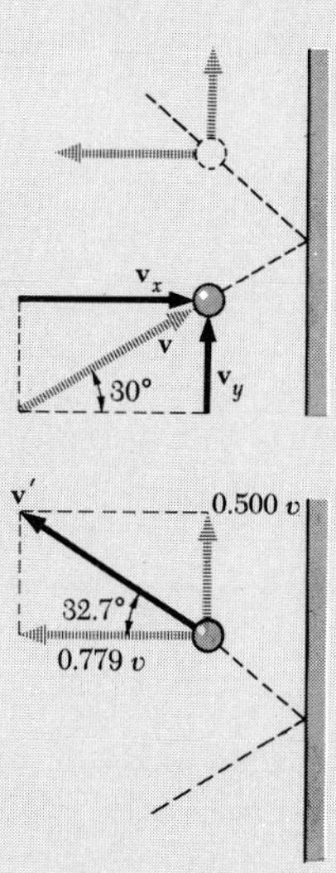

Vertical Motion. Since the wall is smooth, no vertical impulsive force acts on the ball during the time it is in contact with the wall. The vertical component of the momentum, and hence the vertical component of the velocity, of the ball is thus unchanged:

$$\mathbf{v}'_y = \mathbf{v}_y = 0.500v \uparrow$$

Horizontal Motion. Since the mass of the wall (and earth) is essentially infinite, there is no point in expressing that the momentum of the ball-wall system is conserved. Using the coefficient of restitution, we write

$$0 - v'_x = e(v_x - 0)$$
$$v'_x = -(0.90)(0.866v) = -0.779v \qquad \mathbf{v}'_x = 0.779v \leftarrow$$

Resultant Motion. Adding vectorially the components $\mathbf{v}'_x$ and $\mathbf{v}'_y$,

$$\mathbf{v}' = 0.925v \;\nwarrow\; 32.7° \blacktriangleleft$$

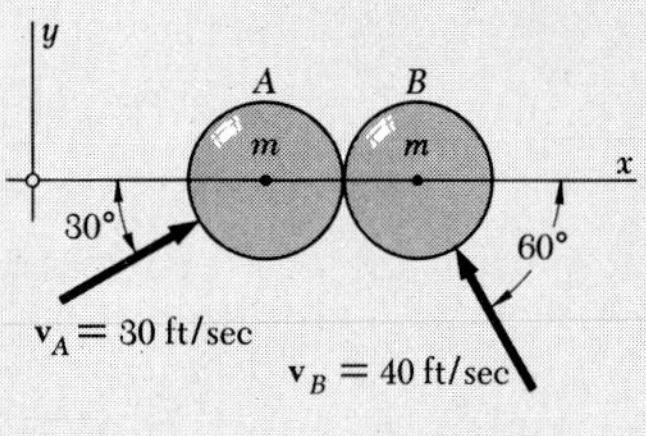

SAMPLE PROBLEM 14.5

The magnitude and direction of the velocities of two identical smooth balls before they strike each other are as shown. Assuming $e = 0.90$, determine the magnitude and direction of the velocity of each ball after the impact.

Solution. The impulsive forces acting between the balls during the impact are directed along a line joining the centers of the balls called the *line of impact*. Choosing x and y axes, respectively, parallel and perpendicular to the line of impact and directed as shown, we write:

$$(v_A)_x = v_A \cos 30^\circ = +26.0 \text{ ft/sec}$$
$$(v_A)_y = v_A \sin 30^\circ = +15.0 \text{ ft/sec}$$
$$(v_B)_x = v_B \cos 60^\circ = -20.0 \text{ ft/sec}$$
$$(v_B)_y = v_B \sin 60^\circ = +34.6 \text{ ft/sec}$$

Principle of Impulse and Momentum. In the following sketches we show in turn the initial momenta, the impulsive reactions, and the final momenta.

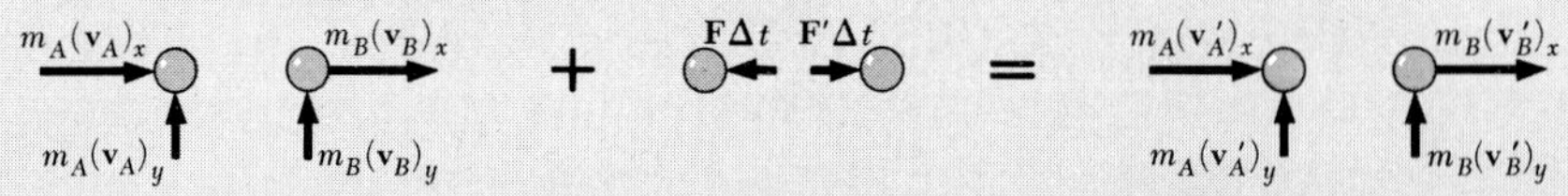

Motion Perpendicular to the Line of Impact. Considering only the y components, we apply the principle of impulse and momentum to each ball *separately*. Since no vertical impulsive force acts during the impact, the vertical component of the momentum, and hence the vertical component of the velocity, of each ball is unchanged.

$$(\mathbf{v}_A')_y = 15.0 \text{ ft/sec} \uparrow \qquad (\mathbf{v}_B')_y = 34.6 \text{ ft/sec} \uparrow$$

Motion Parallel to the Line of Impact. In the x direction, we consider the two balls as a *single* system and note that, by Newton's third law, the impulsive reactions $\mathbf{F}\,\Delta t$ and $\mathbf{F}'\,\Delta t$ cancel. Applying the principle of conservation of momentum, we write

$$m_A(v_A)_x + m_B(v_B)_x = m_A(v_A')_x + m_B(v_B')_x$$
$$m(26.0) + m(-20.0) = m(v_A')_x + m(v_B')_x \qquad (v_A')_x + (v_B')_x = 6.0 \qquad (1)$$

Using the coefficient of restitution, we write

$$(v_B')_x - (v_A')_x = e[(v_A)_x - (v_B)_x]$$
$$(v_B')_x - (v_A')_x = (0.90)[26.0 - (-20.0)] \qquad (v_B')_x - (v_A')_x = 41.4 \qquad (2)$$

Solving Eqs. (1) and (2) simultaneously, we obtain

$$(v_A')_x = -17.7 \qquad (v_B')_x = +23.7$$
$$(\mathbf{v}_A')_x = 17.7 \text{ ft/sec} \leftarrow \qquad (\mathbf{v}_B')_x = 23.7 \text{ ft/sec} \rightarrow$$

Resultant Motion. Adding vectorially the velocity components of each ball, we obtain

$$\mathbf{v}_A' = 23.2 \text{ ft/sec} \nwarrow 40.3^\circ \qquad \mathbf{v}_B' = 42.0 \text{ ft/sec} \nearrow 55.6^\circ \blacktriangleleft$$

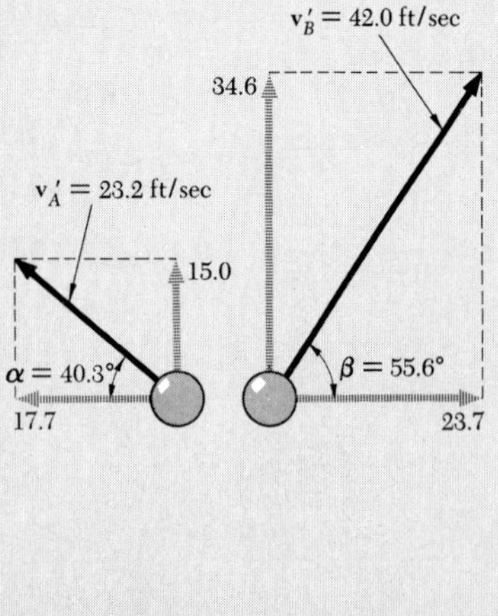

SAMPLE PROBLEM 14.6

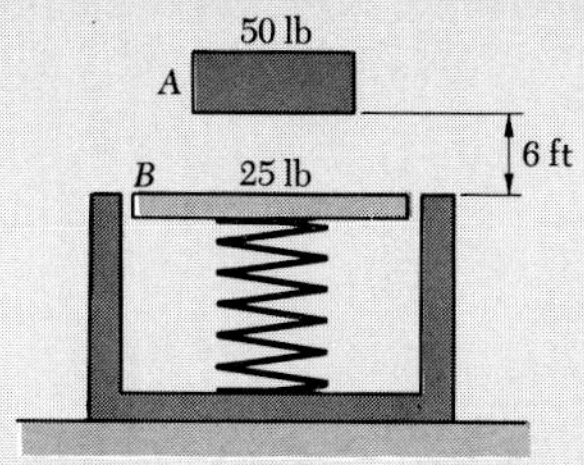

A 50-lb block is dropped from a height of 6 ft onto the 25-lb pan of a spring scale. Assuming the impact to be perfectly plastic, determine the maximum deflection of the pan. The constant of the spring is $k = 100$ lb/in.

Solution. The impact between the block and the pan *must* be treated separately; therefore we divide the solution into three parts.

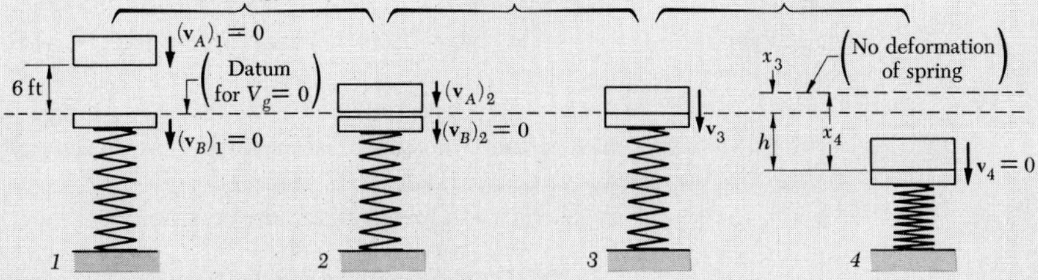

Conservation of Energy

$$T_1 = \tfrac{1}{2}m_A(v_A)_1^2 = 0 \qquad V_1 = Wy = (50 \text{ lb})(6 \text{ ft}) = 300 \text{ ft-lb}$$

$$T_2 = \tfrac{1}{2}m_A(v_A)_2^2 \qquad \frac{1}{2}\frac{50}{32.2}(v_A)_2^2 = 0.776(v_A)_2^2 \qquad V_2 = 0$$

$$T_1 + V_1 = T_2 + V_2 \qquad 0 + 300 = 0.776(v_A)_2^2 + 0$$

$$(v_A)_2 = +19.66 \text{ ft/sec} \qquad (\mathbf{v}_A)_2 = 19.66 \text{ ft/sec}\downarrow$$

Impact: Conservation of Momentum. Since the impact is perfectly plastic, $e = 0$; the block and pan move together with a velocity $\mathbf{v}_3$ after the impact.

$$m_A(v_A)_2 + m_B(v_B)_2 = (m_A + m_B)v_3$$

$$\frac{50}{32.2}(19.66) + 0 = \frac{50 + 25}{32.2}v_3$$

$$v_3 = +13.11 \text{ ft/sec} \qquad \mathbf{v}_3 = 13.11 \text{ ft/sec}\downarrow$$

Conservation of Energy. Initially the spring supports the 25-lb pan; thus the initial deflection of the spring is $x_3 = \frac{1}{4}$ in. Denoting by x_4 the total maximum deflection of the spring, we write

$$T_3 = \tfrac{1}{2}(m_A + m_B)v_3^2 = \frac{1}{2}\frac{50 + 25}{32.2}(13.11)^2 = 200 \text{ ft-lb} = 2{,}400 \text{ in.-lb}$$

$$V_3 = V_g + V_e = 0 + \tfrac{1}{2}kx_3^2 = \tfrac{1}{2}(100 \text{ lb/in.})(\tfrac{1}{4} \text{ in.})^2 = 3.12 \text{ in.-lb}$$

$$T_4 = 0$$

$$V_4 = V_g + V_e = (W_A + W_B)(-h) + \tfrac{1}{2}kx_4^2 = -75h + (\tfrac{1}{2})(100)x_4^2$$

Noting that the displacement of the pan is $h = x_4 - x_3 = x_4 - \frac{1}{4}$ in., we write

$$T_3 + V_3 = T_4 + V_4 \qquad 2{,}400 + 3.12 = 0 - 75(x_4 - \tfrac{1}{4}) + (\tfrac{1}{2})(100)x_4^2$$

$$x_4 = 7.70 \text{ in.} \qquad h = x_4 - x_3 = 7.70 \text{ in.} - 0.25 \text{ in.}$$

$$h = 7.45 \text{ in.} \blacktriangleleft$$

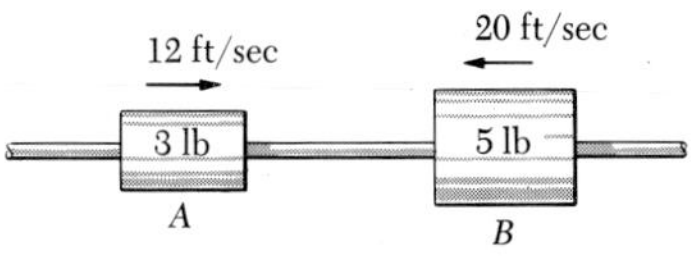

FIG. P 14.42, P 14.44, AND P 14.45

PROBLEMS

14.42. The coefficient of restitution between the two collars is known to be 0.75; determine (*a*) their velocities after impact, (*b*) the energy loss during the impact.

14.43. Solve Prob. 14.42 assuming that the velocity of collar *A* is 12 ft/sec to the left.

14.44. Knowing that $e = 0.75$, determine how much additional weight should be attached to collar *B* if its velocity after impact is to be zero.

14.45. The velocities of the two collars before impact are as shown. If after the impact the velocity of collar *B* is observed to be 2 ft/sec to the left, determine the coefficient of restitution between the two collars.

14.46. Several identical steel balls *B*, *C*, and *D* are at rest when ball *B* is struck by a ball *A* of the same weight, moving with an initial velocity $\mathbf{v}_A$. This causes a series of collisions between the various balls. Determine the final velocity of ball *D* in terms of the initial velocity $\mathbf{v}_A$ and the coefficient of restitution *e*.

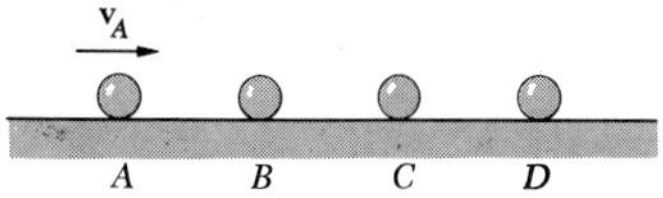

FIG. P 14.46

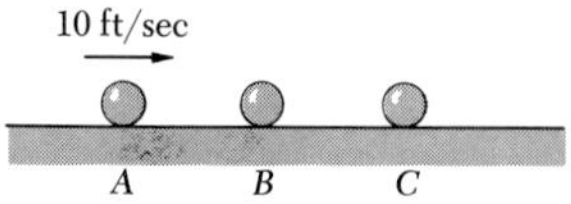

FIG. P 14.47

14.47. Two identical balls *B* and *C* are at rest when ball *B* is struck by a ball *A* of the same weight, moving with a velocity of 10 ft/sec. This causes a series of collisions between the various balls. Knowing that $e = 0.40$, determine the velocity of each ball after *all* collisions have taken place.

14.48. The official weights of various United States coins are: silver dollar, 412.5 grains; half dollar, 192.9 grains; quarter dollar, 96.45 grains; dime, 38.58 grains. Determine the velocity imparted to a quarter dollar which is at rest on a smooth surface when it is struck squarely by each of the following coins moving with a velocity $\mathbf{v}_1$: (*a*) a silver dollar, (*b*) a half dollar, (*c*) a dime. Assume the impact to be perfectly elastic.

14.49. A dime which is at rest on a *rough* surface is struck squarely by a half dollar moving to the right. After the impact, each coin slides and comes to rest; the dime slides 22.6 in. to the right, and the half dollar slides 4.2 in. to the right. Assuming the coefficient of friction is the same for each coin, determine the value of the coefficient of restitution between the coins. (See Prob. 14.48 for the weight of United States coins.)

14.50. Two identical billiard balls A and B of radius r may move freely on a horizontal table. If B is at rest and A has an initial velocity of components $v_x = v$ and $v_y = 0$, determine the distance a so that the y component of the velocity of B after impact is maximum. Also determine the corresponding resultant velocity of B and the direction in which B will move. Assume $e = 1$.

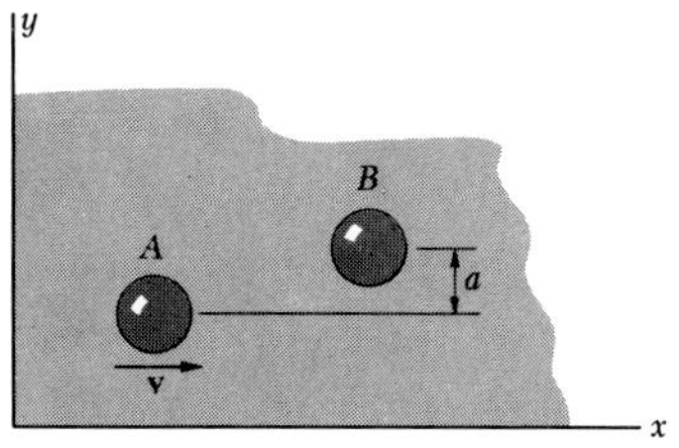

FIG. P 14.50 AND P 14.51

14.51. Ball B weighs 2 lb and is initially at rest. Ball A weighs 4 lb and has an initial velocity of 8 ft/sec to the right. It is desired to have ball B, after the impact, move to the right in a direction forming an angle of 30° with the x axis. (*a*) Knowing that the diameter of each ball is 2 in., determine the required distance a. (*b*) Assuming $e = 0.80$, determine the final velocity of each ball.

14.52. In Sample Prob. 14.5, determine the required value of the coefficient of restitution if the angles α and β between the horizontal and the respective directions of the final velocities are to be equal.

***14.53.** Three identical balls A, B, and C may roll freely on a horizontal surface. Balls B and C are at rest and in contact when struck by ball A, which was moving to the right with a velocity $\mathbf{v}_A$. Determine the final velocity of each ball assuming (*a*) that the path of A is perfectly centered and that A strikes B and C simultaneously, (*b*) that the path of A is not perfectly centered and that A strikes B slightly before it strikes C. Assume perfectly elastic impact and conservation of energy.

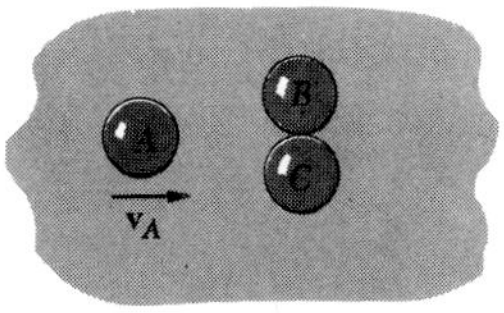

FIG. P 14.53

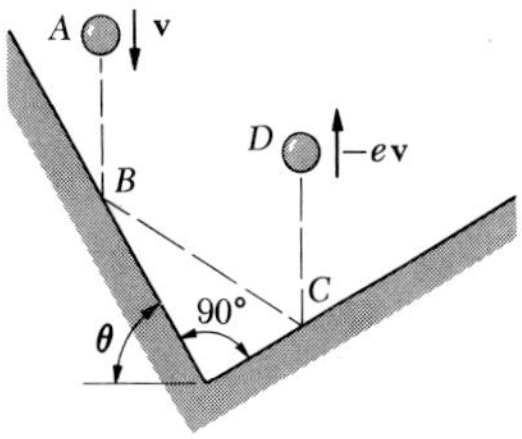

FIG. P 14.54

14.54. A steel ball strikes a 90° corner at B, is deflected, and again strikes the corner at C. The coefficient of restitution is denoted by e. If the ball strikes B with a velocity of magnitude v, show (*a*) that the magnitude of its final velocity after striking C is ev and (*b*) that the initial and final paths AB and CD are parallel. Assume that v is large and that the short intermediate path BC is a straight line.

14.55. In Prob. 14.54, derive an expression for θ, knowing that path BC is to be perpendicular to paths AB and CD.

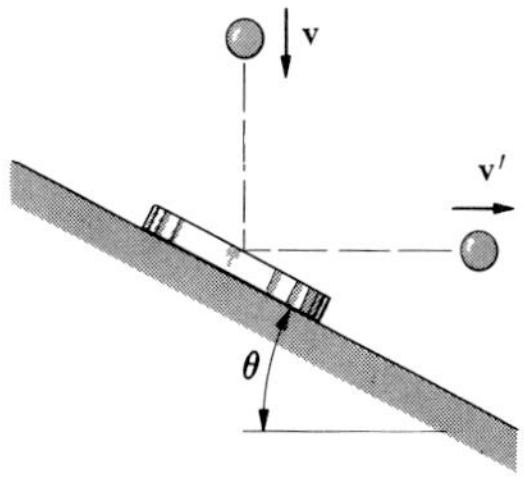

FIG. P 14.56

14.56. A steel ball falling vertically strikes a rigid plate and rebounds horizontally as shown. Denoting by e the coefficient of restitution, determine (*a*) the required angle θ, (*b*) the magnitude of the velocity $\mathbf{v}'$.

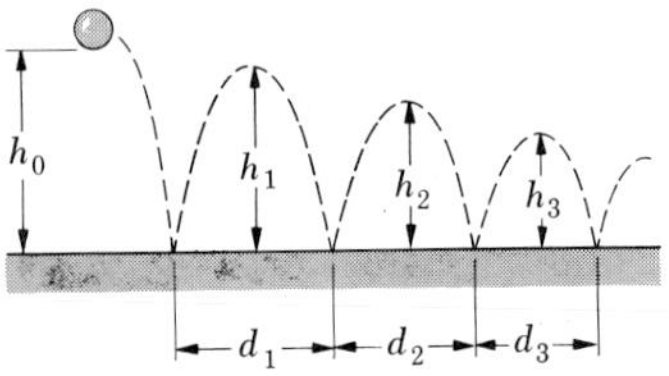

FIG. P 14.57, P 14.58, AND P 14.59

14.57. A ball is dropped from a height $h_0 = 36$ in. onto a smooth floor. Knowing that the height of the first bounce is $h_1 = 32$ in., determine (*a*) the coefficient of restitution, (*b*) the expected height h_2 of the second bounce.

14.58. A ball is dropped onto a smooth floor and bounces as shown. The lengths of the first two bounces are measured and found to be $d_1 = 14.5$ in. and $d_2 = 13.7$ in. Determine (*a*) the coefficient of restitution, (*b*) the expected length d_3 of the third bounce.

14.59. A ball is dropped onto a smooth floor and allowed to bounce several times as shown. Derive an expression for the coefficient of restitution in terms of (*a*) the height of two successive bounces h_n and h_{n+1}, (*b*) the length of two successive bounces d_n and d_{n+1}, (*c*) the duration of two successive bounces t_n and t_{n+1}.

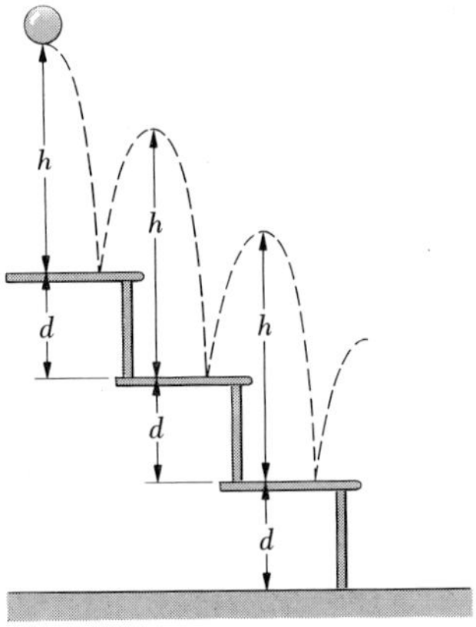

FIG. P 14.60

14.60. A ball is dropped from a height h above the landing and bounces down a flight of stairs. Determine the value of h for which the ball will bounce to the same height above each step.

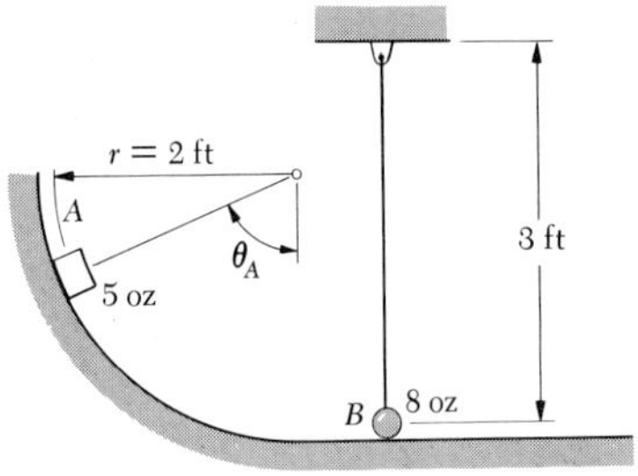

FIG. P 14.61

14.61. Block *A* is released when $\theta_A = 90°$ and slides without friction until it strikes ball *B*. Knowing that $e = 0.90$, determine (*a*) the velocity of *B* immediately after impact, (*b*) the maximum tension in the cord holding *B*, (*c*) the maximum height to which ball *B* will rise.

14.62. What should be the value of the angle θ_A in Prob. 14.61 if the maximum angle between the cord holding ball *B* and the vertical is to be 45°?

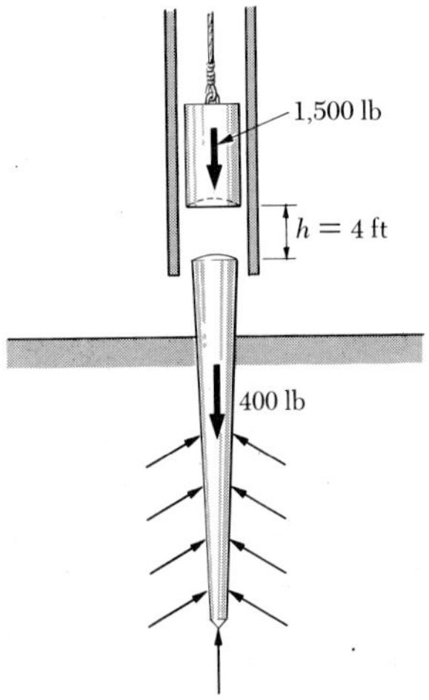

FIG. P 14.63 AND P 14.64

14.63. The 1,500-lb hammer of a drop-hammer pile driver falls from a height of 4 ft onto the top of a 400-lb pile. The pile is driven 8 in. into the ground. Assuming perfectly plastic impact, determine the average resistance of the ground to penetration.

14.64. If the average resistance of the ground to the penetration of a 400-lb pile is 2 tons, determine the height h of drop required by a 1,500-lb hammer to drive the pile 9 in. into the ground. Assume that the impact is perfectly plastic.

14.65. A $\frac{3}{4}$-oz bullet is fired with a velocity of 1,800 ft/sec into a 10-lb block. Knowing that the coefficient of friction between the block and the floor is 0.30, determine (*a*) through what distance the block will slide, (*b*) the percentage of the initial kinetic energy lost in friction between the block and the floor.

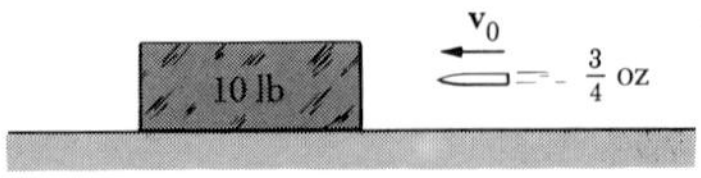

FIG. P 14.65

14.66. Cylinder A is dropped 8 ft onto cylinder B, which is resting on a spring of constant $k = 10$ lb/in. Assuming a perfectly plastic impact, determine (a) the maximum deflection of cylinder B, (b) the energy loss during the impact.

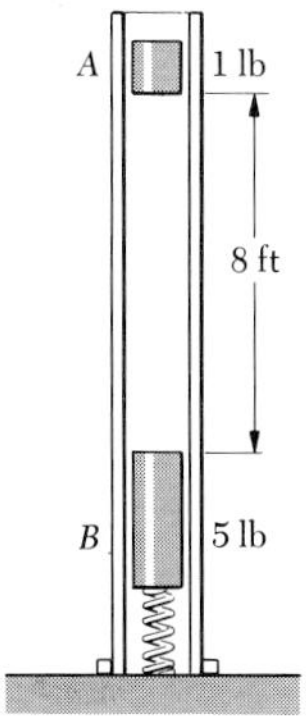

FIG. P 14.66

14.67. Collars A and B of weight $W_A = 2$ lb and $W_B = 3$ lb, respectively, may slide without friction on the horizontal rod shown. Collar A is released from rest when spring C is compressed 6 in.; it slides and strikes collar B. Assuming $e = 0.80$, determine the maximum deflection of spring D.

14.68. Block A is released when spring C is compressed a distance δ; it slides without friction and strikes collar B. The coefficient of restitution between the collars is denoted by e. What should be the weight of collar A if the velocity of collar B immediately after impact is to be as large as possible?

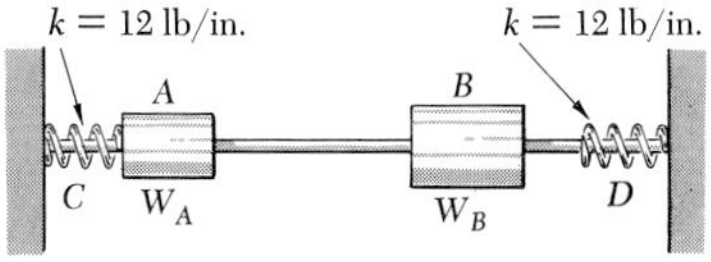

FIG. P 14.67 AND P 14.68

14.69. Three steel rods of uniform cross section may slide without friction on a horizontal surface. Rods B and C are at rest when B is struck by rod A, which was moving with a velocity $\mathbf{v}_0$. (a) Denoting by e the coefficient of restitution of the rods, determine the length x of rod B for which we obtain the maximum velocity of rod C after it has been struck by B for the first time. (b) Using the value of x found in part a, determine the kinetic energy of C after impact as a fraction of the initial kinetic energy of A.

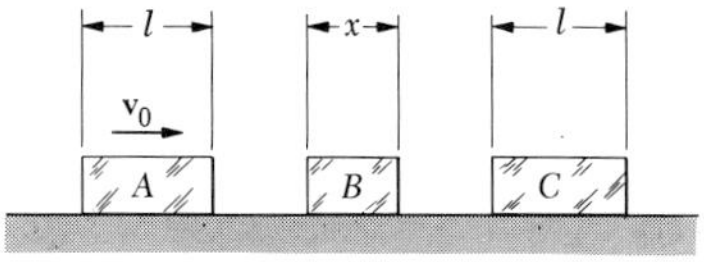

FIG. 14.69

***14.70.** Determine the energy absorbed by the chain of Prob. 14.40 under each condition of support. Assume perfectly plastic impact.

***14.71.** Determine the energy absorbed by the machine part of Prob. 14.41 under each condition of support. Assume perfectly plastic impact.

***14.72.** A small rivet connecting two pieces of sheet metal is being clinched by hammering. Determine the energy absorbed by the rivet under each blow, knowing that the head of the hammer weighs 1 lb and that it strikes the rivet with a velocity of 16 ft/sec. Assume that the anvil is supported by springs and (a) is infinite in weight (rigid support), (b) weighs 10 lb.

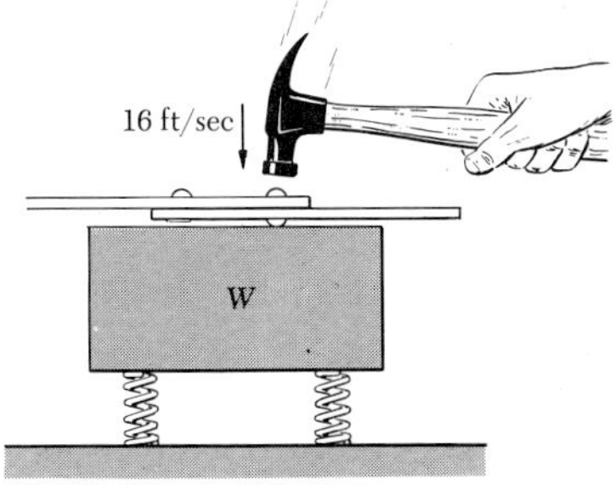

FIG. P 14.72

***14.73.** In Prob. 14.72, determine the weight of the hammer required to deliver to the rivet an amount of energy equal to 5-ft-lb per blow if the hammer strikes the rivet with a velocity of 16 ft/sec. Consider both types of support.

***14.74.** In Prob. 14.66, determine the maximum deflection of cylinder B and the height to which cylinder A will rebound, assuming that $e = 0.75$ between the two cylinders.

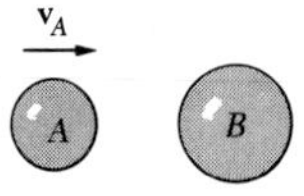

FIG. P 14.75

*14.75. A mass m_A moving to the right with a velocity $\mathbf{v}_A$ strikes a second mass m_B which is at rest. Derive an expression for the kinetic-energy loss during the impact of the two masses. Assume that the balls strike each other squarely, and denote the coefficient of restitution by e.

14.9. Angular Momentum. Consider a particle of mass m moving in the xy plane. As we saw in Sec. 14.1, the momentum of the particle at a given instant is defined as the vector $m\mathbf{v}$ obtained by multiplying the velocity $\mathbf{v}$ of the particle by its mass m. The moment about O of the vector $m\mathbf{v}$ is called the *moment of momentum*, or the *angular momentum*, of the particle about O at that instant and is denoted by h_O. Resolving the vector $m\mathbf{v}$ into its x and y components (Fig. 14.12*a*), and recalling that counterclockwise is positive, we write

$$h_O = x(mv_y) - y(mv_x)$$
$$h_O = m(xv_y - yv_x) \qquad (14.24)$$

We shall now compute the derivative of the angular momentum h_O with respect to t; we have

$$\frac{dh_O}{dt} = m\frac{d}{dt}(xv_y - yv_x)$$
$$= m\left(\frac{dx}{dt}v_y + x\frac{dv_y}{dt} - \frac{dy}{dt}v_x - y\frac{dv_x}{dt}\right)$$

or, since $dx/dt = v_x$ and $dy/dt = v_y$,

$$\frac{dh_O}{dt} = m\left(x\frac{dv_y}{dt} - y\frac{dv_x}{dt}\right) \qquad (14.25)$$

But, according to Newton's second law, we have

$$m\frac{dv_x}{dt} = F_x \qquad m\frac{dv_y}{dt} = F_y$$

where F_x and F_y are the rectangular components of the force $\mathbf{F}$ acting on the particle. Equation (14.25) may therefore be written in the form

$$\frac{dh_O}{dt} = xF_y - yF_x$$

or, since the right-hand member of the equation obtained represents the moment M_O of $\mathbf{F}$ about O (Fig. 14.12*b*),

$$M_O = \frac{dh_O}{dt} \qquad (14.26)$$

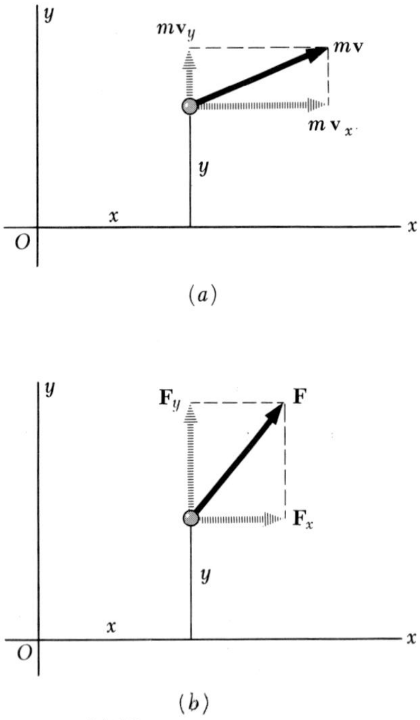

FIG. 14.12

Equation (14.26) expresses that *the moment about O of the force* **F** *acting on the particle is equal to the rate of change of the moment of momentum, or angular momentum, of the particle about O.*

In the case of a system of particles, the moment of momentum, or angular momentum, of the system of particles about O is defined as the sum of the moments about O of the momenta of the various particles of the system; we write

$$h_O = \Sigma m(xv_y - yv_x) \tag{14.27}$$

Since Eq. (14.26) is verified for each particle, we may write that the sum of the moments of all the forces acting on the various particles of the system is equal to the rate of change of the angular momentum of the system. However, since the internal forces occur by pairs of equal and opposite forces having the same line of action, the sum of their moments is zero and we need consider only the sum of the moments of the external forces. We thus write

$$\Sigma(M_O)_{\text{ext}} = \frac{dh_O}{dt} \tag{14.28}$$

where h_O is the angular momentum of the system defined by the relation (14.27).

14.10. Generalized Principle of Impulse and Momentum. We saw in Sec. 14.1 that the linear impulse of a force **F**, of components F_x and F_y, during a given time interval may be defined by the integrals of F_x and F_y over that time interval. We shall now, in a similar way, define the *angular impulse* of a couple **M** over a time interval from t_1 to t_2 as the integral

$$\int_{t_1}^{t_2} M dt$$

of the moment M of the couple over the given time interval. This new concept, as we shall see presently, will enable us to express in a more general form the principle of impulse and momentum for a system of particles.

Consider a system of particles and the *external forces* acting on the various particles. Each external force **F** may be replaced by an equal force **F** attached at the origin O, plus a couple $\mathbf{M}_O$ of moment equal to the moment about O of the original force (Chap. 3). Now we shall draw three separate sketches (Fig. 14.13). The first and third sketches will show the systems of vectors representing the momenta of the various particles at a time t_1 and a time t_2, respectively. The second sketch will show the resultant of the vectors representing the

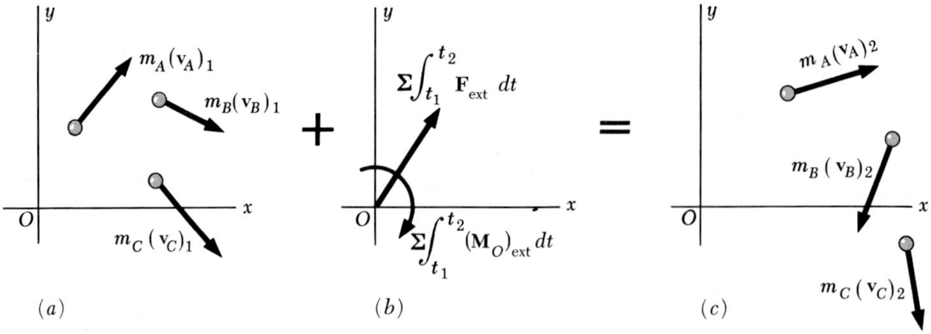

FIG. 14.13

linear impulses of the external forces **F** during the given time interval, as well as the sum of the couples representing the angular impulses of the couples $\mathbf{M}_O$ during the same time interval. We recall from Sec. 14.2 that the sums of the x and y components of the vectors shown in parts a and b of Fig. 14.13 must be respectively equal to the sums of the x and y components of the vectors in part c of the same figure. Indeed, rewriting Eq. (14.8) in terms of x and y components, we have

$$\Sigma m(v_x)_1 + \Sigma \int_{t_1}^{t_2} (F_x)_{ext}\,dt = \Sigma m(v_x)_2$$
$$\Sigma m(v_y)_1 + \Sigma \int_{t_1}^{t_2} (F_y)_{ext}\,dt = \Sigma m(v_y)_2 \qquad (14.29)$$

Returning now to Eq. (14.28), which was derived in the preceding section, and integrating both members over the time interval from t_1 to t_2, we write

$$(h_O)_1 + \Sigma \int_{t_1}^{t_2} (M_O)_{ext}\,dt = (h_O)_2 \qquad (14.30)$$

The equation obtained expresses that the sum of the moments about O of the vectors shown in parts a and b of Fig. 14.13 must be equal to the sum of the moments about O of the vectors shown in part c of the same figure. Together, Eqs. (14.29) and (14.30) express therefore that the vectors shown in parts a and b of the figure and the vectors shown in part c form *two equivalent vector systems*, from the point of view of their moments about any given point, as well as from the point of view of their x and y components. We write

Syst Momenta$_1$ + Syst Ext Imp$_{1\to2}$ = Syst Momenta$_2$ (14.31)

This more general statement of the principle of impulse and momentum for a system of particles will prove particularly useful for the study of the motion of rigid bodies (Chap. 18).

14.11. Conservation of Angular Momentum. We saw in Sec. 14.9 that the rate of change of the angular momentum of a particle about a point O is equal to the moment M_O about O of the force **F** acting on the particle. If M_O is zero for every value of t, Eq. (14.26) yields

$$\frac{dh_O}{dt} = 0$$

for any t or, integrating with respect to t,

$$h_O = \text{constant} \tag{14.32}$$

Thus, if the moment about O of the force $\mathbf{F}$ acting on a particle is zero for every value of t, *the angular momentum of the particle about O is conserved.*

Clearly, the angular momentum of a particle about a fixed point O will be conserved if the resultant of the forces acting on the particle is zero. But the angular momentum of the particle about O will also be conserved when the particle is acted upon by an unbalanced force $\mathbf{F}$ *if the force* $\mathbf{F}$ *is a central force whose line of action passes through O* (Fig. 14.14).

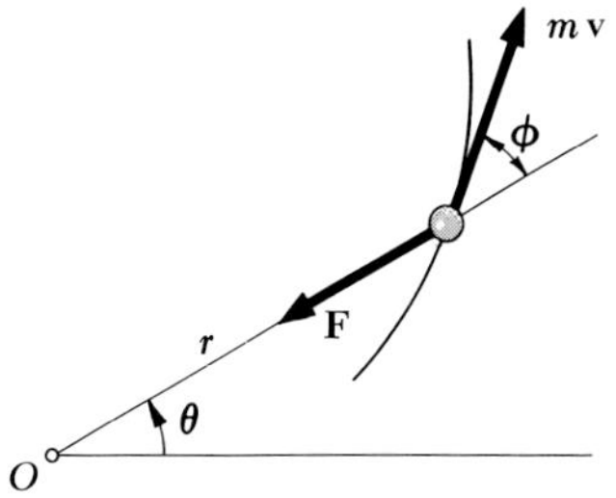

FIG. 14.14

The angular momentum h_O of a particle was expressed in (14.24) in terms of the rectangular coordinates of the particle and of the rectangular components of its momentum. In the case of a particle moving under a central force $\mathbf{F}$, it is found more convenient to use polar coordinates. Recalling that h_O is, by definition, the moment about O of the momentum $m\mathbf{v}$ of the particle, and denoting by ϕ the angle formed by the radius vector and the tangent to the path of the particle, we write Eq. (14.32) in the form

$$h_O = r(mv \sin \phi) = \text{constant} \tag{14.33}$$

Observing that $v \sin \phi$ represents the transverse component v_θ of the velocity, which is equal to $r d\theta/dt$ (Sec. 11.13), we may also write

$$h_O = mr^2 \frac{d\theta}{dt} = \text{constant} \tag{14.34}$$

Comparing Eq. (14.34) and Eq. (12.15), we note that, when a particle moves under a central force, its angular momentum h_O about the center of force O is equal to the product of its mass and of the constant h introduced in Sec. 12.9. It follows that the angular momentum of the particle is equal to twice the product of its mass and of its areal velocity; thus, stating that the areal velocity of the particle is constant is equivalent to stating that its angular momentum is conserved.

14.12. Application to Space Mechanics. The principles of conservation of energy and of conservation of angular momentum may be used to solve many problems concerning the motion of earth satellites and other space vehicles.

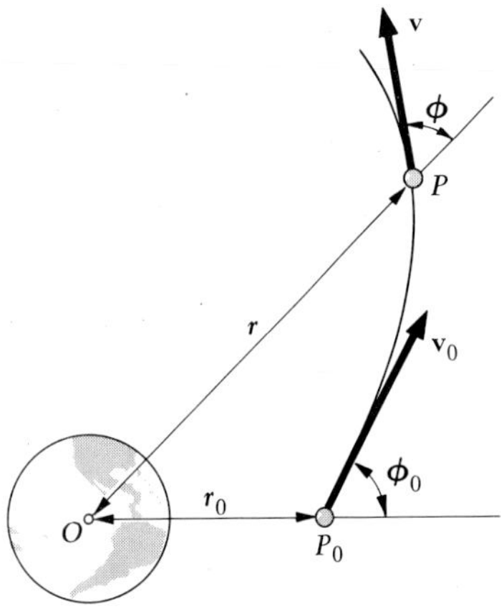

FIG. 14.15

Consider a space vehicle which begins its free flight at point P_0, at a distance r_0 from the center of the earth, with a velocity $\mathbf{v}_0$ forming an angle ϕ_0 with the radius vector OP_0 (Fig. 14.15). Let P be a point of the trajectory described by the vehicle; we denote by r the distance from O to P, by $\mathbf{v}$ the velocity of the vehicle at P, and by ϕ the angle formed by $\mathbf{v}$ and the radius vector OP.

Recalling from Sec. 13.6 that the potential energy due to the force of gravity is

$$V = -\frac{GMm}{r}$$

where M is the mass of the earth, we apply the principle of conservation of energy between P_0 and P and write

$$T_0 + V_0 = T + V$$

$$\tfrac{1}{2}mv_0^2 - \frac{GMm}{r_0} = \tfrac{1}{2}mv^2 - \frac{GMm}{r} \qquad (14.35)$$

Since the force of gravity acting on the space vehicle is directed toward the center O of the earth, the angular momentum of the vehicle about O is conserved. Using the expression (14.33), we write

$$r_0mv_0 \sin \phi_0 = rmv \sin \phi \qquad (14.36)$$

Equation (14.35) may be solved for the magnitude v of the velocity of the vehicle at P when the distance r from O to P is known; Eq. (14.36) may then be used to determine the angle ϕ that the velocity forms with the radius vector OP.

Equations (14.35) and (14.36) may also be used to determine the maximum and minimum values of r in the case of a satellite launched from P_0 in a direction forming an angle ϕ_0 with the vertical OP_0 (Fig. 14.16). The desired values of r are obtained by making $\phi = 90°$ in (14.36) and eliminating v between Eqs. (14.35) and (14.36).

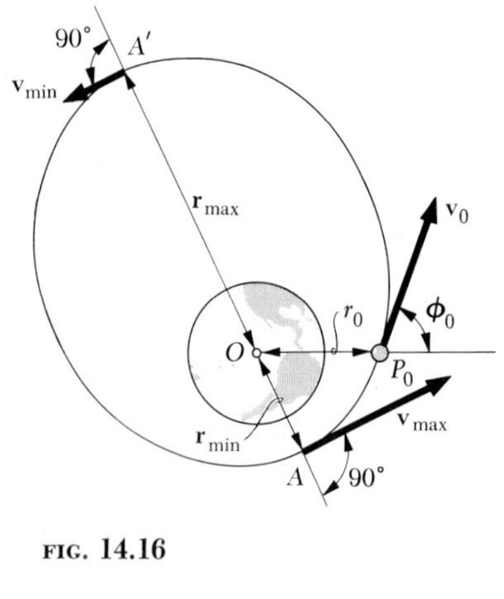

FIG. 14.16

It should be noted that the application of the principles of conservation of energy and of conservation of angular momentum leads to a more fundamental formulation of the problems of space mechanics than the method indicated in Sec. 12.11. In all cases involving oblique launchings, it will also result in much simpler computations. And while the method of Sec. 12.11 must be used when the actual trajectory or the periodic time of a space vehicle is to be determined, the calculations will be simplified if the conservation principles are first used to compute the maximum and minimum values of the radius vector r.

SAMPLE PROBLEM 14.7

A 2-lb block P rests on a smooth horizontal table at a distance of 1 ft from a fixed pin O. The block is attached to pin O by an elastic cord of constant $k = 2$ lb/in. and of undeformed length 2 ft. If the block is set in motion to the right as shown, determine (*a*) the speed v_1 for which the distance from O to the block P will reach a maximum value of 3 ft, (*b*) the speed v_2 when $OP = 3$ ft, (*c*) the radius of curvature of the path of the block when $OP = 3$ ft.

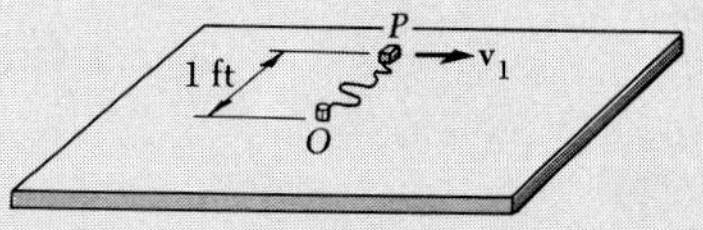

Principle of Impulse and Momentum. We note that the force **T** exerted on P by the cord passes through the fixed point O and that the velocity $\mathbf{v}_2$ is perpendicular to OP when OP has reached its maximum value of 3 ft.

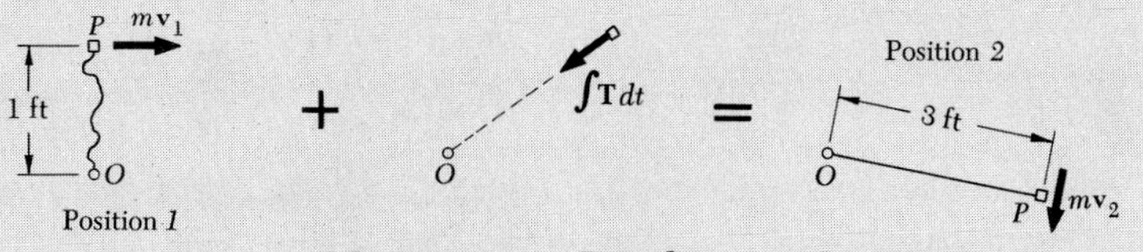

$$\textbf{Momentum}_1 + \textbf{Impulse}_{1\to 2} = \textbf{Momentum}_2$$

$+\circlearrowright$ moments about O: $\quad -(mv_1)(1 \text{ ft}) + 0 = -(mv_2)(3 \text{ ft})$

$$v_1 = 3v_2 \qquad (1)$$

Conservation of Energy. *Kinetic Energy*

$$T_1 = \tfrac{1}{2}mv_1^2 = \frac{1}{2}\frac{W}{g}v_1^2 = \frac{1}{2}\frac{2}{g}v_1^2 \qquad T_2 = \frac{1}{2}\frac{2}{g}v_2^2$$

Potential Energy. Since the cord is unstretched in position *1*, $V_1 = 0$. In position 2 the elongation of the cord is $x = 3 \text{ ft} - 2 \text{ ft} = 1$ ft. Recalling that $k = 2$ lb/in. $= 24$ lb/ft, we have

$$V_2 = \tfrac{1}{2}kx^2 = \tfrac{1}{2}(24 \text{ lb/ft})(1 \text{ ft})^2 = 12 \text{ ft-lb}$$

Applying the principle of conservation of energy, we write

$$T_1 + V_1 = T_2 + V_2 \qquad \frac{1}{2}\frac{2}{g}v_1^2 + 0 = \frac{1}{2}\frac{2}{g}v_2^2 + 12 \qquad (2)$$

Substituting $v_1 = 3v_2$ from (1) into (2), we find

$$\frac{(3v_2)^2}{g} = \frac{v_2^2}{g} + 12 \qquad v_2^2 = \frac{12g}{8} = 48.3 \qquad v_2 = 6.95 \text{ ft/sec} \blacktriangleleft$$

$$v_1 = 3v_2 = 3(6.95) \qquad v_1 = 20.85 \text{ ft/sec} \blacktriangleleft$$

Radius of Curvature. When the block is 3 ft from O, we have $v_2 = 6.95$ ft/sec and the tension in the cord is

$$T = kx = (24 \text{ lb/ft})(1 \text{ ft}) = 24 \text{ lb}$$

Since the acceleration of the block is directed toward O, we write

$$\mathbf{F} = m\mathbf{a}_n: \qquad T = \frac{W}{g}\frac{v_2^2}{\rho} \qquad 24 = \frac{2}{g}\frac{(48.3)}{\rho}$$

$$\rho = 0.1250 \text{ ft} = 1.500 \text{ in.} \blacktriangleleft$$

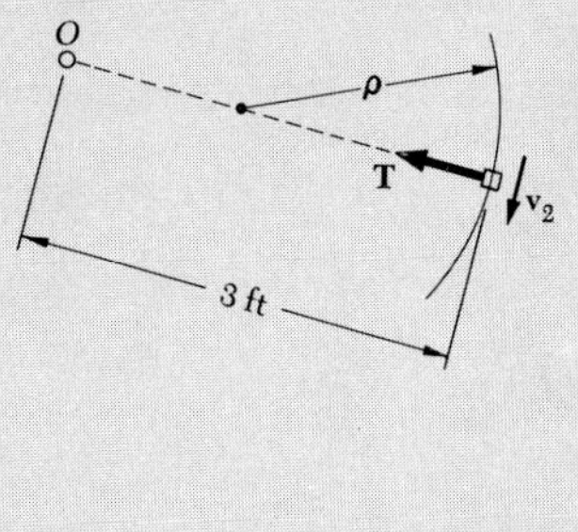

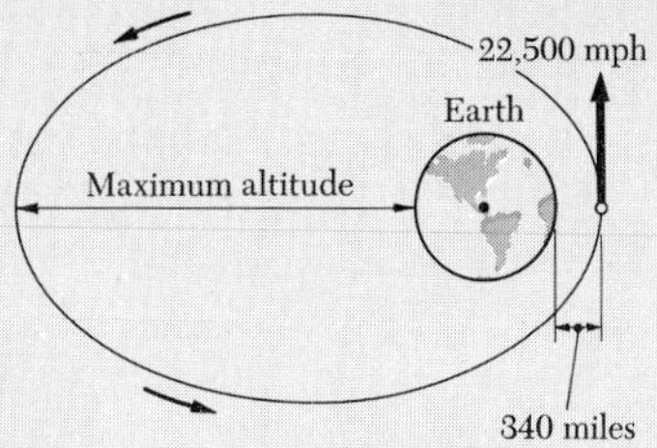

SAMPLE PROBLEM 14.8

A satellite is launched in a direction parallel to the surface of the earth with a velocity of 22,500 mph from an altitude of 340 miles. Determine (*a*) the maximum altitude reached by the satellite, (*b*) the maximum allowable error in the direction of launching if the satellite is to go into orbit and to come not closer than 140 miles to the surface of the earth.

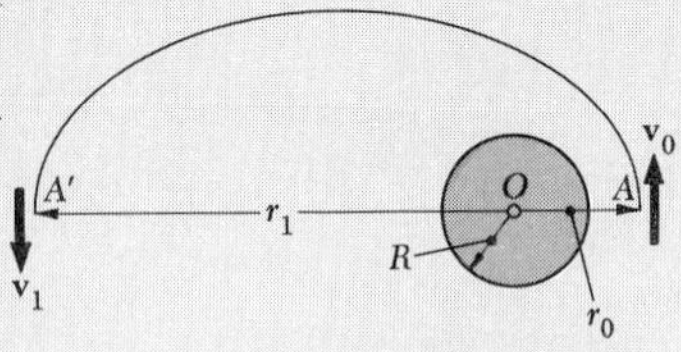

a. **Maximum Altitude.** We denote by A' the point of the orbit farthest from the earth and by r_1 the corresponding distance from the center of the earth. Since the satellite is in free flight between A and A', we apply the principle of conservation of energy.

$$T_A + V_A = T_{A'} + V_{A'}$$

$$\tfrac{1}{2}mv_0^2 - \frac{GMm}{r_0} = \tfrac{1}{2}mv_1^2 - \frac{GMm}{r_1} \qquad (1)$$

Since the only force acting on the satellite is the force of gravity, which is a central force, the angular momentum of the satellite about O is conserved. Considering points A and A', we write

$$mr_0v_0 = mr_1v_1 \qquad v_1 = v_0\frac{r_0}{r_1} \qquad (2)$$

Substituting this expression for v_1 into Eq. (1) and dividing each term by the mass m, we obtain, after rearranging the terms,

$$\tfrac{1}{2}v_0^2\left(1 - \frac{r_0^2}{r_1^2}\right) = \frac{GM}{r_0}\left(1 - \frac{r_0}{r_1}\right) \qquad 1 + \frac{r_0}{r_1} = \frac{2GM}{r_0v_0^2} \qquad (3)$$

Recalling that the radius R of the earth is 3,960 miles, we compute

$$r_0 = 3{,}960 + 340 = 4{,}300 \text{ miles} = 22.7 \times 10^6 \text{ ft}$$
$$v_0 = 22{,}500 \text{ mph} = 33{,}000 \text{ ft/sec}$$
$$GM = gR^2 = (32.2)(3{,}960 \times 5{,}280)^2 = 1.408 \times 10^{16}$$

Substituting these values into (3), we obtain $r_1 = 30{,}940$ miles.

Maximum altitude = 30,940 − 3,960 = 26,980 miles ◄

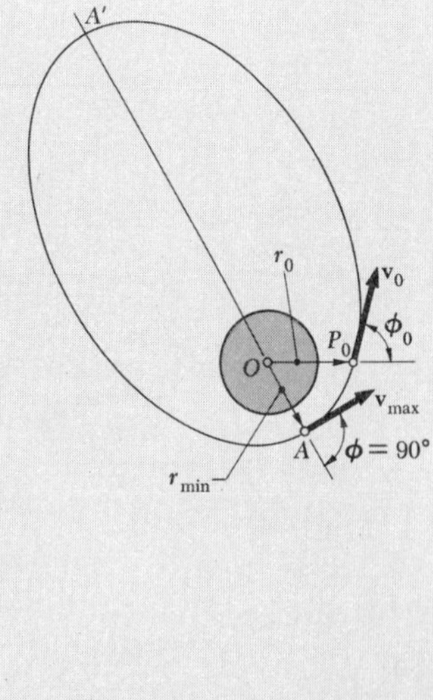

b. **Allowable Error in Direction of Launching.** The satellite is launched from P_0 in a direction forming an angle ϕ_0 with the vertical OP_0. The value of ϕ_0 corresponding to $r_{min} = 3{,}960 + 140 = 4{,}100$ miles is obtained by applying the principles of conservation of energy and of conservation of momentum between P_0 and the perigee A.

$$\tfrac{1}{2}mv_0^2 - \frac{GMm}{r_0} = \tfrac{1}{2}mv_{max}^2 - \frac{GMm}{r_{min}} \qquad (4)$$

$$mr_0v_0 \sin\phi_0 = mr_{min}v_{max} \qquad (5)$$

Solving (5) for v_{max} and then substituting for v_{max} into (4), we may solve (4) for $\sin\phi_0$. Using the values of v_0 and GM computed in part *a* and noting that $r_0/r_{min} = 4{,}300/4{,}100 = 1.0488$, we find

$$\sin\phi_0 = 0.9796 \qquad \phi_0 = 90° \pm 11.6°$$

Allowable error = ±11.6° ◄

PROBLEMS

14.76. A heavy ball is mounted on a horizontal rod which rotates freely about a vertical shaft. In the position shown, the speed of the ball is $v_1 = 50$ in./sec and the ball is held by a cord attached to the shaft. The cord is suddenly cut and the ball moves to position A' as the rod rotates. Neglecting the mass of the rod, determine (*a*) the speed of the ball in position A', (*b*) the change in the kinetic energy of the system, (*c*) the path (on the xz plane) of the ball as it moves from A to A'.

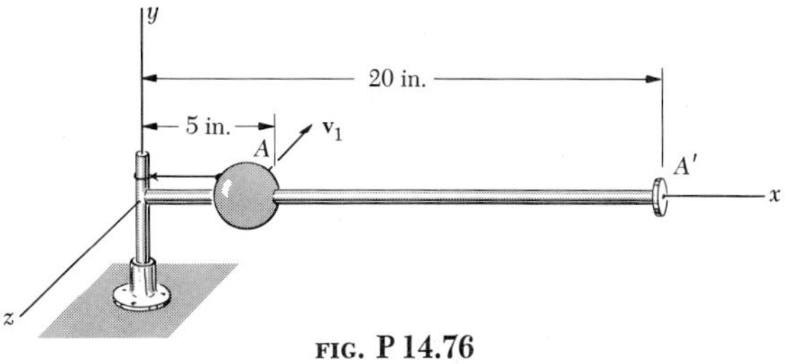

FIG. P 14.76

14.77. A particle is set in motion in a hemispherical cup by projecting it horizontally along the inside of the rim with an arbitrary initial velocity $\mathbf{v}_0$. If the particle slides without friction, show that its path will never pass through the base of the cup.

14.78. A ball of mass m slides on a smooth horizontal table at the end of a string which passes through a small hole in the table at O. When the length of string above the table is r_1, the speed of the ball is v_1. If the string is drawn in until the length of string above the table is $r_2 = \frac{1}{2}r_1$, determine (*a*) the speed v_2, (*b*) the per cent change in the magnitude of the linear momentum of the ball, (*c*) the per cent change in the angular momentum of the ball with respect to O, (*d*) the per cent change in the kinetic energy of the ball.

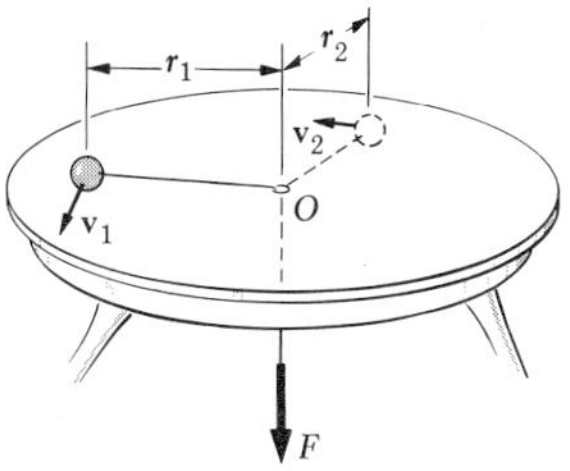

FIG. P 14.78

14.79. Solve Prob. 14.78 assuming that the string wraps around a rod at O of very small diameter instead of being drawn through a hole at O. (*Hint.* No work is done by the forces acting on the system.)

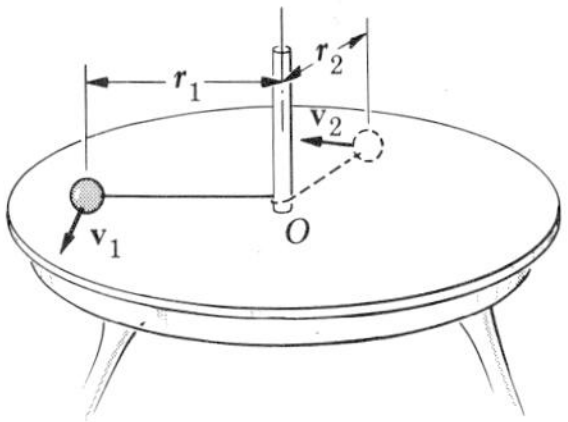

FIG. P 14.79

14.80. A $\frac{1}{2}$-lb ball is attached to a fixed point O by means of an elastic cord of constant $k = 10$ lb/ft and of undeformed length 2 ft. The ball slides on a smooth horizontal surface. When the ball is in position *1*, the length of the cord is 3 ft and the velocity of the ball is 10 ft/sec, directed as shown. Determine (*a*) the speed of the ball after the cord has become slack, (*b*) the distance d when the ball is closest to point O.

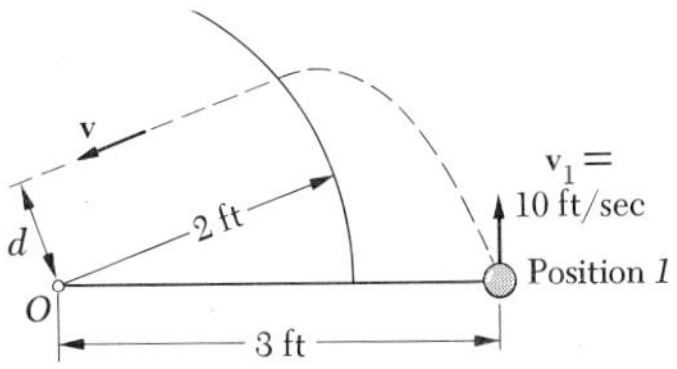

FIG. P 14.80

14.81. In Prob. 14.80, determine the required magnitude of $\mathbf{v}_1$ if the ball is to pass at a distance $d = 4$ in. from point O. The direction of $\mathbf{v}_1$ is not changed.

14.82. In Prob. 14.80, determine the smallest magnitude of $\mathbf{v}_1$ for which the elastic cord will remain taut at all times.

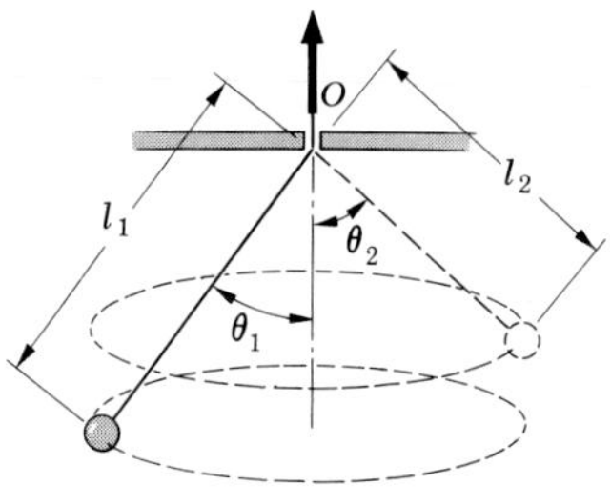

FIG. P 14.83

14.83. A small ball swings in a horizontal circle at the end of a cord of length l_1 which forms an angle θ_1 with the vertical. If the cord is slowly drawn through the support at O until the free length is l_2, derive a relation between l_1, l_2, θ_1, and θ_2.

14.84. The ball of Prob. 14.83 is set in motion so that, initially, $l_1 = 20$ in. and $\theta_1 = 30°$. Determine the length l_2 for which $\theta_2 = 60°$.

14.85. The ball of Prob. 14.83 is set in motion so that, initially, $l_1 = 20$ in. and $\theta_1 = 30°$. Determine the angle θ_2 when $l_2 = 15$ in.

14.86 through 14.89. Using the principles of conservation of energy and of conservation of angular momentum, solve the following problems:

14.86. Prob. 12.84.
14.87. Prob. 12.85.
14.88. Prob. 12.86.
14.89. Prob. 12.89.

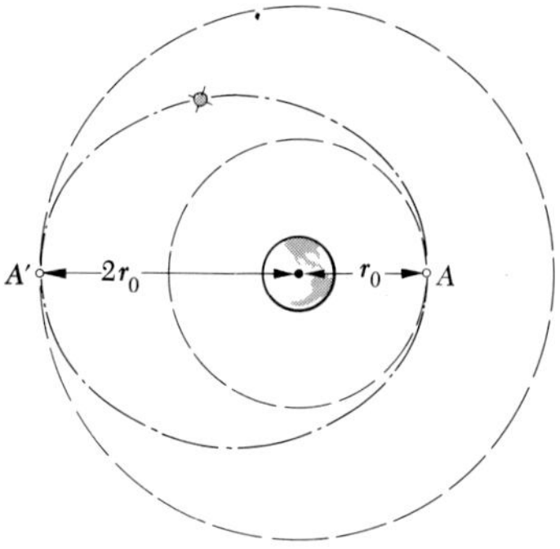

FIG. P 14.91

14.90. A satellite is describing a circular orbit of radius r_0 around the earth. By firing auxiliary rockets, its kinetic energy is suddenly increased by 50 per cent. Determine the maximum distance from the center of the earth reached by the satellite in its new orbit.

14.91. A satellite is describing a circular orbit of radius r_0 around the earth. (*a*) How much should the kinetic energy of the satellite be increased to place it in an elliptic orbit with apogee A' at a distance $2r_0$ from the center of the earth? (*b*) What further increase in energy would be required to place the satellite in a circular orbit of radius $2r_0$?

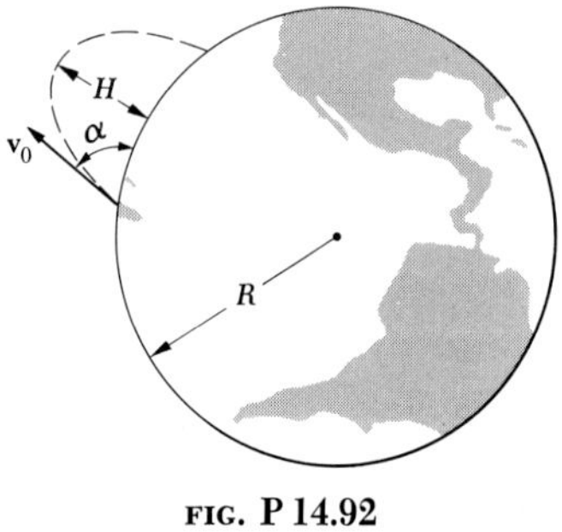

FIG. P 14.92

14.92. A missile is fired from the ground with an initial velocity of magnitude $v_0 = \sqrt{gR}$, where R is the radius of the earth. Determine the firing angle α if the missile is to reach a maximum height H equal to half the radius of the earth.

14.93. An artificial satellite is projected into space with a velocity $\mathbf{v}_0$ at a distance r_0 from the center of the earth by the last stage of its launching rocket. The initial velocity $\mathbf{v}_0$ was designed to send the satellite into a circular orbit around the earth. However, owing to a malfunction of control, the satellite is not projected horizontally but at an angle α with the horizontal and, as a result, is propelled into an elliptic orbit. Determine the maximum and minimum values of the distance from the center of the earth to the satellite.

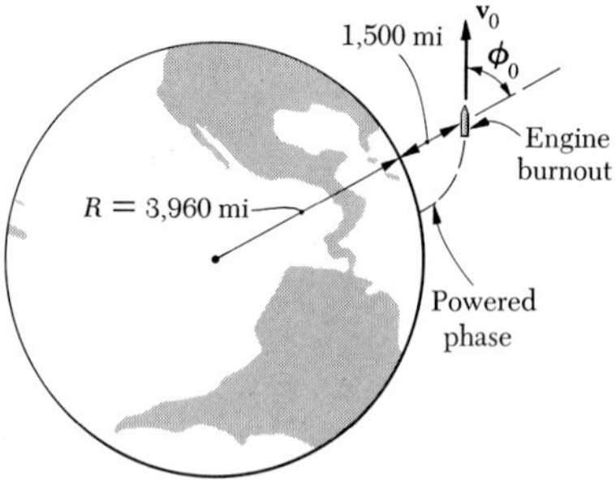

FIG. P 14.94 AND P 14.95

14.94. At engine burnout a satellite has reached an altitude of 1,500 miles and has a velocity $\mathbf{v}_0$ of 26,700 ft/sec forming an angle $\phi_0 = 76°$ with the vertical. Determine the maximum and minimum heights reached by the satellite.

14.95. At engine burnout a satellite has reached an altitude of 1,500 miles and has a velocity $\mathbf{v}_0$ of magnitude 26,700 ft/sec. For what range of values of the angle ϕ_0, formed by $\mathbf{v}_0$ and the vertical, will the satellite go into a permanent orbit? (Assume that if the satellite gets closer than 200 miles from the earth's surface, it will soon burn up.)

14.96. A satellite describing a circular orbit around the earth at an altitude $H = 4{,}000$ miles ejects a capsule. If the speed of the capsule is reduced to $v_0 = 6{,}000$ ft/sec by means of rockets, determine the speed with which the capsule will reach the earth's surface and the angle of impact ϕ with the vertical. (Neglect the effect of the atmosphere.)

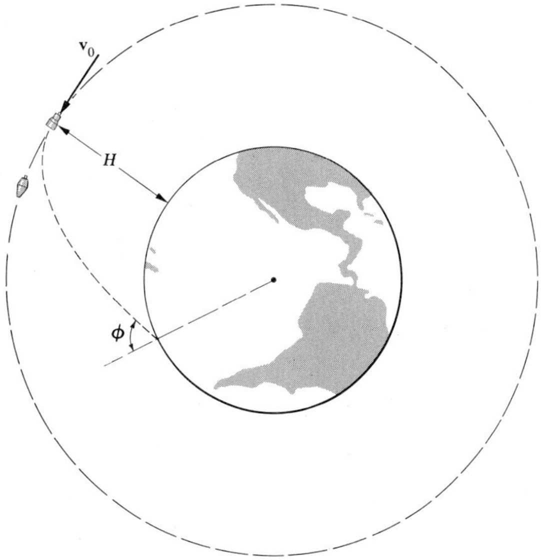

FIG. P 14.96 AND P 14.97

14.97. A capsule is ejected from a satellite describing a circular orbit around the earth at an altitude $H = 1{,}000$ miles and is slowed by means of rockets. To what value v_0 should the magnitude of the absolute velocity of the capsule be reduced by the rockets if it is to strike the earth at an angle $\phi = 60°$ with the vertical? (Neglect the effect of the atmosphere.)

14.98. A missile fired from the ground with an initial velocity of magnitude v_0 is to reach a maximum altitude equal to the radius of the earth. (*a*) Show that the required firing angle α is defined by the relation

$$\cos \alpha = 2\sqrt{1 - \tfrac{1}{2}(v_{esc}/v_0)^2}$$

where v_{esc} is the escape velocity. (*b*) Determine the maximum and minimum allowable values of v_0.

***14.99.** Solve Prob. 12.95.

***14.13. Variable Systems of Particles.** All the systems of particles considered so far consisted of well-defined particles. These systems did not gain or lose any particles during their motion. In a large number of engineering applications, however, it is necessary to consider *variable systems of particles*, i.e., systems which are continuously gaining or losing particles, or doing both at the same time. Consider, for example, a hydraulic turbine. Its analysis involves the determination of the forces exerted by a stream of water on rotating blades, and we note that the particles of water in contact with the blades form an ever-changing system which continuously acquires and loses particles. Rockets furnish another example of variable systems, since their propulsion depends upon the continuous ejection of fuel particles.

We recall that all the kinetics principles established so far were derived for constant systems of particles, which neither gain nor lose particles. We must therefore find a way to reduce the analysis of a variable system of particles to that of an auxiliary constant system. The procedure to follow is indicated in Secs. 14.14 and 14.15 for two broad categories of applications.

***14.14. Steady Stream of Particles.** Consider a steady stream of particles, such as a stream of water diverted by a fixed vane or a flow of air through a duct or through a blower. In order to determine the resultant of the forces exerted on the particles in contact with the vane, duct, or blower, we isolate these particles and denote by S the system thus defined (Fig. 14.17). We observe that S is a variable system of particles, since it continuously gains particles flowing in and loses an equal number of particles flowing out. Therefore, the kinetics principles that have been established so far cannot be directly applied to S.

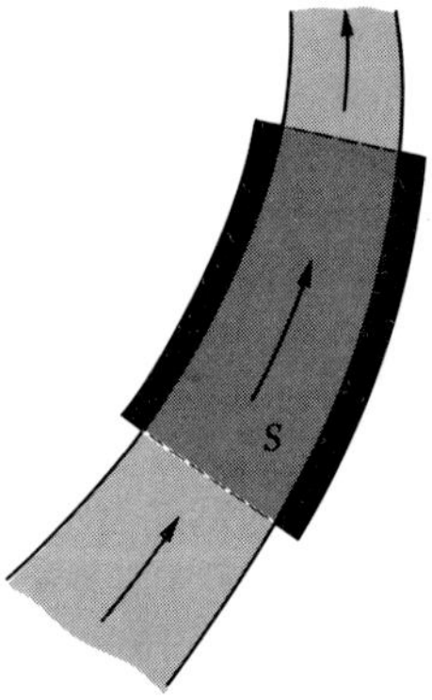

FIG. 14.17

However, we may easily define an auxiliary system of particles which does remain constant for a short interval of time Δt. Consider at time t the system S *plus* the particles which will enter S during the interval of time Δt (Fig. 14.18*a*). Next, consider at time $t + \Delta t$ the system S *plus* the particles which have left S during the interval Δt (Fig. 14.18*c*). Clearly, *the same particles are involved in both cases*, and we may apply to these particles the principle of impulse and momentum. Since the total mass m of the system S remains constant, the particles entering the system and those leaving the system in the time Δt must have the same mass Δm. Denoting by $\mathbf{v}_1$ and $\mathbf{v}_2$, respectively, the velocities of the particles entering and leaving

S and by $\Sigma m\mathbf{v}$ the sum of the momenta of the particles of S, we express the principle of impulse and momentum as follows:

$$(\Delta m)\mathbf{v}_1 + \Sigma m\mathbf{v} + \Sigma\mathbf{F}\,\Delta t = \Sigma m\mathbf{v} + (\Delta m)\mathbf{v}_2$$

or, canceling the term $\Sigma m\mathbf{v}$ which appears in both members,

$$(\Delta m)\mathbf{v}_1 + \Sigma\mathbf{F}\,\Delta t = (\Delta m)\mathbf{v}_2 \tag{14.37}$$

This equation expresses that *the momentum of the particles leaving S in the time Δt may be obtained by adding vectorially the momentum of the particles entering S in the time Δt and the impulses of the forces exerted on S during the same time interval.* Dividing all terms of (14.37) by Δt and letting Δt approach zero, we obtain at the limit

$$\Sigma\mathbf{F} = \frac{dm}{dt}(\mathbf{v}_2 - \mathbf{v}_1) \tag{14.38}$$

where $\mathbf{v}_2 - \mathbf{v}_1$ represents the difference between the vectors $\mathbf{v}_2$ and $\mathbf{v}_1$.

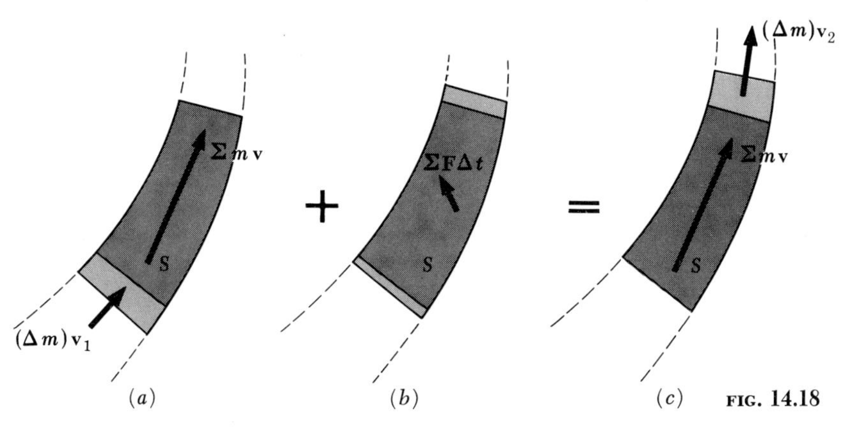

FIG. 14.18

The principle we have just established may be used to analyze a large number of engineering applications. Some of the most common are indicated below.

Fluid Stream Diverted by a Vane. If the vane is fixed, the method of analysis given above may be applied directly to find the force **F** exerted by the vane on the stream. We note that **F** is the only force which needs to be considered since the pressure in the stream is constant (atmospheric pressure). The force exerted by the stream on the vane will be equal and opposite to **F**. If the vane moves with a constant velocity, the stream is not steady. However, it will appear steady to an observer moving with the vane. We should therefore choose a system of axes moving with the vane. Since this system of axes is not accelerated, Eq. (14.37) may still be used, but $\mathbf{v}_1$ and $\mathbf{v}_2$ must be replaced by the *relative velocities* of the stream with respect to the vane (see Sample Prob. 14.9).

Fluid Flowing through a Pipe. The force exerted by the fluid on a pipe transition such as a bend or a contraction may be determined by considering the system of particles S in contact with the transition. Since, in general, the pressure in the flow will vary, we should also consider the forces exerted on S by the adjoining portions of the fluid.

Jet Engine. In a jet engine, air enters with no velocity through the front of the engine and leaves through the rear with a high velocity. The energy required to accelerate the air particles is obtained by burning fuel. While the exhaust gases contain burned fuel, the mass of the fuel is small compared with the mass of the air flowing through the engine and usually may be neglected. Thus, the analysis of a jet engine reduces to that of an air stream. This stream may be considered as a steady stream if all velocities are measured with respect to the airplane. The air stream should be assumed, therefore, to enter the engine with a velocity $\mathbf{v}$ of magnitude equal to the speed of the airplane and to leave with a velocity $\mathbf{u}$ equal to the relative velocity of the exhaust gases (Fig. 14.19). Since the intake and exhaust pressures are nearly atmospheric, the only external force which needs to be considered is the force exerted by the engine on the air stream. This force is equal and opposite to the thrust.

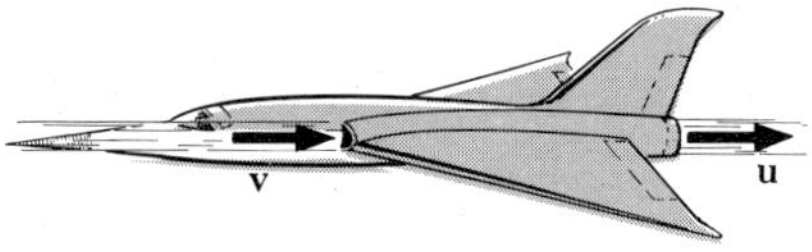

FIG. 14.19

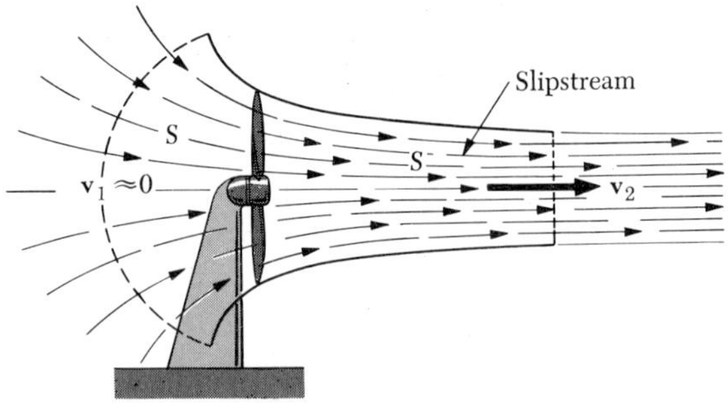

FIG. 14.20

Fan. We consider the system of particles S shown in Fig. 14.20. The velocity $\mathbf{v}_1$ of the particles entering the system is assumed equal to zero, and the velocity $\mathbf{v}_2$ of the particles leaving the system is the velocity of the *slipstream*. The rate of flow may be obtained by multiplying v_2 by the cross-sectional area of the slipstream. Since the pressure all around S is atmospheric, the only external force acting on S is the thrust of the fan.

Airplane Propeller. In order to obtain a steady stream of air, velocities should be measured with respect to the airplane. Thus, the air particles should be assumed to enter the system with a velocity **v** of magnitude equal to the speed of the airplane and to leave with a velocity **u** equal to the relative velocity of the slipstream.

***14.15. Systems Gaining or Losing Mass.** We shall now analyze a different type of variable system of particles, namely, a system which gains mass by continuously absorbing particles or loses mass by continually expelling particles. Consider the system S shown in Fig. 14.21. Its mass, equal to m at the instant t, increases by Δm in the interval of time Δt. In order to apply the principle of impulse and momentum to the analysis of this system, we must consider at time t the system S *plus* the particles of mass Δm which S absorbs during the time interval Δt. The velocity of S at time t is denoted by **v**, and its velocity at time $t + \Delta t$ is denoted by $\mathbf{v} + \Delta\mathbf{v}$, while the absolute velocity of the particles which are absorbed is denoted by $\mathbf{v}_a$.

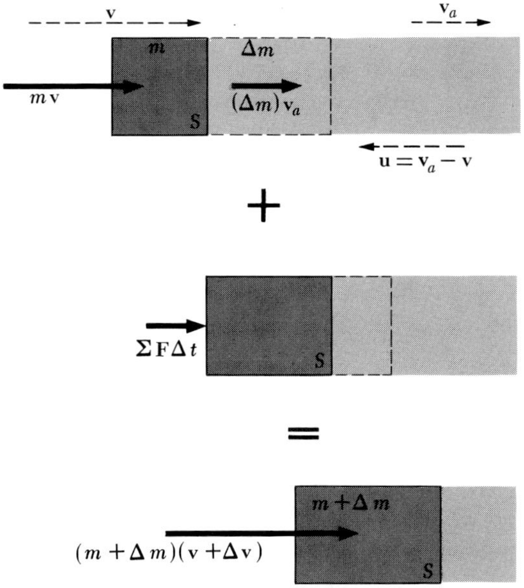

FIG. 14.21

Applying the principle of impulse and momentum, we write

$$m\mathbf{v} + (\Delta m)\mathbf{v}_a + \Sigma\mathbf{F}\,\Delta t = (m + \Delta m)(\mathbf{v} + \Delta\mathbf{v})$$

Solving for the sum $\Sigma\mathbf{F}\,\Delta t$ of the impulses of the external forces acting on S (excluding the forces exerted by the particles being absorbed), we have

$$\Sigma\mathbf{F}\,\Delta t = m\,\Delta\mathbf{v} + \Delta m(\mathbf{v} - \mathbf{v}_a) + (\Delta m)(\Delta\mathbf{v}) \qquad (14.39)$$

Introducing the *relative velocity* $\mathbf{u}$ with respect to S of the particles which are absorbed, we write $\mathbf{u} = \mathbf{v}_a - \mathbf{v}$ and note, since $v_a < v$, that the relative velocity $\mathbf{u}$ is directed to the left, as shown in Fig. 14.21. Neglecting the last term in Eq. (14.39), which is of the second order, we write

$$\Sigma\mathbf{F}\,\Delta t = m\,\Delta\mathbf{v} - (\Delta m)\mathbf{u}$$

Dividing through by Δt and letting Δt approach zero, we have at the limit†

$$\Sigma\mathbf{F} = m\frac{d\mathbf{v}}{dt} - \frac{dm}{dt}\mathbf{u} \qquad (14.40)$$

Rearranging the terms, we obtain the equation

$$\Sigma\mathbf{F} + \frac{dm}{dt}\mathbf{u} = m\frac{d\mathbf{v}}{dt} \qquad (14.41)$$

which shows that the action on S of the particles being absorbed is equivalent to a thrust of magnitude $(dm/dt)u$ which tends to slow down the motion of S, since the relative velocity $\mathbf{u}$ of the particles is directed to the left.

The equations obtained may also be used to determine the motion of a system S losing mass. In this case, the rate of change of mass is negative, and the action on S of the particles being expelled is equivalent to a thrust in the direction of $-\mathbf{u}$, i.e., in the direction opposite to that in which the particles are being expelled. A *rocket* represents a typical case of a system continuously losing mass (see Sample Prob. 14.10).

† When the absolute velocity $\mathbf{v}_a$ of the particles absorbed is zero, we have $\mathbf{u} = -\mathbf{v}$, and formula (14.40) becomes

$$\Sigma\mathbf{F} = \frac{d}{dt}(m\mathbf{v})$$

Comparing the formula obtained to Eq. (14.2) of Sec. 14.1, we observe that Newton's second law may be applied to a system gaining mass, *provided that the particles absorbed are initially at rest.* It may also be applied to a system losing mass, *provided that the velocity of the particles expelled is zero* with respect to the frame of reference selected.

SAMPLE PROBLEM 14.9

A nozzle discharges a stream of water of cross-sectional area A with a velocity $\mathbf{v}_1$. The stream is deflected by a *single* blade which moves to the right with a constant velocity $\mathbf{V}$. Assuming that the water moves along the blade at constant speed, determine (*a*) the components of the force $\mathbf{F}$ exerted by the blade on the stream, (*b*) the velocity $\mathbf{V}$ for which maximum power is developed.

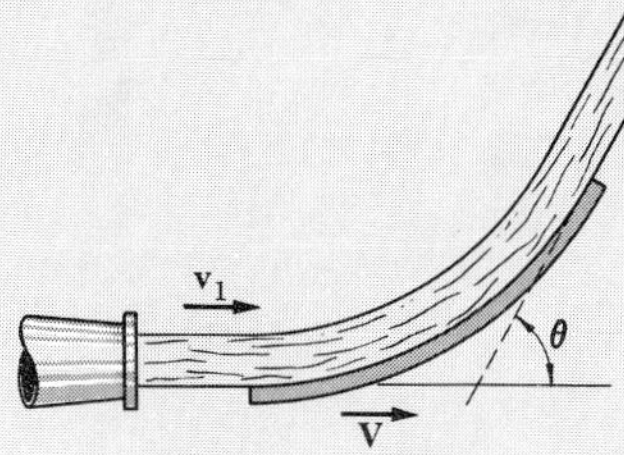

a. **Components of Force Exerted on Stream.** We choose a coordinate system which moves with the blade at a constant velocity $\mathbf{V}$. The particles of water strike the blade with a relative velocity $\mathbf{u}_1 = \mathbf{v}_1 - \mathbf{V}$ and leave the blade with a relative velocity $\mathbf{u}_2$. Since the particles move along the blade at a constant speed, the relative velocities $\mathbf{u}_1$ and $\mathbf{u}_2$ have the same magnitude u. Denoting the density of water by ρ, the mass of the particles striking the blade during the time interval Δt is $\Delta m = A\rho(v_1 - V)\,\Delta t$; an equal mass of particles leaves the blade during Δt. Since the momentum of the particles leaving the blade is equal to the momentum of the particles striking the blade plus the impulses of the forces exerted by the blade, we write

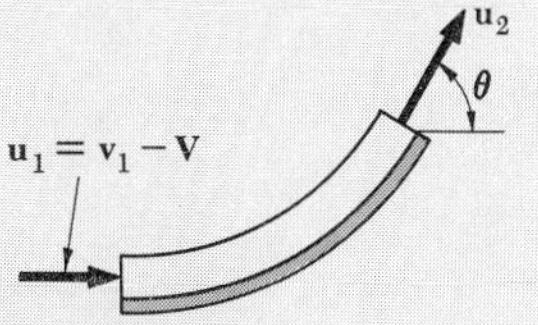

$$(\Delta m)\mathbf{u}_1 + \Sigma\mathbf{F}\,\Delta t = (\Delta m)\mathbf{u}_2$$

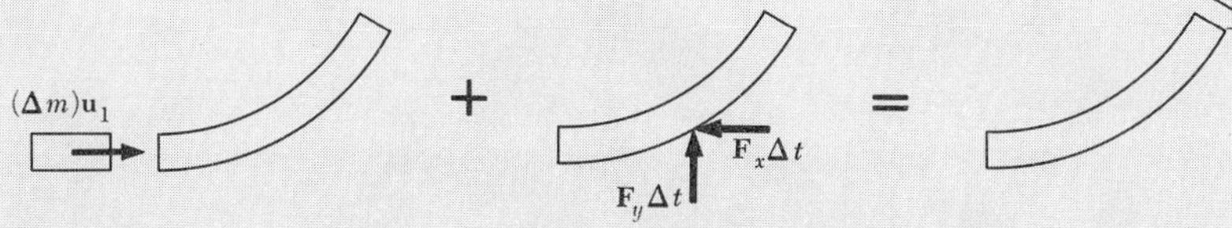

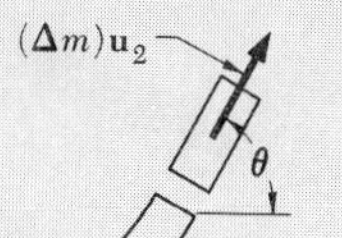

Recalling that $\mathbf{u}_1$ and $\mathbf{u}_2$ have the same magnitude u, we write

$\xrightarrow{+}$ x components: $\quad (\Delta m)u - F_x\,\Delta t = (\Delta m)u\cos\theta$

$+\uparrow$ y components: $\quad +F_y\,\Delta t = (\Delta m)u\sin\theta$

Substituting $\Delta m = A\rho(v_1 - V)\,\Delta t$ and $u = v_1 - V$, we obtain

$$\mathbf{F}_x = A\rho(v_1 - V)^2(1 - \cos\theta)\leftarrow \qquad \mathbf{F}_y = A\rho(v_1 - V)^2\sin\theta\uparrow \quad ◄$$

b. **Velocity of Blade for Maximum Power.** The power is obtained by multiplying the velocity V of the blade by the component $-F_x$ of the force exerted by the stream on the blade.

$$\text{Power} = -F_xV = A\rho(v_1 - V)^2(1 - \cos\theta)V$$

Differentiating the power with respect to V and setting the derivative equal to zero, we obtain

$$\frac{d(\text{power})}{dV} = A\rho(v_1^2 - 4v_1V + 3V^2)(1 - \cos\theta) = 0$$

$$V = v_1 \qquad V = \tfrac{1}{3}v_1 \qquad \text{For maximum power } \mathbf{V} = \tfrac{1}{3}v_1 \rightarrow \quad ◄$$

Note. These results are valid only when a *single* blade deflects the stream. Different results are obtained when a series of blades deflects the stream, as in a Pelton-wheel turbine. (See Prob. 14.144.)

SAMPLE PROBLEM 14.10

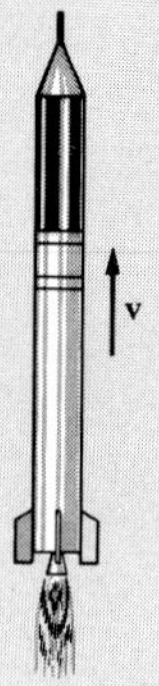

A rocket of initial mass m_0 (including shell and fuel) is fired vertically at time $t = 0$. The fuel is consumed at a constant rate $q = dm/dt$ and is expelled at a constant speed u relative to the rocket. Derive an expression for the velocity of the rocket at time t, neglecting the resistance of the air.

Solution. At time t, the mass of the rocket shell and remaining fuel is $m = m_0 - qt$, and the velocity is $\mathbf{v}$. During the time interval Δt, a mass of fuel $\Delta m = q\,\Delta t$ is expelled with a speed u relative to the rocket. Denoting by $\mathbf{v}_e$ the absolute velocity of the expelled fuel, we apply the principle of impulse and momentum between time t and time $t + \Delta t$.

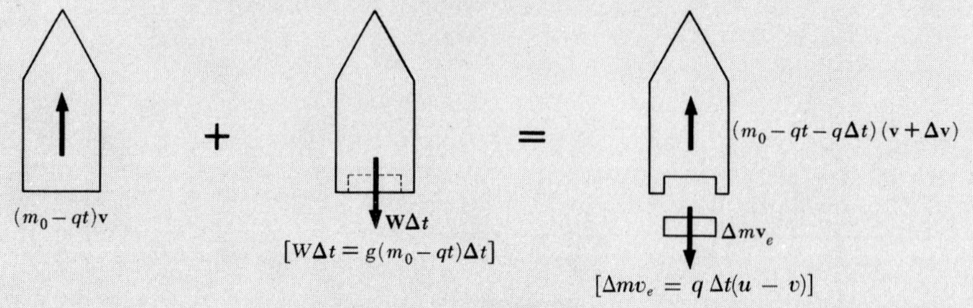

$$(m_0 - qt)v - g(m_0 - qt)\,\Delta t$$
$$= (m_0 - qt - q\,\Delta t)(v + \Delta v) - q\,\Delta t(u - v)$$

Dividing through by Δt, and letting Δt approach zero, we obtain

$$-g(m_0 - qt) = (m_0 - qt)\frac{dv}{dt} - qu$$

Separating variables and integrating from $t = 0, v = 0$ to $t = t, v = v$,

$$dv = \left(\frac{qu}{m_0 - qt} - g\right)dt \qquad \int_0^v dv = \int_0^t \left(\frac{qu}{m_0 - qt} - g\right)dt$$

$$v = [-u \ln (m_0 - qt) - gt]_0^t \qquad v = u \ln \frac{m_0}{m_0 - qt} - gt \quad ◄$$

Remark. The mass remaining at time t_f, after all of the fuel has been expended, is equal to the mass of the rocket shell $m_s = m_0 - qt_f$ and the maximum velocity attained by the rocket is $v_m = u \ln (m_0/m_s) - gt_f$. Assuming that the fuel is expelled in a relatively short period of time, the term gt_f is small and we have $v_m \approx u \ln (m_0/m_s)$. In order to escape the gravitational field of the earth, a rocket must reach a velocity of 36,700 ft/sec. Assuming $u = 7{,}000$ ft/sec and $v_m = 36{,}700$ ft/sec, we obtain $m_0/m_s = 188$. Thus, to project each pound of the rocket shell into space, it is necessary to consume more than 188 lb of fuel if a propellant yielding $u = 7{,}000$ ft/sec is used.

PROBLEMS

14.100. A hose discharges 2,000 gal/min from the stern of a 20-ton fireboat. If the velocity of the water stream is 90 ft/sec, determine the reaction on the boat.

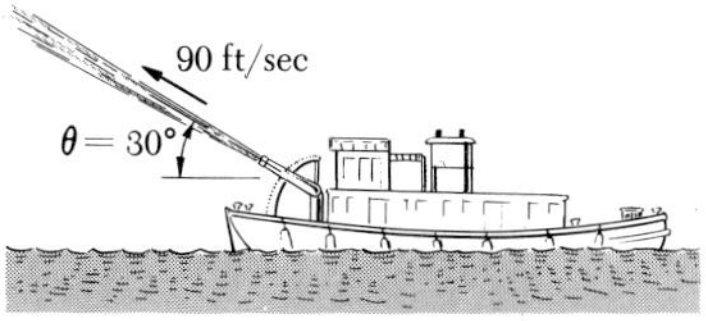

FIG. P 14.100

14.101. Neglecting the frictional resistance of the water, determine the acceleration of the fireboat of Prob. 14.100.

14.102. A 15-lb machine gun fires 600 bullets per minute. Knowing that each bullet weighs 1.5 oz and that the muzzle velocity is 2,400 ft/sec, determine the magnitude of the average force required to hold the gun motionless.

14.103. The speed of the water issuing from an orifice in a tank car is $v = \sqrt{2gh}$, where h is the height of the water surface above the orifice. Denoting by W the total weight of the car, by γ the specific weight of water, and by A the cross-sectional area of the stream, determine (*a*) the magnitude of the force **P** required to prevent the car from moving, (*b*) the acceleration of the car if $\mathbf{P} = 0$.

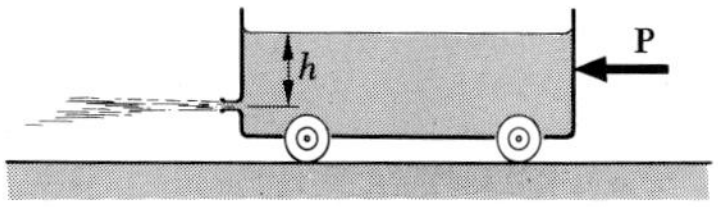

FIG. 14.103

14.104. Solve Prob. 14.103 assuming $h = 5$ ft, $A = 6$ in.^{2}, and $W = 1{,}200$ lb.

14.105. A rocket engine is attached to a test stand and fired; fuel is consumed and expelled with a velocity of 6,000 ft/sec. Knowing that the thrust of the engine is to be 300,000 lb, determine the required rate of fuel consumption.

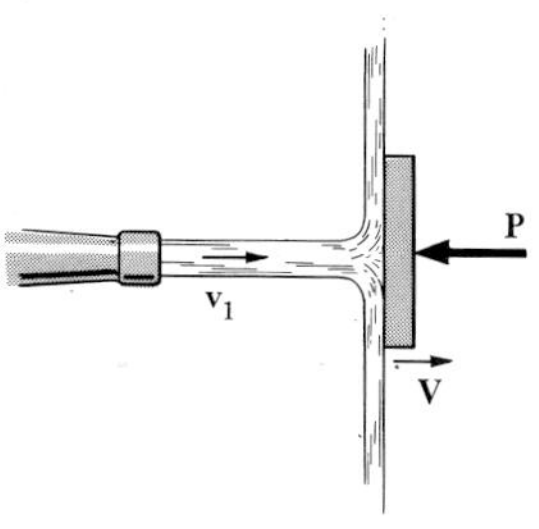

FIG. P 14.106 AND P 14.107

14.106. A fire nozzle discharges water with an initial velocity $\mathbf{v}_1$. If the cross-sectional area of the stream is A, derive an expression for the magnitude of the force **P** required to hold the plate motionless. Determine the numerical value of P, if $A = 3$ in.^{2}, $v_1 = 90$ ft/sec, and $V = 0$.

14.107. A fire nozzle discharges water with an initial velocity $\mathbf{v}_1$. If the cross-sectional area of the stream is A, derive an expression for the magnitude of the force **P** required to hold the plate when the velocity of the plate is **V** directed to the right.

14.108. Sand is discharged at the rate of w lb/sec from a conveyor belt moving with a velocity $\mathbf{v}_0$. The sand is deflected by a plate at B so that it falls in a vertical stream. Neglecting frictional resistance between the sand and the plate, determine the force required to hold the plate in the position shown.

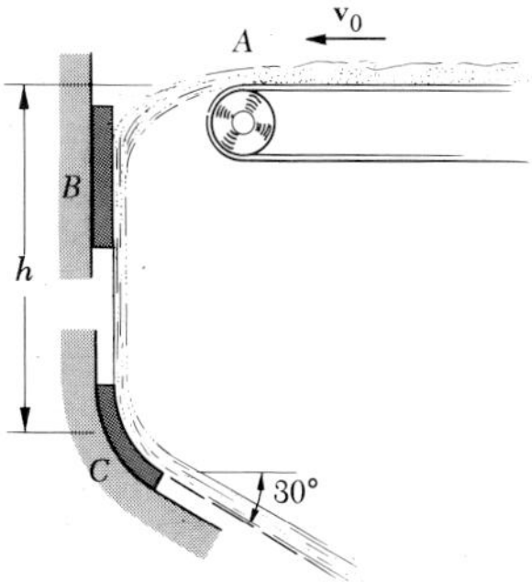

FIG. P 14.108

14.109. After falling a distance h, the sand of Prob. 14.108 is deflected as shown by a small vane at C. Neglecting the frictional resistance between the sand and the vane, determine the force required to hold vane C in the position shown.

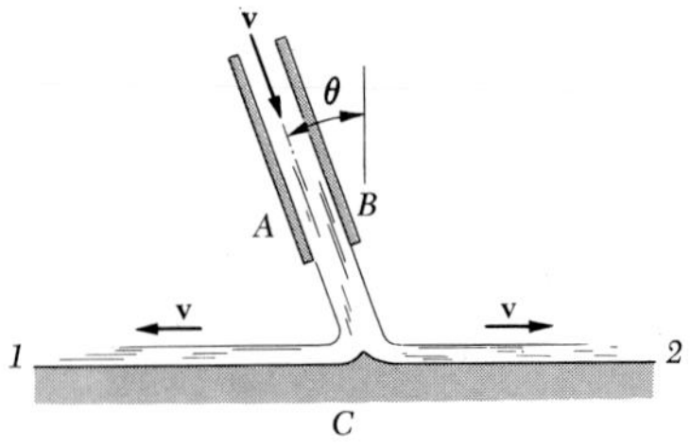

FIG. P 14.110

14.110. Water flows in a continuous sheet from between two plates *A* and *B* with a velocity **v**. The stream is split into two equal streams *1* and 2 by a vane attached to plate *C*. Denoting the total rate of flow by *Q*, determine the force exerted by the stream on plate *C*.

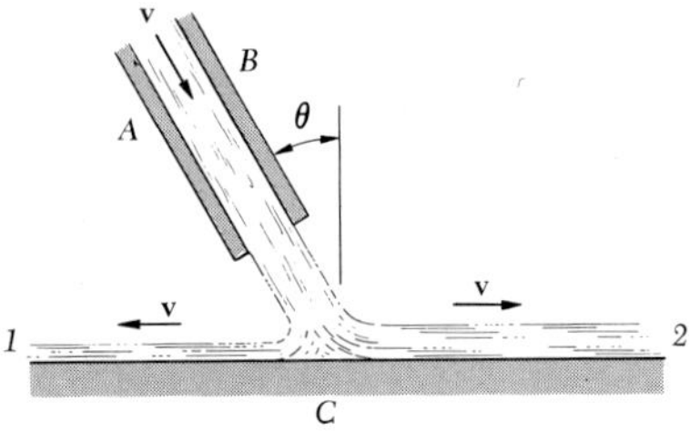

FIG. P 14.111

14.111. Water flows in a continuous sheet from between two plates *A* and *B* with a velocity **v**. The stream is split into two parts by a smooth horizontal plate *C*. Denoting the total rate of flow by *Q*, determine the rate of flow of each of the resulting streams. (*Hint.* The plate *C* can exert only a vertical force on the water.)

14.112. A jet airplane scoops in air at the rate of 190 lb/sec and discharges it with a velocity of 2,200 ft/sec relative to the airplane. If the speed of the airplane is 650 mph, determine (*a*) the propulsive force developed, (*b*) the horsepower developed by the engine, (*c*) the horsepower actually used to propel the airplane.

14.113. The total drag due to air friction of a jet airplane traveling at 600 mph is 3,500 lb. Knowing that the exhaust velocity is 2,000 ft/sec relative to the airplane, determine the weight of air which must pass through the engine per second to maintain the speed of 600 mph in level flight.

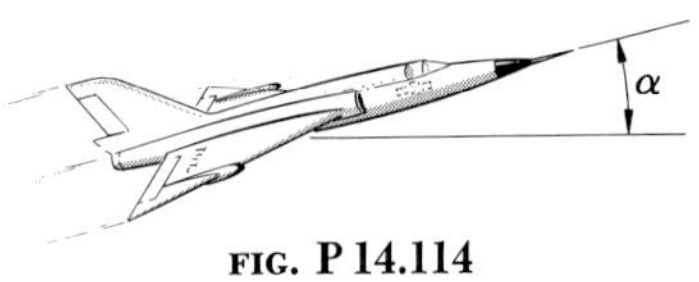

FIG. P 14.114

14.114. A jet airplane weighing 15,000 lb scoops in air at the rate of 200 lb/sec and discharges it with a velocity of 2,000 ft/sec relative to the airplane. If the total drag due to air friction is 5,000 lb, determine the angle of climb α at which the airplane can maintain a constant speed of 600 mph.

14.115. If the jet airplane of Prob. 14.114 climbs at an angle $\alpha = 4°$, determine (*a*) the acceleration of the airplane when its speed is 600 mph, (*b*) the maximum speed possible, assuming that the drag due to air friction increases 150 lb for each additional 10 mph in the speed of the airplane. (*Note.* Drag is 5,000 lb at 600 mph.)

14.116. A jet airplane scoops in w lb of air per second and discharges it with a speed u relative to the airplane. (*a*) Denoting the speed of the airplane by v, derive an expression for the thrust provided by the jet engine. (*b*) Using the results of part *a*, show that the speed v of the airplane must be less than the relative speed u.

14.117. The maximum speed of a jet airliner is known to be 600 mph. Each of the four engines discharges air with a velocity of 2,000 ft/sec relative to the plane. Assuming that the drag due to air resistance is proportional to the square of the speed, determine the maximum cruising speed of the airliner when only two of the engines are in operation.

14.118. A rotary power plow is used to remove snow from a level section of railroad track. The plow car is placed ahead of an engine which propels it at a constant speed of 15 mph. The plow clears 180 tons of snow per minute, projecting it in the direction shown with a velocity of 40 ft/sec relative to the plow car. Neglecting rolling friction, determine (*a*) the magnitude of the force **P** exerted by the engine on the plow car, (*b*) the lateral force exerted on the plow car by the track.

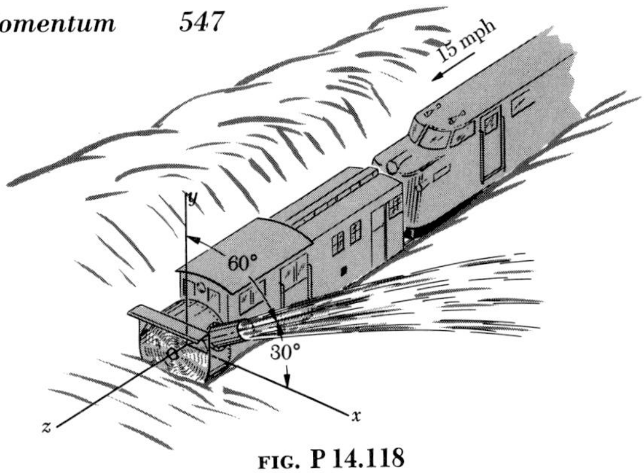

FIG. P 14.118

14.119. In Prob. 14.118, what angle should the discharge duct form with the z axis, if, at the speed considered, the force **P** exerted by the engine on the plow car is to be zero?

14.120. The slipstream of a fan has an area A and a speed v. Derive an expression (*a*) for the magnitude of the force **F** required to hold the fan motionless, (*b*) for the kinetic energy imparted per second to the air of the slipstream.

14.121. The propeller of an airplane produces a thrust of 800 lb when the airplane is at rest on the ground and has a slipstream of 6-ft diameter. Assuming that air weighs 0.076 lb/ft^3, determine (*a*) the speed of the air in the slipstream, (*b*) the volume of air passing through the propeller per second, (*c*) the kinetic energy imparted per second to the air of the slipstream.

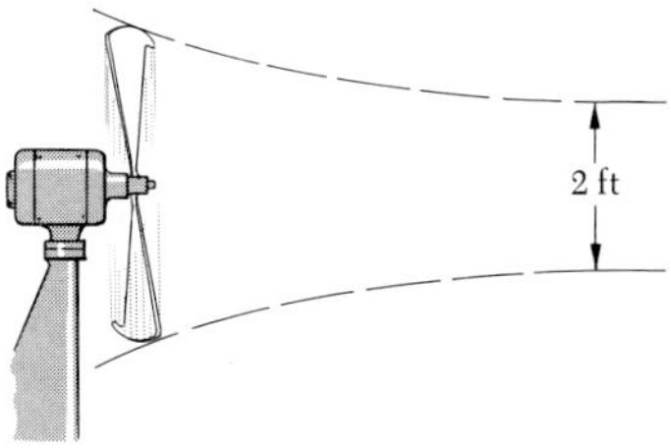

FIG. P 14.122

14.122. The slipstream of a fan has a diameter of 2 ft and a velocity of 40 ft/sec relative to the fan. Assuming air weighs 0.076 lb/ft^3 and neglecting the velocity of approach of the air, determine the force required to hold the fan motionless.

***14.123.** The depth of water flowing in a rectangular channel of width b at a speed v_1 and depth d_1 increases to a depth d_2 at a *hydraulic jump*. Determine the relation between the depth d_1 and the depth d_2 for a given total flow Q.

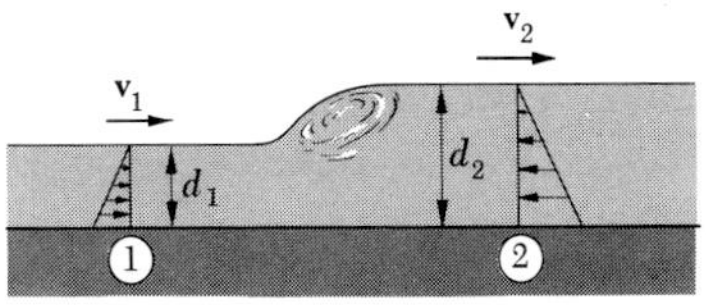

FIG. P 14.123

14.124. Determine the rate of flow of water in the channel of Prob. 14.123, knowing that $d_1 = 2$ ft, $d_2 = 4$ ft, and that the rectangular channel is 10 ft wide.

14.125. A circular reentrant orifice (also called Borda's mouthpiece) of diameter D is placed at a depth h below the surface of a tank. Knowing that the speed of the issuing stream is $v = \sqrt{2gh}$ and assuming that the speed of approach v_1 is zero, show that the diameter of the stream is $d = D/\sqrt{2}$. (*Hint.* Consider the section of water indicated, and note that P is equal to the pressure at a depth h multiplied by the area of the orifice.)

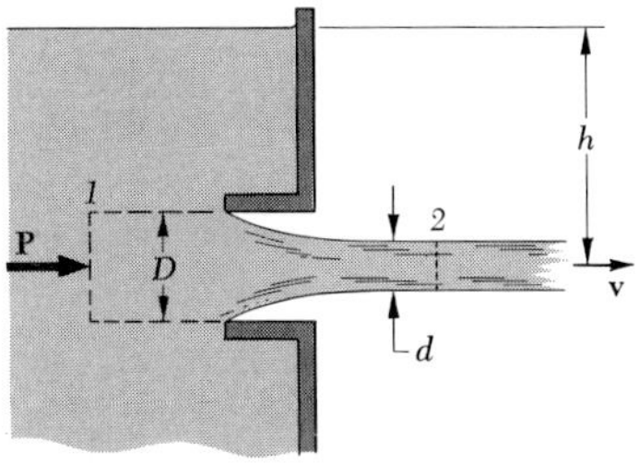

FIG. P 14.125

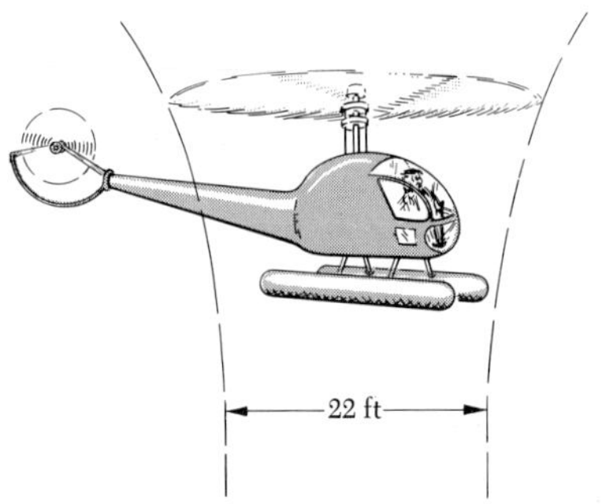

FIG. P 14.126 AND P 14.127

14.126. A helicopter of gross weight 1,500 lb produces a slipstream of 22-ft diameter. Assuming that air weighs 0.076 lb/ft^3, determine the vertical component of the velocity of the air in the slipstream when the helicopter is hovering in mid-air.

14.127. Knowing that the helicopter shown weighs 1,500 lb and can produce a maximum downward air speed of 160 ft/sec in the 22-ft diameter slipstream, determine the maximum load which the helicopter can carry while hovering in mid-air. Air weighs 0.076 lb/ft^3.

14.128. On some long-distance runs, steam locomotives used to scoop up water from long troughs placed between the rails. Assuming that a locomotive scoops up water at the rate of 4,000 gal/min while traveling at a constant speed of 45 mph, determine (*a*) the magnitude of the additional force **P** which must be exerted by the locomotive to maintain the constant speed, (*b*) the additional power required to maintain the constant speed. Neglect the drag on the scoop and the change in potential energy of the water as it is raised into the tender of the locomotive.

14.129. Because of the play existing in the couplings of railroad freight cars, a long train may be started by successively setting each car in motion. If the engine moves at a constant speed v, (*a*) show that the magnitude of the constant force required to set the cars in motion is $F = v(dm/dt)$, where dm/dt is the rate at which the mass of the cars is set in motion. (*b*) Show that the work done in setting each car in motion is m_0v^2, where m_0 is the mass of a car. (*Note.* Although only half the work done is used to increase the kinetic energy of the train, this method of starting long trains is frequently used in order to overcome static friction.)

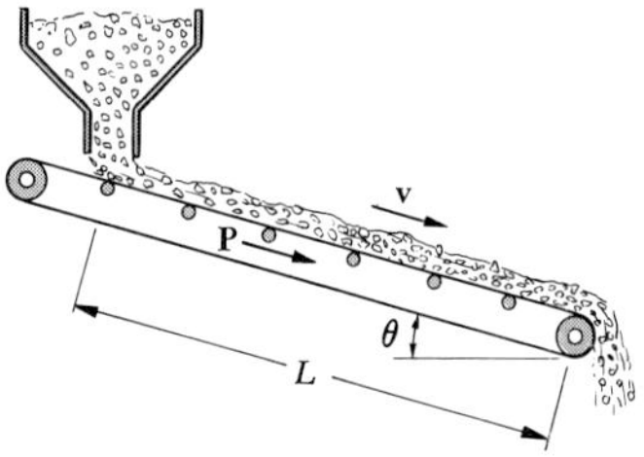

FIG. P 14.130 AND P 14.131

14.130. Coal falls onto a conveyor belt at the constant rate of w lb/sec. (*a*) Determine the magnitude of the force **P** required to maintain a constant belt speed v, when $\theta = 0$. (*b*) Solve part *a* when $w = 50$ lb/sec and $v = 6$ ft/sec.

14.131. Coal falls onto a conveyor belt at the constant rate of w lb/sec. A force **P** is applied to the belt to maintain a constant speed v. Derive an expression for the angle θ for which the force **P** is zero.

FIG. P 14.132

14.132. A chain of weight w lb/ft and total length l is held at end A by a force **P**. If end B of the chain is just in contact with the floor at time $t = 0$ and the velocity of the chain is **v** directed downward, determine (*a*) the magnitude of the force **P** required to lower the chain with the constant velocity **v**, (*b*) the magnitude of the upward force exerted by the floor as the chain is lowered.

14.133. A chain of weight w lb/ft and total length l lies in a pile on the floor. At time $t = 0$ a force **P** is applied and the chain is raised with a constant velocity v. Determine (a) the required magnitude of the force **P**, (b) the magnitude of the upward force exerted by the floor as the chain is raised.

FIG. P 14.133

14.134. The *specific impulse* of a rocket fuel is defined as the propulsive thrust produced by burning the fuel at the rate of 1 lb per second. Determine the specific impulse of a fuel which is consumed and expelled at a constant speed u relative to the rocket.

14.135. A booster rocket is attached to the fuselage of an airplane weighing 40,000 lb. The rocket fuel is consumed at the rate of 20 lb/sec and is ejected with a relative velocity of 5,000 ft/sec. Determine the additional propulsive thrust available while the rocket is being fired (a) if the speed of the airplane is 500 mph, (b) if the airplane is at rest on the ground.

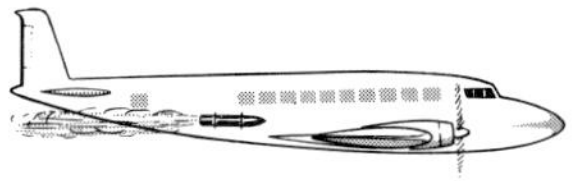

FIG. P 14.135

14.136. A space vehicle describing a circular orbit at a speed of 15,000 mph releases a capsule which has a gross weight of 1,000 lb, including 750 lb of fuel. If the fuel is consumed at the constant rate of 30 lb/sec and is ejected with a relative velocity of 6,000 ft/sec, determine the tangential acceleration of the capsule (a) as the engine is fired, (b) as the last particle of fuel is being consumed.

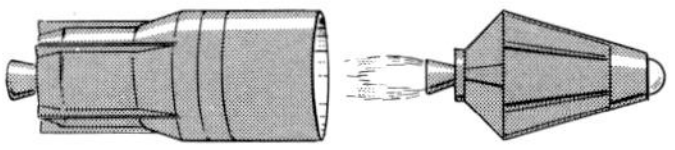

FIG. P 14.136

14.137. A test rocket is designed to hover motionless above the ground. The shell of the rocket weighs 2,000 lb, and the initial fuel load is 8,000 lb. The fuel is burned and ejected with a velocity of 6,000 ft/sec. Determine the required rate of fuel consumption (a) when the rocket is fired, (b) as the last particle of fuel is being consumed.

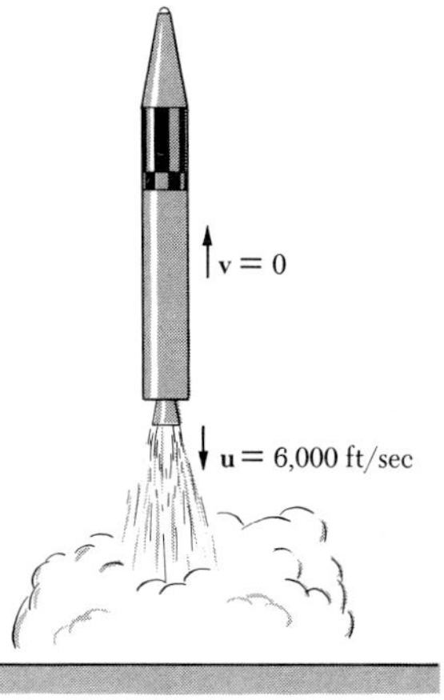

FIG. P 14.137

14.138. A test rocket consists of a shell weighing 50 lb and 450 lb of fuel. The fuel is consumed at a rate of 10 lb/sec and is ejected with a relative velocity of 5,000 ft/sec. Determine the maximum speed attained by the rocket when it is fired vertically. Neglect the effect of air friction.

14.139. A multiple-stage rocket is more efficient than a rocket consisting of a single shell because expendable mass such as emptied fuel tanks can be discarded when no longer required. Assume that the rocket of Sample Prob. 14.10 is the second stage of a two-stage rocket and that, as the first section of the rocket is discarded, the velocity of the second section is $\mathbf{v}_0$ directed vertically upward. Taking $t = 0$ when the second stage begins, derive an expression for the velocity of the rocket at any time t.

FIG. P 14.140

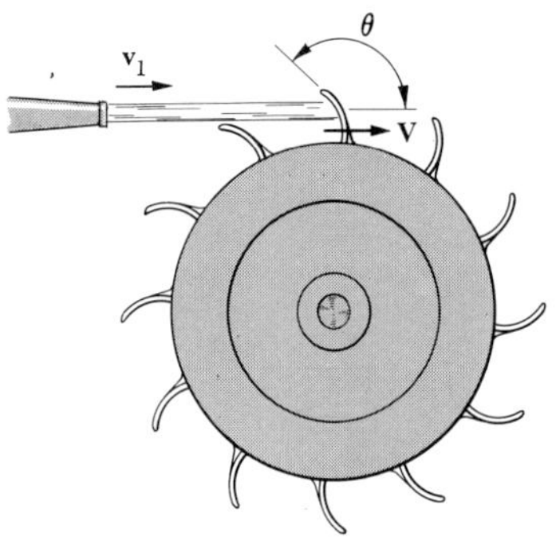

FIG. P 14.144

14.140. Two rockets A and B similar to the rocket of Prob. 14.138 are used to form a two-stage rocket which is fired vertically. When rocket A expels its last particle of fuel, its shell is released and rocket B is fired. Determine (*a*) the speed when rocket A is released, (*b*) the maximum speed attained by rocket B.

14.141. A space vehicle equipped with a retrorocket, which may expel fuel with a relative velocity $\mathbf{u}$, is moving with a velocity $\mathbf{v}_0$. Denoting by m_s the net mass of the vehicle and by m_f the mass of the unexpended fuel, determine the minimum ratio m_f/m_s for which the velocity of the vehicle can be reduced to zero.

14.142. In Prob. 14.136, determine the final velocity of the capsule after all its fuel has been expended, assuming (*a*) that the capsule is ejected forward, (*b*) that the capsule is ejected to the rear.

14.143. The kinetic energy available per second from the stream of Sample Prob. 14.9 is $\frac{1}{2}Q\rho v_1^2$, where Q is the flow of water per second, $Q = Av_1$. Derive an expression for the mechanical efficiency of the single blade, and determine the maximum possible value of the efficiency.

14.144. In a Pelton-wheel turbine, a stream of water is deflected by a series of blades so that the rate at which water is deflected by the blades is equal to the rate at which water issues from the nozzle ($\Delta m/\Delta t = A\rho v_1$). Using the same notation as in Sample Prob. 14.9, (*a*) determine the velocity $\mathbf{V}$ of the blades for which maximum power is developed, (*b*) derive an expression for the maximum power, (*c*) derive an expression for the mechanical efficiency.

***14.145.** For the rocket of Sample Prob. 14.10 derive an expression for the height of the rocket as a function of the time t.

***14.146.** Determine the distance between the capsule and the space vehicle of Prob. 14.136 as the last particle of fuel is being ejected by the rocket of the capsule. Both the capsule and the space vehicle may be considered to move in a straight line during the time interval considered.

***14.147.** In a jet airplane, the kinetic energy imparted to the exhaust gases is wasted as far as propelling the airplane is concerned. The useful power is equal to the product of the force available to propel the airplane and the speed of the airplane. If v is the speed of the airplane and u is the relative speed of the expelled gases, show that the efficiency is $\eta = 2v/(u + v)$. Explain why $\eta \neq 1$ when $u = v$.

***14.148.** In a rocket, the kinetic energy imparted to the consumed and ejected fuel is wasted as far as propelling the rocket is concerned. The useful power is equal to the product of the force available to propel the rocket and the speed of the rocket. If v is the speed of the rocket and u is the relative speed of the expelled fuel, show that the efficiency is $\eta = 2uv/(u^2 + v^2)$. Explain why $\eta = 1$ when $u = v$.

REVIEW PROBLEMS

14.149. A steel ball dropped from A strikes a rigid steel plate at B and bounces to point C. Knowing that the distance d is 4.80 ft, determine the coefficient of restitution between the ball and the plate.

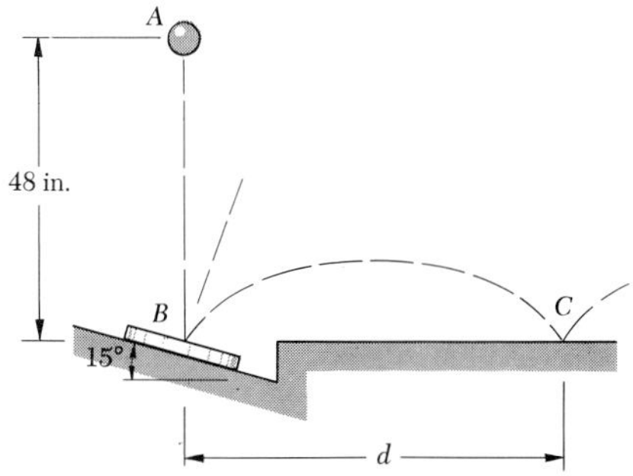

FIG. P 14.149

14.150. A conveyor belt moves with a constant velocity **v** under the action of a force **P**. If coal falls vertically onto the belt at the rate dm/dt, show that the kinetic energy acquired by the coal in a given time interval is equal to one-half of the work done in that interval by the force **P**. Explain what happens to the other half of the work done by **P**.

14.151. The 20-ton truck and the 40-ton railroad flatcar are both at rest with their brakes released. An engine bumps the flatcar and causes the flatcar alone to start moving with a velocity of 3 ft/sec to the right. Assuming $e = 1$ between the truck and the ends of the flatcar, determine the velocities of the truck and of the flatcar after end A strikes the truck. Describe the subsequent motion of the system. Neglect the effect of friction.

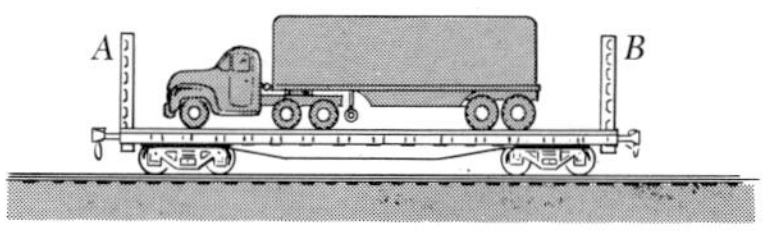

FIG. P 14.151

14.152. A steel ball A weighing 2 oz hits squarely a larger steel ball which is at rest. If ball A bounces back with half its initial speed, determine (a) the weight of ball B, (b) the percentage of the initial kinetic energy acquired by ball B. ($e = 1$.)

*__14.153.__ A chain of weight w lb/ft and length l falls through a small hole in a plate. Initially, when y is very small, the chain is at rest. In each case shown, determine (a) the acceleration of the first link A as a function of y, (b) the velocity of the chain as the last link passes through the hole. In case *1* assume that the individual links are at rest until they fall through the hole; in case 2 assume that at any instant all links have the same speed. Ignore the effect of friction.

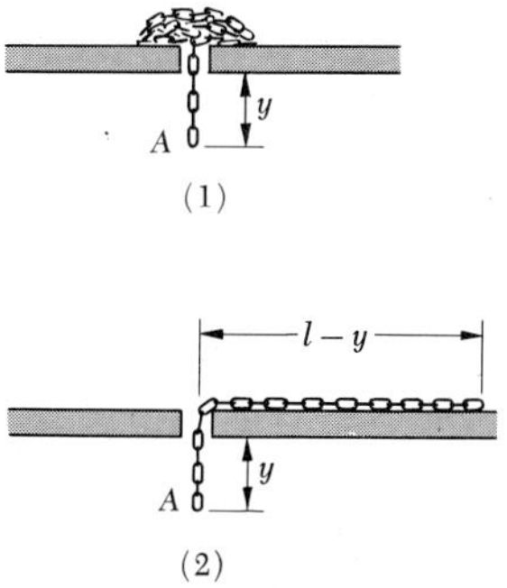

FIG. P 14.153

14.154. An air-to-air missile is test-fired horizontally from a stationary support. The fuel is consumed at a constant rate q and is ejected with a relative velocity of constant magnitude u. Knowing that the atmospheric drag on the missile may be represented by a force of magnitude kv^2, show that the maximum speed v_m attained by the missile is defined by the formula

$$\frac{c + v_m}{c - v_m} = \left(\frac{m_0}{m_s}\right)^{2u/c}$$

where m_0 is the initial gross mass of the missile, m_s the mass of the shell, and $c^2 = qu/k$.

14.155. Derive an expression for the maximum speed attained by the missile of Prob. 14.154 if it is fired horizontally from a plane traveling horizontally at a speed v_0.

14.156. The ends of a chain of weight w lb/ft lie in piles at A and at C; when released, the chain moves over the pulley at B. Determine the required initial speed v for which the chain will move at constant speed. Neglect the effect of friction.

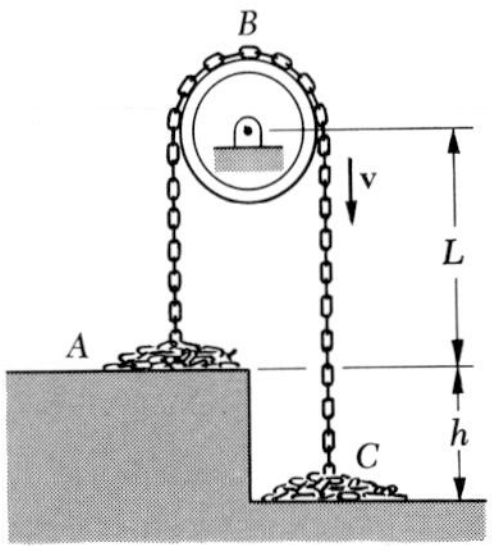

FIG. P 14.156

14.157. Two railroad freight cars move with a velocity **v** through a switchyard. Car B hits a third car C, which was at rest with its brakes released, and it automatically couples with C. Knowing that all three cars have the same weight, determine their common velocity after they are all coupled together, as well as the percentage of their total initial kinetic energy which is absorbed by each coupling mechanism, assuming (*a*) that cars A and B were originally coupled, (*b*) that cars A and B were moving a few feet apart and that the coupling operation between B and C is completed before A hits B and becomes coupled with it.

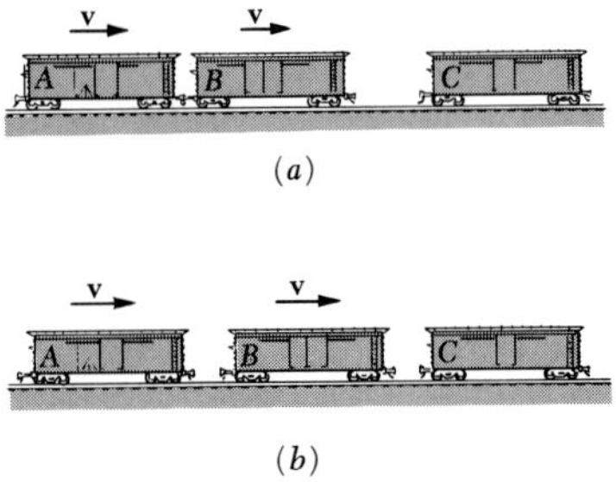

FIG. P 14.157

14.158. A large number of small blocks of total weight W are at rest on a smooth table when a constant force of magnitude P is applied to block A. Knowing that the blocks are in contact with each other but are not connected, determine the speed of block A after half the blocks have been pushed off the table.

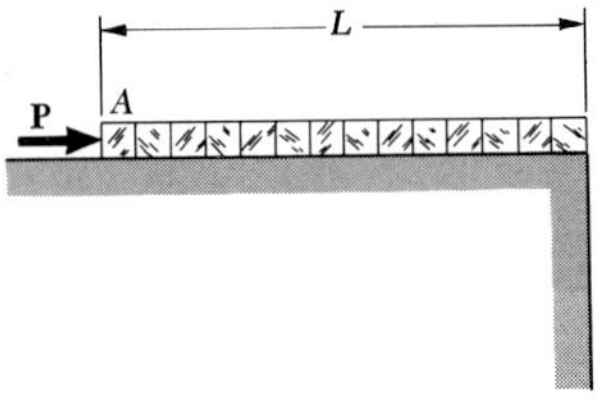

FIG. P 14.158

14.159. Solve Prob. 14.158 assuming that the coefficient of friction between the blocks and the horizontal table is μ.

14.160. A series of 10 castings, each of weight 25 lb, is at rest on an assembly-line belt. Knowing that the tension T in the belt must not exceed 60 lb, determine the time t_1 required for the belt to acquire a speed of 2 ft/sec (*a*) if the T–t curve is parabolic, (*b*) if the T–t curve is triangular. Ignore the effect of friction.

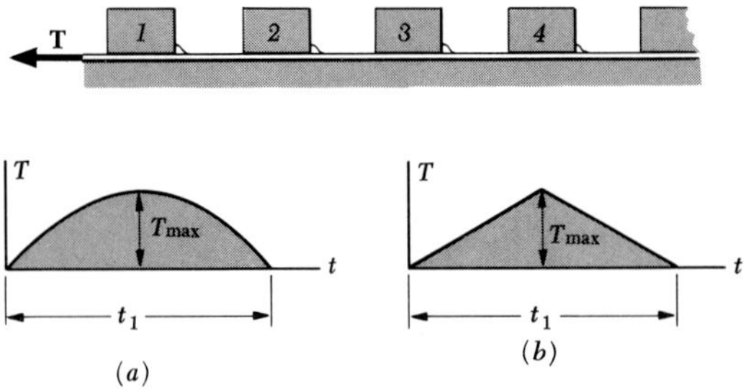

FIG. P 14.160

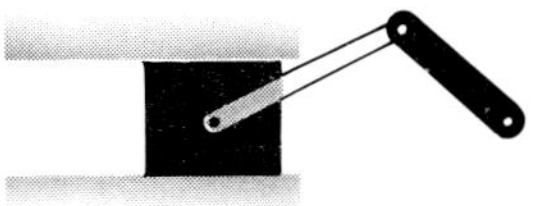

15. KINEMATICS OF RIGID BODIES

15.1. Various Types of Plane Motion. In this chapter, we shall study the kinematics of *rigid bodies*. We shall investigate the relations existing between the time, the positions, the velocities, and the accelerations of the various particles forming a rigid body. Our study will be limited to that of the *plane motion* of a rigid body, which is characterized by the fact that each particle of the body remains at a constant distance from a fixed reference plane. Thus all particles of the body move in parallel planes, and the motion of the body may be represented by the motion of a representative slab in the reference plane.

The various types of plane motion may be grouped as follows:

1. *Translation.* A motion is said to be a translation if any straight line drawn on the body keeps the same direction during the motion. It may also be observed that in a translation all the particles forming the body move along parallel paths. If these paths are straight lines, the motion is said to be a *rectilinear translation* (Fig. 15.1*a*); if the paths are curved lines, the motion is a *curvilinear translation* (Fig. 15.1*b*).

2. *Rotation.* A motion is said to be a rotation when the particles of the representative slab move along concentric circles. If the common center O of the circles is located on the

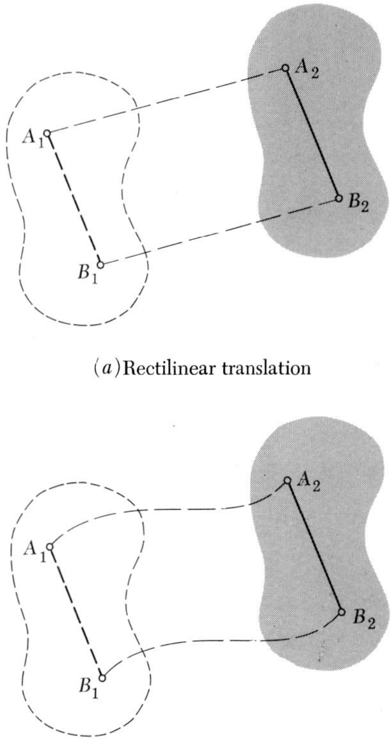

(*a*) Rectilinear translation

(*b*) Curvilinear translation

FIG. 15.1

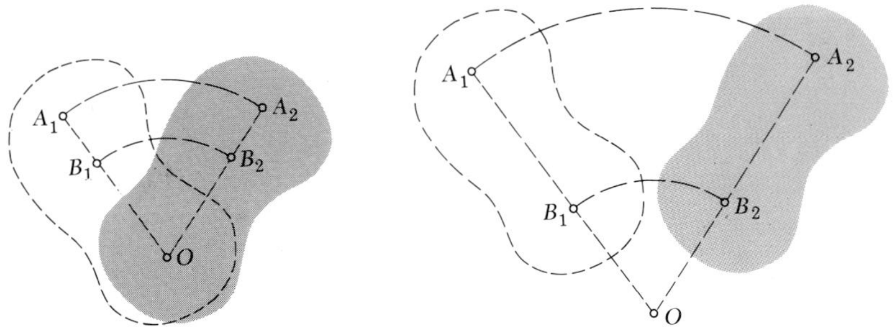

(*a*) (*b*)

FIG. 15.2

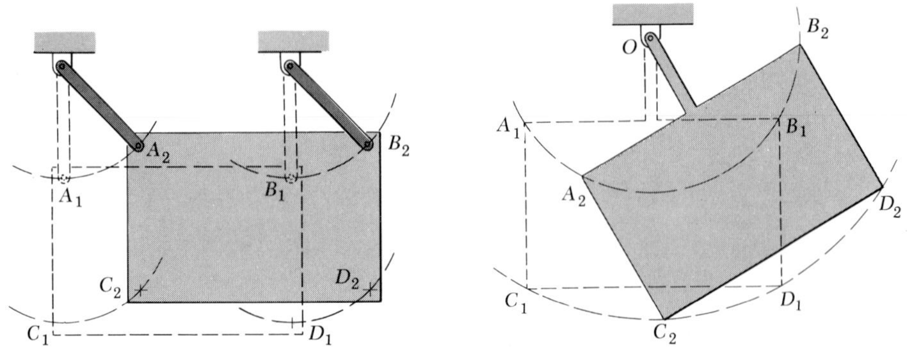

FIG. 15.3 (*a*) Curvilinear translation (*b*) Rotation

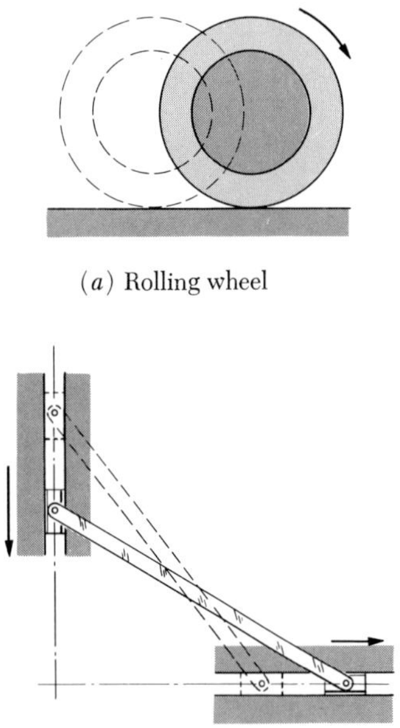

(*a*) Rolling wheel

(*b*) Sliding rod

FIG. 15.4. Examples of general plane motion

slab, the corresponding point remains fixed (Fig. 15.2*a*). In many cases of rotation, however, the common center O is located outside the slab, and none of the points of the slab remains fixed (Fig. 15.2*b*).

Rotation should not be confused with certain types of curvilinear translation. For example, the plate shown in Fig. 15.3*a* is in curvilinear translation, with all its particles moving along *parallel* circles, while the plate shown in Fig. 15.3*b* is in rotation, with all its particles moving along *concentric* circles. In the first case, any given straight line drawn on the plate will maintain the same direction, while, in the second case, point O remains fixed.

3. *General Plane Motion.* Any plane motion which is neither a translation nor a rotation is referred to as a general plane motion. Two examples of general plane motion are given in Fig. 15.4.

15.2. Translation. Consider a rigid slab in translation (either rectilinear or curvilinear translation), and denote by A and B the positions of two of its particles at time t. At time $t + \Delta t$, the two particles will occupy new positions A' and B' (Fig. 15.5*a*). Now, from the very definition of a translation, the line $A'B'$ must be parallel to AB. Besides, since the slab is rigid, we must have $A'B' = AB$. Thus, $ABB'A'$ is a parallelogram, and the two vectors $\Delta\mathbf{r}_A$ and $\Delta\mathbf{r}_B$ representing the displacements of the two particles during the time interval Δt must have the same magnitude and direction. We have, therefore, $\Delta\mathbf{r}_A/\Delta t = \Delta\mathbf{r}_B/\Delta t$ and, at the limit, as Δt approaches zero,

$$\mathbf{v}_A = \mathbf{v}_B \tag{15.1}$$

Since relation (15.1) holds at any time, the vectors $\Delta\mathbf{v}_A$ and $\Delta\mathbf{v}_B$ representing the change in velocity of the two particles during the time interval Δt must be equal. We have, therefore,

$\Delta \mathbf{v}_A / \Delta t = \Delta \mathbf{v}_B / \Delta t$ and, at the limit, as Δt approaches zero,

$$\mathbf{a}_A = \mathbf{a}_B \tag{15.2}$$

Thus, *when a rigid slab is in translation, all the points of the slab have the same velocity and the same acceleration at any given instant* (Fig. 15.5*b* and *c*). In the case of curvilinear translation, the velocity and acceleration change in direction as well as in magnitude at every instant. In the case of rectilinear translation, all particles of the slab move along parallel straight lines, and their velocity and acceleration keep the same direction during the entire motion.

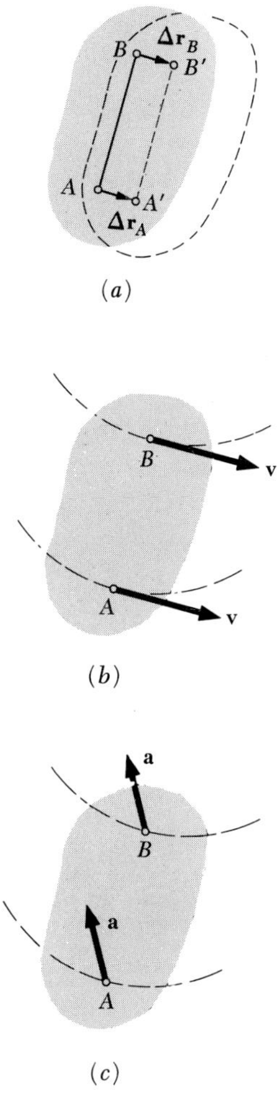

FIG 15.5

15.3. Rotation. Consider a rigid slab which rotates about a fixed axis perpendicular to the plane of the slab and intersecting it at point O. Let P be a point of the slab (Fig. 15.6). The position of the slab will be entirely defined if the angle θ the line OP forms with a fixed direction OQ is given; the angle θ is known as the *angular coordinate* of the slab. The angular coordinate is defined as positive when counterclockwise and will be expressed in radians or, occasionally, in degrees (°) or revolutions (rev). We recall that

$$1 \text{ rev} = 2\pi \text{ radians} = 360°$$

In Chap. 11, the first and second derivatives, respectively, of the coordinate s of a particle were used to define the velocity and acceleration of a particle moving in a straight line. Similarly, the first derivative of the angular coordinate θ of a rotating slab may be used to define the *angular velocity* ω of the slab,

$$\omega = \frac{d\theta}{dt} \tag{15.3}$$

and its second derivative may be used to define the *angular acceleration* α of the slab,

$$\alpha = \frac{d\omega}{dt} = \frac{d^2\theta}{dt^2} \tag{15.4}$$

An alternate form for the angular acceleration is obtained by solving (15.3) for dt and substituting into (15.4). We write $dt = d\theta/\omega$ and

$$\alpha = \omega \frac{d\omega}{d\theta} \tag{15.5}$$

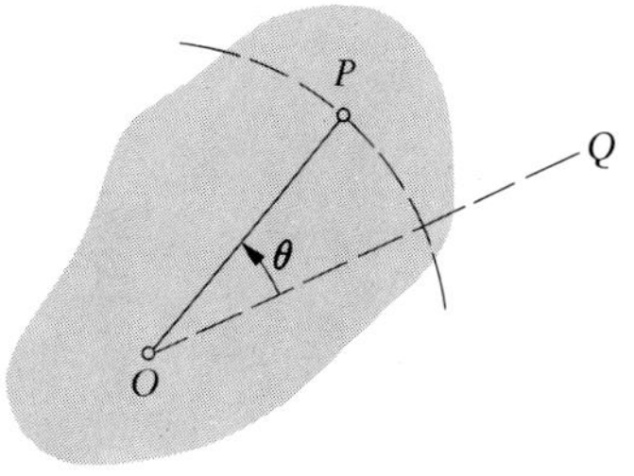

FIG. 15.6

The angular velocity ω is expressed in radians/sec, in rps (revolutions per second), or in rpm (revolutions per minute). The angular acceleration α is generally expressed in radians/sec^2.

Since the angular velocity and the angular acceleration of a slab have a *sense,* as well as a *magnitude,* they should be considered as *vector quantities.*† We may, for instance, represent the angular velocity of the slab of Fig. 15.6 by a vector $\boldsymbol{\omega}$ of magnitude ω directed along the axis of rotation of the slab. This vector will be made to point out of the plane of the figure if the angular velocity is counterclockwise, and into the plane of the figure if the angular velocity is clockwise. The angular acceleration may similarly be represented by a vector $\boldsymbol{\alpha}$ of magnitude α directed along the axis of rotation and pointing out of, or into, the plane of the figure, depending upon the sense of the angular acceleration. However, since in the cases considered in this chapter the axis of rotation will always be perpendicular to the plane of the figure, we need to specify only the sense and the magnitude of the angular velocity and of the angular acceleration. This may be done by using the scalar quantities ω and α, together with a plus or minus sign. As in the case of the angular coordinate θ, the plus sign corresponds to counterclockwise, and the minus sign to clockwise.

It should be observed that the values obtained for the angular velocity and the angular acceleration of a slab are independent of the choice of the reference point P. If a point P' were chosen instead of P (Fig. 15.7), the angular coordinate would be θ', which differs from θ only by the constant angle POP'. The successive derivatives of θ and θ' are thus equal, and the same values are obtained for ω and α.

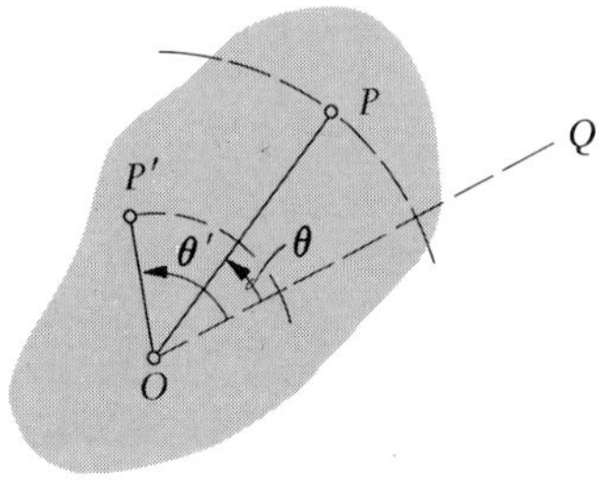

FIG. 15.7

The motion of a slab rotating about a fixed point O is said to be *known* when its coordinate θ may be expressed as a known function of t. In practice, however, the rotation of a slab is seldom defined by a relation between θ and t. More often, the conditions of motion will be specified by the type of angular acceleration that the slab possesses. For example, α may be given as a function of t, or as a function of θ, or as a function of ω. Equations (15.3) to (15.5) may then be used to determine the angular velocity ω and the angular coordinate θ, the procedure to follow being the same as that described in Sec. 11.3 for the rectilinear motion of a particle.

Two particular cases of rotation are frequently encountered:

1. *Uniform Rotation.* This case is characterized by the fact that the angular acceleration is zero. The angular velocity ω

† It may be shown, in the more general case of a rigid body rotating simultaneously about axes having different directions, that angular velocities and angular accelerations obey the parallelogram law of addition.

is thus constant, and the angular coordinate is given by the formula

$$\theta = \theta_0 + \omega t \tag{15.6}$$

2. *Uniformly Accelerated Rotation.* In this case, the angular acceleration α is constant. The following formulas relating angular velocity, angular coordinate, and time may then be derived in a manner similar to that described in Sec. 11.5. The similitude between the formulas derived here and those obtained for the rectilinear uniformly accelerated motion of a particle is easily noted.

$$\omega = \omega_0 + \alpha t \tag{15.7}$$
$$\theta = \theta_0 + \omega_0 t + \tfrac{1}{2}\alpha t^2 \tag{15.8}$$
$$\omega^2 = \omega_0^2 + 2\alpha(\theta - \theta_0) \tag{15.9}$$

It should be emphasized that formula (15.6) may be used only when $\alpha = 0$, and formulas (15.7) to (15.9) only when $\alpha =$ constant. In any other case, the general formulas (15.3) to (15.5) should be used.

15.4. Linear and Angular Velocity, Linear and Angular Acceleration in Rotation. Consider again a point P on a rotating slab (Fig. 15.8a). Point P describes a circle of center O when the slab describes a full rotation. The arc s that P describes while the slab rotates through an angle θ depends not only upon θ but also upon the distance r from O to P. Expressing θ in radians and r and s in the same units of length, we write

$$s = r\theta \tag{15.10}$$

Differentiating, we obtain the following relation between the magnitude v of the *linear velocity* of P (Fig. 15.8b) and the *angular velocity* ω of the slab,

$$\frac{ds}{dt} = r\frac{d\theta}{dt} \qquad v = r\omega \tag{15.11}$$

While the value of the angular velocity ω is independent of the choice of P, the magnitude v of the linear velocity clearly depends upon the distance r. Recalling the definition of the tangential and normal components of the *linear acceleration* of a point P (Sec. 11.12), we write (Fig. 15.8c)

$$a_t = \frac{dv}{dt} = r\frac{d\omega}{dt} \qquad a_t = r\alpha \tag{15.12}$$

$$a_n = \frac{v^2}{r} = \frac{(r\omega)^2}{r} \qquad a_n = r\omega^2 \tag{15.13}$$

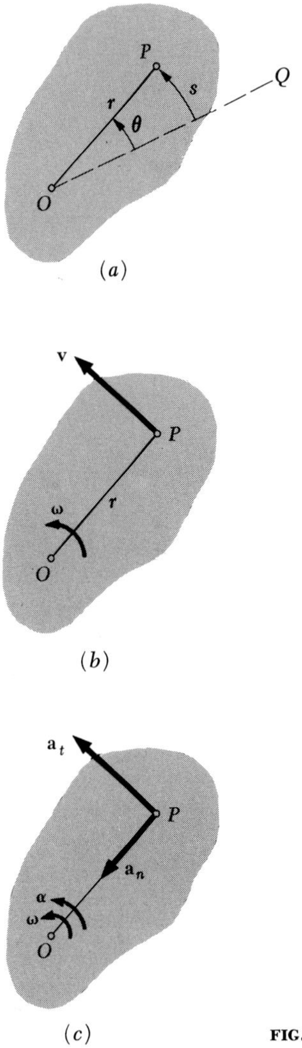

FIG. 15.8

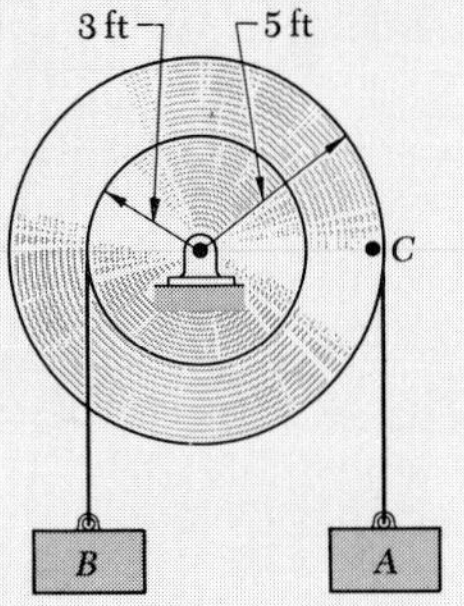

SAMPLE PROBLEM 15.1

A pulley and two loads are connected by inextensible cords as shown. Load A has a constant acceleration of 10 ft/sec^2 and an initial velocity of 15 ft/sec, both directed upward. Determine (*a*) the number of revolutions executed by the pulley in 3 sec, (*b*) the velocity and position of load B after 3 sec, (*c*) the acceleration of point C on the rim of the pulley at $t = 0$.

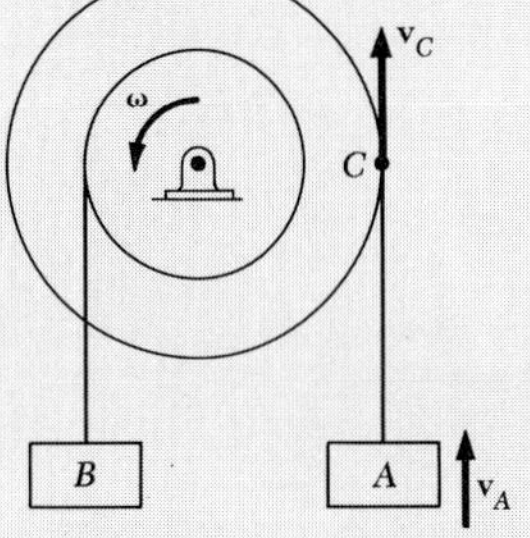

a. **Motion of Pulley.** Since the cord connecting the pulley to load A is inextensible, the velocity of C is equal to the velocity of A and the tangential component of the acceleration of C is equal to the acceleration of A.

$$(\mathbf{v}_C)_0 = (\mathbf{v}_A)_0 = 15 \text{ ft/sec} \uparrow \qquad (\mathbf{a}_C)_t = \mathbf{a}_A = 10 \text{ ft/sec}^2 \uparrow$$

Noting that the distance from C to the center of the pulley is 5 ft, we write

$$(v_C)_0 = r\omega_0 \qquad 15 \text{ ft/sec} = (5 \text{ ft})\omega_0 \qquad \omega_0 = 3 \text{ radians/sec} \circlearrowleft$$
$$(a_C)_t = r\alpha \qquad 10 \text{ ft/sec}^2 = (5 \text{ ft})\alpha \qquad \alpha = 2 \text{ radians/sec}^2 \circlearrowleft$$

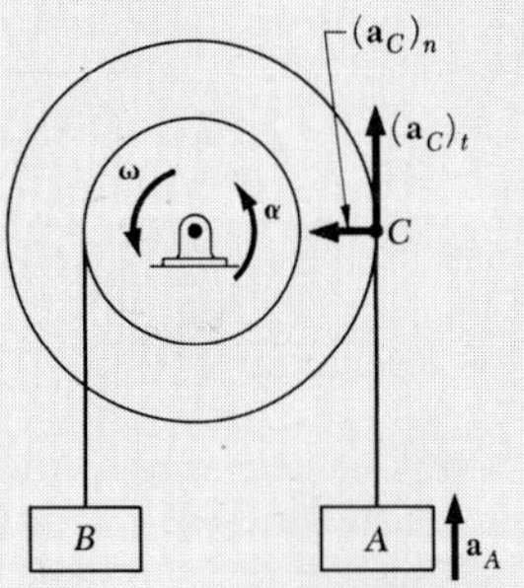

From the equations for uniformly accelerated motion, we obtain, for $t = 3$ sec,

$$\omega = \omega_0 + \alpha t = 3 \text{ radians/sec} + (2 \text{ radians/sec}^2)(3 \text{ sec}) = 9 \text{ radians/sec}$$
$$\omega = 9 \text{ radians/sec} \circlearrowleft$$
$$\theta = \omega_0 t + \tfrac{1}{2}\alpha t^2 = (3 \text{ radians/sec})(3 \text{ sec}) + \tfrac{1}{2}(2 \text{ radians/sec}^2)(3 \text{ sec})^2$$
$$\theta = 18 \text{ radians}$$

$$\text{Number of revolutions} = (18 \text{ radians})\frac{1 \text{ rev}}{2\pi \text{ radians}} = 2.86 \text{ rev} \blacktriangleleft$$

b. **Motion of Load** B. Using the following relations between the linear and angular motion, with $r = 3$ ft, we write

$$v_B = r\omega = (3 \text{ ft})(9 \text{ radians/sec}) \qquad \mathbf{v}_B = 27 \text{ ft/sec} \downarrow \blacktriangleleft$$
$$s_B = r\theta = (3 \text{ ft})(18 \text{ radians}) \qquad \mathbf{s}_B = 54 \text{ ft} \downarrow \blacktriangleleft$$

c. **Acceleration of Point** C **at** $t = 0$. The tangential component of the acceleration is

$$(\mathbf{a}_C)_t = \mathbf{a}_A = 10 \text{ ft/sec}^2 \uparrow$$

Since, at $t = 0$, $\omega_0 = 3$ radians/sec, the normal component of the acceleration is

$$(a_C)_n = r_C\omega_0^2 = (5 \text{ ft})(3 \text{ radians/sec})^2 \qquad (\mathbf{a}_C)_n = 45 \text{ ft/sec}^2 \leftarrow$$

The magnitude and direction of the total acceleration are obtained by writing

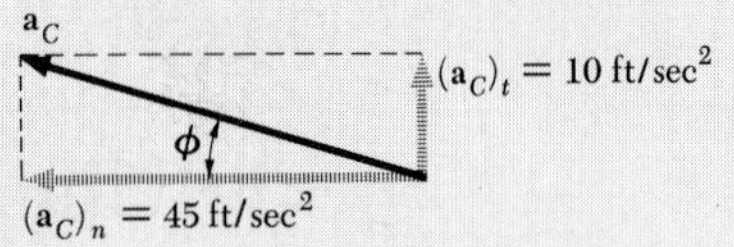

$$(45 \text{ ft/sec}^2)\tan\phi = 10 \text{ ft/sec}^2 \qquad \phi = 12.5°$$
$$a_C \sin 12.5° = 10 \text{ ft/sec}^2 \qquad a_C = 46.1 \text{ ft/sec}^2$$
$$\mathbf{a}_C = 46.1 \text{ ft/sec}^2 \measuredangle 12.5° \blacktriangleleft$$

PROBLEMS

15.1. The motion of a cam is defined by the relation $\theta = \frac{1}{10}t(12 - t^2)$, where θ is expressed in radians and t in seconds. Determine the angular coordinate, the angular velocity, and the angular acceleration of the cam when (*a*) $t = 0$, (*b*) $t = 3$ sec.

15.2. For the cam of Prob. 15.1 determine (*a*) the time at which the angular velocity is zero, (*b*) the corresponding angular coordinate and angular acceleration.

15.3. The motion of an oscillating crank is defined by the relation $\theta = \theta_0 \sin (2\pi t/T)$, where θ is expressed in radians and t in seconds. Knowing that $\theta_0 = 0.60$ radians and $T = 0.50$ sec, determine the maximum angular velocity and the maximum angular acceleration of the crank.

15.4. The motion of a disk rotating in an oil bath is defined by the relation $\theta = \theta_0(1 - e^{-t/4})$, where θ is expressed in radians and t in seconds. Knowing that $\theta_0 = 0.80$ radians, determine the angular coordinate, velocity, and acceleration of the disk when (*a*) $t = 0$, (*b*) $t = 4$ sec, (*c*) $t = \infty$.

15.5. A small grinding wheel is attached to the shaft of an electric motor which has a rated speed of 3,600 rpm. When the power is turned on, the unit reaches its rated speed in 5 sec, and when the power is turned off, the unit coasts to rest in 70 sec. Assuming uniformly accelerated motion, determine the number of revolutions that the motor executes (*a*) in reaching its rated speed, (*b*) in coasting to rest.

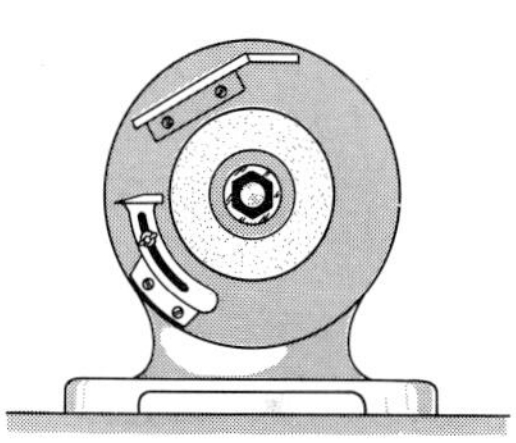

FIG. P 15.5

15.6. The rotor of a steam turbine is rotating at a speed of 10,800 rpm when the steam supply is suddenly cut off. It is observed that 6 min 20 sec are required for the rotor to come to rest. Assuming uniformly accelerated motion, determine (*a*) the angular acceleration, (*b*) the total number of revolutions that the rotor executes before coming to rest.

15.7. As steam is slowly injected into a turbine, the angular acceleration of the rotor is observed to increase linearly with the time t. Knowing that the rotor starts from rest at $t = 0$ and that after 10 sec the rotor has completed 20 revolutions, write the equations of motion for the rotor, and determine (*a*) the angular velocity at $t = 20$ sec, (*b*) the time required for the rotor to complete its first 40 revolutions.

15.8. The deceleration of a flywheel when coasting freely is defined by the relation $\alpha = -0.0002\omega^2$, where α is the angular acceleration in radians/sec^2 and ω is the angular velocity in radians/sec. If the flywheel starts coasting freely when the angular velocity is ω_0, determine the number of revolutions that it will execute before the angular velocity drops to $\frac{1}{2}\omega_0$.

15.9. The earth makes one complete revolution on its axis in 23.93 hr. Knowing that the mean radius of the earth is 3,960 miles, determine the linear velocity and acceleration of a point on the surface of the earth (*a*) at the equator, (*b*) at Philadelphia, latitude 40° north, (*c*) at the north pole.

15.10. The earth makes one complete revolution about the sun in 365.24 days. Assuming that the orbit of the earth is circular and has a radius of 93,000,000 miles, determine the velocity and acceleration of the earth.

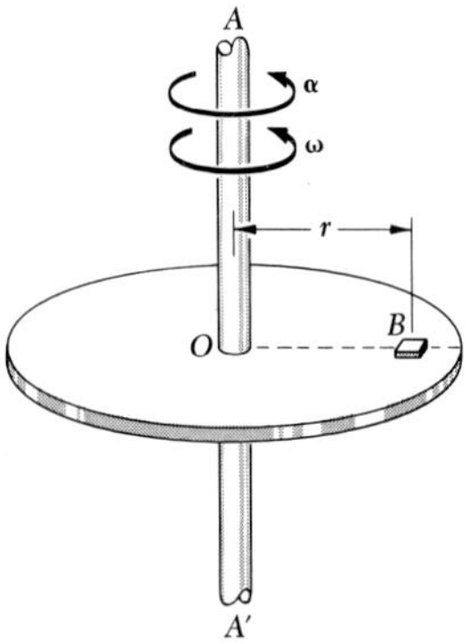

FIG. P 15.11 AND P 15.12

15.11. A small block B rests on a horizontal plate which can rotate about a fixed vertical axis AA'. If the plate is initially at rest at $t = 0$ and is accelerated at the constant rate of α radians/sec^2, derive an expression (*a*) for the total acceleration of the block at time t, (*b*) for the angle between the total acceleration and the radius OB at time t.

15.12. It is known that the static-friction force between block B and the plate will be exceeded and that the block will start sliding on the plate when the total acceleration of the block reaches 15 ft/sec^2. If the plate starts from rest at $t = 0$ and is accelerated at the constant rate of 4 radians/sec^2, determine the time t and the angular velocity of the plate when the block starts sliding, assuming $r = 6$ in.

15.13. In Prob. 15.12, determine the constant value α of the angular acceleration for which the block will start sliding when the angle between the total acceleration of the block and the radius OB is 45°. What is the value of the angular velocity when the block starts sliding?

15.14. The angular acceleration of the circular plate is defined by the relation $\alpha = \alpha_0 e^{-t}$. The plate has a radius of 2 ft and starts from rest at $t = 0$. Knowing that $\alpha_0 = 10$ radians/sec^2, determine the total acceleration of point B when (*a*) $t = 0$, (*b*) $t = 1$ sec, (*c*) $t = \infty$.

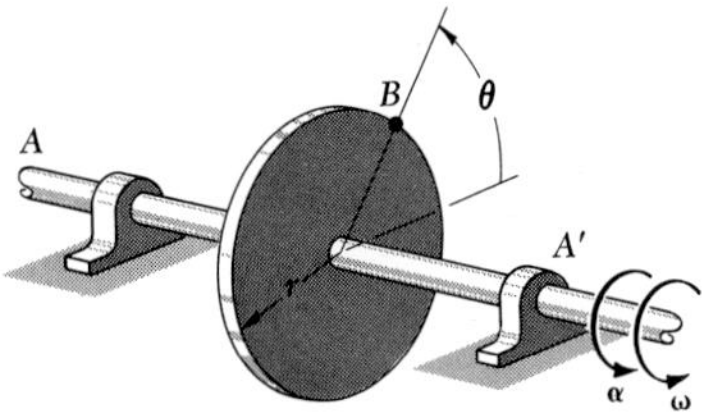

FIG. P 15.14

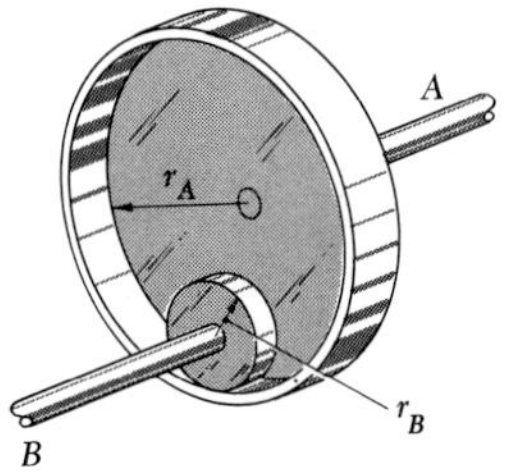

FIG. P 15.15 AND P 15.16

15.15. The friction wheel B rolls without slipping on the inside rim of wheel A. Knowing that shaft B rotates at a constant angular velocity ω_B, determine (*a*) the angular velocity of shaft A, (*b*) the linear acceleration of a point on the inside rim of wheel A.

15.16. The angular velocity of wheel B increases uniformly from 200 rpm to 500 rpm over a 10-sec interval. Knowing that $r_A = 6$ in. and $r_B = 2$ in., determine (*a*) the angular acceleration of wheel A, (*b*) the number of revolutions executed by wheel A during the 10-sec interval.

15.17. When released from rest at $t = 0$, the load is observed to fall 48 ft in 4 sec. Assuming uniformly accelerated motion, determine (*a*) the angular acceleration of the drum, (*b*) the angular velocity of the drum at $t = 3$ sec.

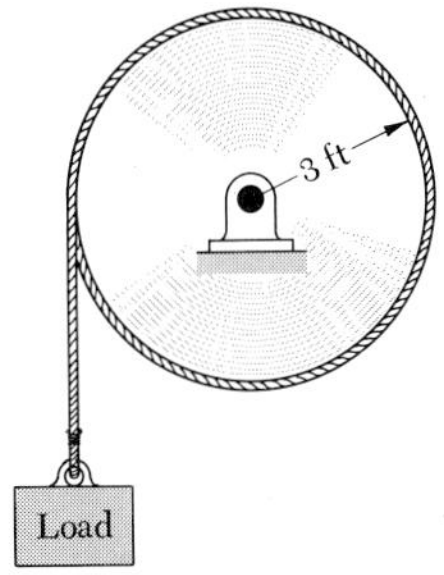

FIG. P 15.17 AND P 15.18

15.18. The hoisting drum shown has an angular velocity of 120 rpm when the power is suddenly cut off. Knowing that the load rises through 60 more feet before coming to rest, determine (*a*) the angular acceleration of the drum, (*b*) the time required for the drum to come to rest.

15.19. The two friction wheels A and B are to be brought together. Wheel A has an initial angular velocity of 600 rpm clockwise and will coast to rest in 40 sec, while wheel B is initially at rest and is given a constant counterclockwise angular acceleration of 2 radians/sec^2. Determine (*a*) at what time the wheels may be brought together if they are not to slip, (*b*) the angular velocity of each wheel as contact is made.

15.20. Two friction wheels A and B are both rotating freely at 300 rpm clockwise when they are brought into contact. After 3 sec of slippage, during which each wheel has a constant angular acceleration, wheel A reaches a final angular velocity of 60 rpm clockwise. Determine (*a*) the angular acceleration of each wheel during the period of slippage, (*b*) the time at which the angular velocity of wheel B is equal to zero.

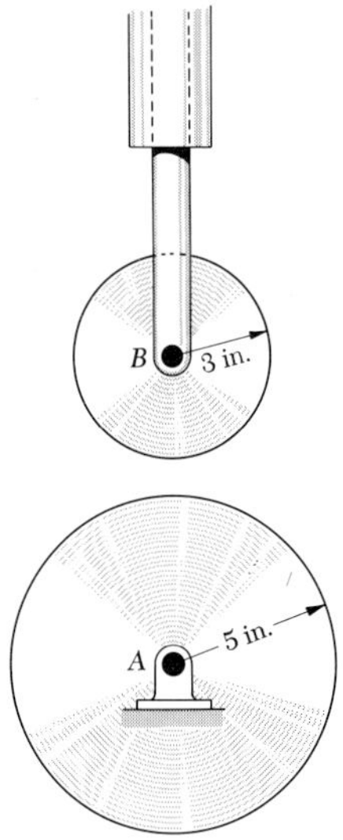

FIG. P 15.19 AND P 15.20

***15.21.** In a continuous printing process, paper is drawn into the presses at a constant speed v. Denoting by r the radius of paper on the roll at any given time and by a the thickness of the paper, derive an expression for the angular acceleration of the paper roll.

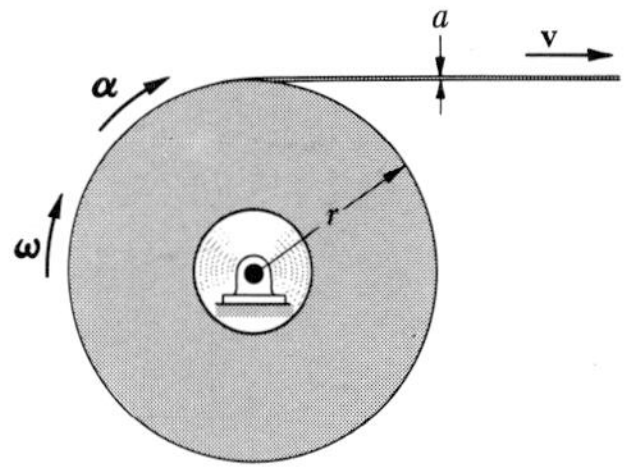

FIG. P 15.21

***15.22.** The motion of the circular plate of Fig. P 15.14 is defined by the relation $\theta = \theta_0 \sin(2\pi t/T)$, where θ is expressed in radians and t in seconds. Derive expressions (*a*) for the magnitude of the total acceleration of point B on the rim of the plate, (*b*) for the values of θ at which the total acceleration of point B reaches its maximum and minimum values, and for the corresponding values of the total acceleration of point B.

15.5. General Plane Motion. As indicated in Sec. 15.1, we understand by general plane motion a plane motion which is neither a translation nor a rotation. As we shall presently see, however, *a general plane motion may always be considered as the sum of a translation and a rotation.*

Consider, for example, a wheel rolling on a straight track (Fig. 15.9). Over a certain interval of time, two given points A and B will have moved, respectively, from A_1 to A_2 and from B_1 to B_2. The same result could be obtained through a translation which would bring A and B into A_2 and B_1' (the line AB remaining vertical), followed by a rotation about A bringing B into B_2. Although the original rolling motion differs from the combination of translation and rotation when these motions are taken in succession, the original motion may be completely duplicated by a combination of simultaneous translation and rotation.

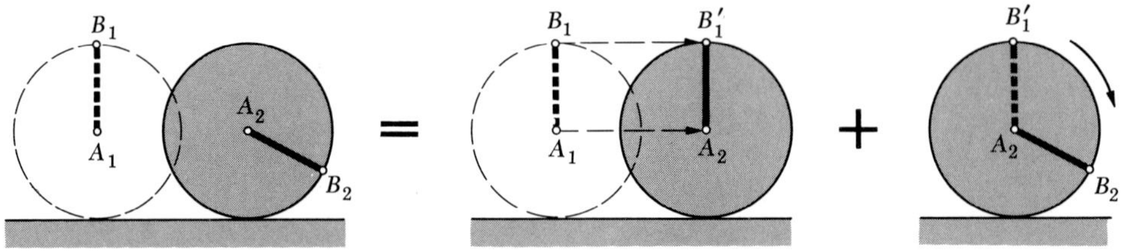

FIG. 15.9 Plane motion = Translation with A + Rotation about A

Another example of plane motion is given in Fig. 15.10, which represents a rod whose extremities slide, respectively, along a horizontal and a vertical track. This motion may be replaced by a translation in a horizontal direction and a rotation about A (Fig. 15.10*a*) or by a translation in a vertical direction and a rotation about B (Fig. 15.10*b*).

In general, any plane motion of a rigid slab may be replaced by a translation in which all the particles of the slab move along paths parallel to the path actually followed by some arbitrary reference point A, and by a rotation about the reference point A. We saw in Sec. 11.11 that, when two particles A and B move in a plane, the absolute motion of B may be obtained by combining the motion of A and the relative motion of B with respect to A. We recall that by "absolute motion of B" we mean the motion of B with respect to fixed axes, while by "relative motion of B with respect to A" we mean the motion of B with respect to a system of axes whose origin moves with A but which does not rotate. Now, in the present case, the two particles belong to the same rigid body. Particle B must thus remain at a constant distance from A and, *to an observer*

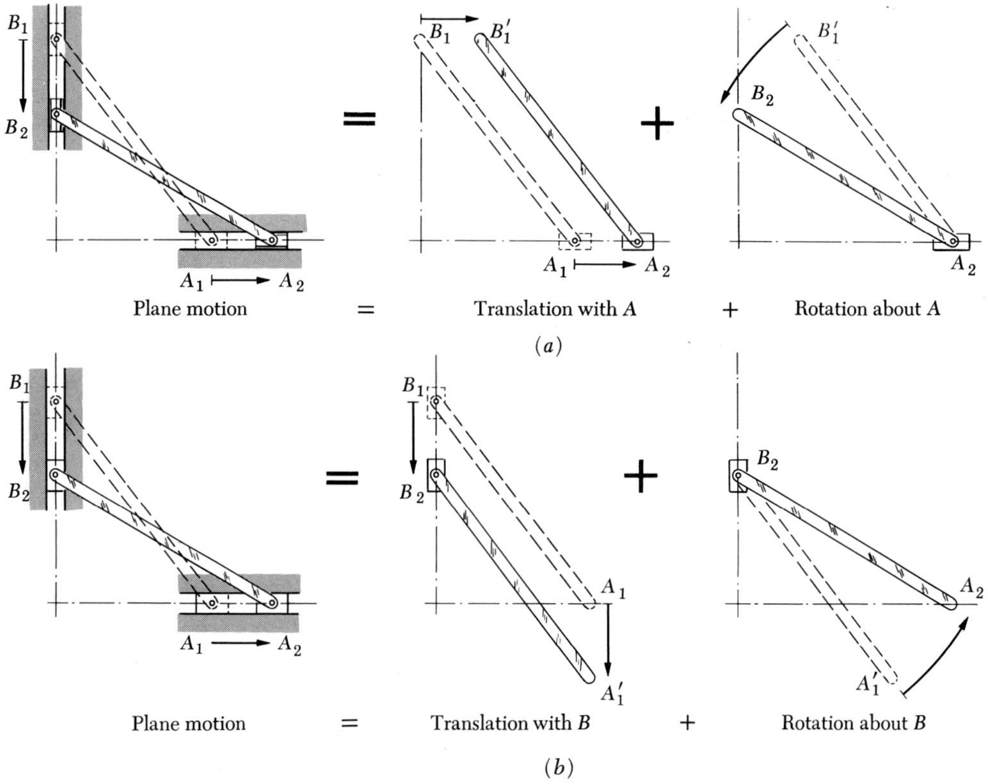

FIG. 15.10

moving with A, but not rotating, particle B will appear to describe an arc of circle centered at A. Considering successively each particle of the slab, and resolving its motion into the motion of A and its relative motion about A, we thus conclude that any plane motion of a rigid slab is the sum of a translation with A and a rotation about A.

15.6. Absolute and Relative Velocity in Plane Motion. We saw in the preceding section that any plane motion of a slab may be replaced by a translation defined by the motion of an arbitrary reference point A, and by a rotation about A. The absolute velocity $\mathbf{v}_B$ of a particle B of the slab is obtained from the relative-velocity formula derived in Sec. 11.11,

$$\mathbf{v}_B = \mathbf{v}_A + \mathbf{v}_{B/A} \tag{15.14}$$

where the right-hand member represents a vector sum. The velocity $\mathbf{v}_A$ corresponds to the translation of the slab with A, while the relative velocity $\mathbf{v}_{B/A}$ is associated with the rotation of the slab about A and is measured with respect to axes centered at A and of fixed orientation (Fig. 15.11). Denoting by

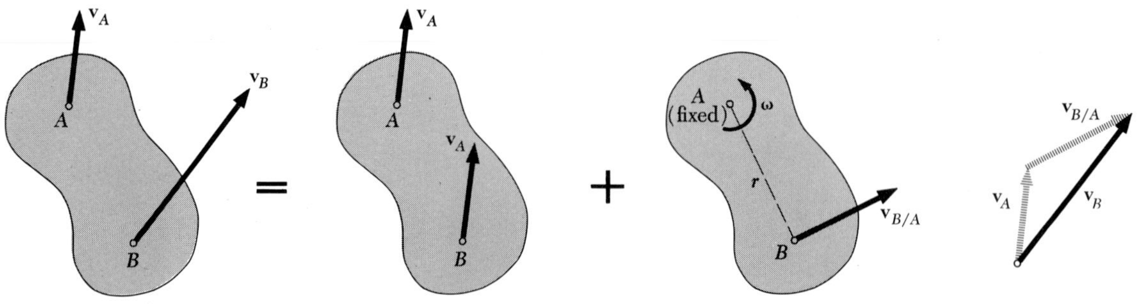

Plane motion = Translation with *A* + Rotation about *A* $\mathbf{v}_B = \mathbf{v}_A + \mathbf{v}_{B/A}$

FIG. 15.11

r the distance from A to B, and by ω the magnitude of the angular velocity $\boldsymbol{\omega}$ of the slab with respect to axes of fixed orientation, we find that the magnitude of the relative velocity $\mathbf{v}_{B/A}$ is

$$v_{B/A} = r\omega \qquad (15.15)$$

As an example, we shall consider again the rod AB of Fig. 15.10. Assuming that the velocity $\mathbf{v}_A$ of end A is known, we propose to find the velocity $\mathbf{v}_B$ of end B and the angular velocity $\boldsymbol{\omega}$ of the rod, in terms of the velocity $\mathbf{v}_A$, the length l, and the angle θ. Choosing A as reference point, we express that the given motion is equivalent to a translation with A and a rotation about A (Fig. 15.12). The absolute velocity of B must therefore be equal to the vector sum

$$\mathbf{v}_B = \mathbf{v}_A + \mathbf{v}_{B/A} \qquad (15.14)$$

We note that, while the direction of $\mathbf{v}_{B/A}$ is known, its magnitude $l\omega$ is unknown. However, this is compensated by the fact that the direction of $\mathbf{v}_B$ is known. We may therefore complete the diagram of Fig. 15.12. Solving for the magnitudes v_B and ω, we write

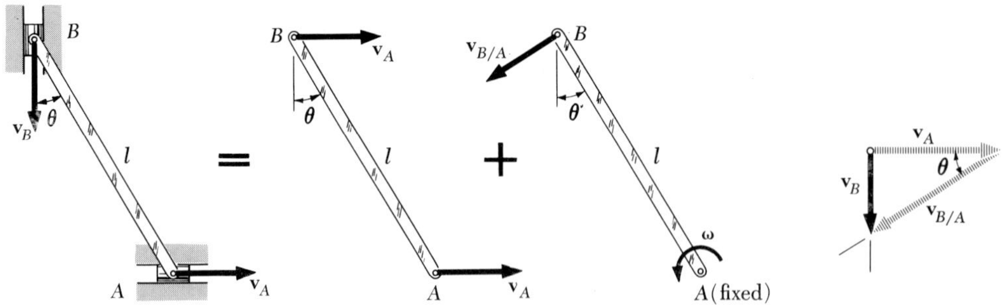

FIG. 15.12 Plane motion = Translation with *A* + Rotation about *A* $\mathbf{v}_B = \mathbf{v}_A + \mathbf{v}_{B/A}$

$$v_B = v_A \tan\theta \qquad \omega = \frac{v_{B/A}}{l} = \frac{v_A}{l\cos\theta} \tag{15.16}$$

The same result may be obtained by using B as a point of reference. Resolving the given motion into a translation with B and a rotation about B (Fig. 15.13), we write the equation

$$\mathbf{v}_A = \mathbf{v}_B + \mathbf{v}_{A/B} \tag{15.17}$$

which is represented graphically in Fig. 15.13. We note that $\mathbf{v}_{A/B}$ and $\mathbf{v}_{B/A}$ have the same magnitude $l\omega$ but opposite sense. The sense of the relative velocity depends, therefore, upon the point of reference which has been selected and should be carefully ascertained from the appropriate diagram (Fig. 15.12 or 15.13).

Finally, we observe that the angular velocity ω of the rod in its rotation about B is the same as in its rotation about A. It is measured in both cases by the rate of change of the angle θ. This result is quite general; we should therefore bear in mind that *the angular velocity* ω *of a rigid body in plane motion is independent of the reference point.*

Most mechanisms consist, not of one, but of *several* moving parts. When the various parts of a mechanism are pin-connected, its analysis may be carried out by considering each part as a rigid body, while keeping in mind that the points where two parts are connected must have the same absolute velocity (see Sample Prob. 15.3). A similar analysis may be used when gears are involved, since the teeth in contact must also have the same absolute velocity. However, when a mechanism contains parts which slide on each other, the relative velocity of the parts in contact must be taken into account (see Secs. 15.10 and 15.11).

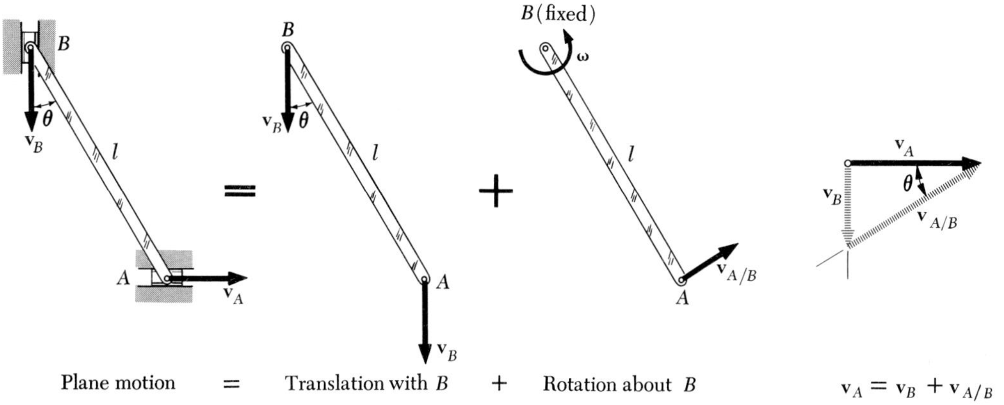

FIG. 15.13

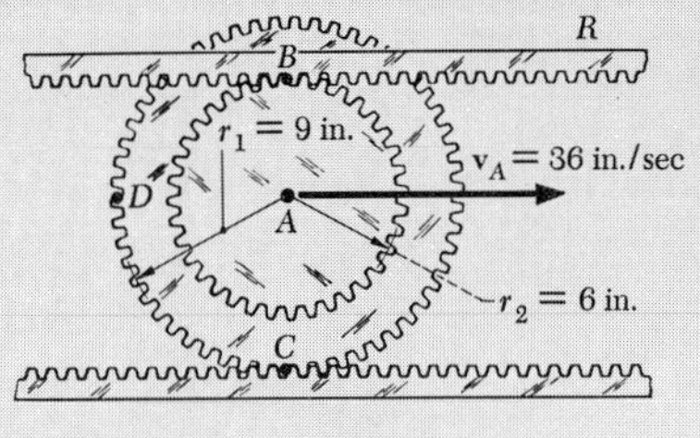

SAMPLE PROBLEM 15.2

The double gear shown rolls on the stationary lower rack; the velocity of its center A is 36 in./sec directed to the right. Determine (a) the angular velocity of the gear, (b) the velocities of the upper rack R and of point D of the gear.

a. **Angular Velocity of the Gear.** Since the gear rolls on the lower rack, its center A moves through a distance equal to the outer circumference $2\pi r_1$ for each full revolution of the gear. Noting that 1 rev $=$ 2π radians, we obtain the coordinate s_A in terms of the corresponding angular coordinate θ (in radians) of the gear by a proportion,

$$\frac{s_A}{2\pi r_1} = \frac{\theta}{2\pi} \qquad s_A = r_1\theta$$

Differentiating with respect to the time t and substituting the known values $v_A = 36$ in./sec and $r_1 = 9$ in., we obtain

$$v_A = r_1\omega \qquad 36 \text{ in./sec} = (9 \text{ in.})\omega \qquad \omega = 4 \text{ radians/sec} \circlearrowright \blacktriangleleft$$

b. **Velocities.** The rolling motion is resolved into two component motions: a translation with the center A and a rotation about the center A. In the translation, all points of the gear move with the same velocity $\mathbf{v}_A$. In the rotation, each point of the gear moves about A with a relative velocity of magnitude $r\omega$, where r is the distance from A.

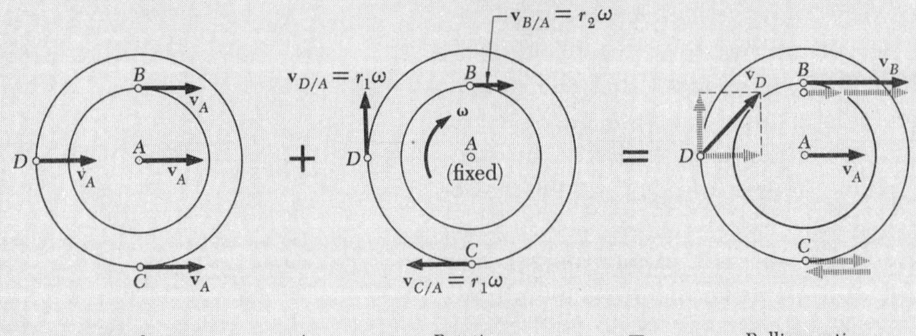

Translation + Rotation = Rolling motion

Velocity of Upper Rack. The velocity of the upper rack is equal to the velocity of point B; we write

$$\mathbf{v}_R = \mathbf{v}_B = \mathbf{v}_A + \mathbf{v}_{B/A}$$

where $\qquad \mathbf{v}_A = 36 \text{ in./sec} \rightarrow$

$$v_{B/A} = (6 \text{ in.})(4 \text{ radians/sec}) = 24 \text{ in./sec} \qquad \mathbf{v}_{B/A} = 24 \text{ in./sec} \rightarrow$$

Since $\mathbf{v}_A$ and $\mathbf{v}_{B/A}$ are collinear, we add their magnitudes and obtain

$$\mathbf{v}_R = 60 \text{ in./sec} \rightarrow \blacktriangleleft$$

Velocity of Point D: $\mathbf{v}_D = \mathbf{v}_A + \mathbf{v}_{D/A}$

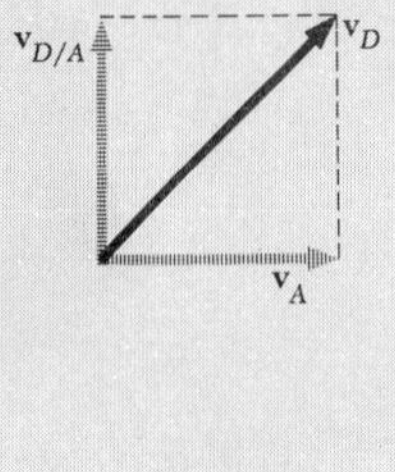

where $\qquad \mathbf{v}_A = 36 \text{ in./sec} \rightarrow$

$$v_{D/A} = (9)(4) = 36 \text{ in./sec} \qquad \mathbf{v}_{D/A} = 36 \text{ in./sec} \uparrow$$

Adding these velocities vectorially, we obtain

$$\mathbf{v}_D = 50.9 \text{ in./sec} \measuredangle 45^\circ \blacktriangleleft$$

SAMPLE PROBLEM 15.3

In the engine system shown, the crank AB has a constant clockwise angular velocity of 2,000 rpm. For the crank position indicated, determine (*a*) the angular velocity of the connecting rod BD, (*b*) the velocity of the piston P.

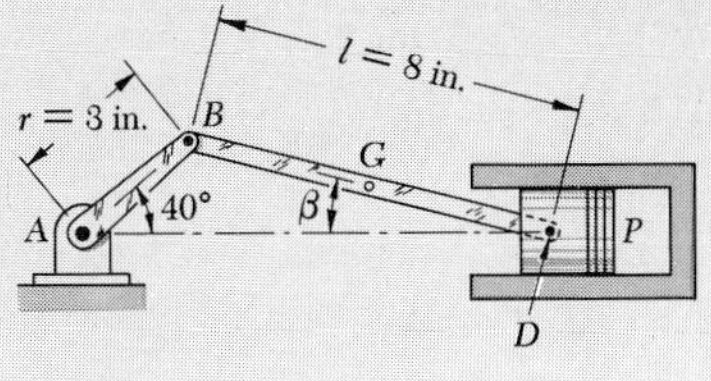

Motion of Crank AB. The crank AB rotates about point A. Expressing ω_{AB} in radians/sec and writing $v_B = r\omega_{AB}$, we obtain

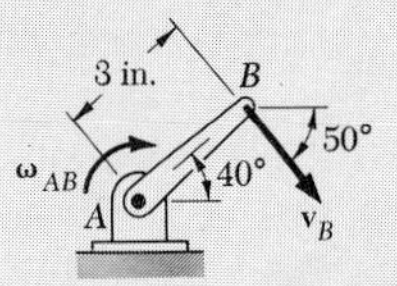

$$\omega_{AB} = \left(2{,}000\ \frac{\text{rev}}{\text{min}}\right)\left(\frac{1\ \text{min}}{60\ \text{sec}}\right)\left(\frac{2\pi\ \text{radians}}{1\ \text{rev}}\right) = 209\ \text{radians/sec}$$

$$v_B = (AB)\omega_{AB} = (3\ \text{in.})(209\ \text{radians/sec}) = 627\ \text{in./sec}$$
$$\mathbf{v}_B = 627\ \text{in./sec} \searrow 50^\circ$$

Motion of Connecting Rod BD. We consider this motion as a general plane motion. Using the law of sines, we compute the angle β between the connecting rod and the horizontal,

$$\frac{\sin 40^\circ}{8\ \text{in.}} = \frac{\sin \beta}{3\ \text{in.}} \qquad \beta = 13.9^\circ$$

The velocity $\mathbf{v}_D$ of the point D where the rod is attached to the piston must be horizontal, while the velocity of point B is equal to the velocity $\mathbf{v}_B$ obtained above. Resolving the motion of BD into a translation with B and a rotation about B, we obtain

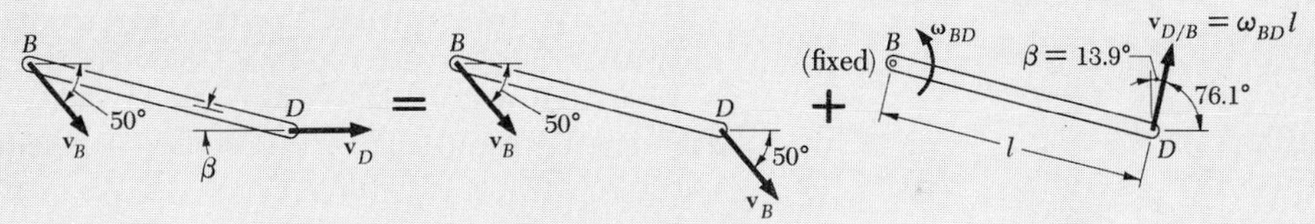

Plane motion = Translation + Rotation

Expressing the relation between the velocities $\mathbf{v}_D$, $\mathbf{v}_B$, and $\mathbf{v}_{D/B}$, we write

$$\mathbf{v}_D = \mathbf{v}_B + \mathbf{v}_{D/B}$$

We draw the vector diagram corresponding to this equation. Recalling that $\beta = 13.9^\circ$, we determine the angles of the triangle and write

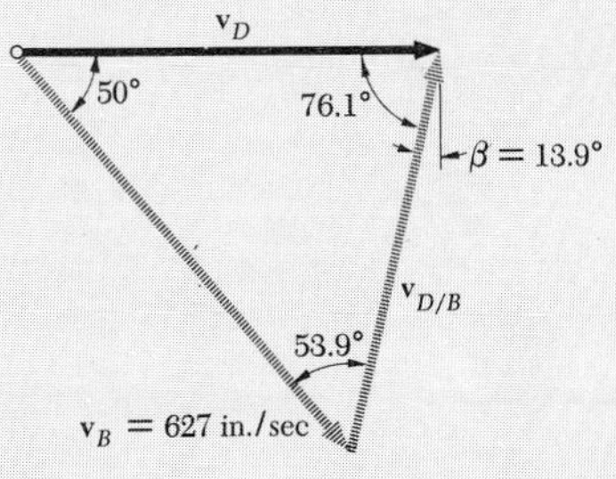

$$\frac{v_D}{\sin 53.9^\circ} = \frac{v_{D/B}}{\sin 50^\circ} = \frac{627\ \text{in./sec}}{\sin 76.1^\circ}$$

$$v_{D/B} = 495\ \text{in./sec} \qquad \mathbf{v}_{D/B} = 495\ \text{in./sec} \measuredangle 76.1^\circ$$
$$v_D = 522\ \text{in./sec} = 43.5\ \text{ft/sec} \qquad \mathbf{v}_D = 43.5\ \text{ft/sec} \rightarrow$$
$$\mathbf{v}_P = \mathbf{v}_D = 43.5\ \text{ft/sec} \rightarrow \quad ◄$$

Since $v_{D/B} = l\omega_{BD}$, we have

$$495\ \text{in./sec} = (8\ \text{in.})\omega_{BD} \qquad \omega_{BD} = 61.9\ \text{radians/sec} \circlearrowleft \quad ◄$$

PROBLEMS

15.23. An automobile travels to the right at a constant speed of 60 mph. If the diameter of a wheel is 26 in., determine the velocities of points *B, C, D,* and *E* on the rim of the wheel.

15.24. Solve Prob. 15.23 assuming that the diameter of the wheel is reduced to 24 in.

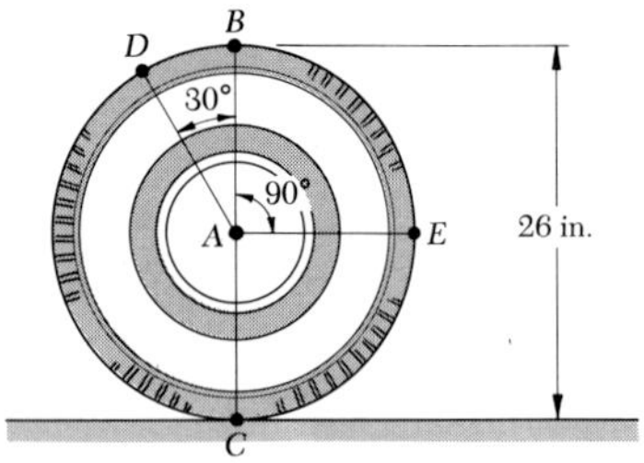

FIG. P 15.23

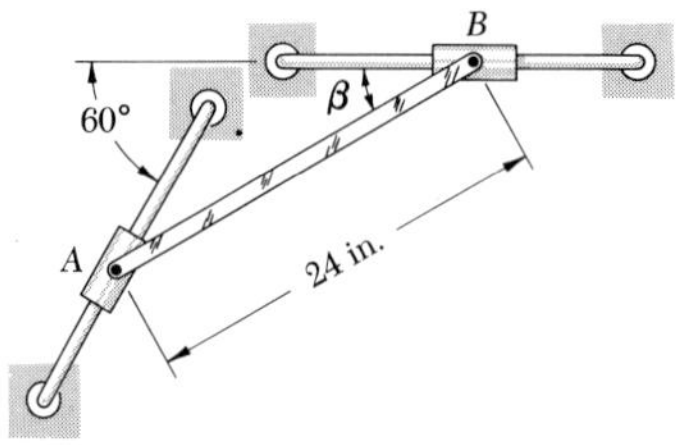

FIG. P 15.25

15.25. Collar *B* moves with a constant velocity of 30 in./sec to the left. At the instant when $\beta = 30°$, determine (*a*) the angular velocity of rod *AB*, (*b*) the velocity of collar *A*.

15.26. Solve Prob. 15.25 assuming that $\beta = 45°$.

15.27. Two rollers *A* and *B* of radius *r* are joined by a link *AB* and roll along a horizontal surface. A drum *C* of radius 2*r* is placed on the rollers as shown. If the link moves to the right with a constant velocity **v**, determine (*a*) the angular velocity of the rollers and of the drum, (*b*) the velocity of point *E* on the drum.

15.28. In Prob. 15.27, determine the velocities of points *D* and *F* on the drum.

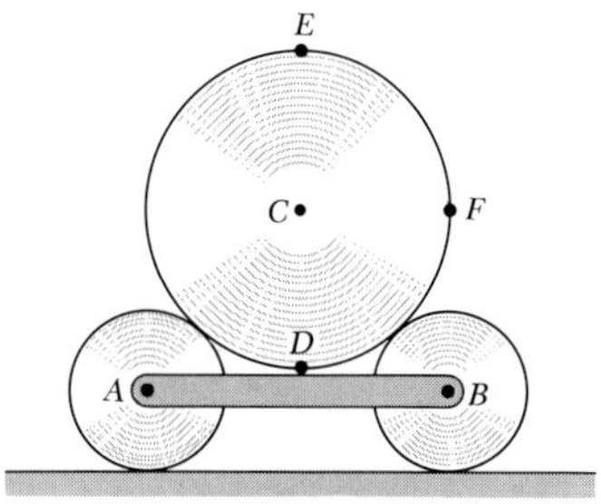

FIG. P 15.27

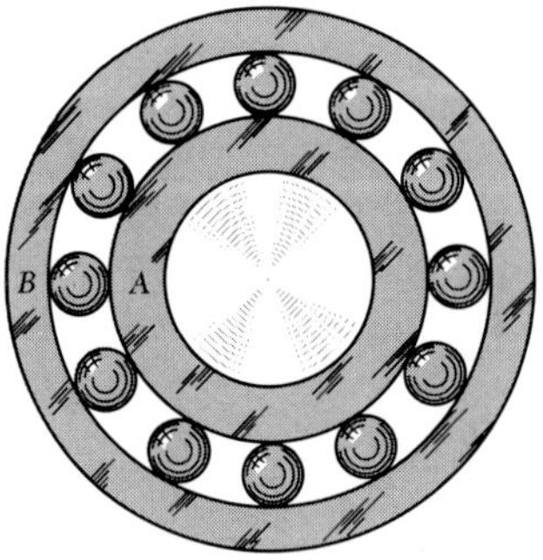

FIG. P 15.29

15.29. In the simplified sketch of a ball bearing shown, the diameter of the inner race *A* is 2.5 in. and the diameter of each ball is 0.5 in. The outer race *B* is stationary while the inner race has an angular velocity of 3,600 rpm. Determine (*a*) the linear velocity of the center of each ball, (*b*) the angular velocity of each ball, (*c*) the number of times per minute each ball describes a complete circle.

FIG. P 15.30 AND P 15.31

15.30. In the planetary gear system shown, the radius of the central gear A is a, the radius of each planetary gear is b, and the radius of the outer gear E is $a + 2b$. In a particular gear system where $a = b = 2\frac{1}{4}$ in., the angular velocity of gear A is ω_A clockwise. Knowing that the outer gear is stationary, determine (a) the angular velocity of the spider connecting the planetary gears, (b) the angular velocity of each planetary gear.

15.31. In the planetary gear system shown, the radius of the central gear A is a, the radius of each of the planetary gears is b, and the radius of the outer gear E is $a + 2b$. The angular velocity of gear A is ω_A clockwise and the outer gear is stationary. If the angular velocity of the spider BCD is to be $\omega_A/5$, determine (a) the required value of the ratio b/a, (b) the corresponding angular velocity of each planetary gear.

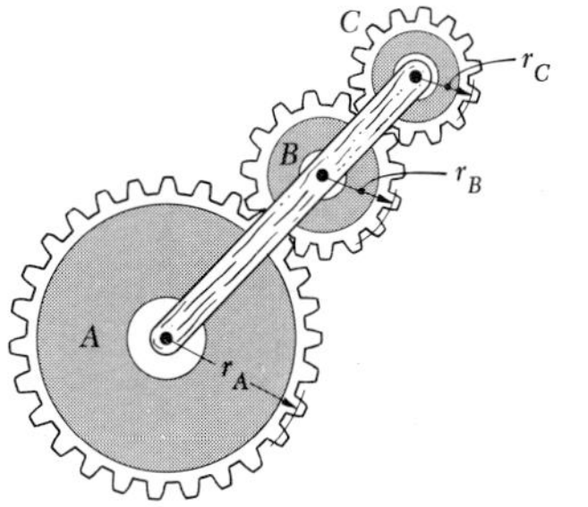

FIG. P 15.32

15.32. Three gears A, B, and C are pinned at their centers to rod ABC. Knowing that $r_A = 3r_B = 3r_C$ and that gear A does not rotate, determine the angular velocity of gears B and C when the rod ABC rotates clockwise with an angular velocity of 10 rpm.

15.33. Crank AB has a constant angular velocity of 200 rpm counterclockwise. Determine the angular velocity of rod BD and the velocity of collar D when (a) $\theta = 0$, (b) $\theta = 90°$, (c) $\theta = 180°$.

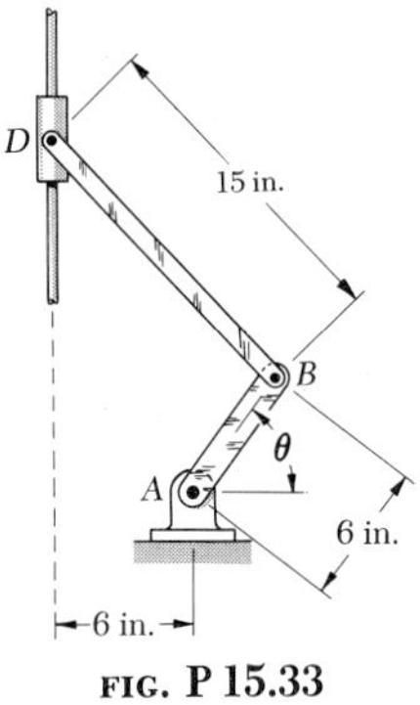

FIG. P 15.33

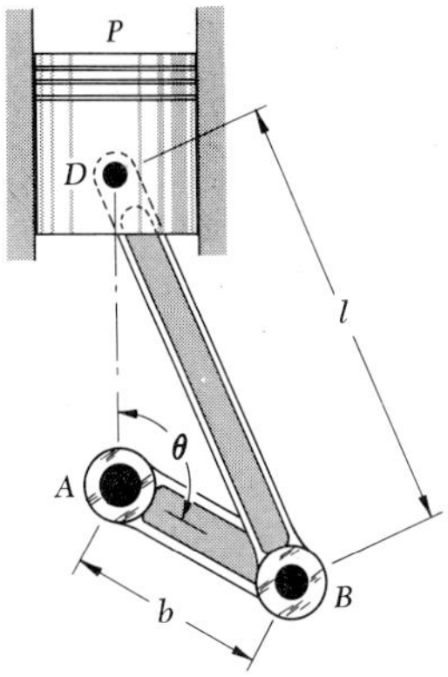

FIG. P 15.34

15.34. In the engine system shown, $l = 8$ in. and $b = 2$ in.; the crank AB rotates with a constant angular velocity of 1,000 rpm clockwise. Determine the velocity of the piston P and the angular velocity of the connecting rod for the position corresponding to (a) $\theta = 0$, (b) $\theta = 90°$, (c) $\theta = 180°$.

15.35. Solve Prob. 15.33 for the position corresponding to $\theta = 30°$.

15.36. Solve Prob. 15.34 for the position corresponding to $\theta = 60°$.

15.37 through 15.40. In the position shown, bar AB has a constant angular velocity of 4 radians/sec counterclockwise. Determine the angular velocity of bars BD and DE.

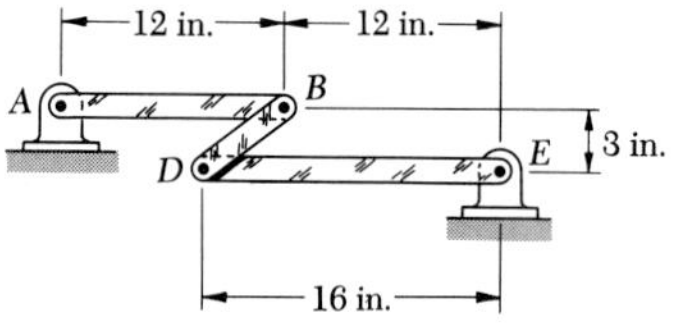

FIG. P 15.37

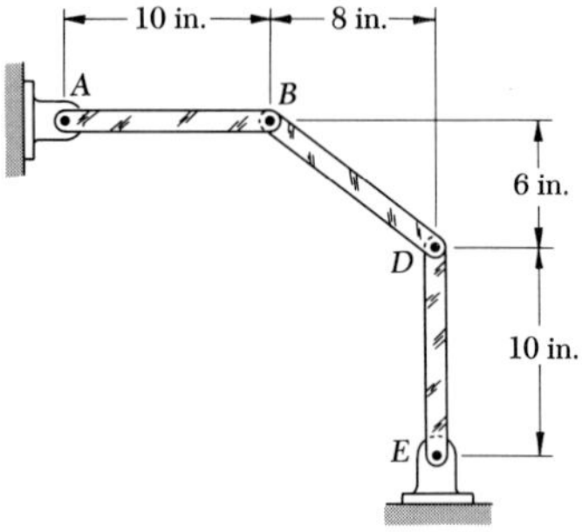

FIG. P 15.38

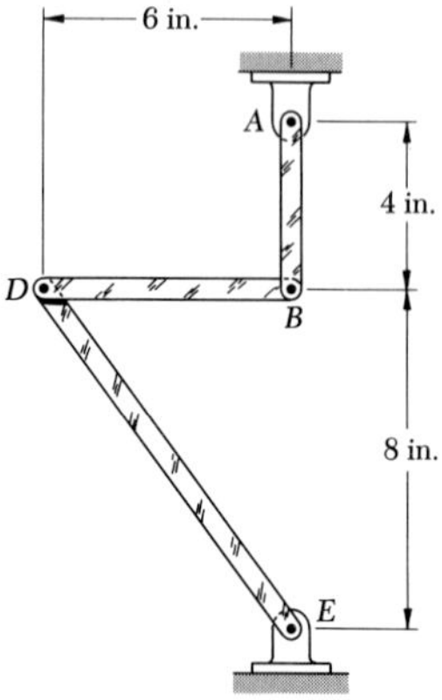

FIG. P 15.39

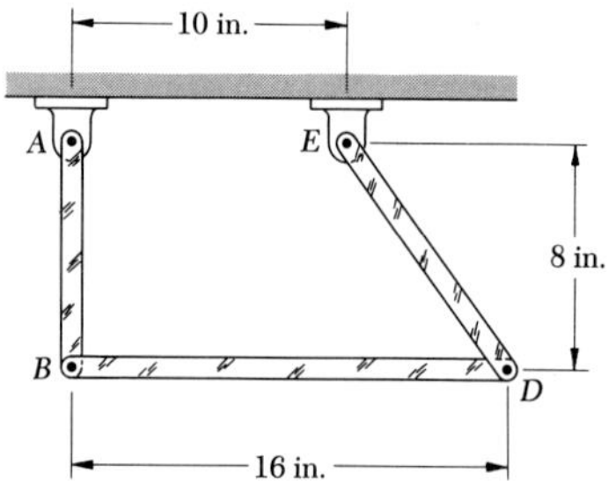

FIG. P 15.40

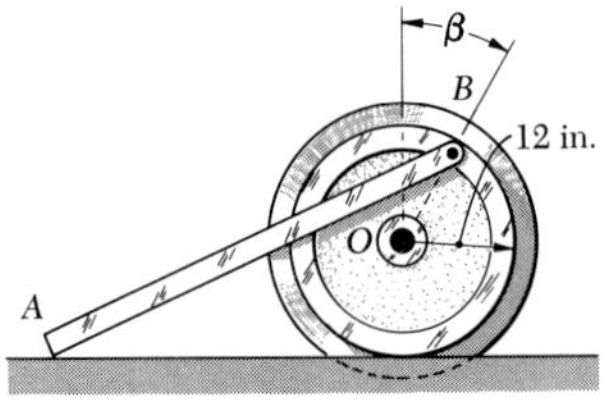

FIG. P 15.41

15.41. The flanged wheel rolls to the right with a constant velocity of 4 ft/sec. The rod AB is 48 in. long and is attached to the wheel at B. Determine the angular velocity of AB and the linear velocity of A (*a*) when $\beta = 0$, (*b*) when $\beta = 90°$.

15.42. Solve Prob. 15.41 assuming (*a*) $\beta = 180°$, (*b*) $\beta = 60°$.

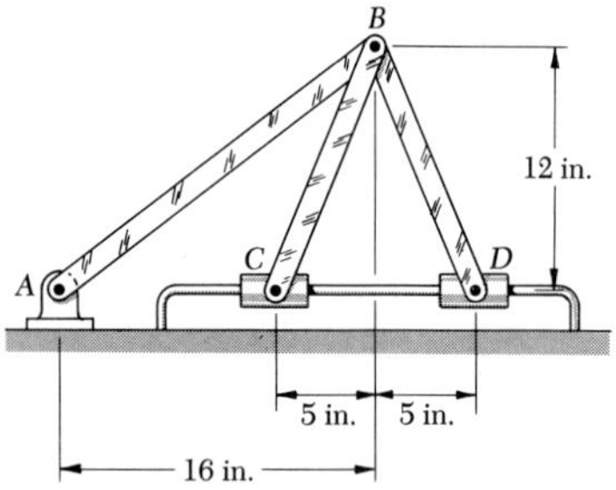

FIG. P 15.43

15.43. Two collars C and D move along the horizontal rod shown. Knowing that the velocity of collar D is 42 in./sec to the left, determine (*a*) the velocity of collar C, (*b*) the angular velocity of member AB.

***15.44.** Prove for any given position of the mechanism of Prob. 15.43 that the ratio of the magnitudes of the velocities of collars C and D is equal to the ratio of the distances AC and AD.

***15.45.** Derive an expression for the angular velocity ω_C of gear C of the system of Prob. 15.32 and show that ω_C is independent of the radius of gear B. Assume that point A is fixed and denote the angular velocities of rod ABC and gear A by ω_{ABC} and ω_A respectively.

*15.46. Assuming that the crank AB of Prob. 15.34 rotates with a constant clockwise angular velocity ω and that $\theta = 0$ at $t = 0$, derive an expression for the velocity of the piston P in terms of the time t.

15.7. Instantaneous Center of Rotation in Plane Motion. Consider the general plane motion of a slab. We shall show that at any given instant the velocities of the various particles of the slab are the same as if the slab were rotating about a certain axis perpendicular to the plane of the slab, called the *instantaneous axis of rotation.* This axis intersects the plane of the slab at a point C, called the *instantaneous center of rotation* of the slab.

To prove our statement, we first recall that the plane motion of a slab may always be replaced by a translation defined by the motion of an arbitrary reference point A, and by a rotation about A. As far as the velocities are concerned, the translation is characterized by the velocity $\mathbf{v}_A$ of the reference point A and the rotation is characterized by the angular velocity ω of the slab (which is independent of the choice of A). Thus, the velocity $\mathbf{v}_A$ of point A and the angular velocity ω of the slab define completely the velocities of all the other particles of the slab (Fig. 15.14*a*). Now let us assume that $\mathbf{v}_A$ and ω are known and that they are both different from zero. (If $\mathbf{v}_A = 0$, point A is itself the instantaneous center of rotation, and if $\omega = 0$, the slab is in translation.) These velocities could be obtained by letting the slab rotate with the angular velocity ω about a point C located on the perpendicular to $\mathbf{v}_A$ at a distance $r = v_A/\omega$ from A as shown in Fig. 15.14*b*. We check that the velocity of A would be perpendicular to AC and that its magnitude would be $r\omega = (v_A/\omega)\omega = v_A$. Thus the velocities of all the other particles of the slab would be the same as originally defined. Therefore, *as far as the velocities are concerned, the slab seems to rotate about the instantaneous center C at the instant considered.*

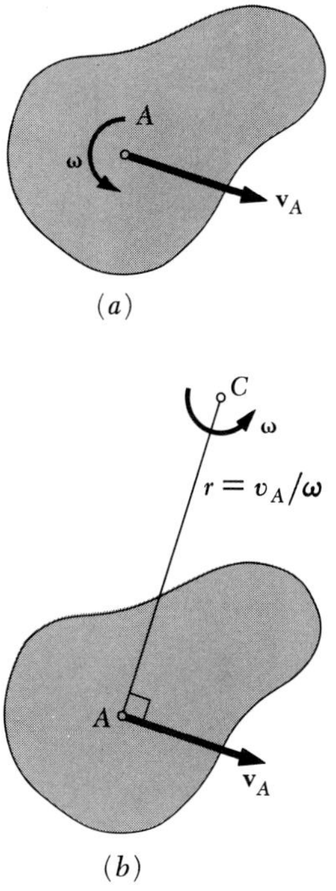

FIG. 15.14

The position of the instantaneous center may be defined in two other ways. If the directions of the velocities of two particles A and B of the slab are known, and if they are different, the instantaneous center C is obtained by drawing the perpendicular to $\mathbf{v}_A$ through A and the perpendicular to $\mathbf{v}_B$ through B and determining the point in which these two lines intersect (Fig. 15.15*a*). If the velocities $\mathbf{v}_A$ and $\mathbf{v}_B$ of two particles A and B are perpendicular to the line AB, and if their magnitudes are known, the instantaneous center may be found by intersecting the line AB with the line joining the extremities of the vectors

$\mathbf{v}_A$ and $\mathbf{v}_B$ (Fig. 15.15*b*). Note that, if $\mathbf{v}_A$ and $\mathbf{v}_B$ were parallel in Fig. 15.15*a*, or if $\mathbf{v}_A$ and $\mathbf{v}_B$ had the same magnitude in Fig. 15.15*b*, the instantaneous center C would be at an infinite distance and ω would be zero; the slab would be in translation.

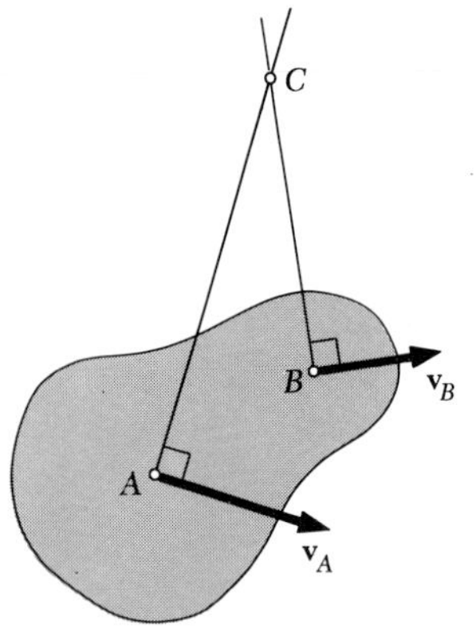

(*a*)

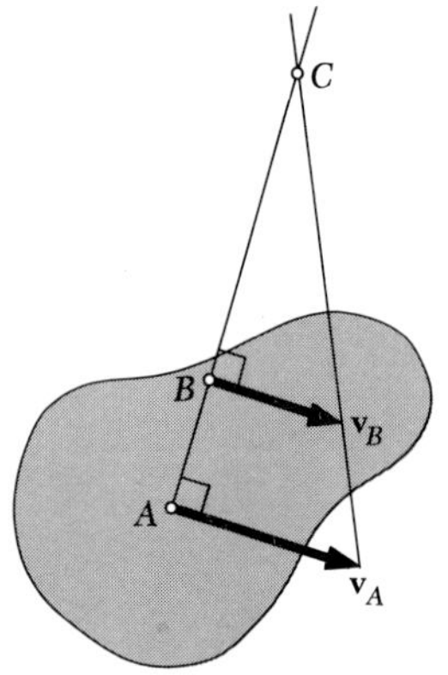

(*b*)

FIG. 15.15

To see how the concept of instantaneous center of rotation may be put to use, let us consider again the rod of Sec. 15.6. Drawing the perpendicular to $\mathbf{v}_A$ through A and the perpendicular to $\mathbf{v}_B$ through B (Fig. 15.16), we obtain the instantaneous center C. At the instant considered, the velocities of all the particles of the rod are thus the same as if the rod rotated about C. Now, if the magnitude v_A of the velocity of A is known, the magnitude ω of the angular velocity of the rod may be obtained by writing

$$\omega = \frac{v_A}{AC} = \frac{v_A}{l \cos \theta}$$

The magnitude of the velocity of B may then be obtained by writing

$$v_B = (BC)\omega = l \sin \theta \frac{v_A}{l \cos \theta} = v_A \tan \theta$$

Note that only *absolute* velocities are involved in the computation.

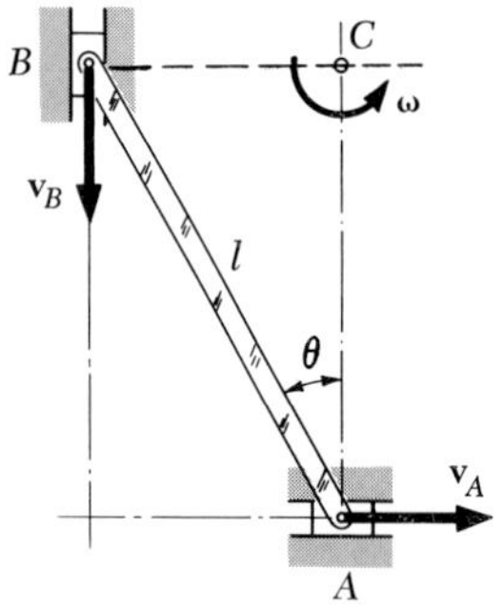

FIG. 15.16

The instantaneous center of a slab in plane motion may be located either on the slab or outside the slab. If it is located on the slab, the particle C coinciding with the instantaneous center at a given instant t must have zero velocity at that instant. The instantaneous-center method for the determination of velocities may thus be considered as a particular case of the method of relative velocities, where C is chosen as point of reference. Since $\mathbf{v}_C = 0$, the general formula $\mathbf{v}_B = \mathbf{v}_C + \mathbf{v}_{B/C}$ reduces to $\mathbf{v}_B = \mathbf{v}_{B/C}$, which means that the velocities of the various particles of the slab may be determined as if the slab were rotating about C.

It should be noted that the instantaneous center of rotation is valid only at a given instant. As the motion of the slab proceeds, other instantaneous centers should be used. The particle C of the slab which coincides with the instantaneous center at time t will generally not coincide with the instantaneous center at time $t + \Delta t$; while its velocity is zero at time t, it will probably be different from zero at time $t + \Delta t$. This means that, in general, the particle C *does not have zero acceleration*, and therefore that the *accelerations* of the various particles of the slab *cannot* be determined as if the slab were rotating about C.

SAMPLE PROBLEM 15.4

Solve Sample Prob. 15.2, using the method of the instantaneous center of rotation.

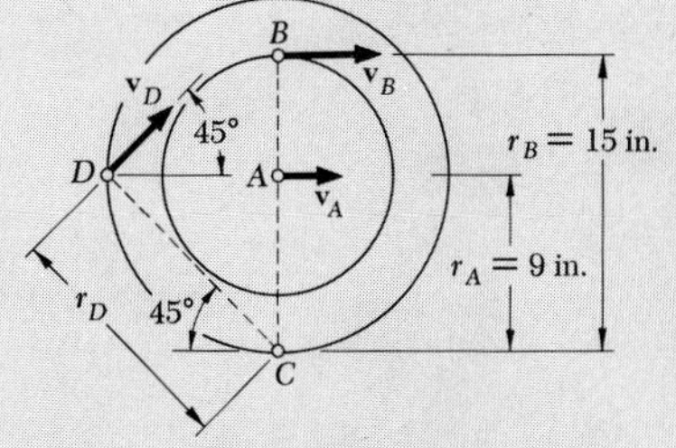

Solution *a.* **Angular Velocity of the Gear.** Since the gear rolls on the stationary lower rack, the point of contact C of the gear with the rack has no velocity; point C is therefore the instantaneous center of rotation. We write

$$v_A = r_A\omega \qquad 36 \text{ in./sec} = (9 \text{ in.})\omega \qquad \omega = 4 \text{ radians/sec} \curvearrowright$$

b. **Velocities.** All points of the gear seem to rotate about the instantaneous center as far as velocities are concerned.

Velocity of Upper Rack. Recalling that $v_R = v_B$, we write

$$v_R = v_B = r_B\omega \qquad v_R = (15 \text{ in.})(4 \text{ radians/sec}) = 60 \text{ in./sec}$$
$$\mathbf{v}_R = 60 \text{ in./sec} \rightarrow$$

Velocity of Point D. Since $r_D = (9 \text{ in.})\sqrt{2} = 12.72$ in., we write

$$v_D = r_D\omega \qquad v_D = (12.72 \text{ in.})(4 \text{ radians/sec}) = 50.9 \text{ in./sec}$$
$$\mathbf{v}_D = 50.9 \text{ in./sec} \measuredangle 45°$$

SAMPLE PROBLEM 15.5

Solve Sample Prob. 15.3, using the method of the instantaneous center of rotation.

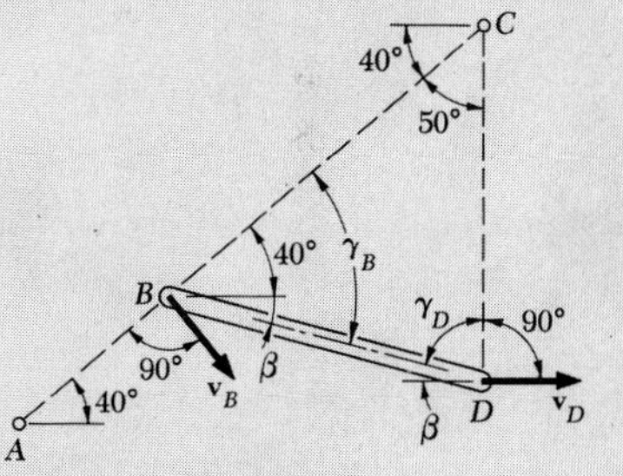

Solution. Motion of Crank ***AB.*** Referring to Sample Prob. 15.3, we obtain the velocity of point B; $\mathbf{v}_B = 627$ in./sec $\measuredangle$ 50°.

Motion of the Connecting Rod ***BD.*** We first locate the instantaneous center C by drawing lines perpendicular to the absolute velocities $\mathbf{v}_B$ and $\mathbf{v}_D$. Recalling from Sample Prob. 15.3 that $\beta = 13.9°$ and that $BD = 8$ in., we solve the triangle BCD.

$$\gamma_B = 40° + \beta = 53.9° \qquad \gamma_D = 90° - \beta = 76.1°$$

$$\frac{BC}{\sin 76.1°} = \frac{CD}{\sin 53.9°} = \frac{8 \text{ in.}}{\sin 50°}$$

$$BC = 10.14 \text{ in.} \qquad CD = 8.44 \text{ in.}$$

Since the connecting rod BD seems to rotate about point C, we write

$$v_B = (BC)\omega_{BD}$$
$$627 \text{ in./sec} = (10.14 \text{ in.})\omega_{BD}$$
$$\omega_{BD} = 61.9 \text{ radians/sec} \curvearrowleft$$

$$v_D = (CD)\omega_{BD} = (8.44 \text{ in.})(61.9 \text{ radians/sec})$$
$$= 522 \text{ in./sec} = 43.5 \text{ ft/sec}$$
$$\mathbf{v}_P = \mathbf{v}_D = 43.5 \text{ ft/sec} \rightarrow$$

PROBLEMS

15.47. A disk of radius 5 in. rolls and slides on a smooth horizontal surface. Knowing that the center of the disk has a constant velocity of 16 ft/sec to the right and that the disk rotates counterclockwise at a constant angular velocity of 8 radians/sec, (*a*) locate the instantaneous center of rotation, (*b*) determine the velocity of the point of the disk that is in contact with the surface.

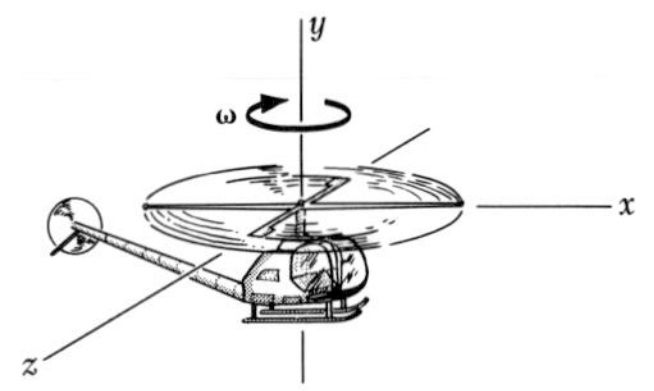

FIG. P 15.48

15.48. A helicopter moves horizontally in the *x* direction at a speed of 45 mph. Knowing that the main blades rotate clockwise at an angular velocity of 120 rpm, determine the instantaneous axis of rotation of the main blades.

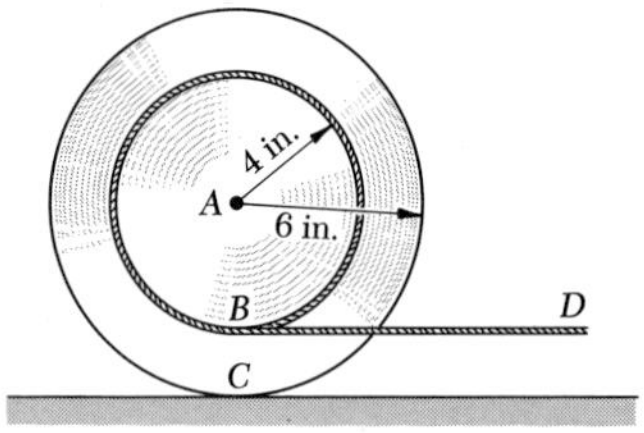

FIG. P 15.49

15.49. A drum, of radius 4 in., is mounted on a cylinder of radius 6 in. A cord is wound around the drum, and its extremity *D* is pulled to the right at a constant velocity of 5 in./sec, causing the cylinder to roll without sliding. Determine (*a*) the angular velocity of the cylinder, (*b*) the velocity of the center of the cylinder, (*c*) the number of inches of cord which are wound or unwound per second.

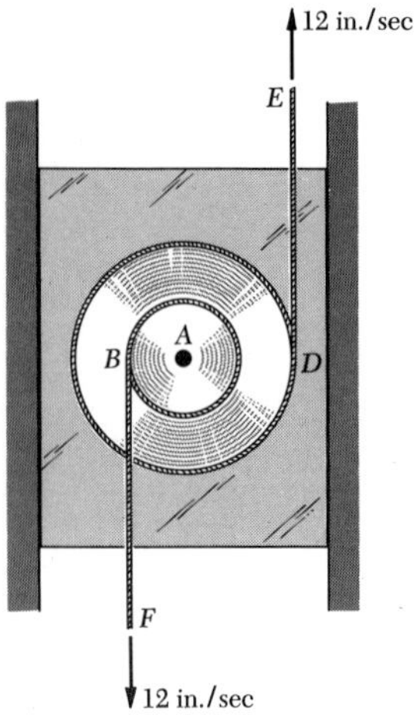

FIG. P 15.50

15.50. A double pulley is attached to a slider block by a pin at *A*. The 2-in.-radius inner pulley is rigidly attached to the 4-in.-radius outer pulley. Knowing that each of the two cords is pulled at a constant speed of 12 in./sec as shown, determine (*a*) the instantaneous center of rotation of the double pulley, (*b*) the velocity of the slider block, (*c*) the number of inches of cord wrapped or unwrapped on each pulley per second.

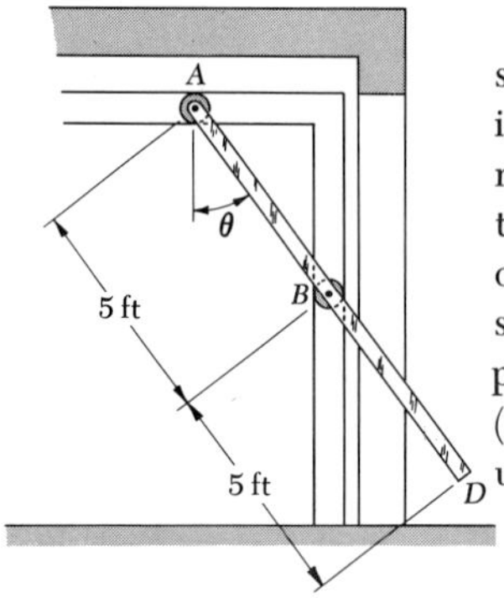

FIG. P 15.51

15.51. A 10-ft channel, used to form one edge of an overhead door, is guided by wheels at *A* and *B* which roll in horizontal and vertical tracks as shown. Knowing that $\theta = 30°$ and that the velocity of *B* is 2 ft/sec upward, determine the angular velocity of the door and the velocity of *D*.

15.52. Solve Prob. 15.51 assuming $\theta = 60°$.

15.53. Knowing that at the instant shown the velocity of collar *D* is 12 in./sec upward, determine (*a*) the instantaneous center of rotation of link *BD*, (*b*) the angular velocities of crank *AB* and link *BD*, (*c*) the velocity of the mid-point of link *BD*.

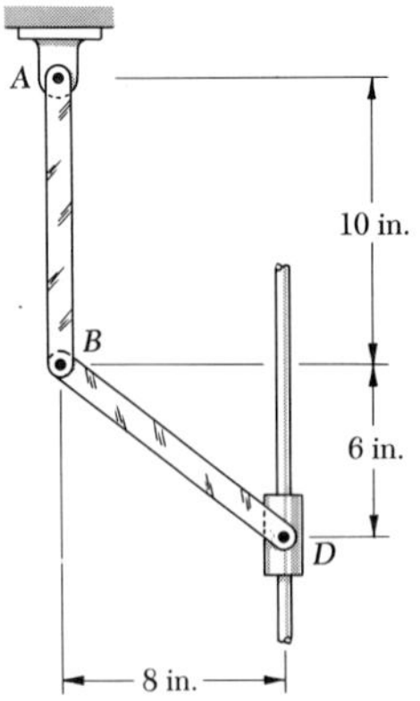

FIG. P 15.53 AND P 15.54

15.54. Knowing that at the instant shown the angular velocity of crank *AB* is 3 radians/sec clockwise, determine (*a*) the angular velocity of link *BD*, (*b*) the velocity of collar *D*, (*c*) the velocity of the mid-point of link *BD*.

15.55. Two rods *AB* and *BD* are connected to three collars as shown. Knowing that collar *A* moves downward with a constant velocity of 6 in./sec, determine (*a*) the angular velocity of each rod, (*b*) the velocity of collar *D*.

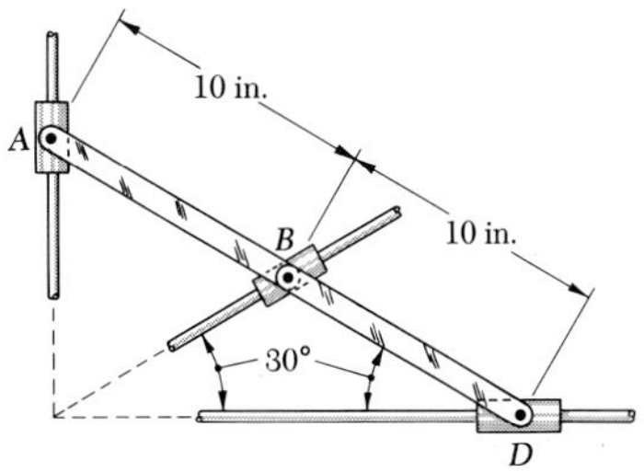

FIG. **P 15.55**

15.56. Two links *AB* and *BD*, each of length *l*, are connected to three collars as shown. Collar *A* moves downward at a constant speed v_A. Show that $\omega_{AB} \sin \beta = \omega_{BD} \sin \gamma$ and that $v_A \tan \beta = v_D \tan \gamma$.

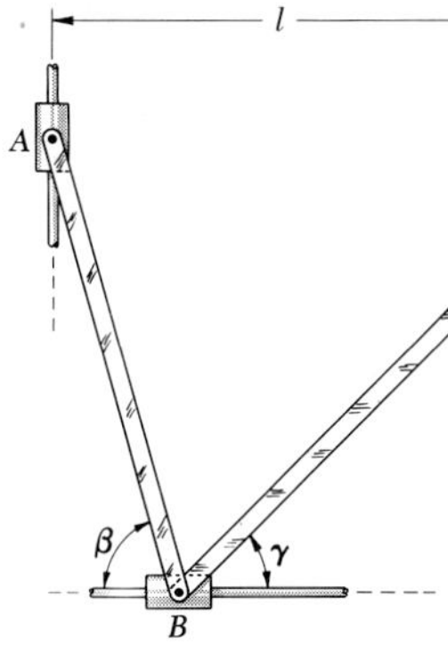

FIG. **P 15.56**

15.57. In the position shown, the piston *A* has a velocity of 3 ft/sec upward. Determine the instantaneous center of rotation and the angular velocity (*a*) of gear *D*, (*b*) of the connecting rod *AB*.

15.58. In the position shown, the velocity of the center of gear *D* is 24 in./sec to the left. Determine (*a*) the angular velocity of the connecting rod *AB*, (*b*) the velocity of the piston *A*.

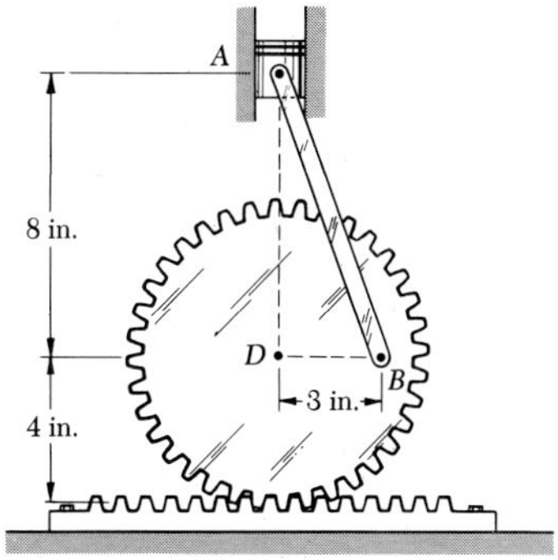

FIG. **P 15.57** AND **P 15.58**

15.59. Using the method of Sec. 15.7, solve Prob. 15.33.

15.60. Using the method of Sec. 15.7, solve Prob. 15.34.

15.61. Using the method of Sec. 15.7, solve Prob. 15.37.

15.62. Using the method of Sec. 15.7, solve Prob. 15.38.

15.63. Using the method of Sec. 15.7, solve Prob. 15.39.

15.64. Using the method of Sec. 15.7, solve Prob. 15.40.

15.65. Using the method of Sec. 15.7, solve Prob. 15.41.

15.66. Using the method of Sec. 15.7, solve Prob. 15.43.

15.67. Using the method of Sec. 15.7, solve Prob. 15.27.

15.68. Using the method of Sec. 15.7, solve Prob. 15.30.

15.69. Using the method of Sec. 15.7, solve Prob. 15.31.

15.70. Using the method of Sec. 15.7, solve Prob. 15.32.

15.71. Using the method of Sec. 15.7, solve Prob. 15.29.

15.8. Absolute and Relative Acceleration in Plane Motion. We saw in Sec. 15.5 that any plane motion may be replaced by a translation defined by the motion of an arbitrary reference point *A*, and by a rotation about *A*. This property was used in Sec. 15.6 to determine the velocity of the various points of a moving slab. We shall now use the same property to determine the acceleration of the points of the slab.

We first recall that the absolute acceleration $\mathbf{a}_B$ of a particle of the slab may be obtained from the relative-acceleration formula derived in Sec. 11.11,

$$\mathbf{a}_B = \mathbf{a}_A + \mathbf{a}_{B/A} \tag{15.18}$$

where the right-hand member represents a vector sum. The acceleration $\mathbf{a}_A$ corresponds to the translation of the slab with A, while the relative acceleration $\mathbf{a}_{B/A}$ is associated with the rotation of the slab about A and is measured with respect to axes of fixed orientation centered at A (Fig. 15.17). Denot-

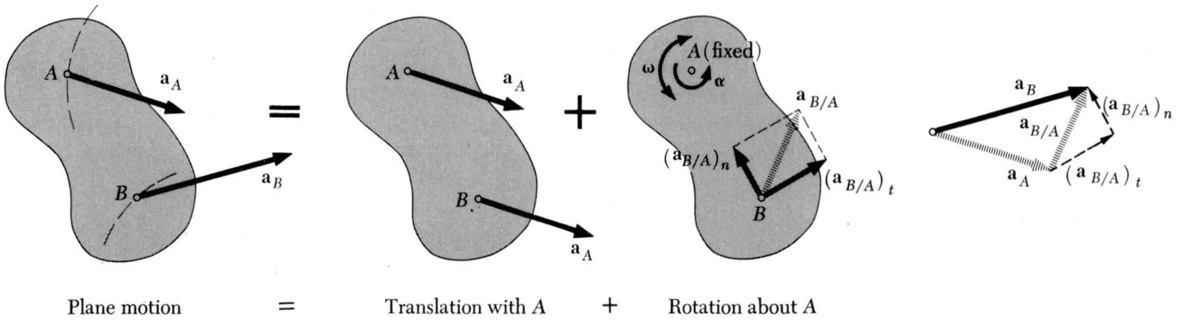

FIG. 15.17

ing by r the distance from A to B and, respectively, by ω and α the angular velocity and angular acceleration of the slab with respect to axes of fixed orientation, we find that the relative acceleration $\mathbf{a}_{B/A}$ of B with respect to A consists of two components, a *normal component* $(\mathbf{a}_{B/A})_n$ of magnitude $r\omega^2$ directed toward A, and a *tangential component* $(\mathbf{a}_{B/A})_t$ of magnitude $r\alpha$ perpendicular to the line AB.

As an example, we shall consider again the rod AB whose extremities slide, respectively, along a horizontal and a vertical track (Fig. 15.18). Assuming that the velocity $\mathbf{v}_A$ and the

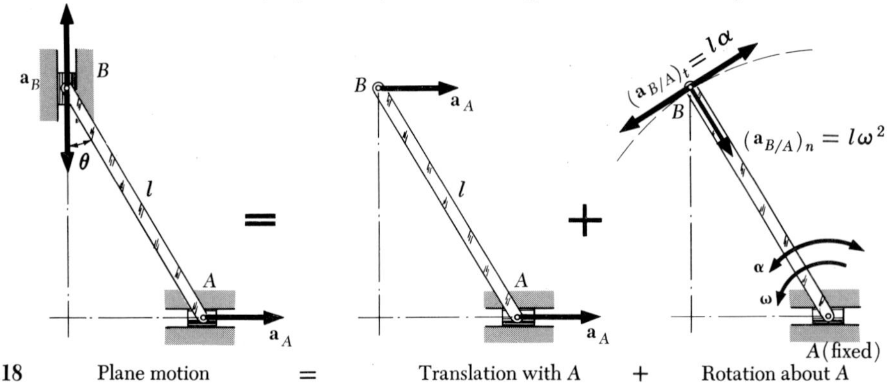

FIG. 15.18

acceleration $\mathbf{a}_A$ of A are known, we propose to determine the acceleration $\mathbf{a}_B$ of B and the angular acceleration $\boldsymbol{\alpha}$ of the rod. Choosing A as a reference point, we express that the given motion is equivalent to a translation with A and a rotation about A. The absolute acceleration of B must be equal to the sum

$$\begin{aligned} \mathbf{a}_B &= \mathbf{a}_A + \mathbf{a}_{B/A} \\ &= \mathbf{a}_A + (\mathbf{a}_{B/A})_n + (\mathbf{a}_{B/A})_t \end{aligned} \tag{15.19}$$

where $(\mathbf{a}_{B/A})_n$ has the magnitude $l\omega^2$ and is *directed toward* A, while $(\mathbf{a}_{B/A})_t$ has the magnitude $l\alpha$ and is perpendicular to AB. There is no way of telling at the present time whether the tangential component $(\mathbf{a}_{B/A})_t$ is directed to the left or to the right, and the student should not rely on his "intuition" in this matter. We shall therefore indicate both possible directions for this component in Fig. 15.18. Similarly, we indicate both possible senses for $\mathbf{a}_B$, since we do not know whether point B is accelerated upward or downward.

Equation (15.19) has been expressed geometrically in Fig. 15.19. Four different vector polygons may be obtained, depending upon the sense of $\mathbf{a}_A$ and the relative magnitude of a_A and $(a_{B/A})_n$. If we are to determine a_B and α from one of these diagrams, we must know not only a_A and θ but also ω. The angular velocity of the rod, therefore, should be separately determined by one of the methods indicated in Secs. 15.6 and 15.7. The values of a_B and α may then be obtained by considering successively the x and y components of the vectors shown in Fig. 15.19. In the case of polygon a, for example, we write the equations

$\xrightarrow{+}$ x components: $\quad 0 = a_A + l\omega^2 \sin\theta - l\alpha\cos\theta$

$+\uparrow$ y components: $\quad -a_B = -l\omega^2\cos\theta - l\alpha\sin\theta$

which may be solved for a_B and α. The two unknowns may also be obtained by direct measurement on the vector polygon. In that case, care should be taken to draw first the known vectors $\mathbf{a}_A$ and $(\mathbf{a}_{B/A})_n$.

It is quite evident that the determination of accelerations is considerably more involved than the determination of velocities. Yet, in the example considered here, the extremities A and B of the rod were moving along straight tracks, and the diagrams drawn were relatively simple. If A and B had moved along curved tracks, the accelerations $\mathbf{a}_A$ and $\mathbf{a}_B$ should have been resolved into normal and tangential components and the solution of the problem would have involved six different vectors.

When a mechanism consists of several moving parts which

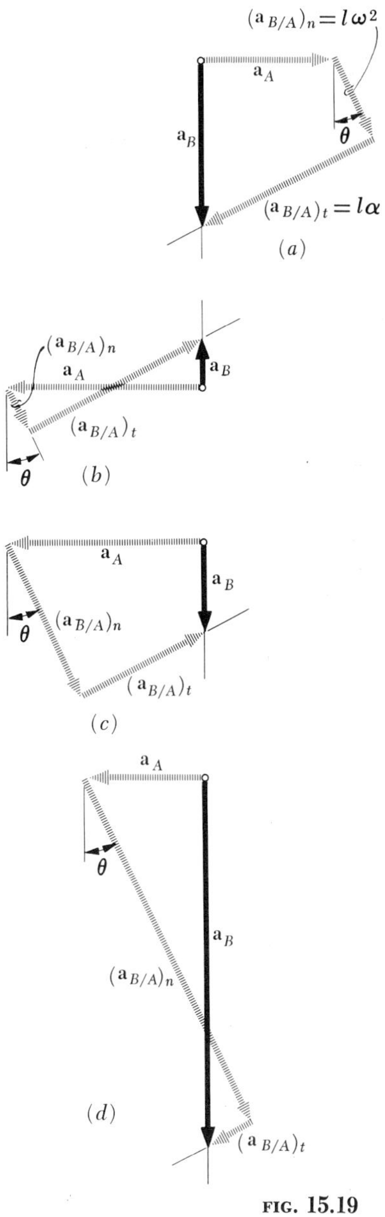

FIG. 15.19

are pin-connected, its analysis may be carried out by considering each part as a rigid body, while keeping in mind that the points where two parts are connected must have the same absolute acceleration (see Sample Prob. 15.7). In the case of meshed gears, the tangential components of the accelerations of the teeth in contact are equal, but their normal components are different.

***15.9. Analysis of Plane Motion in Terms of a Parameter.** In the case of certain mechanisms, it is possible to express the coordinates x and y of all the significant points of the mechanism by means of simple analytic expressions containing a single parameter. It may be advantageous in such a case to determine directly the absolute velocity and the absolute acceleration of the various points of the mechanism, since the components of the velocity and of the acceleration of a given point may be obtained by differentiating the coordinates x and y of that point.

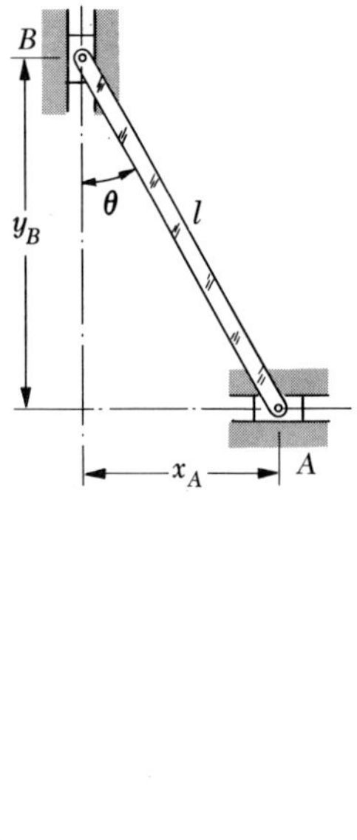

FIG. 15.20

Let us consider again the rod AB whose extremities slide, respectively, in a horizontal and a vertical track (Fig. 15.20). The coordinates x_A and y_B of the extremities of the rod may be expressed in terms of the angle θ the rod forms with the vertical,

$$x_A = l \sin \theta \qquad y_B = l \cos \theta \tag{15.20}$$

Differentiating Eqs. (15.20) twice, we write

$$v_A = \frac{dx_A}{dt} = l \cos \theta \frac{d\theta}{dt} \qquad v_B = \frac{dy_B}{dt} = -l \sin \theta \frac{d\theta}{dt}$$

$$a_A = \frac{d^2x_A}{dt^2} = -l \sin \theta \left(\frac{d\theta}{dt}\right)^2 + l \cos \theta \frac{d^2\theta}{dt^2}$$

$$a_B = \frac{d^2y_B}{dt^2} = -l \cos \theta \left(\frac{d\theta}{dt}\right)^2 - l \sin \theta \frac{d^2\theta}{dt^2}$$

Recalling that $d\theta/dt = \omega$ and $d^2\theta/dt^2 = \alpha$, we obtain

$$v_A = l\omega \cos \theta \qquad v_B = -l\omega \sin \theta \tag{15.21}$$

$$a_A = -l\omega^2 \sin \theta + l\alpha \cos \theta \qquad a_B = -l\omega^2 \cos \theta - l\alpha \sin \theta \tag{15.22}$$

We note that a positive sign for v_A or a_A indicates that the velocity $\mathbf{v}_A$ or the acceleration $\mathbf{a}_A$ is directed to the right; a positive sign for v_B or a_B indicates that $\mathbf{v}_B$ or $\mathbf{a}_B$ is directed upward. Equations (15.21) may be used, for example, to determine v_B and ω when v_A and θ are known. Substituting for ω in (15.22), we may then determine a_B and α if a_A is known.

SAMPLE PROBLEM 15.6

The center of the double gear of Sample Prob. 15.2 has a velocity of 36 in./sec to the right and an acceleration of 45 in./sec² to the right. Determine (*a*) the angular acceleration of the gear, (*b*) the accelerations of points *B*, *C*, and *D* of the gear.

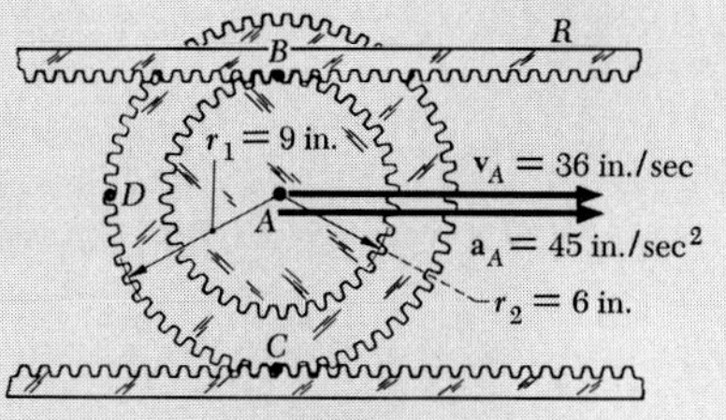

a. **Angular Acceleration of the Gear.** In Sample Prob. 15.2, we found that $s_A = r_1\theta$ and $v_A = r_1\omega$. Differentiating the latter with respect to time, we obtain $a_A = r_1\alpha$.

$$v_A = r_1\omega \qquad 36 \text{ in./sec} = (9 \text{ in.})\omega \qquad \omega = 4 \text{ radians/sec} \curvearrowright$$
$$a_A = r_1\alpha \qquad 45 \text{ in./sec}^2 = (9 \text{ in.})\alpha \qquad \alpha = 5 \text{ radians/sec}^2 \curvearrowright \blacktriangleleft$$

b. **Accelerations.** The rolling motion of the gear is resolved into a translation with *A* and a rotation about *A*.

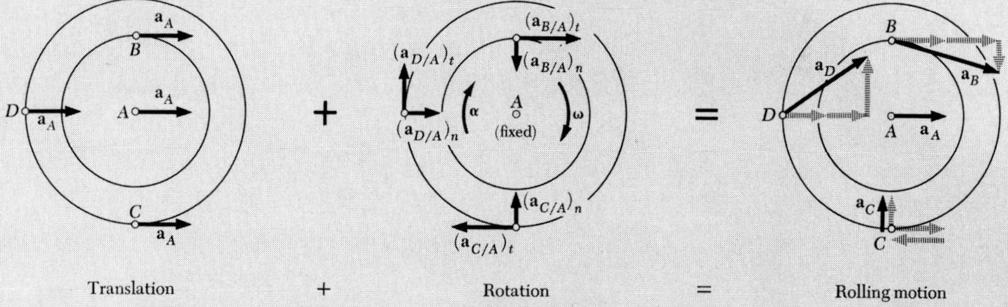

Acceleration of Point B. Adding vectorially the accelerations corresponding to the translation and to the rotation, we obtain

$$\mathbf{a}_B = \mathbf{a}_A + \mathbf{a}_{B/A} = \mathbf{a}_A + (\mathbf{a}_{B/A})_t + (\mathbf{a}_{B/A})_n$$

where $\quad \mathbf{a}_A = 45 \text{ in./sec} \rightarrow$

$$(a_{B/A})_t = r\alpha = (6)(5) = 30 \qquad (\mathbf{a}_{B/A})_t = 30 \text{ in./sec}^2 \rightarrow$$
$$(a_{B/A})_n = r\omega^2 = (6)(4)^2 = 96 \qquad (\mathbf{a}_{B/A})_n = 96 \text{ in./sec}^2 \downarrow$$

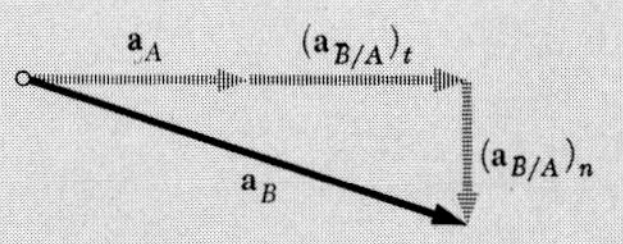

We have $\quad \mathbf{a}_B = [45 \rightarrow] + [30 \rightarrow] + [96 \downarrow]$

$$\mathbf{a}_B = 121.8 \text{ in./sec}^2 \searrow 52.0° \blacktriangleleft$$

Acceleration of Point C

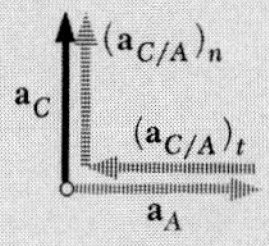

$$\mathbf{a}_C = \mathbf{a}_A + \mathbf{a}_{C/A} = \mathbf{a}_A + (\mathbf{a}_{C/A})_t + (\mathbf{a}_{C/A})_n$$
$$= [45 \rightarrow] + [(9)(5) \leftarrow] + [(9)(4)^2 \uparrow]$$
$$\mathbf{a}_C = 144 \text{ in./sec}^2 \uparrow \blacktriangleleft$$

Acceleration of Point D

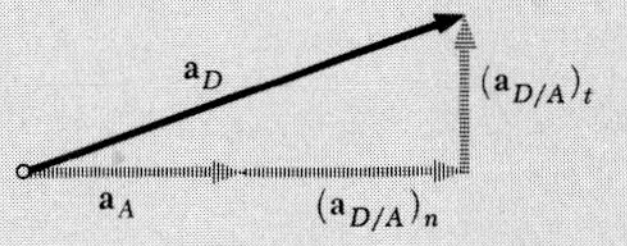

$$\mathbf{a}_D = \mathbf{a}_A + \mathbf{a}_{D/A} = \mathbf{a}_A + (\mathbf{a}_{D/A})_t + (\mathbf{a}_{D/A})_n$$
$$= [45 \rightarrow] + [(9)(5) \uparrow] + [(9)(4)^2 \rightarrow]$$
$$\mathbf{a}_D = 194 \text{ in./sec}^2 \measuredangle 13.4° \blacktriangleleft$$

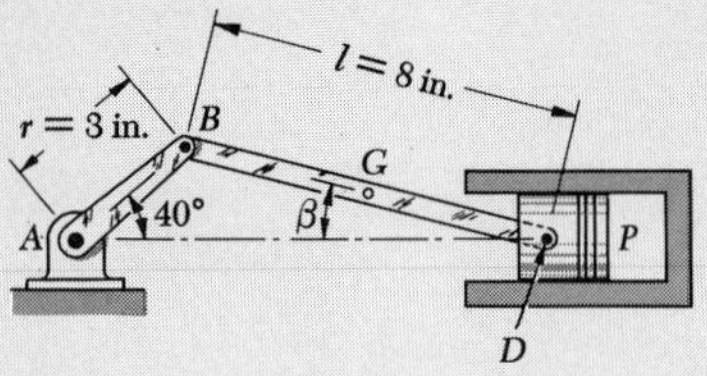

SAMPLE PROBLEM 15.7

Crank AB of the engine system of Sample Prob. 15.3 has a constant clockwise angular velocity of 2,000 rpm. For the crank position shown, determine the angular acceleration of the connecting rod BD and the acceleration of point D.

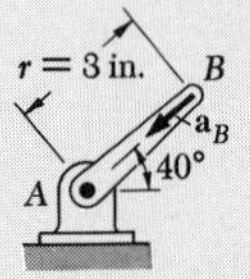

Motion of Crank AB. Since the crank rotates about A with constant $\omega_{AB} = 2{,}000$ rpm $= 209$ radians/sec, we have $\alpha_{AB} = 0$. The acceleration of B is therefore directed toward A and has a magnitude

$$a_B = r\omega_{AB}^2 = (\tfrac{3}{12}\text{ ft})(209)^2 = 10{,}920\text{ ft/sec}^2$$
$$\mathbf{a}_B = 10{,}920\text{ ft/sec} \swarrow 40°$$

Motion of the Connecting Rod BD. The angular velocity ω_{BD} and the value of β were obtained in Sample Prob. 15.3.

$$\omega_{BD} = 61.9\text{ radians/sec} \circlearrowright \qquad \beta = 13.9°$$

The motion of BD is resolved into a translation with B and a rotation about B. The relative acceleration $\mathbf{a}_{D/B}$ is resolved into normal and tangential components.

$$(a_{D/B})_n = (BD)\omega_{BD}^2 = (\tfrac{8}{12})(61.9)^2 = 2{,}560\text{ ft/sec}^2$$
$$(\mathbf{a}_{D/B})_n = 2{,}560\text{ ft/sec}^2 \nwarrow 13.9°$$
$$(a_{D/B})_t = (BD)\alpha_{BD} = (\tfrac{8}{12})\alpha_{BD} = 0.667\alpha_{BD}$$
$$(\mathbf{a}_{D/B})_t = 0.667\alpha_{BD} \nearrow 76.1°$$

While $(\mathbf{a}_{B/D})_t$ must be perpendicular to BD, its sense is not known.

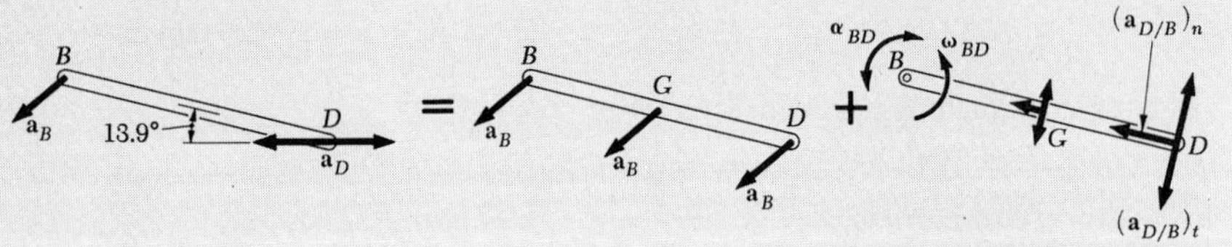

Plane motion = Translation + Rotation

Noting that the acceleration $\mathbf{a}_D$ must be horizontal, we write

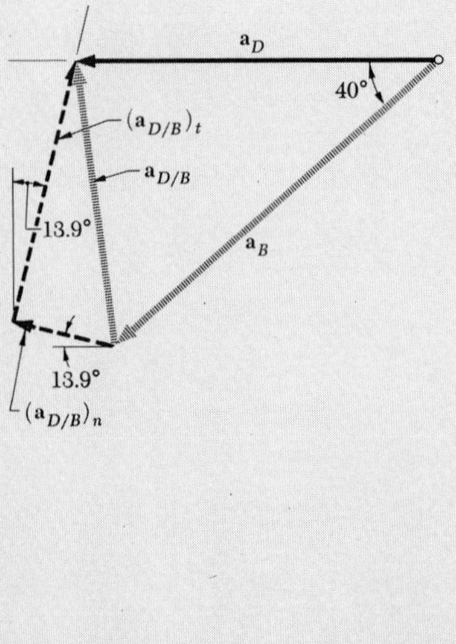

$$\mathbf{a}_D = \mathbf{a}_B + \mathbf{a}_{D/B} = \mathbf{a}_B + (\mathbf{a}_{D/B})_n + (\mathbf{a}_{D/B})_t$$
$$[a_D \leftrightarrow] = [10{,}920 \swarrow 40°] + [2{,}560 \nwarrow 13.9°] + [0.667\alpha_{BD} \nearrow 76.1°]$$

Equating x and y components, we obtain the following scalar equations:

$\xrightarrow{+}$ x components:

$$-a_D = -10{,}920\cos 40° - 2{,}560\cos 13.9° + 0.667\alpha_{BD}\sin 13.9°$$

$+\uparrow$ y components:

$$0 = -10{,}920\sin 40° + 2{,}560\sin 13.9° + 0.667\alpha_{BD}\cos 13.9°$$

Solving the equations simultaneously, we obtain $\alpha_{BD} = +9{,}900$ radians/sec^2 and $a_D = +9{,}260$ ft/sec^2. The positive signs indicate that the senses shown on the vector polygon are correct; we write

$$\boldsymbol{\alpha}_{BD} = 9{,}900\text{ radians/sec}^2 \circlearrowright \quad ◄$$
$$\mathbf{a}_D = 9{,}260\text{ ft/sec}^2 \leftarrow \quad ◄$$

PROBLEMS

15.72. The crate shown is lowered by means of two cables unwinding at the same speed from overhead cranes. As the crate approaches the ground, the crane operators apply brakes to slow down the unwinding motion. The deceleration of the cable attached at A is 10 ft/sec^2, while that of the cable attached at B is 16 ft/sec^2. Determine the acceleration of point C and the angular acceleration of the crate at that instant.

15.73. The acceleration of point C is 5 ft/sec^2 upward and the angular acceleration of the crate is 2 radians/sec^2 clockwise. Knowing that the angular velocity of the crate is zero at the instant considered, determine the acceleration of each cable.

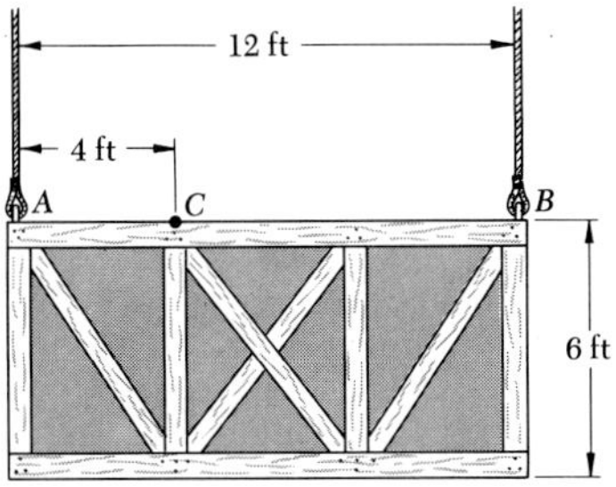

FIG. P 15.72 AND P 15.73

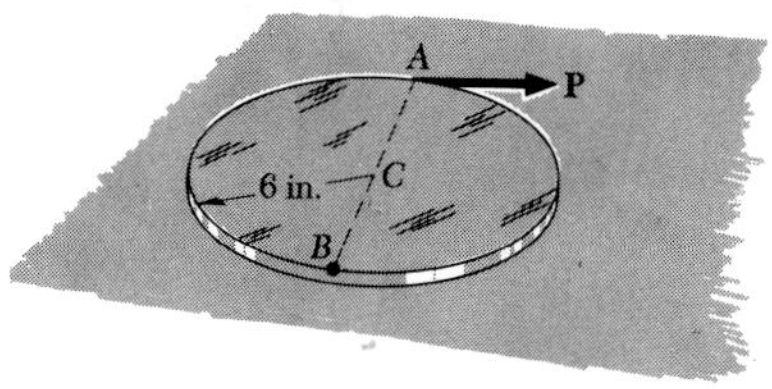

FIG. P 15.74

15.74. A 12-in.-diameter plate rests on a smooth horizontal table. A force **P** applied as shown produces the following accelerations: $\mathbf{a}_A = 36$ in./sec^2 to the right, $\alpha = 4$ radians/sec^2 clockwise as viewed from above. Determine the acceleration (*a*) of point B, (*b*) of point C.

15.75. In Prob. 15.74, determine the point of the plate which (*a*) has no acceleration, (*b*) has an acceleration of 18 in./sec^2 to the right.

15.76. Determine the accelerations of points C and D of the wheel of Prob. 15.23, knowing that the automobile moves at a constant speed of 60 mph.

15.77. Determine the accelerations of points B and E of the wheel of Prob. 15.23, knowing that the automobile moves at a constant speed of 60 mph.

15.78. In Prob. 15.49, the extremity of the cord D has a velocity of 5 in./sec and an acceleration of 2 in./sec^2, both directed to the right. Assuming that the cylinder rolls without slipping, determine the accelerations of points A, B, and C of the cylinder.

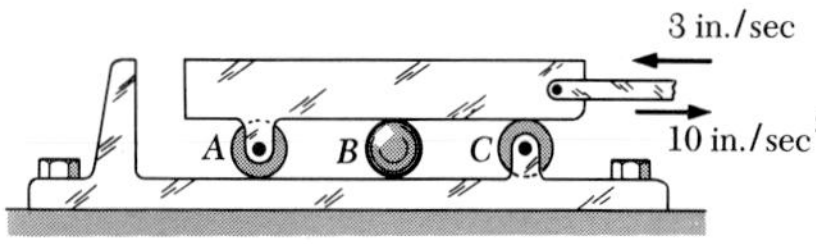

FIG. P 15.79

15.79. The moving carriage is supported by two casters A and C, each of $\frac{1}{2}$-in. diameter, and by a $\frac{1}{2}$-in.-diameter ball B. If at a given instant the velocity and acceleration of the carriage are as shown, determine (*a*) the angular velocities and angular accelerations of the ball and of each caster, (*b*) the velocities and accelerations of the center of the ball and of each caster.

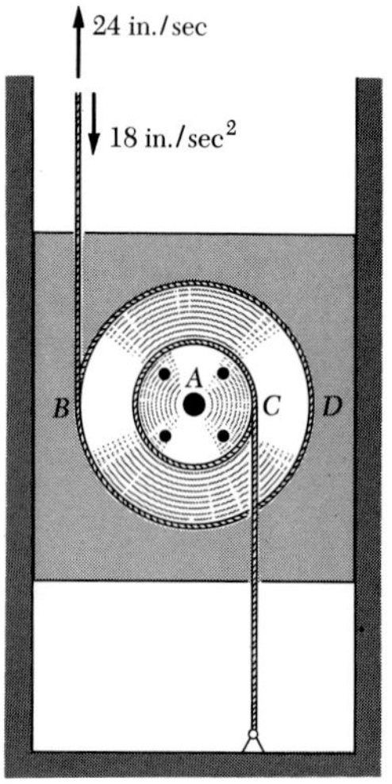

FIG. P 15.80

15.80. A double pulley is attached to a slider block by a pin at A. The 2-in.-radius inner pulley is rigidly attached to the 4-in.-radius outer pulley. Determine the accelerations of points A and B of the pulley at the instant shown.

15.81. In Prob. 15.80 determine the accelerations of points C and D of the pulley.

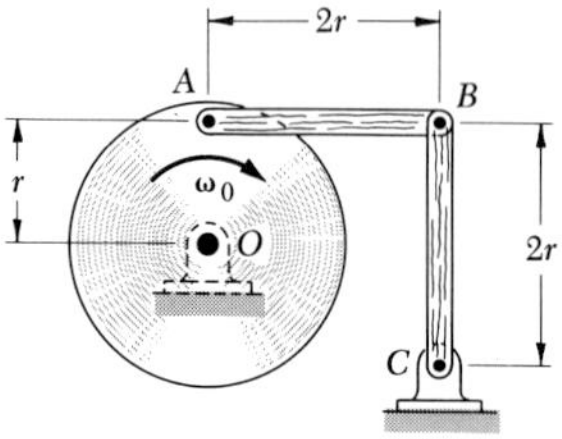

FIG. P 15.82

15.82 and 15.83. At the instant shown, the disk rotates with a constant angular velocity ω_0 clockwise. Determine the angular velocities and the angular accelerations of the rods AB and BC.

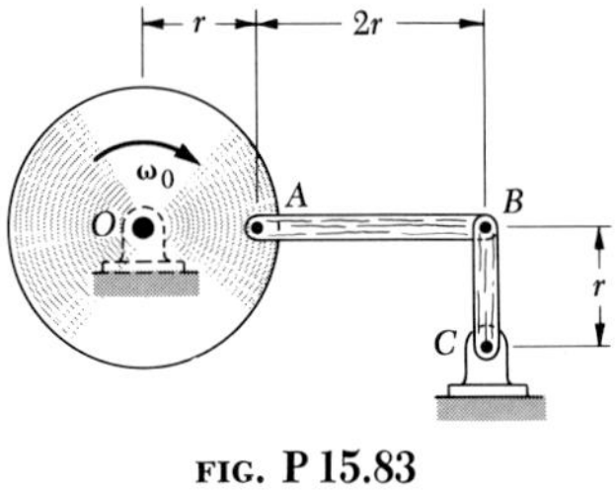

FIG. P 15.83

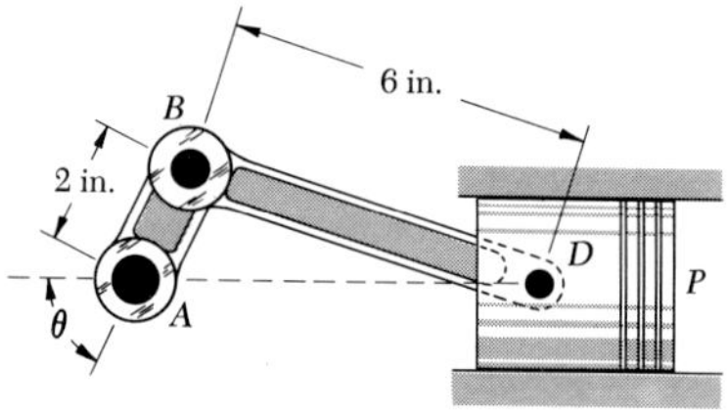

FIG. P 15.84

15.84. Crank AB rotates about A with a constant angular velocity of 600 rpm clockwise. Determine the acceleration of the piston P when (*a*) $\theta = 0$, (*b*) $\theta = 90°$.

15.85. Solve Prob. 15.84 when (*a*) $\theta = 180°$, (*b*) $\theta = 270°$.

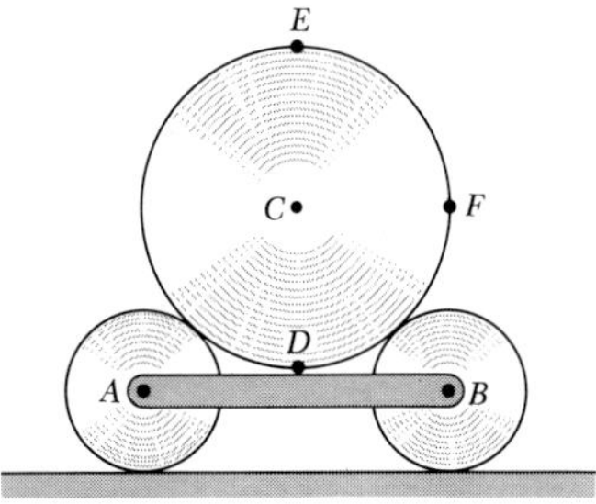

FIG. P 15.86

15.86. Two rollers A and B each of radius 2 in. are connected by a link AB and roll along a horizontal surface. A drum of radius 4 in. is placed on the rollers as shown. If the link moves to the right with a constant velocity of 12 in./sec, determine the accelerations of points D, E, and F on the drum.

15.87. In Prob. 15.86, determine the accelerations of the point of the drum and of the point of roller *A* which are in contact with each other.

15.88 and 15.89. For the linkage indicated, determine the angular acceleration (*a*) of bar *BD*, (*b*) of bar *DE*.

15.88. Linkage of Prob. 15.38.
15.89. Linkage of Prob. 15.37.

15.90 and 15.91. For the linkage indicated, determine (*a*) the angular acceleration of bar *BD*, (*b*) the horizontal and vertical components of the acceleration of the mid-point of bar *BD*.

15.90. Linkage of Prob. 15.40.
15.91. Linkage of Prob. 15.39.

15.92 and 15.93. The disk shown has a constant angular velocity of 8 radians/sec clockwise. For the position shown, determine (*a*) the angular acceleration of each rod, (*b*) the accelerations of points *C* and *D*.

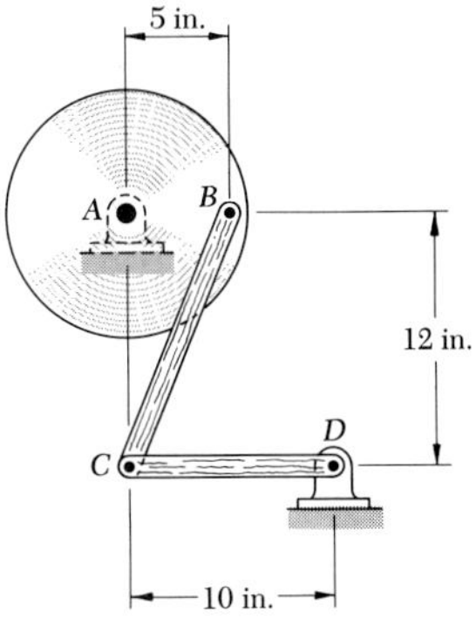

FIG. P 15.92 AND P 15.94

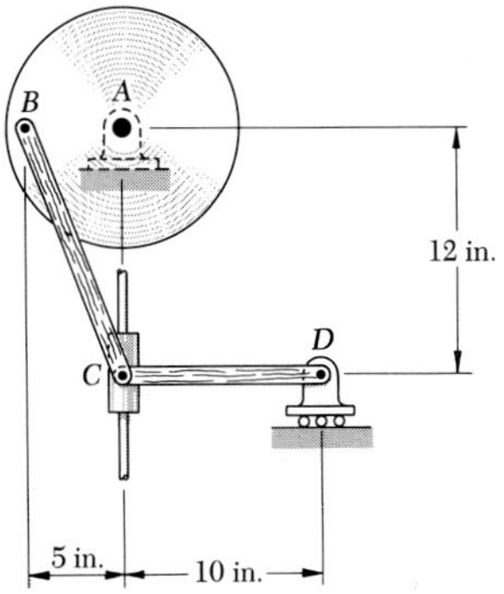

FIG. P 15.93 AND P 15.95

15.94 and 15.95. In the position shown, the disk has an instantaneous angular velocity of 8 radians/sec clockwise and an angular acceleration of 30 radians/sec^2 counterclockwise. Determine (*a*) the angular acceleration of each rod, (*b*) the accelerations of points *C* and *D*.

***15.96.** A disk of radius *r* rolls to the right with a constant velocity **v**. Denoting by *P* the point of the rim in contact with the ground at $t = 0$, derive expressions for the horizontal and vertical components of the velocity of *P* at any time *t*. (The curve described by point *P* is called a *cycloid*.)

***15.97.** The position of a factory window is controlled by the rack and pinion shown. Knowing that the pinion *C* has a radius *r* and rotates counterclockwise at a constant rate ω, derive an expression for the angular velocity of the window.

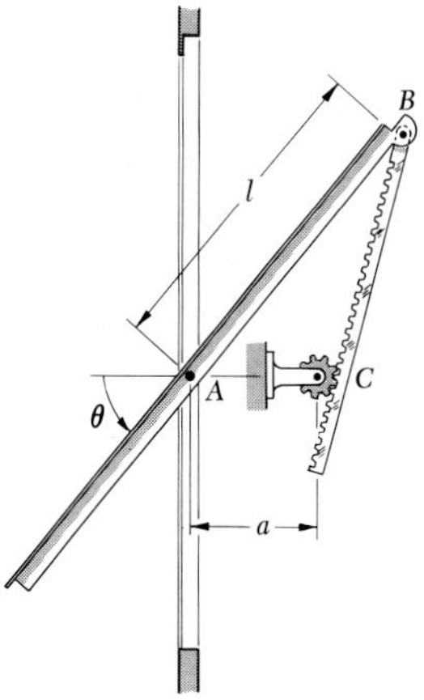

FIG. P 15.97

*15.98. Rod AB slides with its ends in contact with the floor and the inclined plane. Using the method of Sec. 15.9, derive an expression for the angular velocity of the rod in terms of v_B, θ, l, and β.

*15.99. Derive an expression for the angular acceleration of the rod AB in terms of v_B, θ, l, and β, knowing that the acceleration of point B is zero.

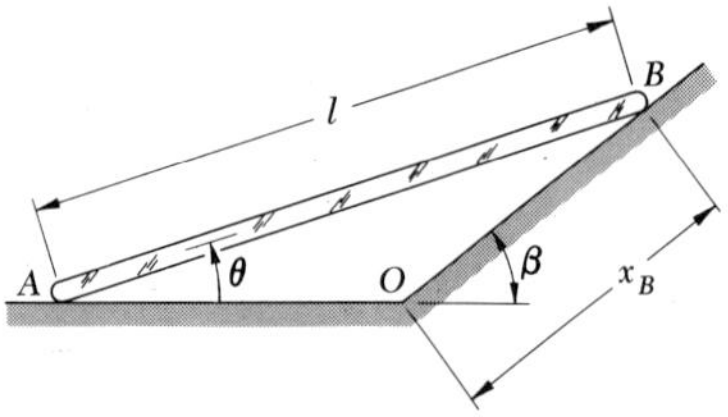

FIG. P 15.98 AND P 15.99

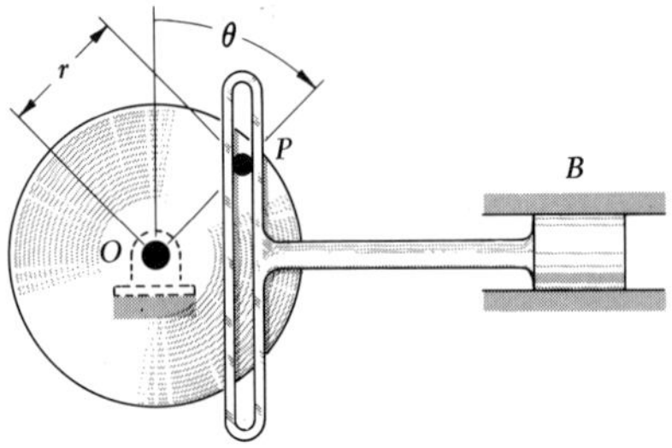

FIG. P 15.100

*15.100. The drive disk of the Scotch crosshead mechanism shown has an angular velocity ω and an angular acceleration α, both directed clockwise. Using the method of Sec. 15.9, derive an expression (*a*) for the velocity of block B, (*b*) for the acceleration of block B.

*15.101. Collar B slides along rod OC and is attached to a sliding block which moves upward with a constant velocity **v** in a vertical slot. Using the method of Sec. 15.9, derive an expression (*a*) for the angular velocity of rod OC, (*b*) for the angular acceleration of rod OC.

*15.102. Collar B slides along rod OC and is attached to a sliding block which moves in a vertical slot. Knowing that rod OC rotates with an angular velocity ω and with an angular acceleration α, both counterclockwise, derive expressions for the velocity and acceleration of collar B.

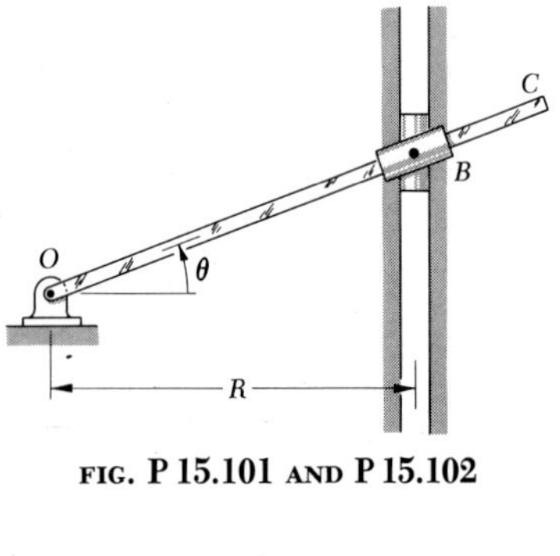

FIG. P 15.101 AND P 15.102

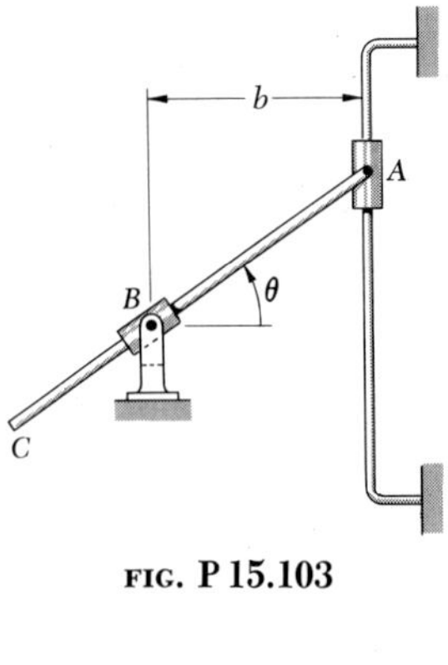

FIG. P 15.103

*15.103. Rod AC of length $2b$ is attached to a collar at A and passes through a pivoted collar at B. Knowing that the collar A moves upward with a constant velocity $\mathbf{v}_A$, derive an expression for (*a*) the angular velocity of rod AC, (*b*) the velocity of the point of the rod in contact with the pivoted collar B.

*15.104. In Prob. 15.103, derive an expression for the angular acceleration of rod AC.

***15.105.** A disk of radius r rolls without slipping along the inside of a fixed cylinder of radius R. The angular velocity ω of the disk is constant. Denoting by P the point of the disk in contact with the cylinder at $t = 0$, derive expressions for the horizontal and vertical components of the velocity of P at any time t. (The curve described by point P is called a *hypocycloid*.)

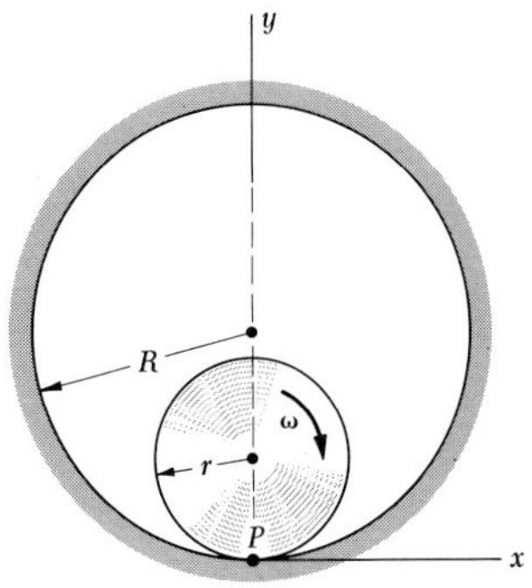

FIG. P 15.105

***15.106.** In Prob. 15.105, show that the path of P is a vertical straight line when $r = \frac{1}{2}R$. Derive expressions for the corresponding velocity and acceleration of P at any time t.

***15.107.** The crank AB of Prob. 15.34 rotates with a constant clockwise angular velocity ω, and $\theta = 0$ at $t = 0$. Using the method of Sec. 15.9, derive an expression for the velocity of the piston P in terms of the time t.

*15.10. Particle Moving on a Slab in Translation.

Let us consider the motion of a particle P which describes a path on a slab S which is itself in translation. The motion of P may be analyzed, either in terms of its coordinates x and y with respect to a fixed set of axes, or in terms of its coordinates x' and y' with respect to a set of axes attached to the slab S and moving with it (Fig. 15.21). We propose to determine the relation existing between the absolute motion of P with respect to the fixed axes and its relative motion with respect to the axes moving with S.

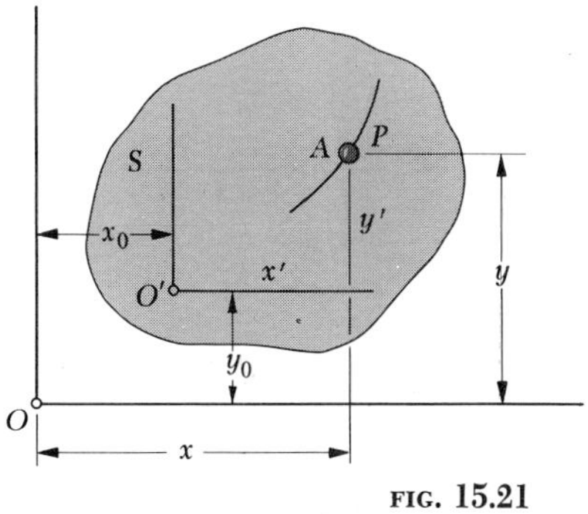

FIG. 15.21

Denoting by x_0 and y_0 the coordinates of O' with respect to the fixed axes, we write

$$x = x_0 + x' \qquad y = y_0 + y' \tag{15.23}$$

Differentiating with respect to t, we have

$$\frac{dx}{dt} = \frac{dx_0}{dt} + \frac{dx'}{dt} \qquad \frac{dy}{dt} = \frac{dy_0}{dt} + \frac{dy'}{dt} \tag{15.24}$$

Now, dx/dt and dy/dt represent the components of the absolute velocity $\mathbf{v}_P$ of P, while dx'/dt and dy'/dt represent the components of the velocity $\mathbf{v}_{P/S}$ of P with respect to S. On the other hand, dx_0/dt and dy_0/dt represent the components of the velocity of O' or, since the slab S is in translation, the components of the velocity of any other point of S. We may, for example, consider that dx_0/dt and dy_0/dt represent the components of the velocity $\mathbf{v}_A$ of the *point A of the slab S which happens to coincide with the particle P at the instant consid-*

ered. We thus write

$$\mathbf{v}_P = \mathbf{v}_A + \mathbf{v}_{P/S} \tag{15.25}$$

where the right-hand member represents a vector sum. We note that the velocity $\mathbf{v}_P$ reduces to $\mathbf{v}_{P/S}$ if the slab is stopped and if the particle is allowed to keep moving on S; it reduces to the velocity $\mathbf{v}_A$ of the coinciding point A if the particle P is immobilized on S while S is allowed to keep moving. Thus, formula (15.25) expresses that the absolute velocity of P may be obtained by adding vectorially these two partial velocities.

Differentiating Eqs. (15.24) with respect to t, we obtain

$$\frac{d^2x}{dt^2} = \frac{d^2x_0}{dt^2} + \frac{d^2x'}{dt^2} \qquad \frac{d^2y}{dt^2} = \frac{d^2y_0}{dt^2} + \frac{d^2y'}{dt^2} \tag{15.26}$$

or, in vector form,

$$\mathbf{a}_P = \mathbf{a}_A + \mathbf{a}_{P/S} \tag{15.27}$$

where $\mathbf{a}_{P/S}$ = acceleration of P with respect to S
$\mathbf{a}_A$ = acceleration of point A of S coinciding with P at the instant considered

Formula (15.27) may be interpreted in the same way as formula (15.25).

Formulas (15.25) and (15.27) actually restate the results obtained in Sec. 11.11. Since S is in translation, the x' and y' axes, respectively, remain parallel to the fixed x and y axes, and the velocity $\mathbf{v}_{P/S}$ is equal to the velocity $\mathbf{v}_{P/A}$ relative to point A as it was defined in Sec. 11.11; similarly, the acceleration $\mathbf{a}_{P/S}$ is equal to the acceleration $\mathbf{a}_{P/A}$ relative to A.

***15.11. Particle Moving on a Rotating Slab. Coriolis Acceleration.** We shall now consider the motion of a particle P which describes a path on a slab S which is itself rotating about a fixed point O. The motion of P may be analyzed either in terms of its polar coordinates r and θ with respect to fixed axes or in terms of its coordinates r and θ' with respect to axes attached to the slab S and rotating with it (Fig. 15.22). Again we propose to determine the relation existing between the absolute motion of P and its relative motion with respect to S.

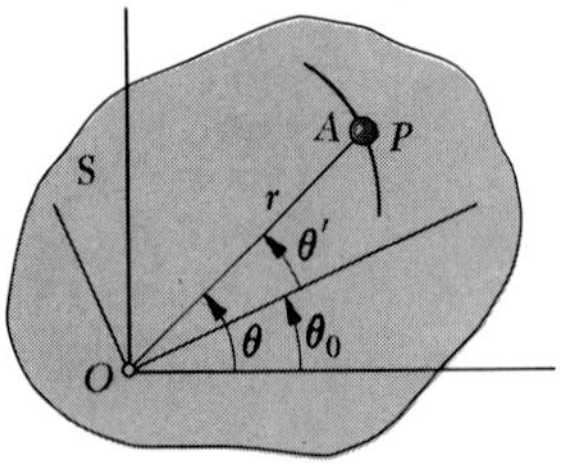

FIG. 15.22

We shall use formulas (11.30) to express the radial and transverse components of the absolute velocity $\mathbf{v}_P$ of P. Observing that $\theta = \theta' + \theta_0$, where θ_0 denotes the angular displacement of the slab at the instant considered, we write

$$(v_P)_r = \frac{dr}{dt} \qquad (v_P)_\theta = r\frac{d\theta}{dt} = r\left(\frac{d\theta'}{dt} + \frac{d\theta_0}{dt}\right) \tag{15.28}$$

Considering the particular case when the slab is maintained

fixed and P is allowed to move, $\mathbf{v}_P$ reduces to the relative velocity $\mathbf{v}_{P/S}$. Making θ_0 constant in (15.28), we obtain, therefore,

$$(v_{P/S})_r = \frac{dr}{dt} \qquad (v_{P/S})_\theta = r\frac{d\theta'}{dt} \tag{15.29}$$

Considering now the particular case when P is immobilized on S and S is allowed to rotate, $\mathbf{v}_P$ reduces to the velocity $\mathbf{v}_A$ of the point A of the slab S which happens to coincide with P at the instant considered. Making $r =$ constant and $\theta' =$ constant in (15.28), we obtain

$$(v_A)_r = 0 \qquad (v_A)_\theta = r\frac{d\theta_0}{dt} \tag{15.30}$$

Comparing formulas (15.28) to (15.30), we find that

$$(v_P)_r = (v_A)_r + (v_{P/S})_r \qquad (v_P)_\theta = (v_A)_\theta + (v_{P/S})_\theta$$

or, in vector form,

$$\mathbf{v}_P = \mathbf{v}_A + \mathbf{v}_{P/S} \tag{15.31}$$

Formula (15.31) expresses that $\mathbf{v}_P$ may be obtained by adding vectorially the velocities corresponding to the two particular cases considered above.

Using formulas (11.33), we now express the radial and transverse components of the absolute acceleration $\mathbf{a}_P$ of P,

$$\begin{aligned}(a_P)_r &= \frac{d^2r}{dt^2} - r\left(\frac{d\theta}{dt}\right)^2 = \frac{d^2r}{dt^2} - r\left(\frac{d\theta'}{dt} + \frac{d\theta_0}{dt}\right)^2 \\ &= \frac{d^2r}{dt^2} - r\left[\left(\frac{d\theta'}{dt}\right)^2 + 2\frac{d\theta'}{dt}\frac{d\theta_0}{dt} + \left(\frac{d\theta_0}{dt}\right)^2\right]\end{aligned} \tag{15.32}$$

$$\begin{aligned}(a_P)_\theta &= r\frac{d^2\theta}{dt^2} + 2\frac{dr}{dt}\frac{d\theta}{dt} \\ &= r\left(\frac{d^2\theta'}{dt^2} + \frac{d^2\theta_0}{dt^2}\right) + 2\frac{dr}{dt}\left(\frac{d\theta'}{dt} + \frac{d\theta_0}{dt}\right)\end{aligned} \tag{15.33}$$

Considering again the particular case when $\theta_0 =$ constant (slab fixed), we obtain

$$(a_{P/S})_r = \frac{d^2r}{dt^2} - r\left(\frac{d\theta'}{dt}\right)^2 \qquad (a_{P/S})_\theta = r\frac{d^2\theta'}{dt^2} + 2\frac{dr}{dt}\frac{d\theta'}{dt} \tag{15.34}$$

Considering now the particular case when $r =$ constant and $\theta' =$ constant (P immobilized on S), we have

$$(a_A)_r = -r\left(\frac{d\theta_0}{dt}\right)^2 \qquad (a_A)_\theta = r\frac{d^2\theta_0}{dt^2} \tag{15.35}$$

Comparing formulas (15.32) to (15.35), we find that the absolute acceleration $\mathbf{a}_P$ *cannot* be obtained by adding the accelerations $\mathbf{a}_A$ and $\mathbf{a}_{P/S}$ corresponding to the two particular cases considered above. We have instead

$$\mathbf{a}_P = \mathbf{a}_A + \mathbf{a}_{P/S} + \mathbf{a}_c \tag{15.36}$$

where $\mathbf{a}_c$ is a vector of components

$$(a_c)_r = -2r\frac{d\theta'}{dt}\frac{d\theta_0}{dt} \qquad (a_c)_\theta = 2\frac{dr}{dt}\frac{d\theta_0}{dt}$$

Noting that $d\theta_0/dt$ represents the angular velocity ω of S, and recalling formulas (15.29), we have

$$(a_c)_r = -2\omega(v_{P/S})_\theta \qquad (a_c)_\theta = 2\omega(v_{P/S})_r \tag{15.37}$$

The vector $\mathbf{a}_c$ is called the *complementary acceleration*, or *Coriolis acceleration*, after the French mathematician De Coriolis (1792–1843). The first of formulas (15.37) indicates that the vector $(\mathbf{a}_c)_r$ is obtained by multiplying the vector $(\mathbf{v}_{P/S})_\theta$ by 2ω and rotating it through 90° in the sense of rotation of the slab (Fig. 15.23); the second formula defines $(\mathbf{a}_c)_\theta$ from $(\mathbf{v}_{P/S})_r$ in a similar way. *The Coriolis acceleration* $\mathbf{a}_c$ *is thus a vector perpendicular to the relative velocity* $\mathbf{v}_{P/S}$, *and of magnitude equal to* $2\omega v_{P/S}$; *the sense of* $\mathbf{a}_c$ *is obtained by rotating the vector* $\mathbf{v}_{P/S}$ *through 90° in the sense of rotation of S.*

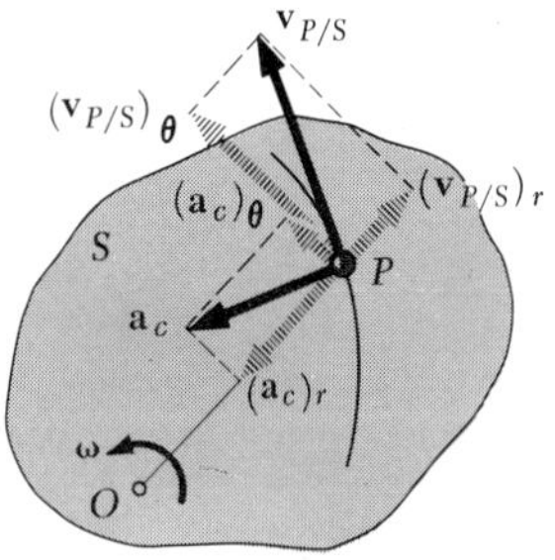

FIG. 15.23

Comparing formulas (15.36) and (11.26), we note that the acceleration $\mathbf{a}_{P/S}$ of P relative to the slab S is *not* equal to the acceleration $\mathbf{a}_{P/A}$ of P relative to the point A of S; this is due to the fact that the first acceleration is defined with respect to *rotating axes*, while the second is defined with respect to *axes of fixed orientation*.

The following example will help in understanding the physical meaning of the Coriolis acceleration. Consider a collar P which is made to slide at a constant relative speed u along a rod OB rotating at a constant angular velocity ω about O (Fig. 15.24a). According to formula (15.36), the absolute acceleration of P may be obtained by adding vectorially the acceleration $\mathbf{a}_A$ of the point of the rod coinciding with P, the relative acceleration $\mathbf{a}_{P/OB}$ of P with respect to the rod, and the Coriolis acceleration $\mathbf{a}_c$. Since the angular velocity ω of the rod is constant, $\mathbf{a}_A$ reduces to its normal component $(\mathbf{a}_A)_n$ of magnitude $r\omega^2$; and since u is constant, the relative acceleration $\mathbf{a}_{P/OB}$ is zero. According to the definition given above, the Coriolis acceleration is a vector perpendicular to OB, of magnitude $2\omega u$, and directed as shown in the figure. The acceleration of the collar P consists, therefore, of the two vectors shown in Fig. 15.24a.

Note that the result obtained may be checked by applying formulas (11.33).

To understand better the significance of the Coriolis acceleration, we shall consider the absolute velocity of P at time t and at time $t + \Delta t$ (Fig. 15.24*b*). At time t, the velocity may be resolved into its components $\mathbf{u}$ and $\mathbf{v}_A$, and at time $t + \Delta t$ into its components $\mathbf{u}'$ and $\mathbf{v}_{A'}$. Drawing these components from the same origin (Fig. 15.24*c*), we note that the change in velocity during the time Δt may be represented by the sum of three vectors $\overrightarrow{RR'}$, $\overrightarrow{TT''}$ and $\overrightarrow{T''T'}$. The vector $\overrightarrow{TT''}$ measures the change in direction of the velocity $\mathbf{v}_A$, and the quotient $\overrightarrow{TT''}/\Delta t$ represents the acceleration $\mathbf{a}_A$ when Δt approaches zero. We check that the direction of $\overrightarrow{TT''}$ is that of $\mathbf{a}_A$ when Δt approaches zero and that

$$\lim_{\Delta t \to 0} \frac{TT''}{\Delta t} = \lim_{\Delta t \to 0} v_A \frac{\Delta \theta}{\Delta t} = r\omega\omega = r\omega^2 = a_A$$

The vector $\overrightarrow{RR'}$ measures the change in direction of $\mathbf{u}$ due to the rotation of the rod; the vector $\overrightarrow{T''T'}$ measures the change in magnitude of $\mathbf{v}_A$ due to the motion of P on the rod. The vectors $\overrightarrow{RR'}$ and $\overrightarrow{T''T'}$ result from the *combined effect* of the relative motion of P and of the rotation of the rod; they would vanish if *either* of these two motions were stopped. We may easily verify that the sum of these two vectors defines the Coriolis acceleration. Their direction is that of $\mathbf{a}_c$ when Δt approaches zero and, since $RR' = u\Delta\theta$ and $T''T' = v_{A'} - v_A = (r + \Delta r)\omega - r\omega = \omega\Delta r$, we check that

$$\lim_{\Delta t \to 0} \left(\frac{RR'}{\Delta t} + \frac{T''T'}{\Delta t} \right) = \lim_{\Delta t \to 0} \left(u \frac{\Delta\theta}{\Delta t} + \omega \frac{\Delta r}{\Delta t} \right)$$
$$= u\omega + \omega u = 2\omega u = a_c$$

Formulas (15.31) and (15.36) may be used to analyze the motion of mechanisms which contain parts sliding on each other. They make it possible, for example, to relate the absolute and relative motions of sliding pins and collars (see Sample Probs. 15.8 and 15.9). The concept of Coriolis acceleration is also very useful in the study of long-range projectiles and of other bodies whose motions are appreciably affected by the rotation of the earth. As was pointed out in Sec. 12.1, a system of axes attached to the earth does not truly constitute a newtonian frame of reference; such a system of axes should actually be considered as rotating. The formulas derived in this section will therefore facilitate the study of the motion of bodies with respect to axes attached to the earth.

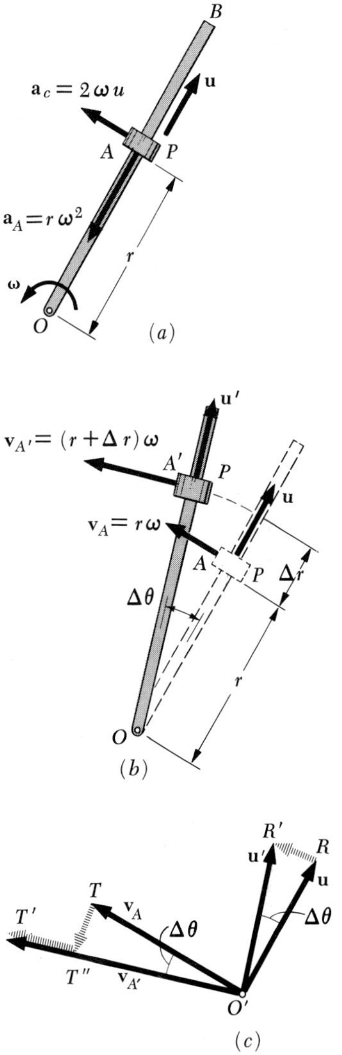

FIG. 15.24

SAMPLE PROBLEM 15.8

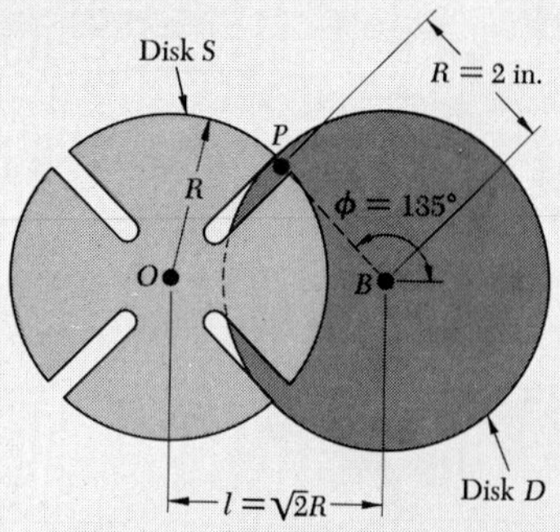

The Geneva mechanism shown is used in many counting instruments and in other applications where an intermittent rotary motion is required. Disk D rotates with a constant counterclockwise angular velocity ω_D of 10 radians/sec. A pin P is attached to disk D and slides along one of several slots cut in disk S. It is desirable that the angular velocity of disk S be zero as the pin enters and leaves each slot; in the case of four slots, this will occur if the distance between the centers of the disks is $l = \sqrt{2}\,R$.

At the instant when $\phi = 150°$, determine (*a*) the angular velocity of disk S, (*b*) the velocity of pin P relative to disk S.

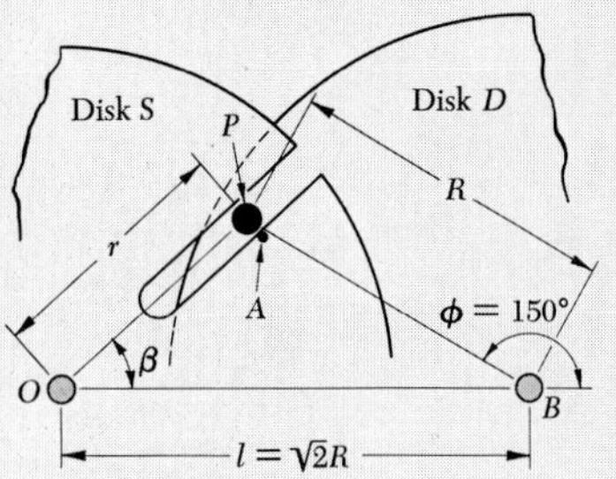

Solution. We solve triangle OPB, which corresponds to the position $\phi = 150°$, and obtain

$$\beta = 42.4° \qquad r = 0.742R = 1.484 \text{ in.}$$

Since pin P is attached to disk D, and since disk D rotates about point B, the magnitude of the absolute velocity of P is

$$v_P = R\omega_D = (2 \text{ in.})(10 \text{ radians/sec}) = 20 \text{ in./sec}$$

$$\mathbf{v}_P = 20 \text{ in./sec} \;\angle\; 60°$$

We consider now the motion of pin P along the slot in disk S. Denoting by A the point of disk S which coincides with P at the instant considered, we write

$$\mathbf{v}_P = \mathbf{v}_A + \mathbf{v}_{P/S}$$

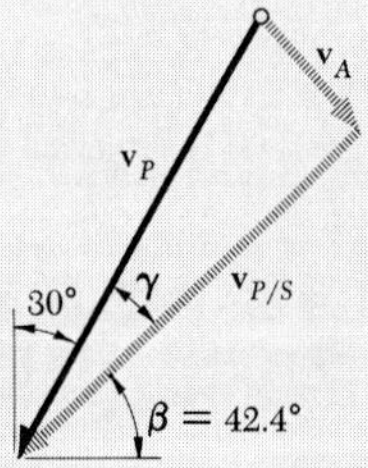

Noting that $\mathbf{v}_A$ is perpendicular to the radius OA and that $\mathbf{v}_{P/S}$ is directed along the slot, we draw the velocity triangle corresponding to the above equation. From the triangle, we compute

$$\gamma = 90° - 42.4° - 30° = 17.6°$$

$$v_A = v_P \sin\gamma = (20 \text{ in./sec}) \sin 17.6°$$

$$\mathbf{v}_A = 6.05 \text{ in./sec} \;⦩\; 42.4°$$

$$v_{P/S} = v_P \cos\gamma = (20 \text{ in./sec}) \cos 17.6°$$

$$\mathbf{v}_{P/S} = 19.06 \text{ in./sec} \;\angle\; 42.4° \quad ◄$$

Since $\mathbf{v}_A$ is perpendicular to the radius OA, we write

$$v_A = r\omega_S \qquad 6.05 \text{ in./sec} = (1.484 \text{ in.})\,\omega_S$$

$$\omega_S = 4.07 \text{ radians/sec} \;↻ \quad ◄$$

SAMPLE PROBLEM 15.9

In the Geneva mechanism of Sample Prob. 15.8, disk D rotates with a constant counterclockwise angular velocity ω_D of 10 radians/sec. At the instant when $\phi = 150°$, determine the angular acceleration of disk S.

Solution. Referring to Sample Prob. 15.8, we obtain the angular velocity of disk S and the velocity of the pin relative to disk S.

$$\omega_S = 4.07 \text{ radians/sec} \circlearrowright$$

$$\beta = 42.4° \qquad \mathbf{v}_{P/S} = 19.06 \text{ in./sec} \searrow 42.4°$$

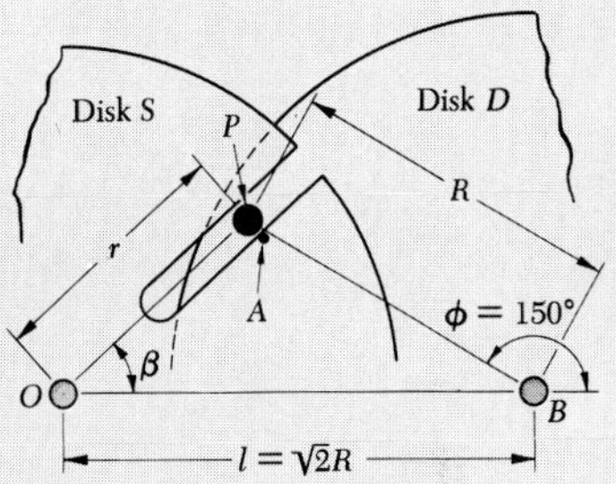

Since pin P moves with respect to the rotating disk S, we write

$$\mathbf{a}_P = \mathbf{a}_A + \mathbf{a}_{P/S} + \mathbf{a}_c \qquad (1)$$

Each term of this vector equation is investigated separately.

Absolute Acceleration $\mathbf{a}_P$. Since disk D rotates with constant ω, the absolute acceleration $\mathbf{a}_P$ is directed toward B.

$$a_P = R\omega_D^2 = (2 \text{ in.})(10 \text{ radians/sec})^2 = 200 \text{ in./sec}^2$$

$$\mathbf{a}_P = 200 \text{ in./sec}^2 \searrow 30°$$

Acceleration $\mathbf{a}_A$ *of the Coinciding Point A.* The acceleration $\mathbf{a}_A$ of the point A of disk S which coincides with P at the instant considered is resolved into normal and tangential components. (We recall from Sample Prob. 15.8 that $r = 1.484$ in.)

$$(a_A)_n = r\omega_S^2 = (1.484)(4.07)^2 = 24.6 \text{ in./sec}^2$$

$$(\mathbf{a}_A)_n = 24.6 \text{ in./sec}^2 \searrow 42.4°$$

$$(a_A)_t = r\alpha_S = 1.484\alpha_S \qquad (\mathbf{a}_A)_t = 1.484\alpha_S \nwarrow 42.4°$$

Relative Acceleration $\mathbf{a}_{P/S}$. Since the pin P moves in a straight slot cut in disk S, the relative acceleration $\mathbf{a}_{P/S}$ must be parallel to the slot, i.e., its direction must be $\swarrow$ 42.4°.

Coriolis Acceleration $\mathbf{a}_c$. Rotating the relative velocity $\mathbf{v}_{P/S}$ through 90° in the sense of ω_S, we obtain the direction of the Coriolis component of the acceleration.

$$a_c = 2\omega_S v_{P/S} = (2)(4.07 \text{ radians/sec})(19.06 \text{ in./sec}) = 155.1 \text{ in./sec}^2$$

$$\mathbf{a}_c = 155.1 \text{ in./sec}^2 \nwarrow 42.4°$$

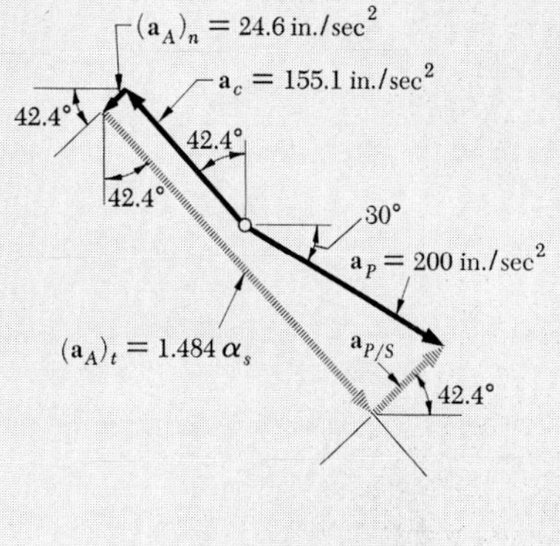

We rewrite Eq. (1) and substitute the accelerations found above.

$$\mathbf{a}_P = (\mathbf{a}_A)_n + (\mathbf{a}_A)_t + \mathbf{a}_{P/S} + \mathbf{a}_c$$

$$[200 \searrow 30°] = [24.6 \searrow 42.4°] + [1.484\alpha_S \nwarrow 42.4°] + [a_{P/S} \swarrow 42.4°] + [155.1 \nwarrow 42.4°]$$

Solving this equation analytically or graphically, we obtain

$$1.484\alpha_S = 346 \text{ in./sec}^2$$

$$\alpha_S = 233 \text{ radians/sec}^2 \circlearrowright \blacktriangleleft$$

PROBLEMS

15.108. The drive disk of the Scotch crosshead mechanism shown has a contant angular velocity of 300 rpm counterclockwise. Knowing that $r = 4$ in., determine the velocity of rod B when (a) $\theta = 0$, (b) $\theta = 30°$, (c) $\theta = 90°$.

15.109. The drive disk of the Scotch crosshead mechanism shown has a constant counterclockwise angular velocity ω. Determine the velocity of rod B in terms of r, θ, and ω.

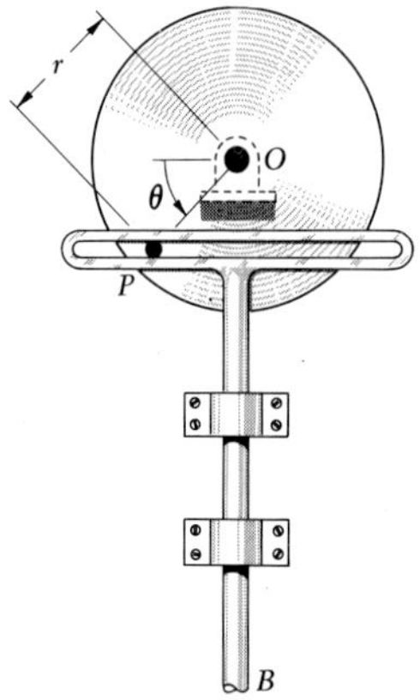

FIG. P 15.108 AND P 15.109

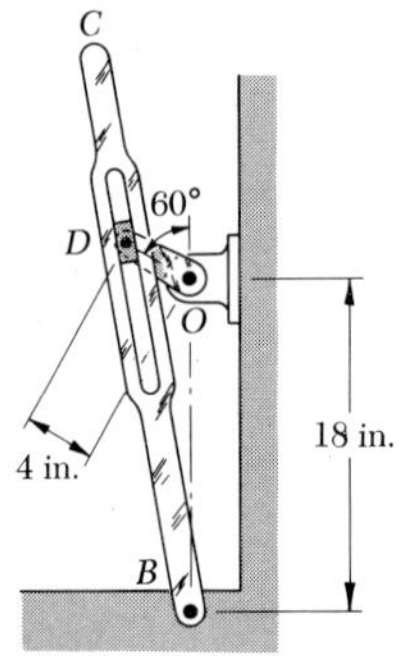

FIG. P 15.111

15.110. For the Geneva mechanism of Sample Prob. 15.8, show that the angular velocity of disk S is zero as the pin P enters or leaves a slot. Also determine the maximum angular velocity of disk S and the corresponding value of ϕ.

15.111. The Whitworth mechanism shown is used to produce a quick-return motion of point C. The drive crank OD has a constant angular velocity of 120 rpm counterclockwise. For the position shown, determine (a) the angular velocity of the arm BC, (b) the velocity of the slider block D with respect to arm BC.

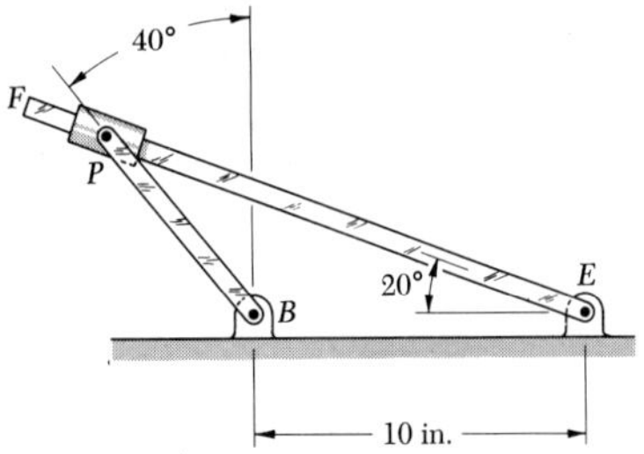

FIG. P 15.112 AND P 15.114

15.112 and 15.113. Two rotating rods are connected by a slider block P. Knowing that the rod attached at B rotates with a constant counterclockwise angular velocity of 5 radians/sec, determine for the position shown (a) the angular velocity of the rod attached at E, (b) the relative velocity of the slider block P with respect to the rod on which it slides.

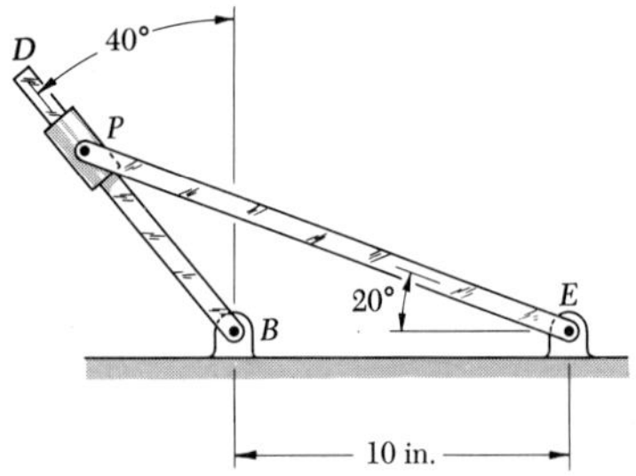

FIG. P 15.113 AND P 15.115

15.114 and 15.115. Two rotating rods are connected by a slider block P. Knowing that the velocity of the slider block relative to the rod on which it slides is 10 in./sec outward, determine the angular velocity of each rod for the position shown.

15.116. Two rods BD and EF pass through smooth holes drilled in a hexagonal block. (The holes are drilled in different planes so that the rods will not hit each other.) Knowing that rod BD rotates counterclockwise at the rate ω, determine the angular velocity of rod EF and the relative velocity of the block with respect to each rod when (a) $\theta = 90°$, (b) $\theta = 60°$.

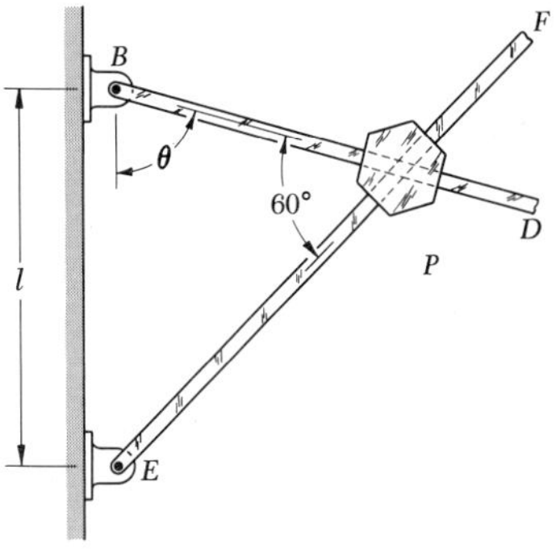

FIG. P 15.116

15.117. Four pins slide in four separate slots cut in a circular plate as shown. When the plate is at rest, each pin has a velocity directed as shown and of the same constant magnitude u. If each pin maintains the same velocity in relation to the plate when the plate rotates about O with a constant *counterclockwise* angular velocity ω, determine the acceleration of each pin.

15.118. Solve Prob. 15.117 assuming that the plate rotates about O with a constant *clockwise* angular velocity ω.

15.119. A pin P slides in a circular slot of radius r_2 which is cut in the plate OE. The velocity of P relative to the plate is of constant magnitude u and is directed as shown. Knowing that the plate rotates counterclockwise with a constant angular velocity ω, derive an expression for (a) the magnitude u for which the acceleration of the pin is zero as it passes through point B, (b) the corresponding magnitude of the acceleration of the pin as it passes through point D.

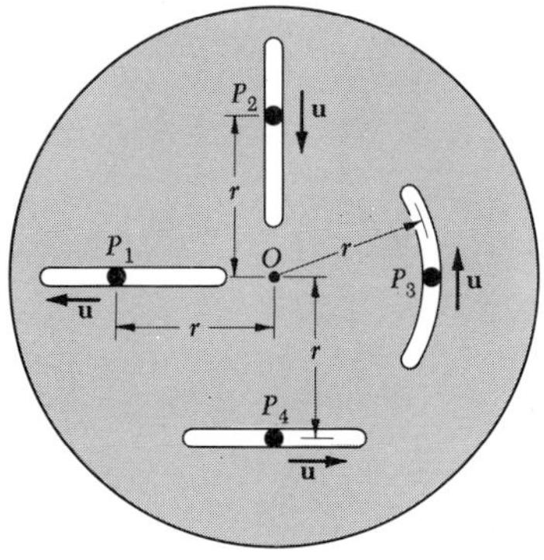

FIG. P 15.117

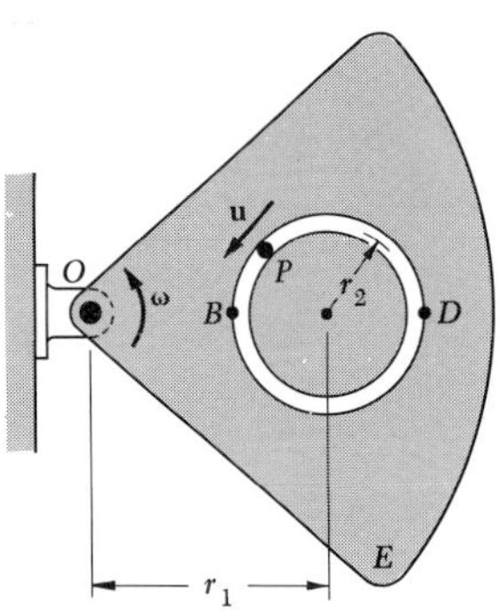

FIG. P 15.119

15.120. The collar P slides outward at a constant relative speed u along the rod BD, which rotates at the constant angular velocity ω. Determine the magnitude of the acceleration of the collar P just before it reaches the end of the rod.

15.121. The collar P slides outward at a constant relative speed u along the rod BD, which rotates at the constant angular velocity ω. Knowing that $r = 0$ when $\theta = 0$ and that the collar reaches D when $\theta = \pi$, determine the magnitude of the acceleration of the collar P just before it reaches the end of the rod.

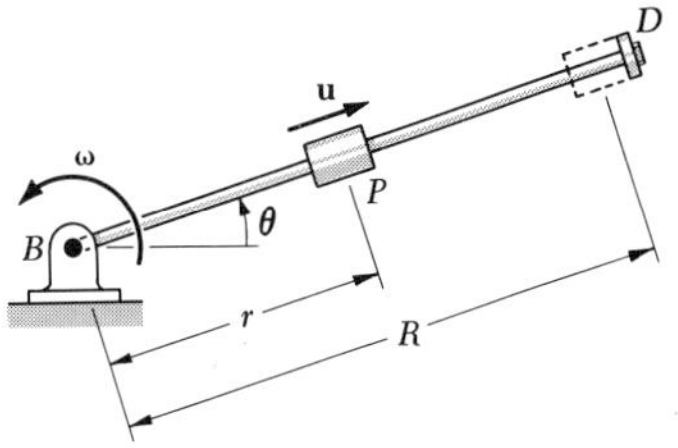

FIG. P 15.120 AND P 15.121

15.122. The cage of a mine elevator moves downward with a constant speed of 40 ft/sec. Determine the magnitude and direction of the Coriolis acceleration of the cage if the elevator is located (a) at the equator, (b) at latitude 40° north, (c) at latitude 40° south. (*Hint.* In parts b and c consider separately the components of the motion parallel and perpendicular to the plane of the equator.)

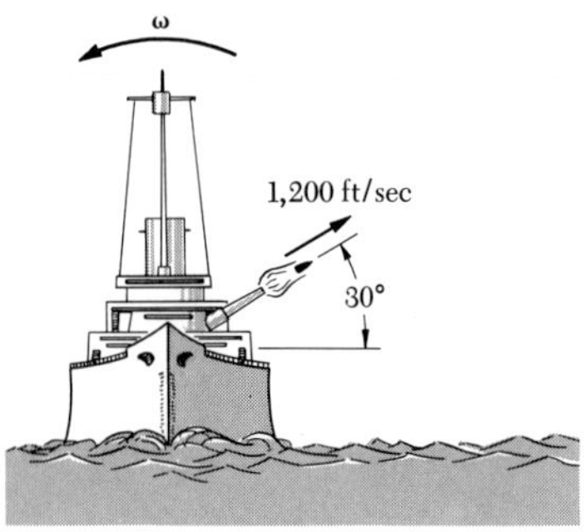

FIG. P 15.124

15.123. A rocket sled is tested on a straight track which is built along a meridian. Knowing that the track is located at a latitude of 40° north, determine the Coriolis acceleration of the sled when its speed is 600 mph. (See hint of Prob. 15.122.)

15.124. A naval gun fires a shell at an angle of 30° with a muzzle velocity of 1,200 ft/sec at a target located directly to the side of the ship. Assuming that the roll of the ship is 2° per second, determine the Coriolis acceleration of the shell just before it leaves the barrel of the gun. (Assume that the gun is rigidly attached to the ship.)

15.125. Solve Prob. 15.124 assuming that the shell is fired at an angle of 30° at a target located directly in front of the ship.

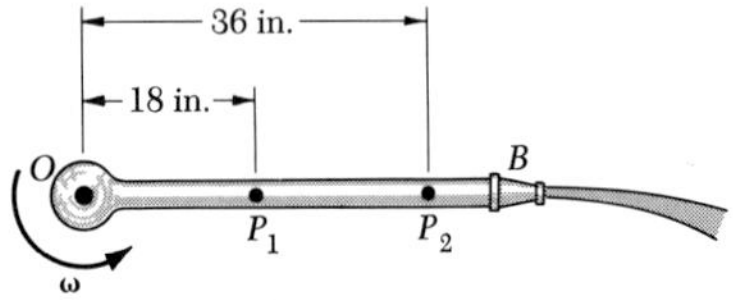

FIG. P 15.126

15.126. Water flows through a straight pipe OB which rotates counterclockwise with an angular velocity of 120 rpm. If the velocity of the water relative to the pipe is 30 ft/sec, determine the total acceleration (*a*) of the particle of water P_1, (*b*) of the particle of water P_2.

15.127. In Prob. 15.126, determine the angular velocity ω of the pipe for which the total acceleration of the particle of water P_2 forms an angle of 45° with the pipe.

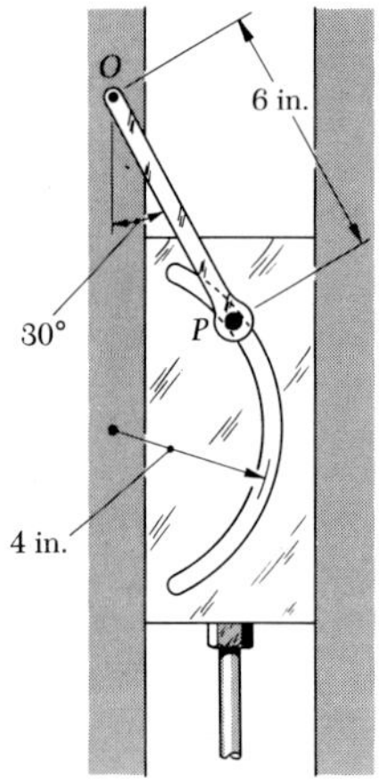

FIG. P 15.128

15.128. At the instant shown, the slotted plate slides with a velocity of 10 in./sec upward and has an acceleration of 40 in./sec² downward. Determine the angular velocity and the angular acceleration of rod OP.

15.129. In Prob. 15.113, determine the angular acceleration of the rod attached at E.

15.130. In Prob. 15.112, determine the angular acceleration of the rod attached at E.

***15.131.** At the instant when $\theta = 90°$ in Prob. 15.116, rod BD has a counterclockwise angular velocity ω and no angular acceleration. Determine at that instant the angular acceleration of rod EF and the total acceleration of the block P.

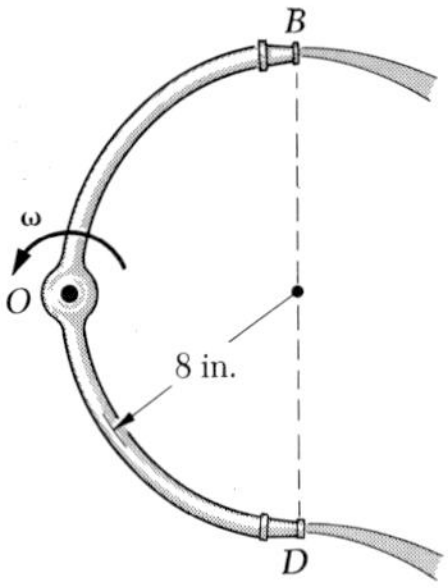

FIG. P 15.132

15.132. Water is introduced into a curved pipe at O, flows through two quarter-circular portions of pipe, and is discharged at points B and D. The pipe rotates about O with a constant counterclockwise angular velocity of 120 rpm. Knowing that the velocity of the water relative to the pipe is 30 ft/sec, determine the absolute acceleration of a particle of water just before it leaves the pipe at B.

15.133. In Prob. 15.132, determine the absolute acceleration of a particle of water just before it leaves the pipe at D.

REVIEW PROBLEMS

15.134. For the bevel-gear system shown, determine the required value of β if the ratio of ω_A to ω_B is to be 3.

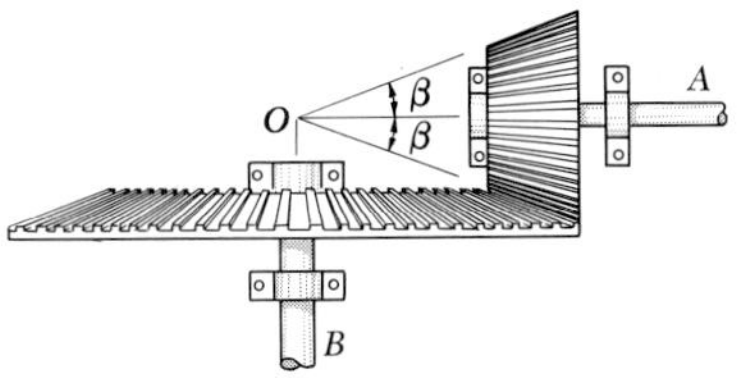

FIG. P 15.134

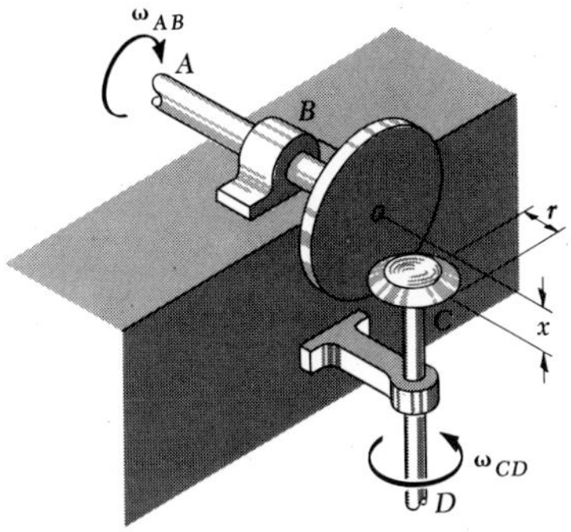

FIG. P 15.135

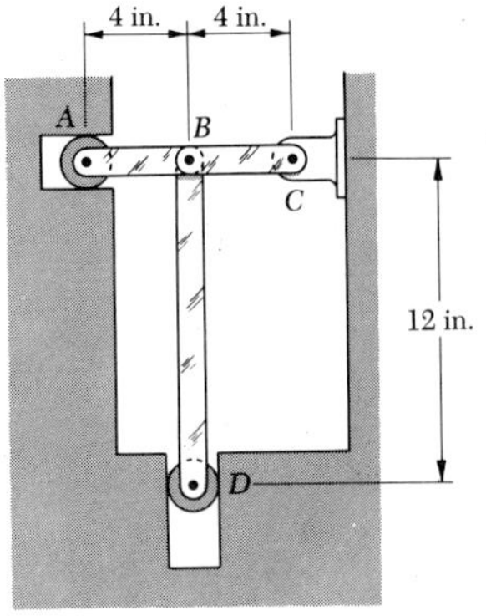

FIG. P 15.136

*15.135. Shafts AB and CD are connected by a friction disk and wheel as shown. Disk C is of radius r and rotates at a constant angular velocity ω_{CD}. If shaft CD is lowered at a constant velocity v, derive an expression for the angular acceleration of shaft AB.

15.136. Three links AB, BC, and BD are connected by a pin B as shown. Knowing that at the instant shown point D has a velocity of 8 in./sec upward and no acceleration, determine (*a*) the angular acceleration of each link, (*b*) the accelerations of points A and B.

15.137. Elliptical gears are used to transform a uniform rotation into a nonuniform rotation; each gear must be pivoted at a focus F of the ellipse. Assuming gear A rotates at a constant speed of 160 rpm, determine the maximum and minimum values of the angular velocity of gear B.

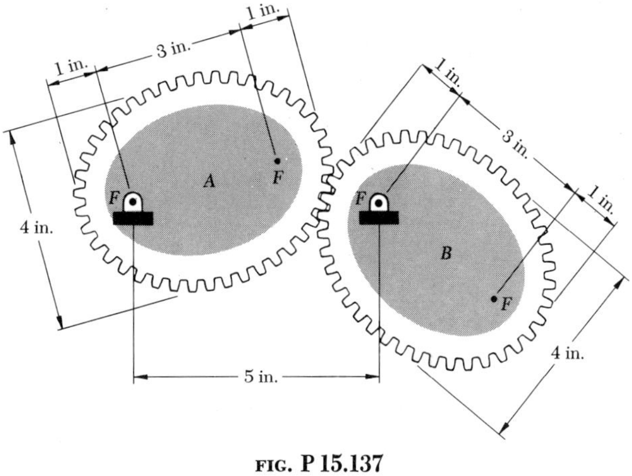

FIG. P 15.137

15.138. The angular velocity of gear A is 250 rpm clockwise. If the motion of gear B is to be a curvilinear translation, determine (*a*) the required angular velocity of rod AB, (*b*) the corresponding velocity of gear B.

15.139. Gear A rotates at the constant angular velocity of 120 rpm clockwise while rod AB rotates at the constant angular velocity of 60 rpm counterclockwise. Determine the magnitude of the accelerations of the two gear teeth which are in contact with each other.

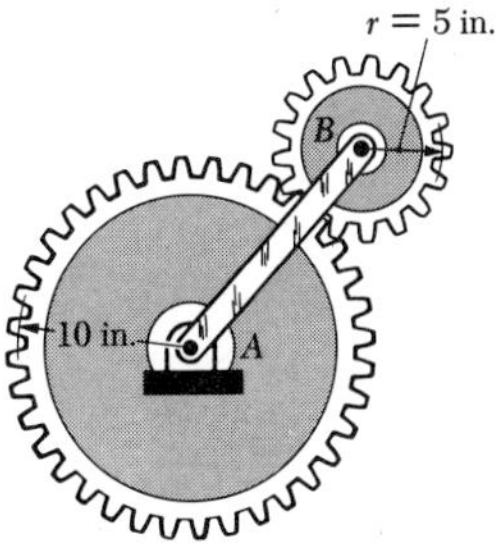

FIG. P 15.138 AND P 15.139

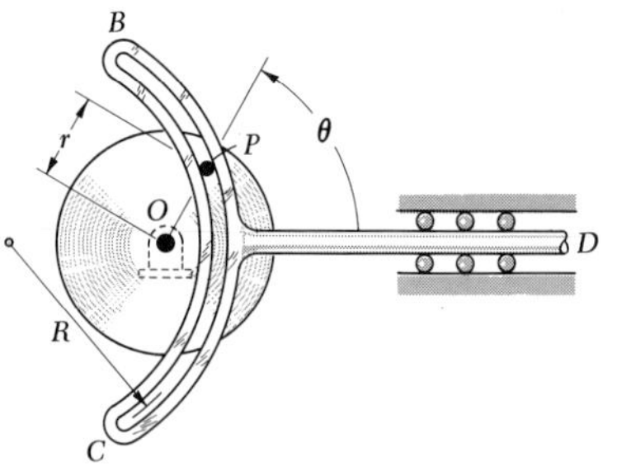

FIG. P 15.140

15.140. The drive disk shown rotates about O with a constant angular velocity of 300 rpm counterclockwise. Knowing that $r = 3$ in. and $R = 6$ in., determine the velocity of member BCD when (a) $\theta = 0$, (b) $\theta = 60°$, (c) $\theta = 90°$.

*15.141. In Prob. 15.140, determine the acceleration of member BCD when (a) $\theta = 0$, (b) $\theta = 60°$, (c) $\theta = 90°$.

15.142. The angular acceleration of a disk is defined by the relation $\alpha = -4\omega$, where α is expressed in radians/sec² and ω in radians/sec. Knowing that at $t = 0$ the angular velocity is 2,000 rpm, determine (a) the number of revolutions executed by the disk before coming to rest, (b) the time required for the disk to come to rest, (c) the time required for the angular velocity of the disk to be reduced to 20 rpm.

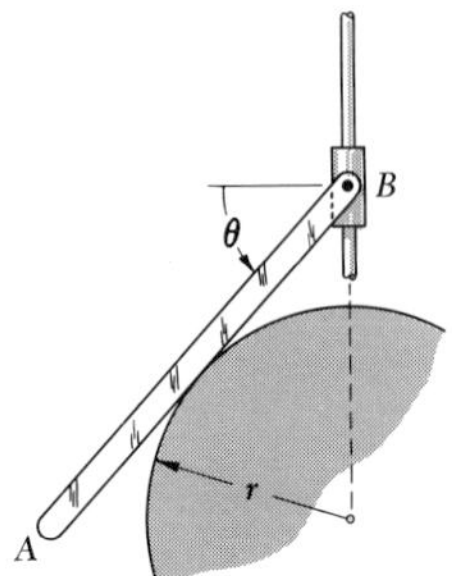

FIG. P 15.143

15.143. A slender rod AB is attached to a collar at B and rests on a smooth circular cylinder of radius r. Knowing that the collar B moves upward with a constant velocity of magnitude v, derive an expression in terms of r, θ, and v (a) for the angular velocity of the rod, (b) for the angular acceleration of the rod.

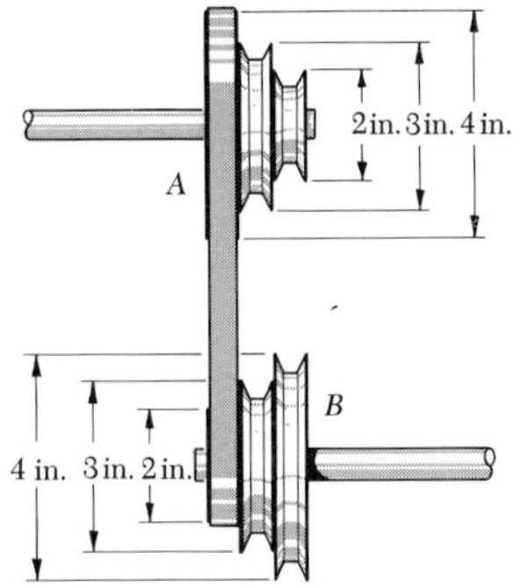

FIG. P 15.144

15.144. The two pulleys shown may be operated with the V belt in any of three positions. If the angular acceleration of shaft A is 8 radians/sec² and if the system is initially at rest, determine the time required for shaft B to reach a speed of 300 rpm with the belt in each of the three positions.

15.145. A straight rack rests on a gear of radius r and is attached to a block B as shown. Knowing that block B slides to the right at a constant speed v, derive an expression for the angular velocity of the rack in terms of r, θ, and v.

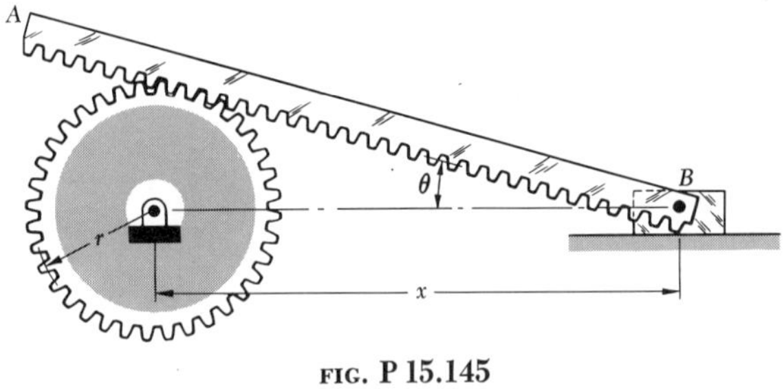

FIG. P 15.145

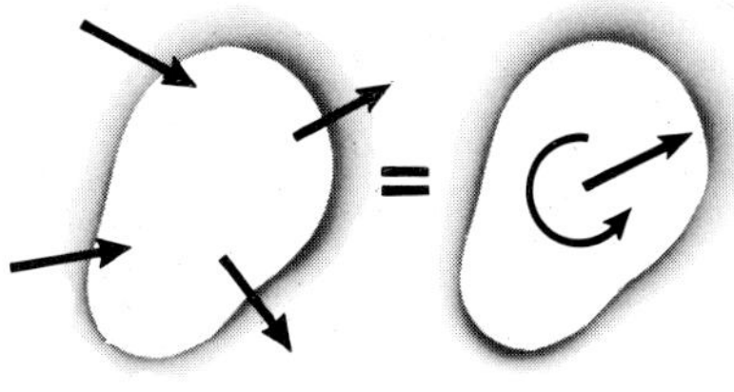

16. KINETICS OF RIGID BODIES: FORCE, MASS, AND ACCELERATION

16.1. Introduction. In this chapter and in Chaps. 17 and 18, we shall study the *kinetics of rigid bodies,* i.e., the relations existing between the forces acting on a rigid body, the shape and mass of the body, and the motion produced. In Chaps. 12 to 14, we studied similar relations, assuming then that the body could be considered as a particle, i.e., that its mass could be concentrated in one point and that all forces acted at that point. We shall now take the shape of the body into account, as well as the exact location of the points of application of the forces. Besides, we shall be concerned not only with the motion of the body as a whole but also with the rotation of the body about its mass center.

In this chapter, our study of the motion of rigid bodies will be based directly on the equation $\mathbf{F} = m\mathbf{a}$, while in the next two chapters we shall make use of the principles of work and energy and of impulse and momentum. Our study will be limited to that of the *plane motion* of rigid bodies. This motion was defined in Sec. 15.1 as a motion in which each particle of the body remains at a constant distance from a fixed reference plane. In the study of the kinetics of plane motion, the reference plane is chosen so that it contains the mass center of the body.

Throughout most of this chapter, our study will be further limited to that of plane slabs and of bodies which are symmetrical with respect to the reference plane.† We shall first study the simplest type of motion, namely, translation. Next we shall consider the motion of rigid bodies which are free to rotate about a fixed axis passing through their mass center. We shall then study the more general types of plane motion. These include the free motion of a rigid body, the rotation of

† Or, more generally, bodies which have a principal centroidal axis of inertia perpendicular to the reference plane.

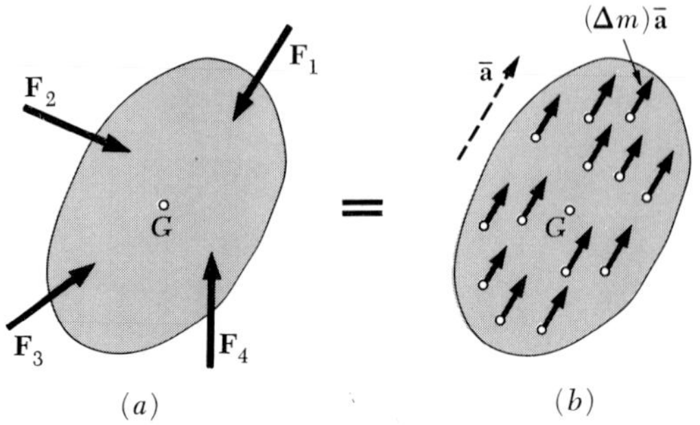

FIG 16.1

rigid bodies about a noncentroidal axis, rolling motion, as well as more complicated constrained motions such as are found in various types of mechanisms. The study of the motion of three-dimensional bodies which are not symmetrical with respect to the reference plane will be postponed until Sec. 16.9, where problems such as the balancing of rotating shafts will be considered.

16.2. Translation. Consider a rigid body of mass m which is in translation under the action of several forces $\mathbf{F}_1$, $\mathbf{F}_2$, $\mathbf{F}_3$, etc., the translation being either rectilinear or curvilinear (Fig. 16.1*a*). Denoting by $\bar{\mathbf{a}}$ the acceleration of the mass center G of the body at a given instant, we shall show that *the system of the external forces* $\mathbf{F}_1$, $\mathbf{F}_2$, $\mathbf{F}_3$, *etc., must be equivalent at that instant to a single vector* $m\bar{\mathbf{a}}$, *attached at the mass center* G *of the body.*

We saw in Sec. 12.4 that, according to D'Alembert's principle, the external forces acting on a system of particles must be equivalent to the effective forces of the various particles of the system. The *effective force* of a particle is defined as the product of the mass Δm of the particle and of its acceleration $\mathbf{a}$; it represents, therefore, the resultant of the forces acting on the particle. Since in the present case all particles have the same acceleration $\bar{\mathbf{a}}$ as the mass center G (Fig. 16.1*b*), the resultant of the effective forces is a vector of the same direction as $\bar{\mathbf{a}}$ and of magnitude equal to

$$\Sigma(\Delta m)\bar{a} = (\Sigma\ \Delta m)\bar{a} = m\bar{a}$$

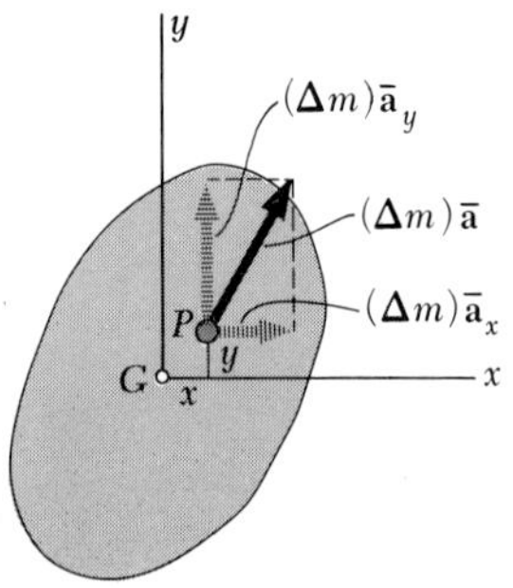

FIG. 16.2

Choosing the origin of the coordinate axes at the mass center G, and denoting by x and y the coordinates of a particle P (Fig. 16.2), we find that the sum of the moments of the effective forces about G is

$$+\circlearrowleft \Sigma(M_G)_{\text{eff}} = \Sigma x(\Delta m)\bar{a}_y - \Sigma y(\Delta m)\bar{a}_x$$
$$= \bar{a}_y\Sigma x\ \Delta m - \bar{a}_x\Sigma y\ \Delta m \qquad (16.1)$$

Now, according to the definition of the mass center of a system of particles (Sec. 12.5), we have

$$\Sigma x\,\Delta m = m\bar{x} \qquad \Sigma y\,\Delta m = m\bar{y} \tag{16.2}$$

where $\bar{x}$ and $\bar{y}$ are the coordinates of the mass center G. But $\bar{x} = \bar{y} = 0$, since the origin of the coordinate axes was chosen at G, and Eq. (16.1) reduces to $\Sigma(M_G)_{\text{eff}} = 0$. The line of action of the resultant of the effective forces, therefore, must pass through G, and the resultant $m\bar{\mathbf{a}}$ may be attached at G.

Replacing the effective forces in Fig. 16.1 by their resultant, we obtain Fig. 16.3 and thus verify that the system of the external forces acting on a rigid body in translation must be equivalent to a single vector $m\bar{\mathbf{a}}$ attached at the mass center G of the body. We write

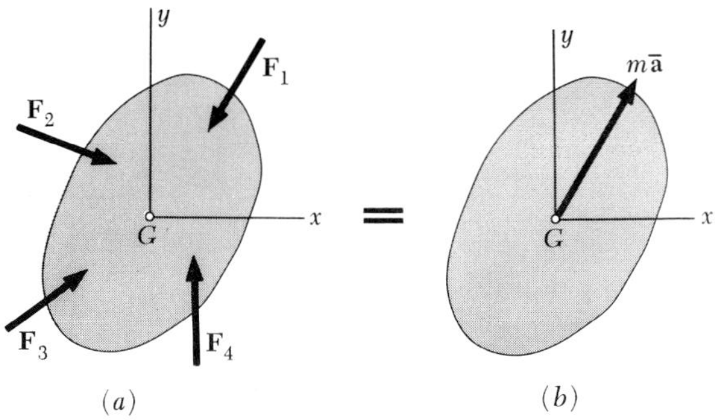

FIG. 16.3

$$\textbf{Syst Ext Forces} = m\bar{\mathbf{a}} \qquad \text{at } G \tag{16.3}$$

The relation obtained is equivalent to three algebraic equations. Two of these equations may be used to express that the sums of the x and y components of the external forces are respectively equal to the x and y components of the vector $m\bar{\mathbf{a}}$, while the third equation will express that the sum of the moments of the external forces about a given point A is equal to the moment of the vector $m\bar{\mathbf{a}}$ about the same point A. When point A is chosen to coincide with the mass center G of the body, the three algebraic equations defining the motion of a rigid body in translation take the particularly simple form

$$\Sigma F_x = m\bar{a}_x \qquad \Sigma F_y = m\bar{a}_y \qquad \Sigma M_G = 0 \tag{16.4}$$
$$\text{(external forces only)}$$

However, as will be recalled from *Statics,* the solution of many problems involving rigid bodies may be considerably simplified by an appropriate choice of the point A about which the moments of the forces are computed. It is therefore preferable to associate with the translation of a rigid body the more general relation (16.3) and to derive from this relation the components or moments equations which fit best the solution of the problem under consideration.

Relation (16.3) may be presented in an alternate form if we consider the vector equal and opposite to $m\bar{\mathbf{a}}$. We may state that if this reversed vector, denoted by $(m\bar{\mathbf{a}})_{rev}$ and called the *inertia vector*, is attached to the mass center G and added to the external forces $\mathbf{F}_1$, $\mathbf{F}_2$, $\mathbf{F}_3$, etc., *the system obtained is equivalent to zero* (Fig. 16.4).† The rigid body is then said to be in dynamic equilibrium under the action of the external forces and of the inertia vector, and the methods developed earlier in statics may be used. We may, for instance, write the equations of equilibrium

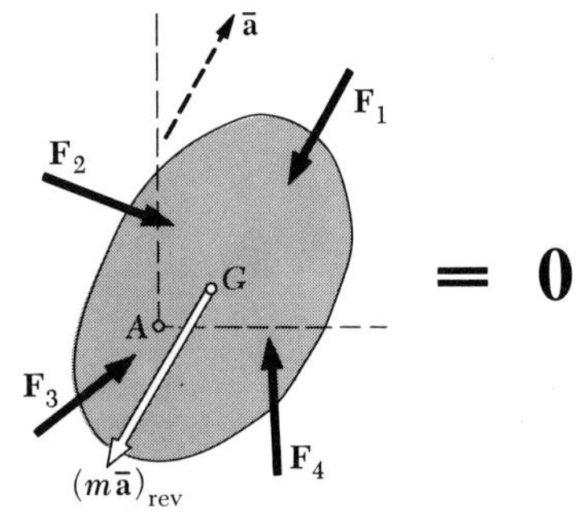

FIG. 16.4

$$\Sigma F_x = 0 \qquad \Sigma F_y = 0 \qquad \Sigma M_A = 0 \qquad (16.5)$$
(including inertia vector)

We note that in Eqs. (16.5), where the inertia vector is included, the moments may be taken with respect to any point A. In Eqs. (16.4), however, where only the actual external forces are considered, the moments, as we observed earlier, must be taken with respect to the mass center G.

Distinguishing now between the two types of translation, we note the following:

1. *Rectilinear Translation.* In this case, all the particles forming the rigid body move along parallel straight lines. The resultant $m\bar{\mathbf{a}}$ of the effective forces and the inertia vector $(m\bar{\mathbf{a}})_{rev}$ have a direction parallel to these lines. The resultant $m\bar{\mathbf{a}}$ has the same sense as the common acceleration $\bar{\mathbf{a}}$ of the particles, while the inertia vector $(m\bar{\mathbf{a}})_{rev}$ has a sense opposite to that of $\bar{\mathbf{a}}$. (See Sample Prob. 16.1.)

2. *Curvilinear Translation.* The particles forming the rigid body move along parallel curved paths, and, at any given instant, they have the same acceleration as the mass center G. It is usually found convenient to split the acceleration of G into a tangential and a normal component. To these components correspond, respectively, a tangential and a normal component of the vector $m\bar{\mathbf{a}}$ or a tangential and a normal component of the inertia vector $(m\bar{\mathbf{a}})_{rev}$. (See Sample Prob. 16.2.)

† The subscript "rev" indicates that the sense of $m\bar{\mathbf{a}}$ has been reversed (see Sec. 12.3).

SAMPLE PROBLEM 16.1

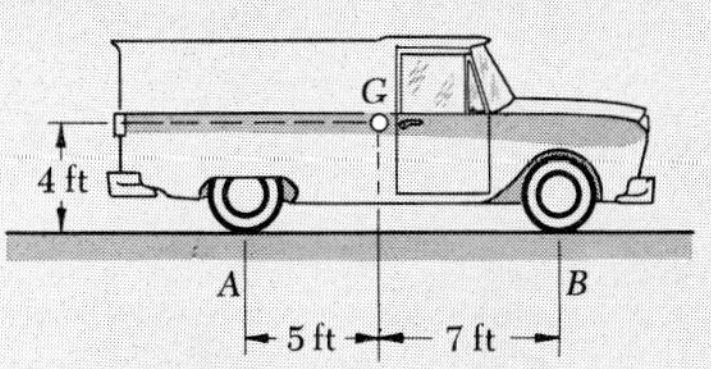

When the forward speed of the truck shown was 30 ft/sec, the brakes were suddenly applied, causing all four wheels to stop rotating. It was observed that the truck skidded to rest in 20 ft. Determine the magnitudes of the normal reactions and of the friction forces at each wheel as the truck skidded to rest.

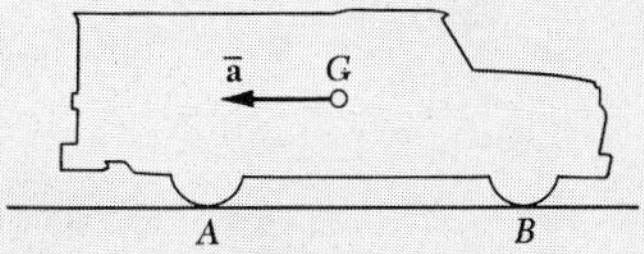

Kinematics of Motion. Choosing the positive sense to the right and using the equations of uniformly accelerated motion, we write

$$\bar{v}_0 = +30 \text{ ft/sec} \qquad \bar{v}^2 = \bar{v}_0^2 + 2\bar{a}\bar{s} \qquad 0 = (30)^2 + 2\bar{a}(20)$$

$$\bar{a} = -22.5 \text{ ft/sec}^2 \qquad \bar{\mathbf{a}} = 22.5 \text{ ft/sec}^2 \leftarrow$$

Dynamic Equilibrium. The truck is in dynamic equilibrium under the action of its weight **W**, the normal reactions and friction forces at the wheels, and the inertia vector $(m\bar{\mathbf{a}})_{\text{rev}}$ directed opposite to $\bar{\mathbf{a}}$ (i.e., directed to the right). The forces $\mathbf{N}_A$ and $\mathbf{F}_A$ represent the sum of the reactions at the rear wheels, while $\mathbf{N}_B$ and $\mathbf{F}_B$ represent the sum of the reactions at the front wheels.

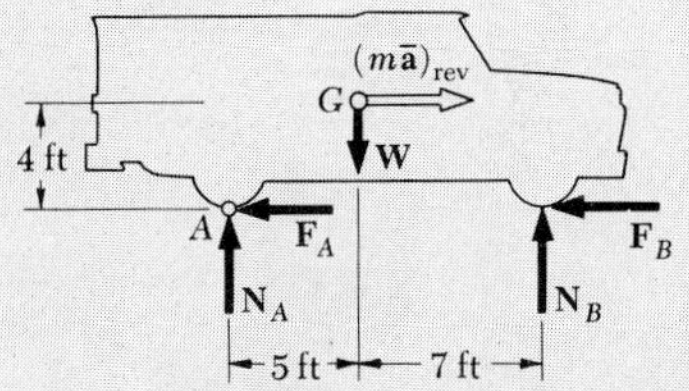

$+\uparrow \Sigma F_y = 0$: $\quad N_A + N_B - W = 0$

Since $F_A = \mu N_A$ and $F_B = \mu N_B$, we find

$$F_A + F_B = \mu(N_A + N_B) = \mu W$$

Noting that the x component of the inertia vector $(m\bar{\mathbf{a}})_{\text{rev}}$ is $+m\bar{a}$, we write

$\overset{+}{\rightarrow} \Sigma F_x = 0$: $\quad -(F_A + F_B) + m\bar{a} = 0$

$$-\mu W + \frac{W}{g}(22.5) = 0 \qquad \mu = 0.699$$

$+\circlearrowleft \Sigma M_A = 0$: $\quad -W(5 \text{ ft}) - m\bar{a}(4 \text{ ft}) + N_B(12 \text{ ft}) = 0$

$$-5W - \frac{W}{g}(22.5)(4) + 12N_B = 0$$

$$N_B = 0.650W$$

$$F_B = \mu N_B = (0.699)(0.650W) \qquad F_B = 0.454W$$

$+\uparrow \Sigma F_y = 0$: $\quad N_A + N_B - W = 0$

$$N_A + 0.650W - W = 0$$

$$N_A = 0.350W$$

$$F_A = \mu N_A = (0.699)(0.350W) \qquad F_A = 0.245W$$

Reactions at Each Wheel. Recalling that the values computed above represent the sum of the reactions at the two front wheels or the two rear wheels, we obtain the magnitudes of the reactions at each wheel by writing

$$N_{\text{front}} = \tfrac{1}{2}N_B = 0.325W \qquad N_{\text{rear}} = \tfrac{1}{2}N_A = 0.175W \quad ◄$$

$$F_{\text{front}} = \tfrac{1}{2}F_B = 0.227W \qquad F_{\text{rear}} = \tfrac{1}{2}F_A = 0.122W \quad ◄$$

SAMPLE PROBLEM 16.2

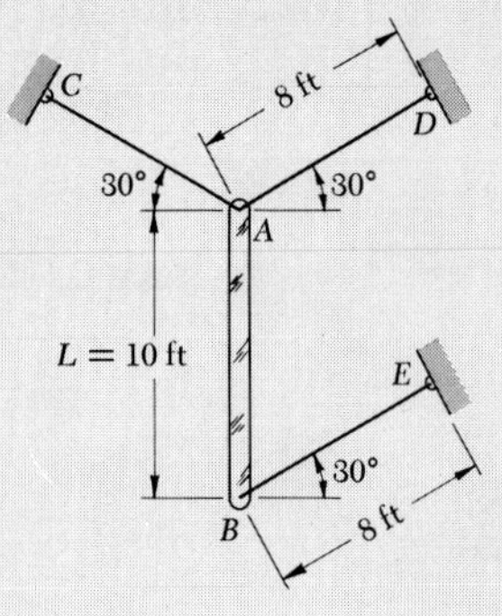

A 10-ft rod AB weighs 50 lb and is held in position by three inextensible wires AC, AD, and BE. Wire AC is then cut. Determine (a) the acceleration of the rod, (b) the tensions in wires AD and BE immediately after wire AC has been cut.

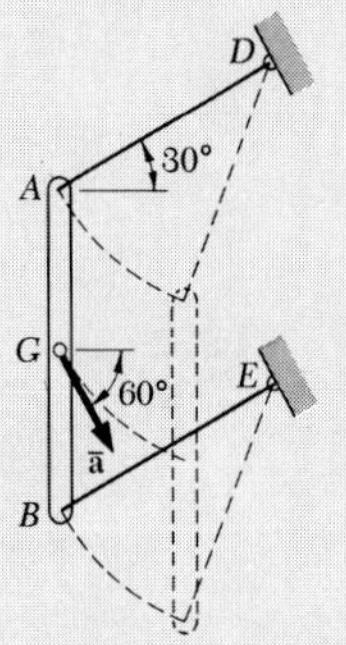

Motion of Rod. After wire AC is cut, we observe that ends A and B move along parallel circles of radius 8 ft centered, respectively, at D and E. The motion of the rod is thus a curvilinear translation; each particle of the rod moves along parallel circles of 8 ft radius.

At the instant wire AC is cut, the velocity of the rod is zero; the acceleration $\bar{\mathbf{a}}$ of the mass center G is thus tangent to the circular path of G.

Equations of Motion. The weight $\mathbf{W}$ and the forces $\mathbf{T}_A$ and $\mathbf{T}_B$ are assumed to act on the rod as shown. Since the acceleration $\bar{\mathbf{a}}$ of the mass center of the rod must be directed along the t axis, we note that the system of forces $\mathbf{W}$, $\mathbf{T}_A$, and $\mathbf{T}_B$ must be equivalent to a vector $m\bar{\mathbf{a}}$ directed along the t axis. We write

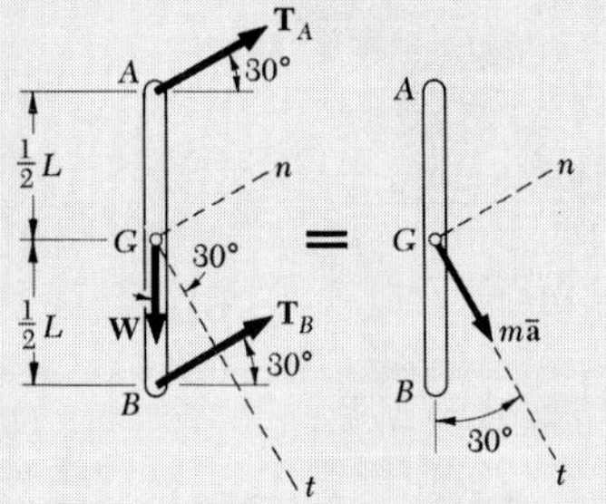

$+\searrow \Sigma F_t = m\bar{a}$: $\quad W \cos 30° = \dfrac{W}{g}\bar{a}$

$$\bar{a} = g \cos 30° = 27.9 \text{ ft/sec}^2$$

$$\bar{\mathbf{a}} = 27.9 \text{ ft/sec}^2 \nwarrow 60°$$

$+\circlearrowleft \Sigma M_G = 0$: $\quad -(T_A \cos 30°)\tfrac{1}{2}L + (T_B \cos 30°)\tfrac{1}{2}L = 0$

$$T_A = T_B$$

$+\nearrow \Sigma F_n = 0$: $\quad T_A + T_B - W \sin 30° = 0$

Since $T_A = T_B$, we have

$$T_A + T_A - W \sin 30° = 0$$

$$T_A = +\tfrac{1}{2} W \sin 30° = +\tfrac{1}{4}W$$

$$T_B = +\tfrac{1}{4}W$$

Recalling that $W = 50$ lb, we have

$$T_A = 12.5 \text{ lb} \qquad T_B = 12.5 \text{ lb} \blacktriangleleft$$

PROBLEMS

16.1. A 6-ft board is placed in a truck so that one end rests against a block *A* on the floor while the other end rests against a vertical wall. Determine the maximum possible uniform acceleration of the truck if the board is to remain in the position shown.

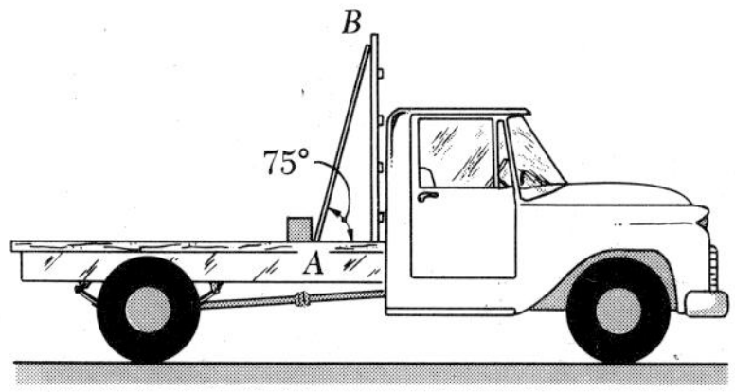

FIG. P 16.1

16.2. A uniform rod *AB* weighs 5 lb and is connected to two collars of negligible weight which slide freely on horizontal rods located in the same vertical plane. If a force **P** of magnitude 10 lb is applied at *A*, determine (*a*) the acceleration of the rod, (*b*) the reactions at *A* and *B*.

16.3. In Prob. 16.2 determine (*a*) the required magnitude of **P** if the reaction at *B* is to be zero, (*b*) the corresponding acceleration of the rod.

16.4. A 90-lb cabinet rests on a rough horizontal floor ($\mu = 0.30$). If a force **P** of magnitude 45 lb is applied as shown, determine (*a*) the acceleration of the cabinet, (*b*) the maximum distance *h* for which the cabinet will not tip about corner *B*.

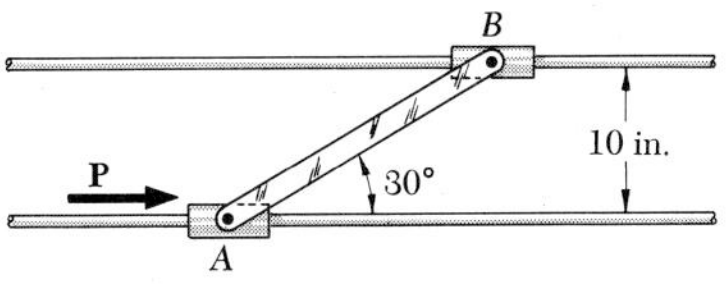

FIG. P 16.2

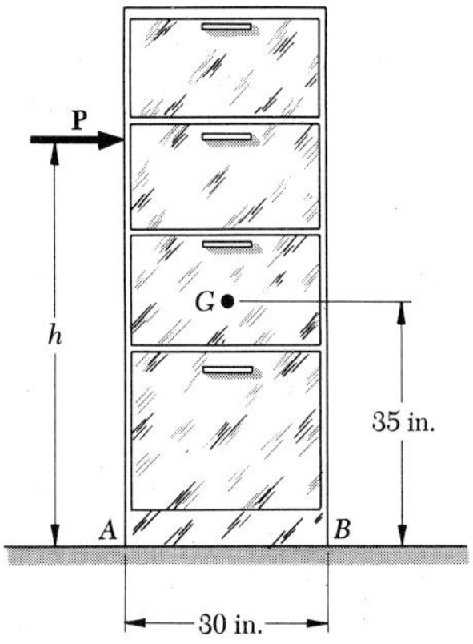

FIG. P 16.4 AND P 16.5

16.5. A horizontal force **P** is applied to the 90-lb cabinet shown at a distance $h = 45$ in. above the floor. Knowing that $\mu = 0.30$ between the cabinet and the floor, determine (*a*) the largest magnitude of **P** for which the cabinet will not tip about *B*, (*b*) the corresponding acceleration of the cabinet.

16.6. Cylindrical cans are transported from one elevation to another by the moving horizontal arms shown. Assuming that $\mu = 0.40$ between the cans and the arms, determine (*a*) the magnitude of the downward acceleration **a** for which the cans slide on the horizontal arms, (*b*) the smallest ratio h/d for which the cans tip before they slide.

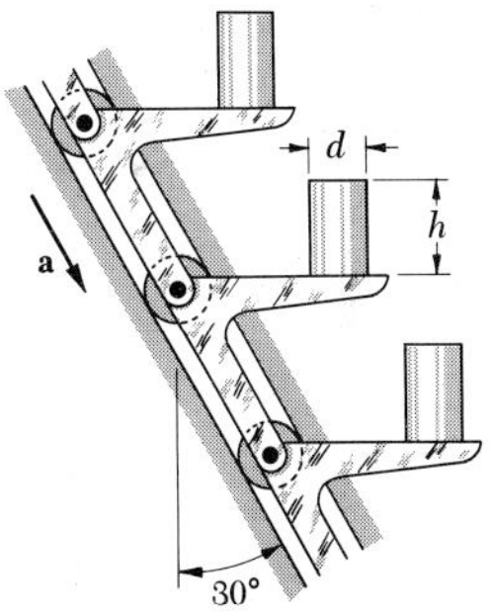

FIG. P 16.6

16.7. Solve Prob. 16.6 assuming that the acceleration **a** of the horizontal arms is directed upward.

16.8. A 15-lb cylinder, 10 in. high and 5 in. in diameter, can slide on a horizontal surface without friction. It is attached to a 30-lb weight as shown. (*a*) Determine the acceleration of the cylinder and the tension in the cord after the weight has been released. (*b*) What is the range of values of the distance *h* for which the cylinder will not tip during the motion?

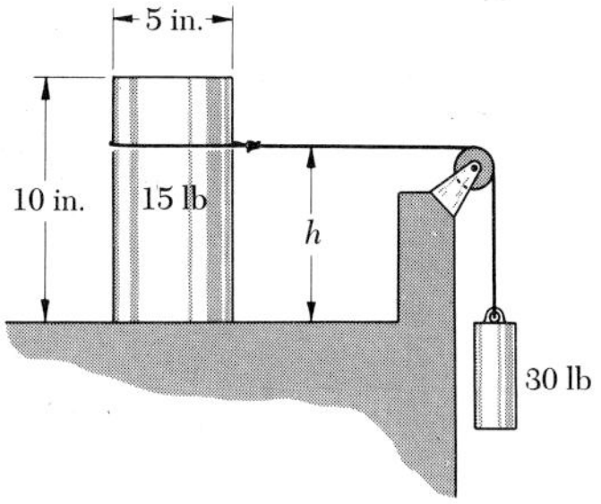

FIG. P 16.8

16.9. Solve Prob. 16.8 assuming the coefficient of friction between the block and the floor to be 0.20.

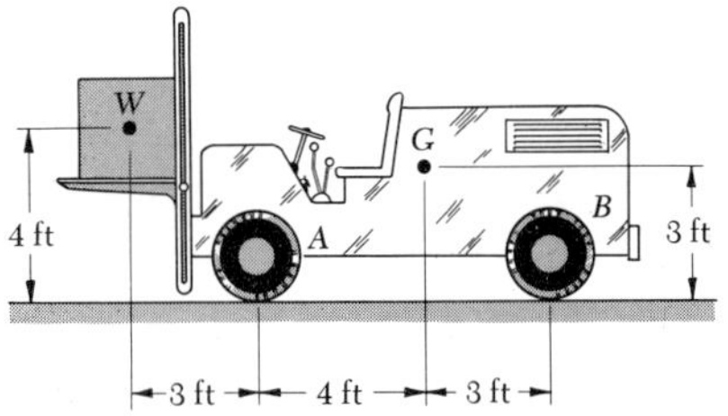

FIG. P 16.10 AND P 16.11

16.10. A fork-lift truck weighs 2,250 lb and is used to lift a crate of weight $W = 2{,}000$ lb. Determine the upward acceleration of the crate for which the reaction at the rear wheels B is zero.

16.11. The fork-lift truck shown weighs 2,250 lb and carries a crate of weight $W = 2{,}000$ lb. It is moving to the left with a speed of 15 ft/sec when the brakes are applied on all four wheels. Determine the shortest distance in which the truck can be brought to a stop if the crate is not to slide and if the truck is not to tip forward. The coefficient of friction between the crate and the fork lift is 0.30.

16.12. Determine the distance through which the truck of Sample Prob. 16.1 will skid if the rear-wheel brakes fail to operate.

16.13. Determine the distance through which the truck of Sample Prob. 16.1 will skid if the front-wheel brakes fail to operate.

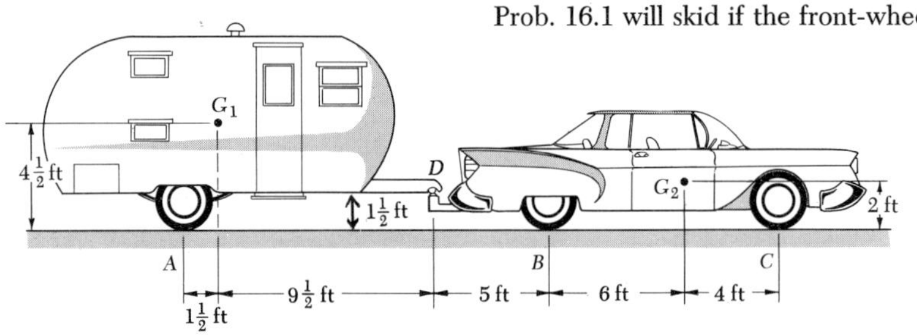

FIG. P 16.14 AND P 16.15

16.14. A trailer weighing 2,750 lb is attached to a 3,200-lb automobile by a ball-and-socket trailer hitch at D. Knowing that the car is being accelerated at the rate of 3 ft/sec², determine the components of the force exerted on the trailer by the hitch at D.

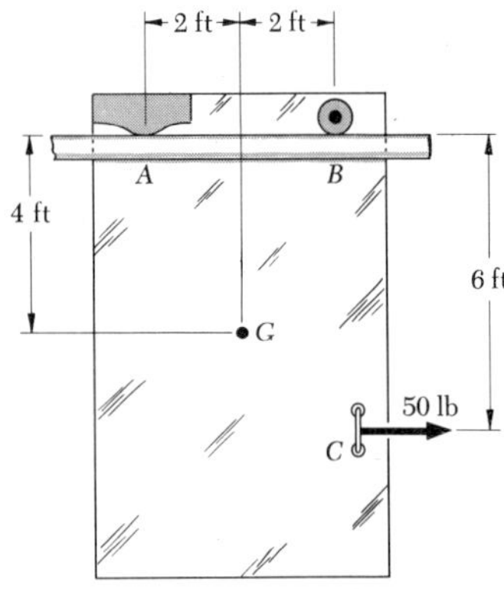

FIG. P 16.16

16.15. A trailer weighing 2,750 lb is attached to a 3,200-lb automobile by a ball-and-socket trailer hitch at D. The automobile and trailer are moving forward at a speed of 30 mph when the brakes are applied. Knowing that $\mu = 0.60$, determine the distance required to stop the automobile and trailer assuming (*a*) that the brakes are fully applied on all six wheels, (*b*) that the brakes are fully applied on the four automobile wheels but that the brakes on the trailer wheels A fail to operate.

16.16. A horizontal force of magnitude 50 lb is applied to the handle C of a 200-lb sliding door as shown. The coefficient of friction between the skid at A and the rail is 0.20. Neglecting the mass and friction of the wheel at B, determine (*a*) the acceleration of the door, (*b*) the components of the reactions at A and B.

16.17. Solve Prob. 16.16 assuming that the 50-lb force applied at C is directed horizontally to the left.

16.18. Disk AB and crank CD both rotate at a constant speed of 180 rpm. For the position $\phi = 30°$, determine the vertical components of the forces exerted on the 15-lb connecting rod BC by the pins B and C.

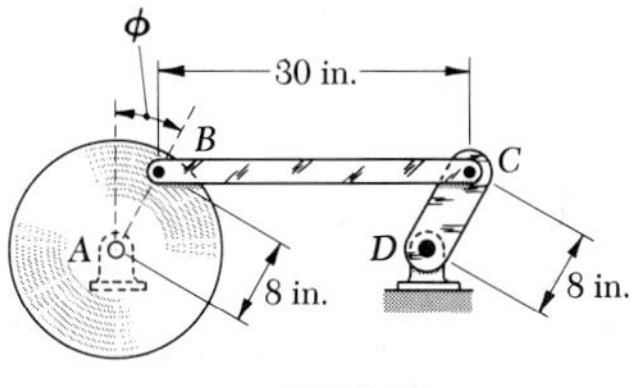

FIG. P 16.18

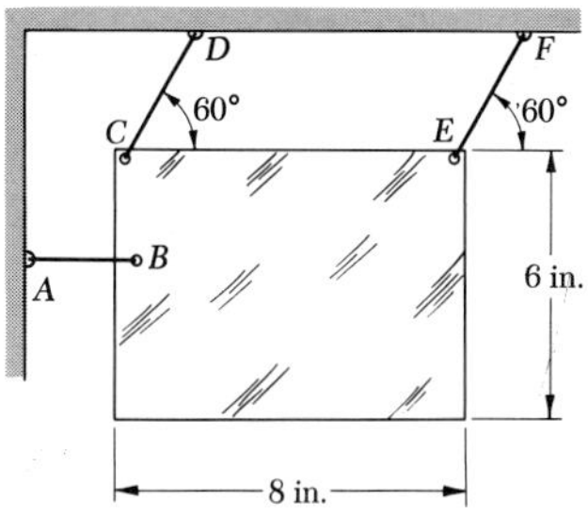

FIG. P 16.19

16.19. A homogeneous rectangular plate, 8 by 6 in. and weighing 10 lb, is held in the position shown by three wires. Determine the tension in wires CD and EF immediately after wire AB has been cut.

16.20. The motion of a 6- by 12-in. plate weighing 10 lb is guided by two pins which slide freely in parallel curved slots. At the instant shown, the velocity of each pin is 36 in./sec. Determine (a) the acceleration of the plate, (b) the pin reactions at A and B.

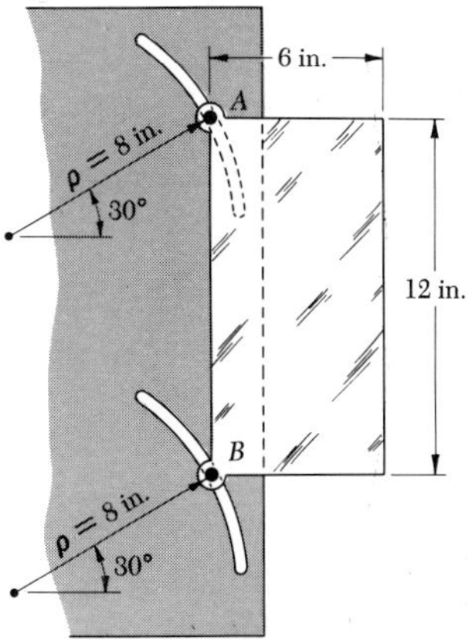

FIG. P 16.20

16.21. Members ACE and DCB are each 20 in. long and are connected by a pin at C. The mass center of the 10-lb member DE is located at G. Determine (a) the acceleration of DE immediately after the system has been released from rest in the position shown, (b) the corresponding force exerted by roller D on member DE. Neglect the weight of members ACE and DCB.

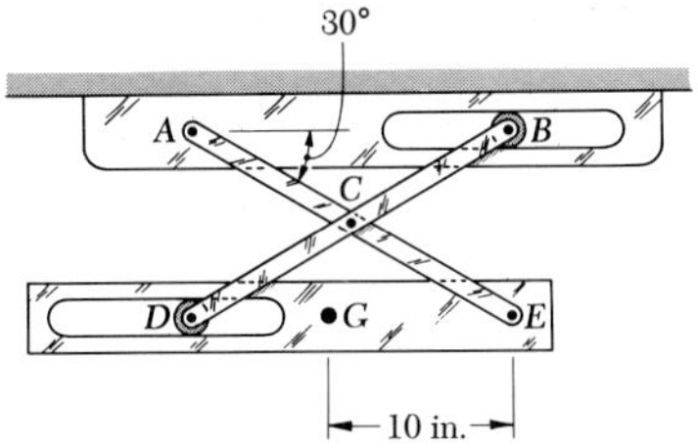

FIG. P 16.21

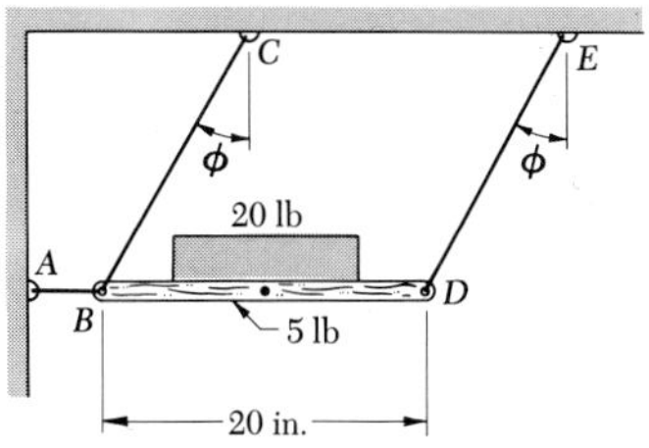

FIG. P 16.22

*16.22. A 20-lb block is placed on a 5-lb platform BD which is held in the position $\phi = 30°$ by the three wires shown. Determine the accelerations of the block and the platform immediately after wire AB has been cut. Assume (a) that the block is rigidly attached to BD, (b) that $\mu = 0$ between the block and BD.

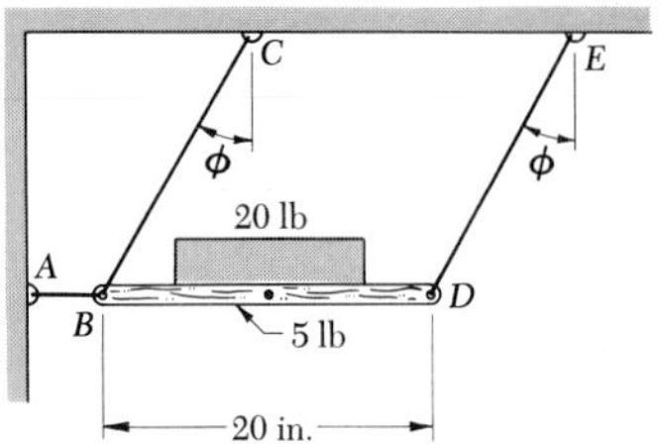

FIG. P 16.23

*16.23. The coefficient of friction between the 20-lb block and the platform BD is 0.50. Knowing that $\phi = 30°$, determine the accelerations of the block and of the platform immediately after wire AB has been cut.

*16.24. Draw the shear and bending-moment diagrams for the connecting rod of Prob. 16.18 when $\phi = 60°$.

*16.25. Draw the shear and bending-moment diagrams for the rod AB of Prob. 16.2.

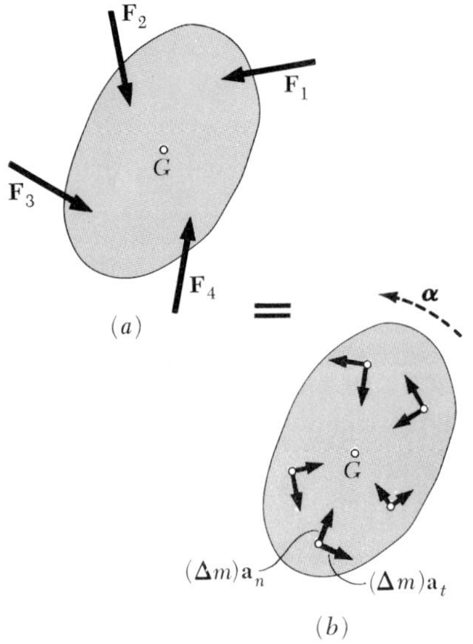

FIG. 16.5

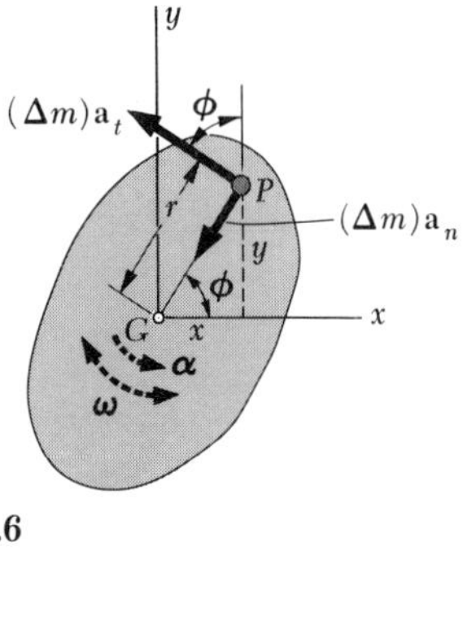

FIG. 16.6

16.3. Centroidal Rotation. Consider a plane slab or, more generally, a body symmetrical with respect to the reference plane, which, under the action of several forces $\mathbf{F}_1$, $\mathbf{F}_2$, $\mathbf{F}_3$, etc., rotates about a fixed axis perpendicular to the reference plane and passing through the mass center G of the body (Fig. 16.5*a*). This motion will be referred to as a *centroidal rotation.* Denoting by $\bar{I}$ the centroidal moment of inertia of the body, and by $\boldsymbol{\alpha}$ its angular acceleration at a given instant, we shall show *that the system of the external forces* $\mathbf{F}_1$, $\mathbf{F}_2$, $\mathbf{F}_3$, *etc., must be equivalent at that instant to a single couple* $\bar{I}\boldsymbol{\alpha}$ of moment $\bar{I}\alpha$ and of the same sense as $\boldsymbol{\alpha}$.

We first recall that, according to D'Alembert's principle (Sec. 12.4), the external forces must be equivalent to the effective forces of the various particles of the system (Fig. 16.5). Considering next a particle P of mass Δm at a distance r from the fixed centroidal axis (Fig. 16.6), we note that its acceleration may be resolved into a normal component $\mathbf{a}_n$ of magnitude $r\omega^2$ and a tangential component $\mathbf{a}_t$ of magnitude $r\alpha$; the effective force of the particle may therefore be similarly resolved into two components, one, $(\Delta m)\mathbf{a}_n$, directed toward the fixed axis and of magnitude $(\Delta m)r\omega^2$, the other, $(\Delta m)\mathbf{a}_t$, perpendicular to the line GP, directed in the sense defined by the angular acceleration and of magnitude $(\Delta m)r\alpha$. We choose the origin of the coordinate axes at G, and denote by x and y the coordinates of the particle P. Observing that $r\cos\phi = x$ and $r\sin\phi = y$, we find that the sums of the x and y components of the effective forces are, respectively,

$$\begin{aligned}\Sigma(F_x)_{\text{eff}} &= -\Sigma(\Delta m)r\alpha\sin\phi - \Sigma(\Delta m)r\omega^2\cos\phi \\ &= -\alpha\Sigma y\,\Delta m - \omega^2\Sigma x\,\Delta m \qquad (16.6)\end{aligned}$$

$$\begin{aligned}\Sigma(F_y)_{\text{eff}} &= \Sigma(\Delta m)r\alpha\cos\phi - \Sigma(\Delta m)r\omega^2\sin\phi \\ &= \alpha\Sigma x\,\Delta m - \omega^2\Sigma y\,\Delta m \qquad (16.7)\end{aligned}$$

Now, according to the definition of the mass center of a system of particles (Sec. 12.5), we have

$$\Sigma x\,\Delta m = m\bar{x} \qquad \Sigma y\,\Delta m = m\bar{y}$$

where $\bar{x}$ and $\bar{y}$ are the coordinates of the mass center G. Since the origin of the coordinate axes was chosen at G, we have $\bar{x} = \bar{y} = 0$ and thus $\Sigma(F_x)_{\text{eff}} = 0$ and $\Sigma(F_y)_{\text{eff}} = 0$. The system of the effective forces reduces, therefore, to a single couple. The moment of this couple is obtained by adding the moments of the effective forces about G. Since the normal components of these forces have no moment about G, the moment of the couple reduces to the sum of the moments of the tangential components of the effective forces,

$$\Sigma(M_G)_{\text{eff}} = \Sigma r(\Delta m)r\alpha = \alpha\Sigma r^2\,\Delta m \qquad (16.8)$$

Letting the mass Δm of each particle decrease, and simultaneously increasing the number of particles into which the rigid body is divided, we find that the sum $\Sigma r^2\,\Delta m$ approaches the integral $\int r^2\,dm$, which represents the moment of inertia $\bar{I}$ of the rigid body about the fixed centroidal axis (Sec. 9.10). We thus write

$$\Sigma(M_G)_{\text{eff}} = \bar{I}\alpha \qquad (16.9)$$

and conclude that the system of the effective forces reduces to a single couple of moment $\bar{I}\alpha$ with the same sense as the angular acceleration $\boldsymbol{\alpha}$. Recalling from Sec. 15.3 that the angular acceleration of a rigid body rotating about a fixed axis may be represented by a vector $\boldsymbol{\alpha}$ of magnitude α directed along that axis, we note that the couple obtained may be represented by the vector $\bar{I}\boldsymbol{\alpha}$ of magnitude $\bar{I}\alpha$ directed along the centroidal axis of rotation.

Replacing the effective forces in Fig. 16.5 by their resultant couple, we obtain Fig. 16.7 and thus verify that the system of the external forces acting on a rigid body in centroidal rotation must be equivalent to a single couple $\bar{I}\boldsymbol{\alpha}$ of moment $\bar{I}\alpha$ and of the same sense as the angular acceleration $\boldsymbol{\alpha}$. The following equations, therefore, must be satisfied by the external forces acting on a rigid body in centroidal rotation:

$$\Sigma F_x = 0 \qquad \Sigma F_y = 0 \qquad \Sigma M_A = \bar{I}\alpha \qquad (16.10)$$
(external forces only)

We note that the moment equation may be written with respect to any point A, since the system of the external forces is equivalent to a couple.

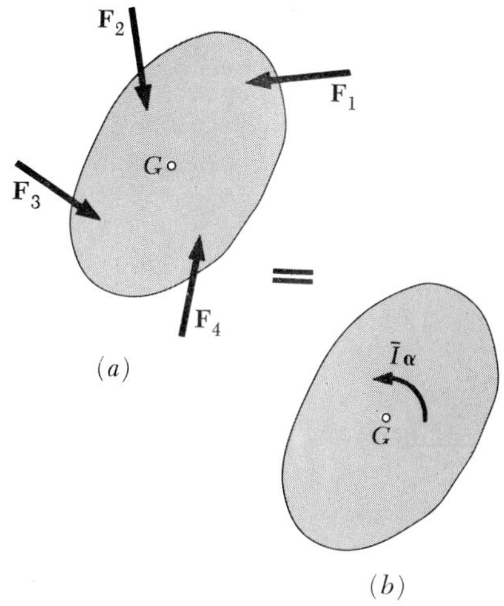

FIG. 16.7

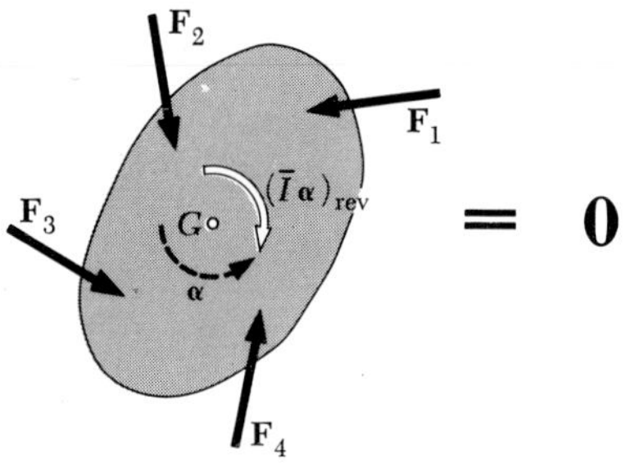

FIG. 16.8

The result obtained may be presented in an alternate form by considering a couple $(\bar{I}\alpha)_{rev}$ of moment equal in magnitude to $\bar{I}\alpha$ and of sense opposite to that of the angular acceleration.† If this couple, called the *inertia couple*, is added to the external forces, the system obtained is equivalent to zero and the rigid body is in dynamic equilibrium (Fig. 16.8). We may then write the equations of equilibrium,

$$\Sigma F_x = 0 \qquad \Sigma F_y = 0 \qquad \Sigma M_A = 0 \qquad \text{(including inertia couple)} \tag{16.11}$$

16.4. Systems of Rigid Bodies. The methods described in the preceding sections may also be used in problems dealing with the motion of several connected rigid bodies. An example is given in Sample Prob. 16.4, where two blocks are attached to a pulley. Since that system has only one degree of freedom, all linear and angular accelerations may be expressed in terms of a single unknown (see Sec. 11.6). If the method of dynamic equilibrium is selected, inertia vectors are then added to the actual forces acting on the various parts of the system. Two alternate approaches may be used to complete the solution of the problem:

1. A free-body diagram of each individual part of the system is drawn. Each free-body diagram should include all the forces acting on the part of the system considered (including tensions in the connecting cables) as well as the inertia vectors. Equations of dynamic equilibrium are written for each part of the system and are solved simultaneously.

2. A single free-body diagram is drawn for the entire system. This diagram should include all external forces and all the inertia vectors associated with the various parts of the system. Tensions in connecting cables, however, will be omitted since they are internal forces as far as the entire system is concerned. This approach will lead to equations which do not contain the tensions and which may therefore be more readily solved for the unknown accelerations.

The second approach suggested may not be used in problems involving more than three unknowns, since only three equations of dynamic equilibrium are available when a single free-body diagram is used. We shall not elaborate upon this point, since the discussion involved would be completely similar to that given in Sec. 6.12 in the case of the static equilibrium of a system of rigid bodies.

† The subscript "rev" indicates that the sense of α has been reversed.

SAMPLE PROBLEM 16.3

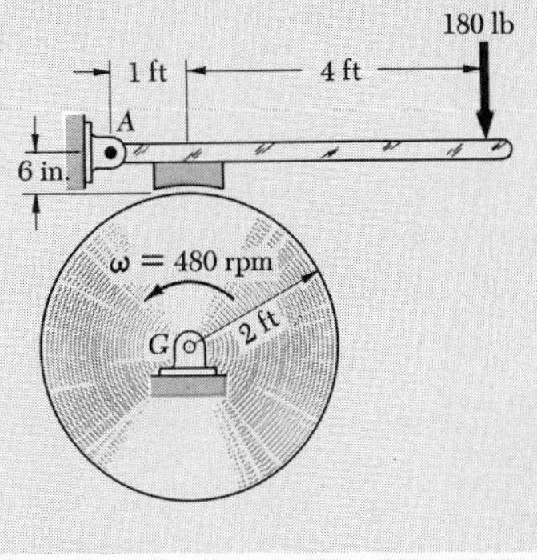

A 150-lb flywheel has a radius of gyration of 1.5 ft and rotates counterclockwise with an angular velocity of 480 rpm when a brake is applied as shown. Knowing that the coefficient of friction between the brake shoe and the flywheel is 0.20, determine the number of revolutions executed by the flywheel before it comes to rest.

Note. In this sample problem and in those which follow, the method of dynamic equilibrium is used exclusively. In *Vector Mechanics for Engineers,* the same problems are solved by the direct application of the principle of equivalence of the systems of applied and effective forces.

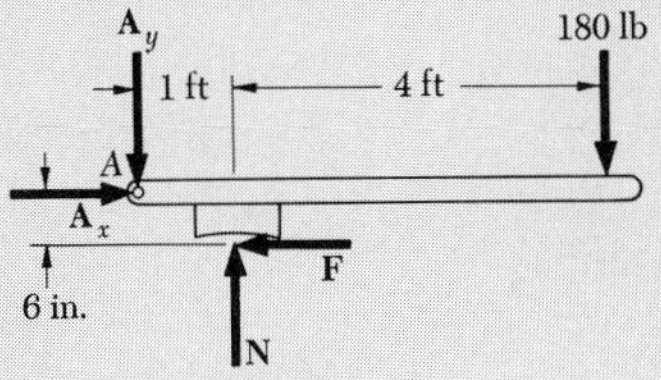

Free Body: Brake. Since the flywheel rotates counterclockwise, the friction force exerted *by the wheel on the brake* is directed to the left. We write

$$+\circlearrowleft \Sigma M_A = 0: \qquad N(1 \text{ ft}) - (180 \text{ lb})(5 \text{ ft}) - F(\tfrac{6}{12} \text{ ft}) = 0$$

Since slipping occurs, the magnitude of the friction force is $F = \mu N = 0.20N$. We substitute this value into the above equation and solve for N.

$$N = 1{,}000 \text{ lb} \qquad F = \mu N = (0.20)(1{,}000) = 200 \text{ lb}$$

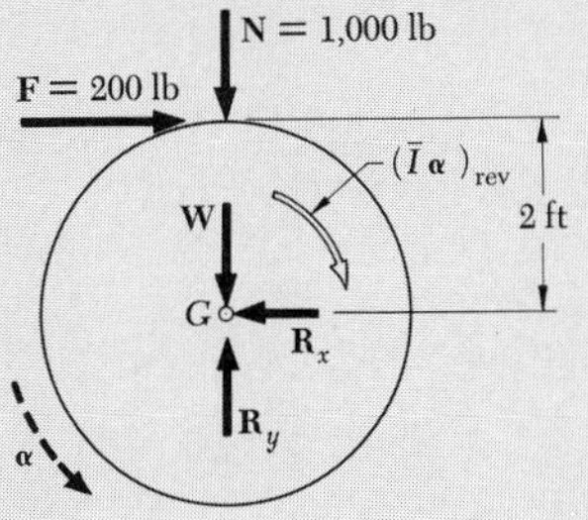

Free Body: Flywheel. Assuming α counterclockwise, we draw the free-body diagram of the flywheel. The diagram includes all external forces and the inertia couple $(\bar{I}\alpha)_{\text{rev}}$ directed clockwise. The centroidal moment of inertia $\bar{I}$ of the flywheel is

$$\bar{I} = m\bar{k}^2 = \frac{150}{32.2}(1.5)^2 = 10.48 \text{ lb-ft-sec}^2$$

The flywheel is in dynamic equilibrium under the action of the forces and inertia couple shown. Noting that the moment of the inertia couple is $-\bar{I}\alpha$, we write

$$+\circlearrowleft \Sigma M_G = 0: \qquad -\bar{I}\alpha - F(2 \text{ ft}) = 0 \qquad -10.48\alpha - (200 \text{ lb})(2 \text{ ft}) = 0$$

$$\alpha = -38.2 \text{ radians/sec}^2$$

The negative sign obtained for α indicates that the senses assumed, respectively, for α and $(\bar{I}\alpha)_{\text{rev}}$ are wrong. The inertia couple is directed counterclockwise, and the angular acceleration clockwise.

Kinematics of Motion. Since the angular acceleration α of the flywheel is constant, we have a uniformly accelerated rotation. The initial angular velocity is

$$\omega_0 = 480 \frac{\text{rev}}{\text{min}} = \left(480 \frac{\text{rev}}{\text{min}}\right)\left(\frac{1 \text{ min}}{60 \text{ sec}}\right)\left(\frac{2\pi \text{ radians}}{1 \text{ rev}}\right) = 50.3 \text{ radians/sec}$$

Using Eq. 15.9 and choosing $\theta_0 = 0$, we write

$$\omega^2 = \omega_0^2 + 2\alpha(\theta - \theta_0)$$

$$0 = (50.3)^2 + (2)(-38.2)\theta \qquad \theta = 33.1 \text{ radians}$$

$$\text{Number of revolutions} = (33.1 \text{ radians})\frac{1 \text{ rev}}{2\pi \text{ radians}} = 5.27 \text{ rev} \blacktriangleleft$$

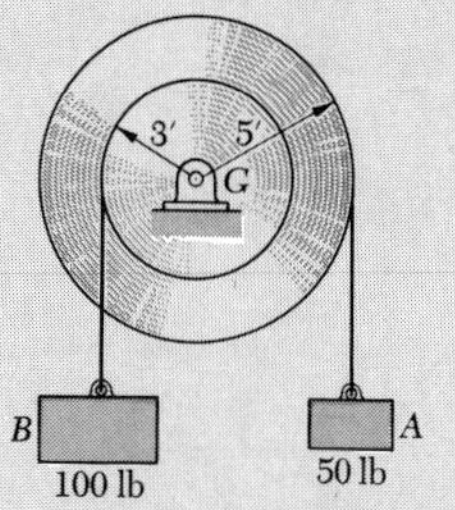

SAMPLE PROBLEM 16.4

A pulley weighing 120 lb and with a radius of gyration of 4 ft is connected to two blocks as shown. Assuming no axle friction, determine the angular acceleration of the pulley.

Sense of Motion. Although an arbitrary sense of motion may be assumed (since no friction forces are involved) and later checked by the sign of the answer, we may prefer first to determine the actual sense of rotation of the pulley. We first find the weight of block *B* required to maintain the equilibrium of the pulley when it is acted upon by the 50-lb block *A*. We write

$$+\circlearrowleft \Sigma M_G = 0: \qquad W_B(3\text{ ft}) - (50\text{ lb})(5\text{ ft}) = 0 \qquad W_B = 83.3\text{ lb}$$

Since block *B* actually weighs 100 lb, the pulley will rotate counterclockwise.

Kinematics of Motion. Assuming α counterclockwise and noting that $a_A = r_A\alpha$ and $a_B = r_B\alpha$, we obtain

$$\mathbf{a}_A = 5\alpha \uparrow \qquad \mathbf{a}_B = 3\alpha \downarrow$$

Dynamic Equilibrium of Each Part of System. The centroidal moment of inertia of the pulley is

$$\bar{I} = m\bar{k}^2 = \frac{120}{32.2}(4)^2 = 59.6\text{ lb-ft-sec}^2$$

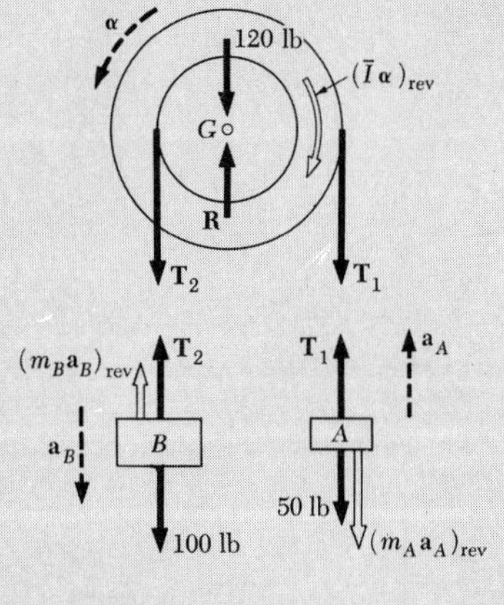

Considering, in turn, the free-body diagrams shown, we write the following equations of dynamic equilibrium:

Pulley, $+\circlearrowleft \Sigma M_G = 0$: $\quad T_2(3\text{ ft}) - T_1(5\text{ ft}) - \bar{I}\alpha = 0$

$$3T_2 - 5T_1 - 59.6\alpha = 0 \qquad (1)$$

Block *A*, $+\uparrow \Sigma F_y = 0$: $\quad T_1 - 50\text{ lb} - m_A a_A = 0$

$$T_1 - 50 - \frac{50}{g}(5\alpha) = 0 \qquad (2)$$

Block *B*, $+\uparrow \Sigma F_y = 0$: $\quad T_2 - 100\text{ lb} + m_B a_B = 0$

$$T_2 - 100 + \frac{100}{g}(3\alpha) = 0 \qquad (3)$$

Solving (1), (2), and (3) simultaneously, we obtain

$$\alpha = +0.396\text{ radian/sec}^2 \qquad \alpha = 0.396\text{ radian/sec}^2 \circlearrowleft \blacktriangleleft$$

Alternate Method: Dynamic Equilibrium of Entire System. We draw the free-body diagram of the entire system, showing all external forces and inertia vectors. (The tensions are now omitted since they are internal to the entire system.) We write

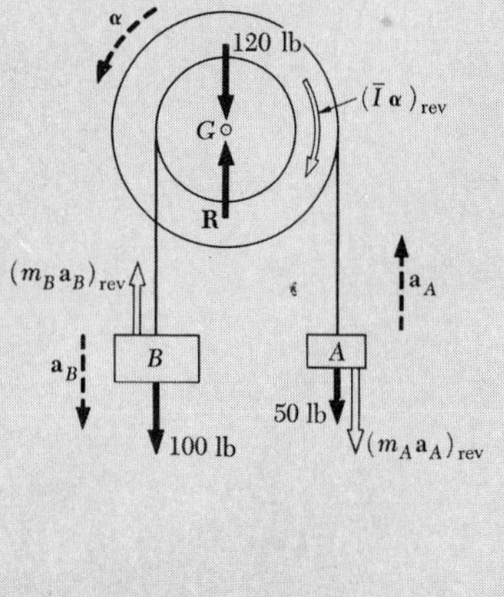

$+\circlearrowleft \Sigma M_G = 0$:

$$(100\text{ lb})(3\text{ ft}) - m_B a_B(3\text{ ft}) - \bar{I}\alpha - (50\text{ lb})(5\text{ ft}) - m_A a_A(5\text{ ft}) = 0$$

$$(100)(3) - \frac{100}{g}(3\alpha)(3) - 59.6\alpha - (50)(5) - \frac{50}{g}(5\alpha)(5) = 0$$

$$\alpha = +0.396\text{ radian/sec}^2 \qquad \alpha = 0.396\text{ radian/sec}^2 \circlearrowleft \blacktriangleleft$$

PROBLEMS

16.26. An electric motor is rotating at 1,200 rpm when the load and power are cut off. The rotor weighs 200 lb and has a radius of gyration of 10 in. If the kinetic friction of the rotor produces a couple of moment 15 lb-in., how many revolutions will the rotor execute before stopping?

16.27. A 2,000-kva turbine-generator unit is shut off when its rotor is rotating at 3,600 rpm; it is observed that the rotor coasts to rest in 7.10 min. Knowing that the rotor weighs 4,100 lb and has a radius of gyration of 9.2 in., determine the average moment of the couple due to bearing friction.

16.28. A bolt located 2 in. from the center of an automobile wheel is tightened by applying the couple shown to a wrench. Assuming the wheel is free to rotate, determine the angular acceleration of the wheel. The wheel weighs 45 lb and has a radius of gyration of 11 in.

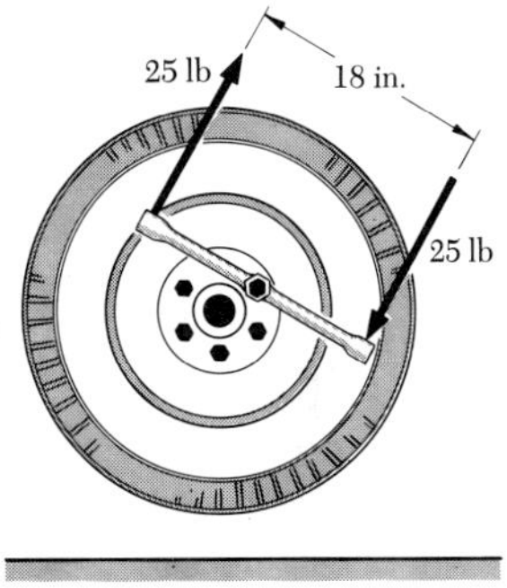

FIG. P 16.28

16.29. Disk A weighs 10 lb and is at rest when it is placed in contact with a conveyor belt moving at a constant speed. The link AB connecting the center of the disk to the support at B is of negligible weight. Knowing that $\mu = 0.40$, determine for each of the arrangements shown the angular acceleration of the disk while slipping occurs.

FIG. P 16.29

16.30. Solve Prob. 16.29 assuming that the direction of motion of the conveyor belt is reversed.

16.31. Referring to the Atwood machine of Prob. 12.20, derive a new formula for g, taking into account the centroidal moment of inertia $\bar{I}$ of the pulley.

16.32. A weight $W = 40$ lb is attached to a cord wrapped around the rim of a flywheel of radius $r = 3$ ft. The flywheel weighs 400 lb and has a radius of gyration of 2.50 ft. Knowing that the system is released from rest, determine the speed of the weight after it has moved 8 ft. Neglect bearing friction.

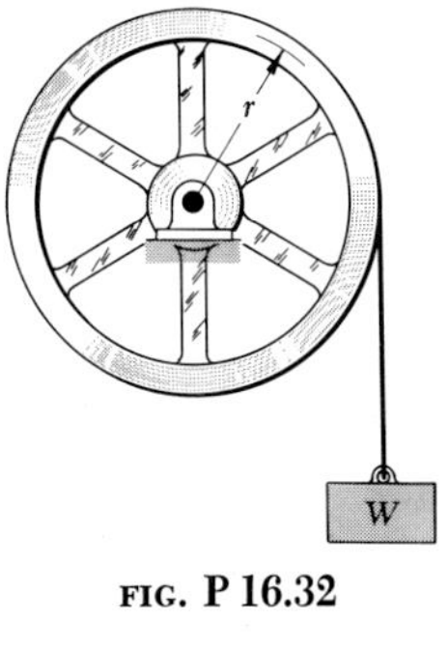

FIG. P 16.32

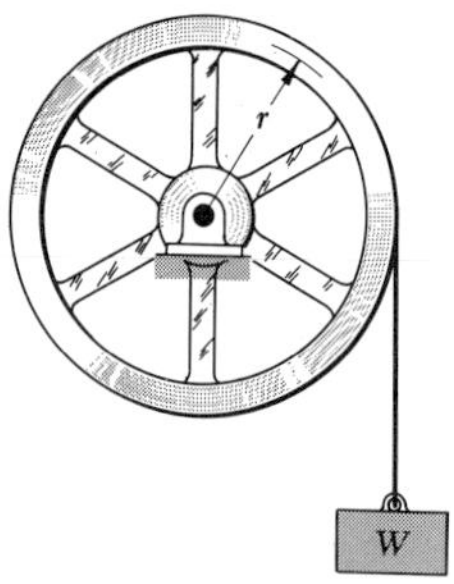

FIG. P 16.33

16.33. In order to determine the mass moment of inertia of a flywheel of radius $r = 2$ ft, a weight $W = 25$ lb is attached to a cord which is wrapped around the rim of the flywheel. The weight is released from rest and is observed to fall 10 ft in 4.80 sec. To eliminate bearing friction from the computation, a second weight $W = 50$ lb is used and is observed to fall 10 ft in 3.10 sec. Assuming that the moment of the couple due to bearing friction is constant, determine the mass moment of inertia of the flywheel.

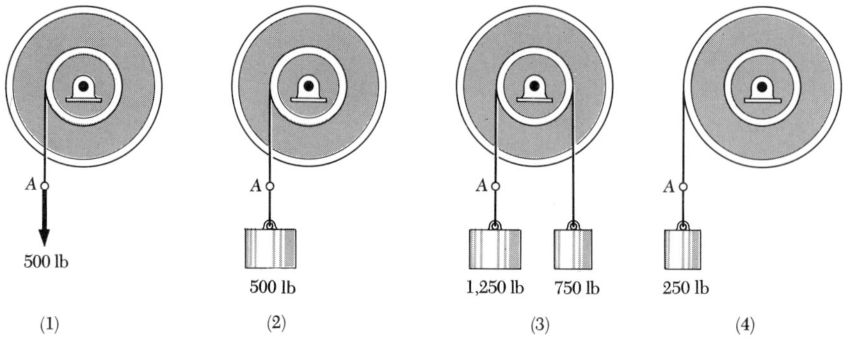

FIG. P 16.34

16.34. Each of the double pulleys shown has a mass moment of inertia of 20 lb-ft-sec^2 and is initially at rest. The outside radius is 2 ft, and the inner radius is 1 ft. Determine (*a*) the angular acceleration of each pulley, (*b*) the angular velocity of each pulley at $t = 2$ sec, (*c*) the angular velocity of each pulley after point A on the cord has moved 10 ft.

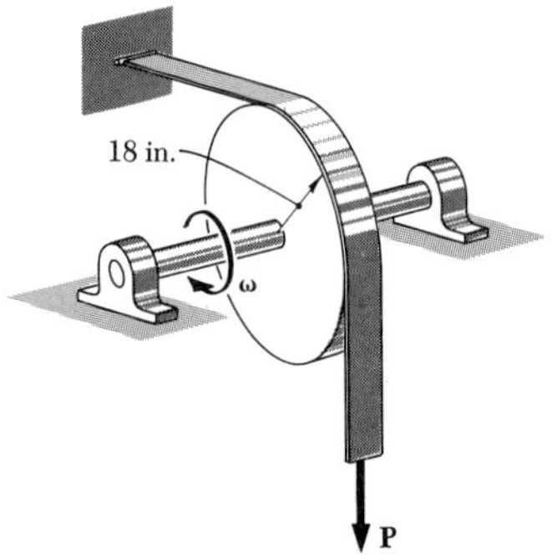

FIG. P 16.35

16.35. The flywheel shown consists of a 3-ft-diameter disk which weighs 300 lb. The coefficient of friction between the band and the flywheel is 0.30. If the initial angular velocity of the flywheel is 300 rpm clockwise, determine the magnitude of the force **P** required to stop the flywheel in 20 revolutions.

16.36. Solve Prob. 16.35 assuming that the initial angular velocity of the flywheel is 300 rpm counterclockwise.

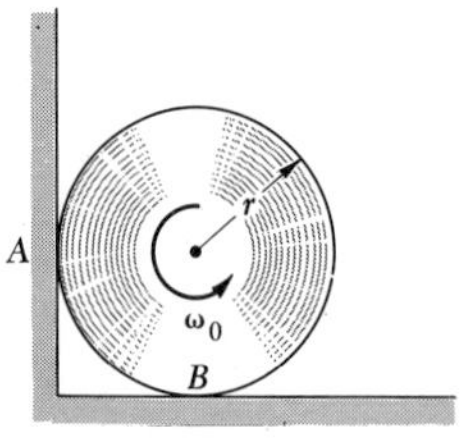

FIG. P 16.38

16.37. Solve Sample Prob. 16.3 assuming that the initial angular velocity of the flywheel is 480 rpm clockwise.

16.38. A cylinder of radius r and weight W is placed in a corner with an initial counterclockwise angular velocity ω_0. Denoting by μ the coefficient of friction at A and at B, determine the angular acceleration α of the cylinder.

16.39. A cylinder of radius r and weight W is placed with no initial velocity on a belt as shown. Denoting by μ the coefficient of friction at A and at B and assuming that $\mu < 1$, determine the angular acceleration α of the cylinder.

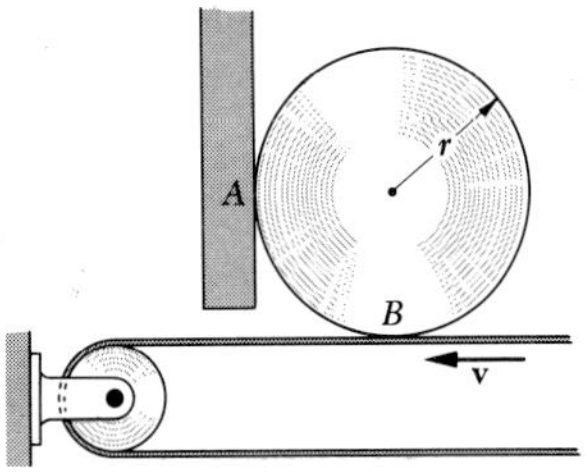

FIG. P 16.39

16.40. A belt of negligible weight is pulled to the right with a force of magnitude P. Cylinder A weighs 5 lb and cylinder B 20 lb. The shaft of cylinder A is free to slide in the vertical slot shown. Knowing that $\mu = 0.50$ between the cylinders and the belt, determine the angular acceleration of each cylinder when $P = 2$ lb.

16.41. Solve Prob. 16.40 assuming $P = 4$ lb.

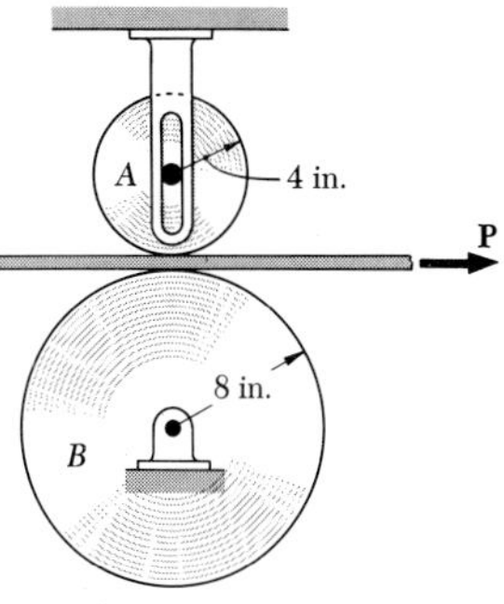

FIG. P 16.40

16.42. Gears A and B weigh 20 lb each and have each a radius of gyration of 9 in.; gear C weighs 5 lb and has a radius of gyration of 3 in. A couple of moment $M = 50$ lb-in. is applied to gear C. Determine (*a*) the angular acceleration of gear A, (*b*) the time required for the angular velocity of gear A to increase from 60 to 660 rpm.

16.43. Solve Prob. 16.42 assuming that the couple of moment $M = 50$ lb-in. is applied to gear A.

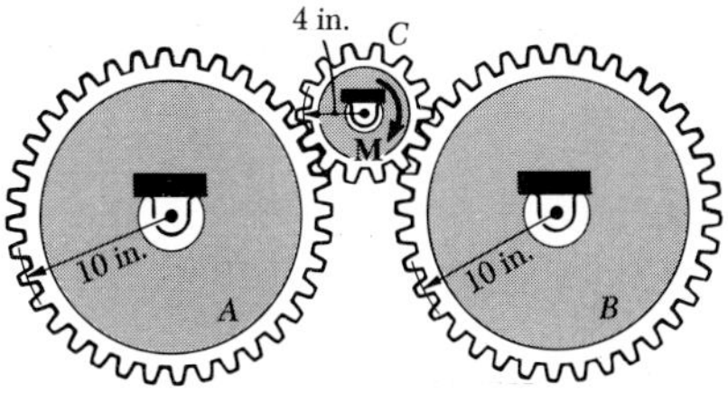

FIG. P 16.42

16.44. A cylinder of radius r and weight W rests on two small casters A and B as shown. Initially, the cylinder is at rest and is set in motion by rotating caster B clockwise at high speed so that slipping occurs between the cylinder and caster B. Denoting by μ the coefficient of friction and neglecting the moment of inertia of the free caster A, derive an expression for the angular acceleration of the cylinder.

16.45. In Prob. 16.44, assume that no slipping can occur between caster B and the cylinder (such a case would exist if the cylinder and caster had gear teeth along their rims). Derive an expression for the maximum counterclockwise acceleration α of the cylinder, if it is not to lose contact with the caster at A.

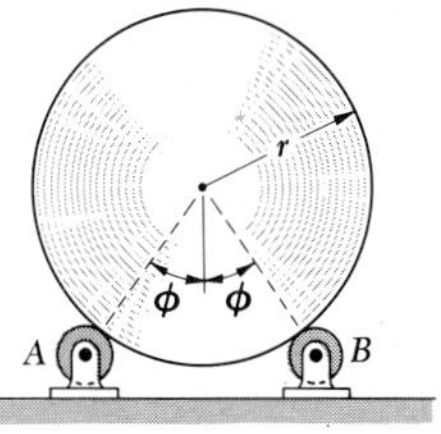

FIG. P 16.44

16.5. Plane Motion. Consider a rigid body of mass m and of centroidal moment of inertia $\bar{I}$ in plane motion under the action of several forces $\mathbf{F}_1$, $\mathbf{F}_2$, $\mathbf{F}_3$, etc. (Fig. 16.9*a*). As in the case of the translation or of the centroidal rotation of a rigid body, the system of the external forces acting on the body must be equivalent at any given instant to the system of the effective forces of the various particles forming the body (Fig. 16.9*b*). Denoting by $\bar{\mathbf{a}}$ the acceleration of the mass center G of the body, and by $\boldsymbol{\alpha}$ the angular acceleration of the body, we shall show that, in the most general case of plane motion, the system of the effective forces reduces to a vector $m\bar{\mathbf{a}}$ attached at G and to a couple $\bar{I}\boldsymbol{\alpha}$ (Fig. 16.10).

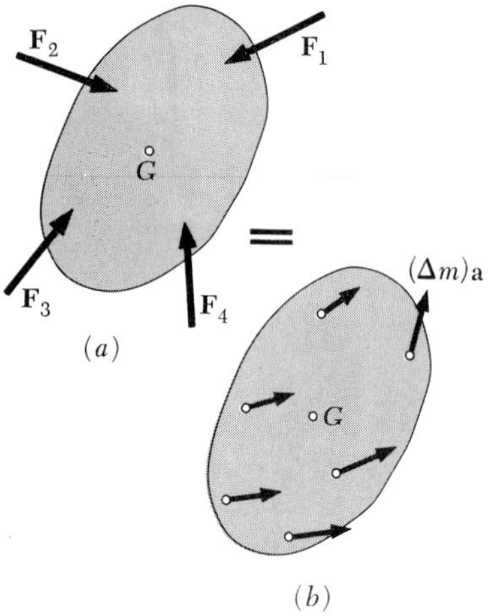

FIG. 16.9

We saw in Chap. 15 that any plane motion of a rigid body may be replaced by a translation plus a rotation about an arbitrary reference point. Choosing the mass center G as the reference point, we may therefore assume that the body has (*a*) a motion of translation in which all its points move with the same acceleration as G and (*b*) a motion of rotation about G (Fig. 16.10*b*). But the system of the effective forces in the translation with G reduces to a single vector $m\bar{\mathbf{a}}$ attached at G (Sec. 16.2), and the system of the effective forces in the rotation about G reduces to a single couple $\bar{I}\alpha$ (Sec. 16.3). The given system of effective forces reduces, therefore, to the vector and couple shown in Fig. 16.10*c*.

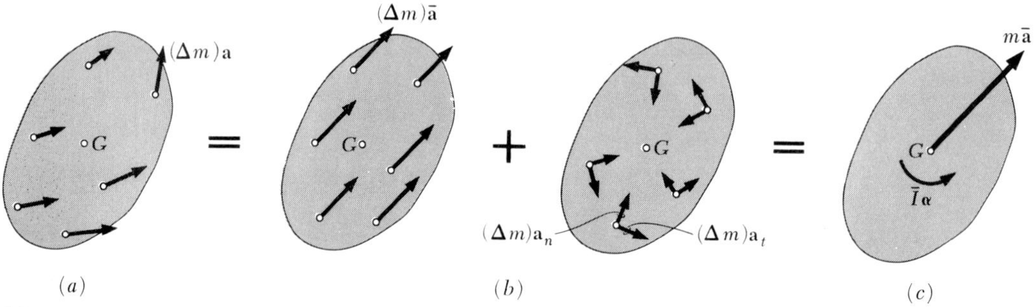

FIG. 16.10

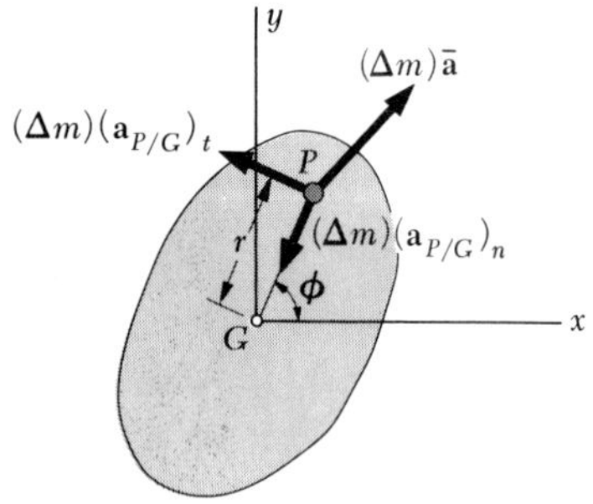

FIG. 16.11

A more rigorous proof of this statement may be obtained as follows: Consider a particle P of the body, at distance r from the mass center G (Fig. 16.11). Choosing G as the reference point, we write that the acceleration of P is equal to

$$\begin{aligned}\mathbf{a}_P &= \mathbf{a}_G + \mathbf{a}_{P/G}\\ &= \bar{\mathbf{a}} + (\mathbf{a}_{P/G})_n + (\mathbf{a}_{P/G})_t\end{aligned}$$

The effective force of particle P may therefore be resolved into the three vectors shown in Fig. 16.11. Resolving similarly the effective forces of all the other particles forming the slab, we obtain three distinct groups of vectors. Recalling the results obtained in Secs. 16.2 and 16.3, we find that the vectors $(\Delta m)\bar{\mathbf{a}}$ may be replaced by their resultant $m\bar{\mathbf{a}}$ attached at G; that the vectors $(\Delta m)(\mathbf{a}_{P/G})_n$ add up to zero; and that the vectors $(\Delta m)(\mathbf{a}_{P/G})_t$ reduce to a single couple $\bar{I}\alpha$. Thus, the entire system of effective forces reduces to the vector and couple shown in Fig. 16.10*c*.

Replacing the effective forces in Fig. 16.9 by the equivalent vector-and-couple system of Fig. 16.10*c*, we obtain Fig. 16.12 and thus conclude that *the system of the external forces is* *equivalent to the vector* $m\bar{\mathbf{a}}$ *attached at G and to the couple* $\bar{I}\alpha$. This relation may be expressed algebraically by writing three equations relating respectively the x and y components and the moments about a given point A of the forces and vectors shown in Fig. 16.12. If the moments are computed about the mass center G of the rigid body, these equations read

$$\Sigma F_x = m\bar{a}_x \qquad \Sigma F_y = m\bar{a}_y \qquad \Sigma M_G = \bar{I}\alpha \qquad \text{(external forces only)} \tag{16.12}$$

The first two equations are identical with the equations of motion of a particle of mass m acted upon by the given forces $\mathbf{F}_1$, $\mathbf{F}_2$, $\mathbf{F}_3$, etc. We thus check that *the mass center G of the body moves as if the entire mass of the body were concentrated at that point, and as if all the external forces acted on it.* We recall that this result has already been obtained in Sec. 12.5 in the general case of a system of particles, the particles being not necessarily rigidly connected. We also note, as we did in Sec. 12.5, that the system of the external forces does not, in general, reduce to a single vector $m\bar{\mathbf{a}}$ attached at G. Therefore, in the general case of the plane motion of a rigid body, *the resultant of the external forces acting on the body does not pass through the mass center of the body.*

The last of Eqs. (16.12) is identical with the equation obtained in Sec. 16.3 for the rotation of a rigid body about a fixed axis through G. Thus, *the body rotates about its mass center as if this point were fixed.*

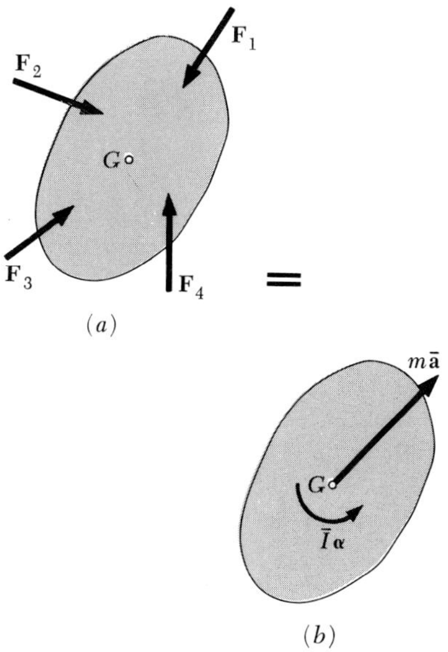

FIG. 16.12

16.6. Solution of Problems Involving Plane Motion. We saw in the preceding section that, when a rigid body is in plane motion, there exists a fundamental relation between the forces $\mathbf{F}_1$, $\mathbf{F}_2$, $\mathbf{F}_3$, etc., acting on the body, the acceleration $\bar{\mathbf{a}}$ of its mass center, and the angular acceleration α of the body. This relation, which is represented in Fig. 16.12, may be used to determine the acceleration $\bar{\mathbf{a}}$ and the angular acceleration α produced by a given system of forces acting on a rigid body or, conversely, to determine the forces which produce a given motion of the rigid body.

While the three algebraic equations (16.12) may be used to solve any problem of plane motion, it is recalled that the solution of many problems involving rigid bodies may be considerably simplified by an appropriate choice of the point about which the moments of the forces are computed. It is therefore preferable to remember the relation existing between the forces and the accelerations in the vectorial form shown in Fig. 16.12, and to derive from this fundamental relation the components or

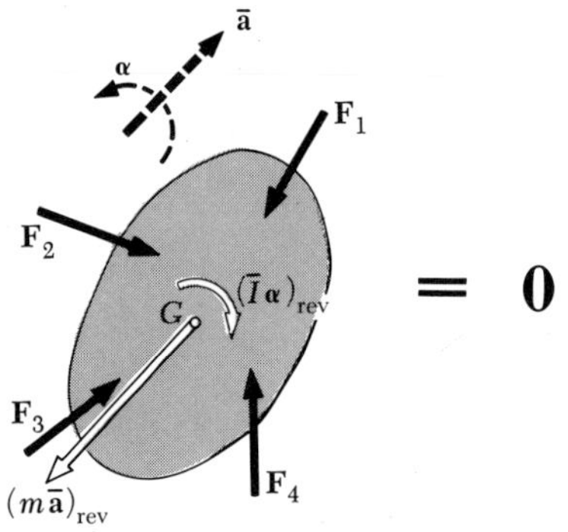

FIG. 16.13

moments equations which fit best the solution of the problem under consideration.

The fundamental relation shown in Fig. 16.12 may be presented in an alternate form if we add to the external forces an inertia vector $(m\bar{\mathbf{a}})_{rev}$ of sense opposite to that of $\bar{\mathbf{a}}$, attached at G, and an inertia couple $(\bar{I}\alpha)_{rev}$ of moment equal in magnitude to $\bar{I}\alpha$ and of sense opposite to that of α (Fig. 16.13). The system obtained is equivalent to zero, and the rigid body is said to be in dynamic equilibrium. We may then write the equations of equilibrium,

$$\Sigma F_x = 0 \qquad \Sigma F_y = 0 \qquad \Sigma M_A = 0 \qquad (16.13)$$

(including inertia vector and inertia couple)

We note that in Eqs. (16.13), where the inertia vector and couple are included, the moments may be computed about any point A. In Eqs. (16.12), however, where only the actual external forces are considered, the moments of the external forces must be computed about the mass center G.

Whether the principle of equivalence of external and effective forces is directly applied, as in Fig. 16.12, or whether the concept of dynamic equilibrium is introduced, as in Fig. 16.13, the use of free-body diagrams showing vectorially the relationship existing between the forces applied on the rigid body and the resulting linear and angular accelerations presents considerable advantages over the blind application of the formulas (16.12). These advantages may be summarized as follows:

1. First of all, a much clearer understanding of the effect of the forces on the motion of the body will result from the use of a pictorial representation.

2. This approach makes it possible to divide the solution of a dynamics problem into two parts: In the first part, the analysis of the kinematic and kinetic characteristics of the problem leads to the free-body diagrams of Fig. 16.12 or 16.13; in the second part, the diagram obtained is used to analyze by the methods learned in statics the various forces and vectors involved.

3. A unified approach is provided for the analysis of the plane motion of a rigid body. Any plane motion is resolved into a translation with the mass center G of the body, and a rotation about G. It should be noted, in this connection, that the motion of translation studied in Sec. 16.2 and the motion of centroidal rotation studied in Sec. 16.3 are particular cases of plane motion, corresponding, respectively, to $\alpha = 0$ and $\bar{\mathbf{a}} = 0$. These two cases were considered first so that the student might familiarize himself with the new concepts introduced. There is no need now, however, to distinguish them

from the general case, and hereafter all problems of plane motion should be solved in the same manner.

4. The resolution of the plane motion of a rigid body into a translation and a centroidal rotation, which is used here, is a basic concept which may be applied effectively throughout the study of mechanics. We shall use it again with the method of work and energy (Chap. 17) and the method of impulse and momentum (Chap. 18).

Various types of plane motion are considered in the following sections; they are grouped according to their *kinematic* characteristics. In Sec. 16.7, the motion of the mass center G of the body considered is independent of the motion of the body about G, while, in Sec. 16.8, a definite relation exists between these two motions. This relation may be such that the body is constrained to rotate about a fixed axis or such that the body must roll without sliding on a given plane; or the relation may be a more complicated one, as in the case of the motion of certain mechanisms. While the kinematics of the various motions considered varies from one case to the other, the approach to the kinetics of the motion is consistently the same. In every case, we shall draw a diagram showing the external forces, the vector $m\bar{\mathbf{a}}$—or $(m\bar{\mathbf{a}})_{\text{rev}}$—associated with the motion of G, and the couple $\bar{I}\alpha$—or $(\bar{I}\alpha)_{\text{rev}}$—associated with the rotation of the body about G.

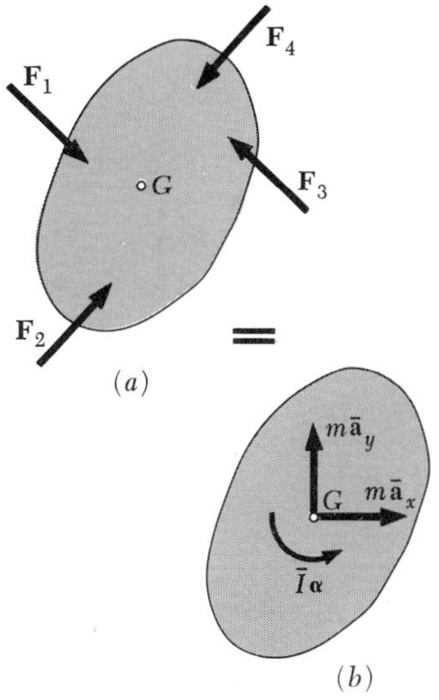

FIG. 16.14

16.7. Plane Motion Consisting of a Translation and of an Unrelated Centroidal Rotation. We shall first consider the case when the motion of the mass center G and the motion of the body about G are unrelated. Each of these two motions may then be studied independently. As we saw in Sec. 16.5, the mass center G will move as if the entire mass were concentrated at G and as if all the external forces acted at G; on the other hand, the body will rotate about G as if G were fixed. Characteristic examples of this type of motion are freely falling bodies, plates pulled on frictionless surfaces, and wheels rolling and sliding at the same time.

Problems involving this type of motion may be solved either by the direct application of D'Alembert's principle (Fig. 16.14) or by the method of dynamic equilibrium (Fig. 16.15). If the problem calls for the determination of the motion of the body under the action of given forces, the components $\bar{a}_x$ and $\bar{a}_y$ of the acceleration of the mass center G and the angular acceleration α of the body will represent *three independent unknowns.* These unknowns may be determined separately by computing respectively the x components, y components, and moments about G of the various forces and vectors involved.

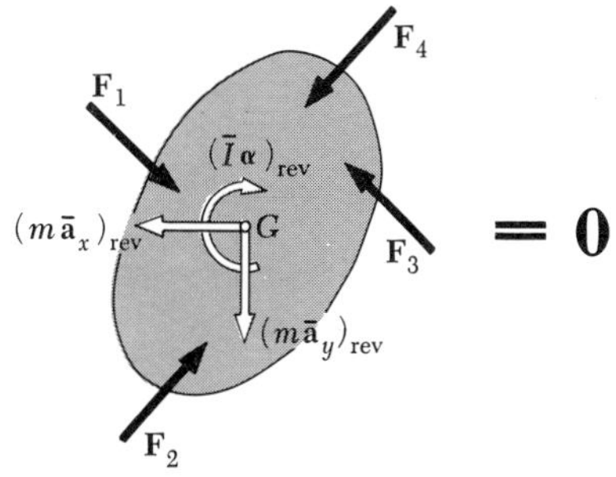

FIG. 16.15

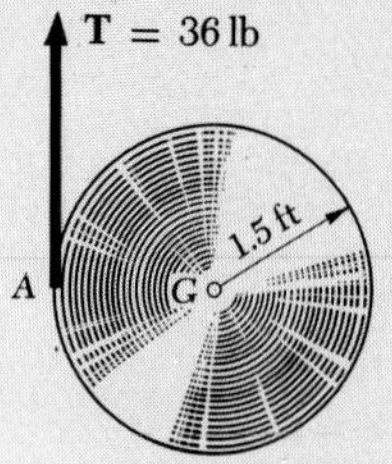

SAMPLE PROBLEM 16.5

A cord is wrapped around a homogeneous disk of radius $r = 1.50$ ft and weight $W = 30$ lb. If the cord is pulled upward with a force **T** of magnitude 36 lb, determine (*a*) the acceleration of the center of the disk, (*b*) the angular acceleration of the disk, (*c*) the acceleration of the cord.

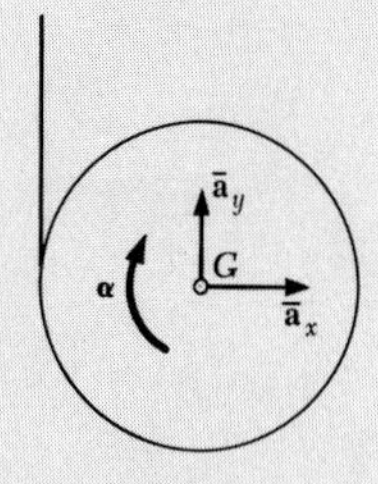

Solution. We assume that the components $\bar{\mathbf{a}}_x$ and $\bar{\mathbf{a}}_y$ of the acceleration of the center are directed, respectively, to the right and upward and that the angular acceleration of the disk is directed clockwise. A free-body diagram of the disk is then drawn, showing the weight, the force exerted by the cord, the components of the inertia vector directed opposite to $\bar{\mathbf{a}}_x$ and $\bar{\mathbf{a}}_y$, and the inertia couple $(\bar{I}\alpha)_{rev}$ directed opposite to $\boldsymbol{\alpha}$.

The mass and centroidal moment of inertia of the disk may be written as follows:

$$m = \frac{W}{g} \qquad \bar{I} = \tfrac{1}{2}mr^2 = \frac{1}{2}\frac{W}{g}r^2$$

Dynamic Equilibrium

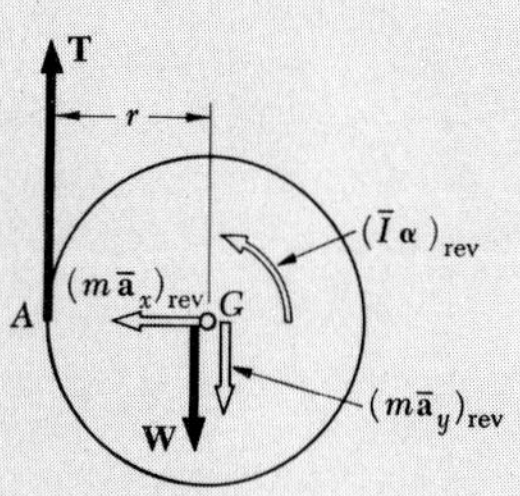

$$\xrightarrow{+} \Sigma F_x = 0: \qquad -m\bar{a}_x = 0 \qquad\qquad \bar{\mathbf{a}}_x = 0 \blacktriangleleft$$

$$+\uparrow \Sigma F_y = 0: \qquad T - W - m\bar{a}_y = 0 \qquad T - W - \frac{W}{g}\bar{a}_y = 0$$

$$\bar{a}_y = \frac{T - W}{W}g$$

Since $T = 36$ lb and $W = 30$ lb, we have

$$\bar{a}_y = \frac{36 - 30}{30}g = +6.44 \text{ ft/sec}^2 \qquad \bar{\mathbf{a}}_y = 6.44 \text{ ft/sec}^2 \uparrow \blacktriangleleft$$

$$+\circlearrowright \Sigma M_G = 0: \qquad \bar{I}\alpha - T(r) = 0 \qquad \frac{1}{2}\frac{W}{g}r^2\alpha - Tr = 0$$

$$\alpha = +\frac{2T}{W}\frac{g}{r} = +\frac{2(36)}{30}\frac{g}{1.5} = +51.5 \text{ radians/sec}^2$$

$$\boldsymbol{\alpha} = 51.5 \text{ radians/sec}^2 \circlearrowright \blacktriangleleft$$

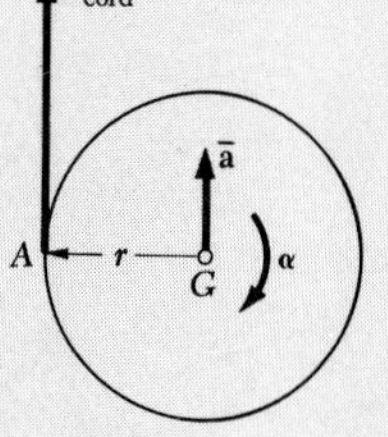

Acceleration of Cord. Since the acceleration of the cord is equal to the tangential component of the acceleration of point *A* on the disk, we write

$$\mathbf{a}_{cord} = (\mathbf{a}_A)_t = \bar{\mathbf{a}} + (\mathbf{a}_{A/G})_t$$
$$= [6.44\uparrow] + [(1.5)(51.5)\uparrow]$$

$$\mathbf{a}_{cord} = 83.7 \text{ ft/sec}^2 \uparrow \blacktriangleleft$$

SAMPLE PROBLEM 16.6

A hoop of radius r and weight W is placed on a horizontal surface with no linear velocity but with a clockwise angular velocity ω_0. Denoting by μ the coefficient of friction between the hoop and the floor, determine (*a*) the time t_1 at which the hoop will start rolling without sliding, (*b*) the linear and angular velocities of the hoop at time t_1.

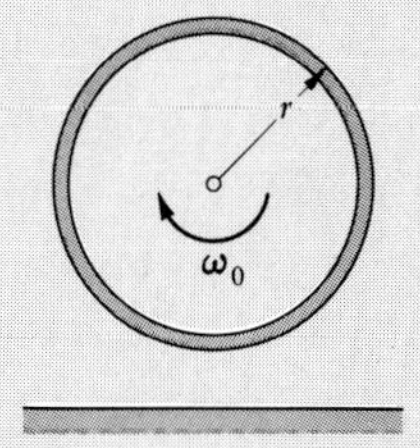

Solution. Since the entire mass, $m = W/g$, is located at a distance r from the center of the hoop, we write $\bar{I} = mr^2 = (W/g)r^2$.

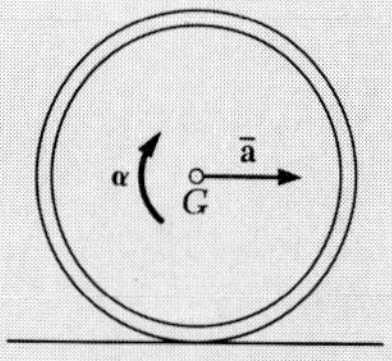

Dynamic Equilibrium. The positive sense is chosen to the right for $\bar{\mathbf{a}}$ and clockwise for α. A free-body diagram of the hoop is drawn, showing its weight **W**, the normal reaction **N**, the friction force **F**, the inertia vector $(m\bar{\mathbf{a}})_{\text{rev}}$, and the inertia couple $(\bar{I}\alpha)_{\text{rev}}$. While the hoop is sliding, the magnitude of the friction force is $F = \mu N$.

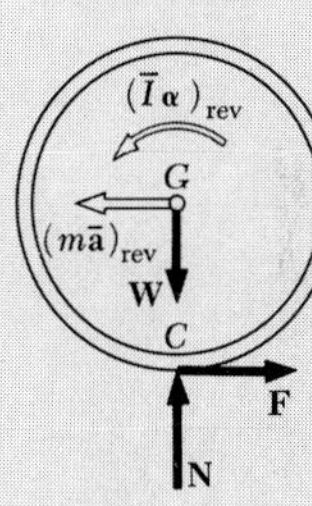

$$+\uparrow \Sigma F_y = 0: \qquad N - W = 0$$

$$N = W \qquad F = \mu N = \mu W$$

$$\xrightarrow{+} \Sigma F_x = 0: \qquad -m\bar{a} + F = 0 \qquad -\frac{W}{g}\bar{a} + \mu W = 0$$

$$\bar{a} = +\mu g$$

$$+\circlearrowright \Sigma M_G = 0: \qquad Fr + \bar{I}\alpha = 0 \qquad \mu W r + \left(\frac{W}{g} r^2\right)\alpha = 0$$

$$\alpha = -\frac{\mu g}{r}$$

Kinematics of Motion. As long as the hoop both rolls and slides, its linear and angular motions are uniformly accelerated.

$$t = 0, \bar{v}_0 = 0 \qquad \bar{v} = \bar{v}_0 + \bar{a}t = 0 + \mu g t \qquad (1)$$

$$t = 0, \omega = \omega_0 \qquad \omega = \omega_0 + \alpha t = \omega_0 + \left(-\frac{\mu g}{r}\right) t \qquad (2)$$

The hoop will start rolling without sliding when the velocity $\mathbf{v}_C$ of the point of contact is zero. At that time, $t = t_1$, point C becomes the instantaneous center of rotation, and we have

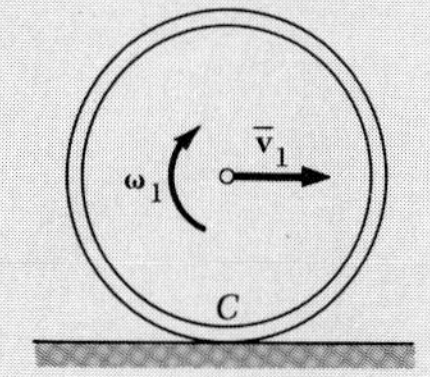

$$\bar{v}_1 = r\omega_1$$

$$\mu g t_1 = r\left(\omega_0 - \frac{\mu g}{r} t_1\right) \qquad t_1 = \frac{r\omega_0}{2\mu g} \quad ◄$$

Substituting for t_1 into (1), we have

$$\bar{v}_1 = \mu g t_1 = \mu g \frac{r\omega_0}{2\mu g} \qquad \bar{v}_1 = \tfrac{1}{2} r\omega_0 \qquad \bar{\mathbf{v}}_1 = \tfrac{1}{2} r\omega_0 \rightarrow \quad ◄$$

$$\bar{v}_1 = r\omega_1 \qquad \tfrac{1}{2} r\omega_0 = r\omega_1 \qquad \omega_1 = \tfrac{1}{2}\omega_0 \qquad \omega_1 = \tfrac{1}{2}\omega_0 \circlearrowright \quad ◄$$

PROBLEMS

16.46. Show that the system of the effective forces for a rigid body in plane motion reduces to a single vector, and express the distance from the mass center G of the body to the line of action of this vector in terms of the centroidal radius of gyration $\bar{k}$ of the body, the magnitude $\bar{a}$ of the acceleration of G, and the angular acceleration α.

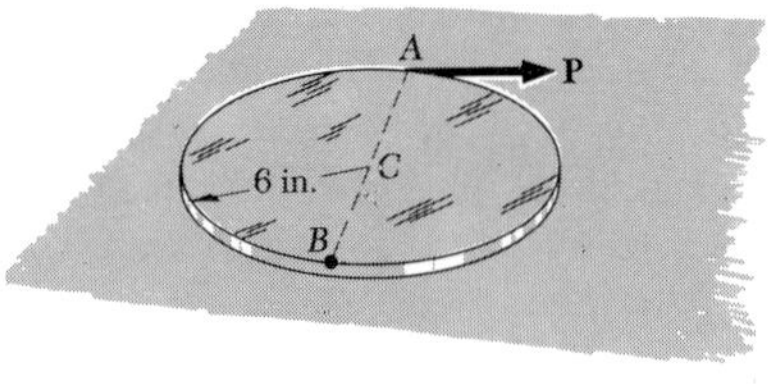

FIG. P 16.47

16.47. A 12-in.-diameter plate weighing 10 lb rests on a smooth horizontal table. A force **P** of magnitude 2 lb is applied to the plate at A in a horizontal direction perpendicular to the diameter AB. Determine (a) the angular acceleration of the plate, (b) the acceleration of the center C of the plate, (c) the point of the plate which has no acceleration.

16.48. In Prob. 16.47, determine the point on the diameter AB at which the force **P** should be applied if the acceleration of point B is to be zero. Knowing that the magnitude of **P** is 2 lb, determine the corresponding angular acceleration of the plate and the acceleration of the center C.

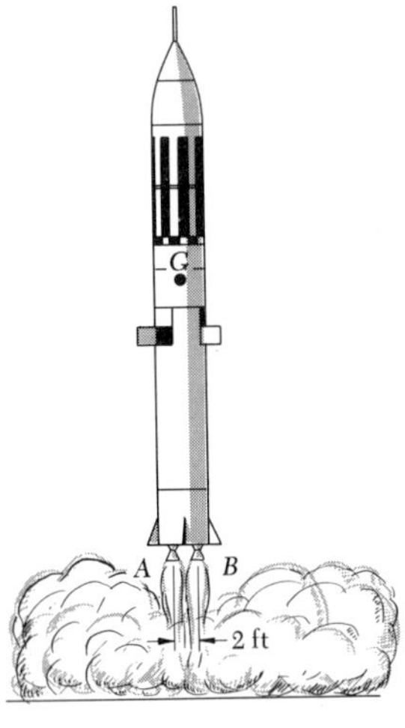

FIG. P 16.49

16.49. Shortly after being fired, the missile shown weighs 20,000 lb and is moving upward with an acceleration of 50 ft/sec^2. If, at this instant, the rocket engine A fails, while rocket engine B continues to operate, determine (a) the acceleration of the mass center of the missile, (b) the angular acceleration of the missile. Assume the missile to be a slender rod 48 ft long.

16.50. A 12-ft beam weighing 644 lb is lowered from a considerable height by means of two cables unwinding from overhead cranes. As the beam approaches the ground, the crane operators apply brakes to slow the unwinding motion. The deceleration of cable A is 4 ft/sec^2, while that of cable B is 28 ft/sec^2. Determine the tension in each cable.

16.51. Solve Prob. 16.50 assuming that the beam has been replaced by the 644-lb crate shown.

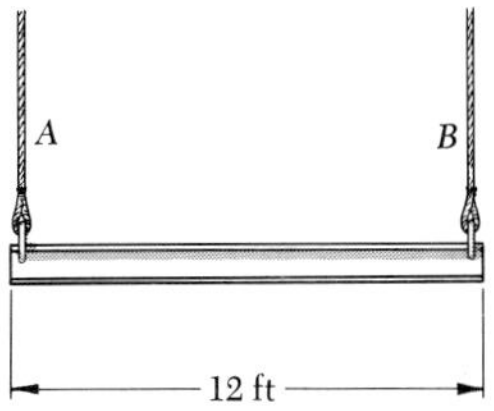

FIG. P 16.50 AND P 16.52

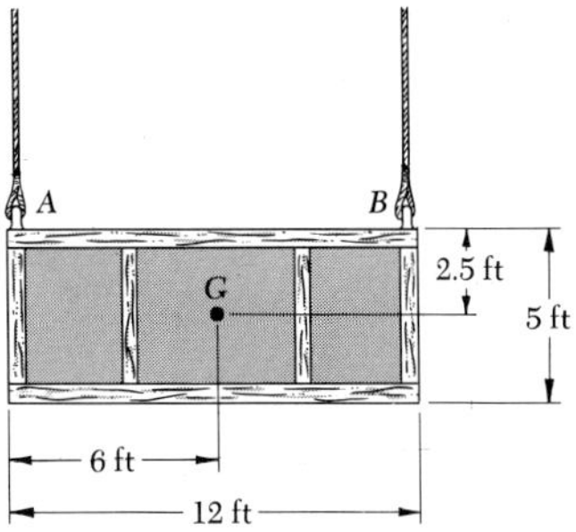

FIG. P 16.51 AND P 16.53

16.52. A 12-ft beam weighing 644 lb is lowered from a considerable height by means of two cables unwinding from overhead cranes. As the beam approaches the ground, the crane operators apply brakes to slow the unwinding motion. Determine the acceleration of each cable at that instant, knowing that $T_A = 502$ lb and $T_B = 542$ lb.

16.53. Solve Prob. 16.52 assuming that the beam has been replaced by the 644-lb crate shown.

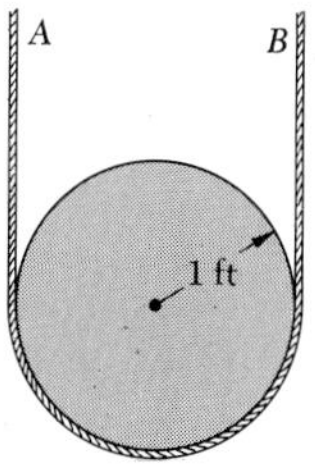

FIG. P 16.54

16.54. A 50-lb cylinder of radius 1 ft is lifted by means of a cable wrapped around it. The two ends of the cable are pulled at different rates, so that the cylinder rotates with an angular acceleration of 6.44 radians/sec^2 counterclockwise, while moving up with an acceleration of 3.22 ft/sec^2. Find the tension in both sections of the cable.

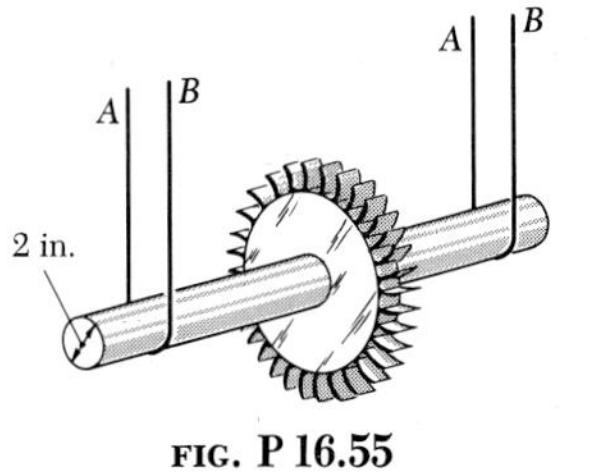

FIG. P 16.55

16.55. A turbine disk and shaft have a combined weight of 200 lb and a centroidal radius of gyration of 2 in. The unit is lifted by two ropes looped around the shaft as shown. Knowing that for each rope $T_A = 55$ lb and $T_B = 65$ lb, determine the angular acceleration of the unit and the acceleration of its mass center.

16.56. In Sample Prob. 16.5, determine (*a*) the magnitude of the force **T** for which the center of the disk has no acceleration, (*b*) the corresponding angular acceleration of the disk, (*c*) the corresponding acceleration of the cord.

16.57. By pulling on the cord of a yo-yo just fast enough, a man manages to make the yo-yo spin clockwise, while remaining at a constant height above the floor. Denoting the weight of the yo-yo by W, the radius of the inner drum on which the cord is wound by r, and the radius of gyration of the yo-yo by $\bar{k}$, determine (*a*) the tension in the cord, (*b*) the angular acceleration of the yo-yo.

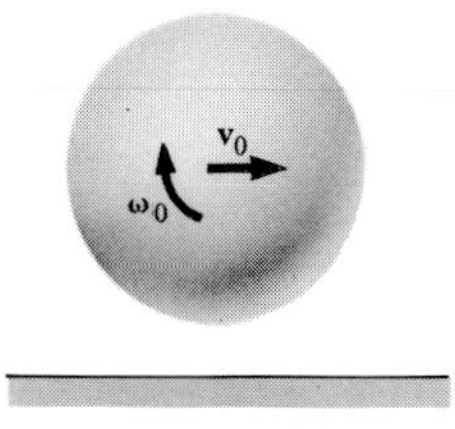

FIG. P 16.58

16.58. A sphere of weight W and radius r is projected horizontally with a linear velocity $\mathbf{v}_0$ and with $\omega_0 = 0$. The sphere will decelerate and then reach a uniform motion. Denoting by μ the coefficient of friction, determine (*a*) the linear and angular acceleration of the sphere before it reaches a uniform motion, (*b*) the time required for the motion to become uniform, (*c*) the distance traveled before the motion becomes uniform, (*d*) the final linear and angular velocity of the sphere.

16.59. Solve Prob. 16.58 assuming that the sphere is replaced by a hoop of radius r and weight W.

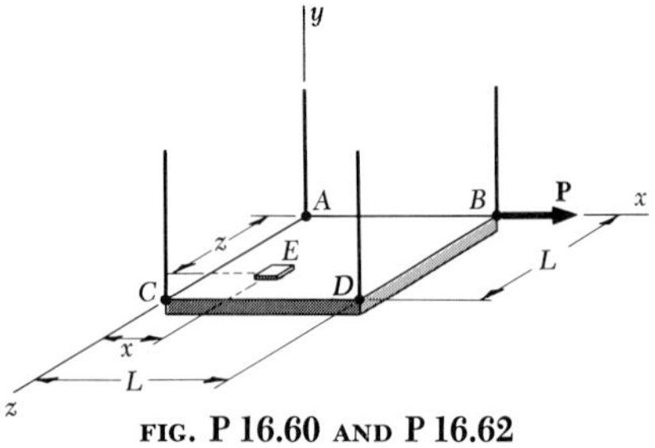

FIG. P 16.60 AND P 16.62

16.60. A heavy square plate of weight W, suspended from four vertical wires, supports a small block E of much smaller weight w. The coefficient of friction between E and the plate is denoted by μ. If the coordinates of E are $x = \frac{1}{4}L$ and $z = \frac{1}{4}L$, derive an expression for the magnitude of the force $\mathbf{P}$ required to cause E to slip with respect to the plate. (*Hint.* Neglect w in all equations containing W.)

16.61. Solve Prob. 16.60 assuming that block E is placed at point D $(x = L, z = L)$.

***16.62.** A square plate of weight $W = 20$ lb and side $L = 3$ ft is suspended from four wires and supports a block E of much smaller weight w. The coefficient of friction between E and the plate is 0.50. If a force $\mathbf{P}$ of magnitude 10 lb is applied as shown, determine the area of the plate where E should be placed if it is not to slip with respect to the plate. (*Hint.* Neglect w in all equations containing W.)

16.8. Constrained Plane Motion. Most engineering applications deal with rigid bodies which are moving under given constraints. Cranks, for example, are constrained to rotate about a fixed axis, wheels roll without sliding, connecting rods must describe certain prescribed motions. In all such cases, definite relations exist between the components of the acceleration $\bar{\mathbf{a}}$ of the mass center G of the body considered and its angular acceleration $\boldsymbol{\alpha}$; the corresponding motion is said to be a *constrained motion.*

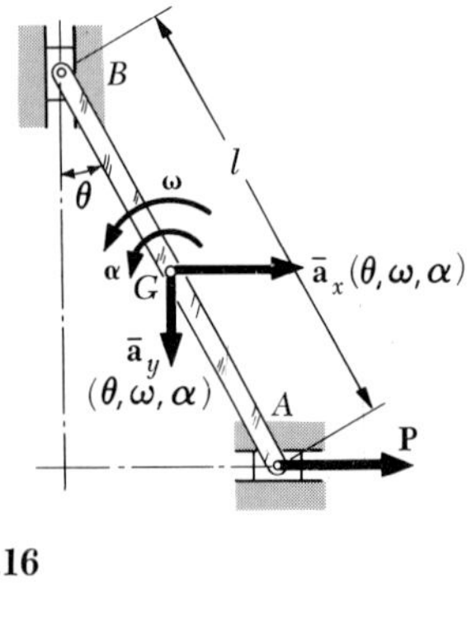

FIG. 16.16

The solution of a problem involving a constrained plane motion calls first for a *kinematic analysis* of the problem. Consider, for example, a slender rod AB of length l and mass m whose extremities are connected to blocks of negligible mass which slide along horizontal and vertical frictionless tracks. The rod is pulled by a force $\mathbf{P}$ applied at A (Fig. 16.16). We know from Sec. 15.8 that the acceleration $\bar{\mathbf{a}}$ of the mass center G of the rod may be determined at any given instant from the position of the rod, its angular velocity, and its angular acceleration

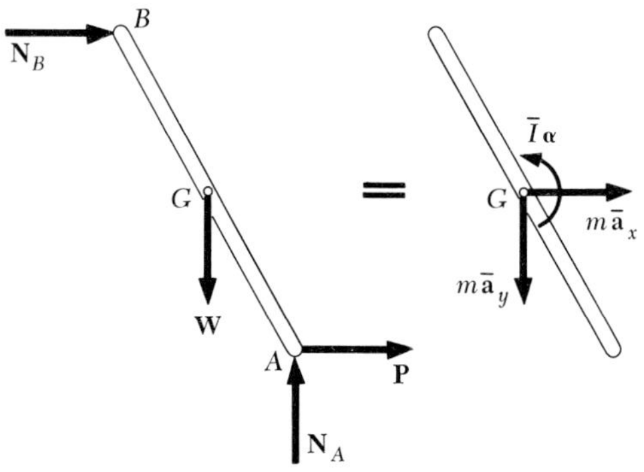

FIG. 16.17

at that instant. Suppose, for instance, that the values of θ, ω, and α are known at a given instant and that we wish to determine the corresponding value of the force **P**, as well as the reactions at A and B. We should first *determine the components* $\bar{a}_x$ *and* $\bar{a}_y$ *of the acceleration of the mass center* G by the method of Sec. 15.8. We then carry the values obtained into Fig. 16.17 or Fig. 16.18, depending upon whether D'Alembert's principle is applied directly or the method of dynamic equilibrium is used. The unknown forces **P**, $\mathbf{N}_A$, and $\mathbf{N}_B$ may then be determined by writing and solving the appropriate equations.

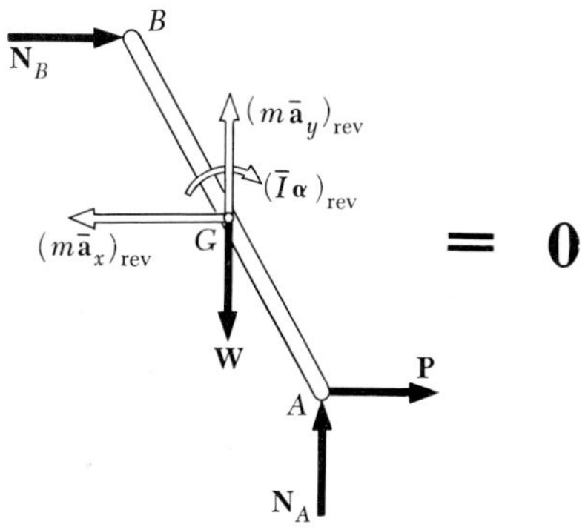

FIG. 16.18

Suppose now that the applied force **P**, the angle θ, and the angular velocity ω of the rod are known at a given instant and that we wish to find the angular acceleration α of the rod and the components $\bar{a}_x$ and $\bar{a}_y$ of the acceleration of its mass center at that instant, as well as the reactions at A and B. The preliminary kinematic study of the problem will have for its object *to express the components* $\bar{a}_x$ *and* $\bar{a}_y$ *of the acceleration of* G *in terms of the angular acceleration* α *of the rod.* This will be done by first expressing the acceleration of a suitable reference point such as A in terms of the angular acceleration α. The components $\bar{a}_x$ and $\bar{a}_y$ of the acceleration of G may then be determined in terms of α, and the expressions obtained carried into Fig. 16.17 or Fig. 16.18. Three equations may then be derived in terms of α, N_A, and N_B, and solved for the three unknowns (see Sample Prob. 16.11).

When a mechanism consists of *several moving parts*, the method just described may be applied to each part of the mechanism. The procedure required to determine the various unknowns is then similar to the procedure followed in the case of the static equilibrium of a system of connected rigid bodies (Sec. 6.12).

We have analyzed earlier two particular cases of constrained

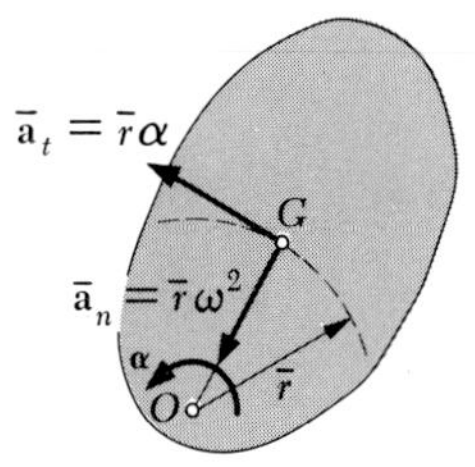

FIG. P16.19

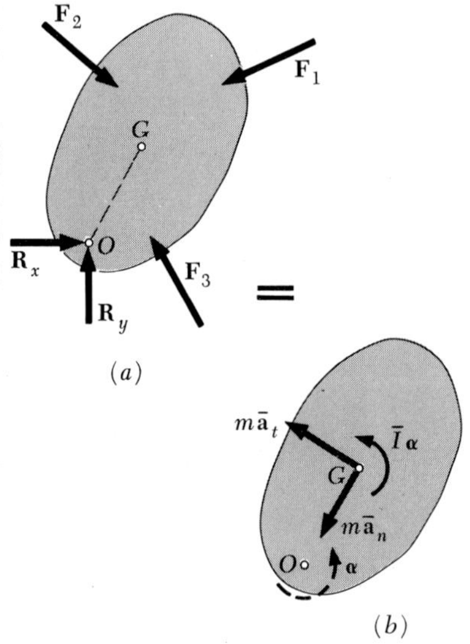

FIG. 16.20

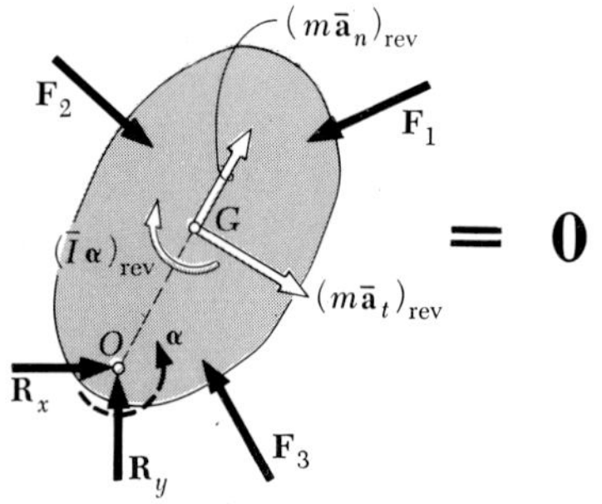

FIG. 16.21

plane motion, the translation of a rigid body (Sec. 16.2), in which the angular acceleration of the body is constrained to be zero, and the centroidal rotation (Sec. 16.3), in which the acceleration $\bar{\mathbf{a}}$ of the mass center of the body is constrained to be zero. Two other particular cases of constrained plane motion are of special interest, the *noncentroidal rotation* of a rigid body and the *rolling motion* of a disk or wheel. These two cases should be analyzed by one of the general methods described above. However, in view of the range of their applications, they deserve a few special comments.

Noncentroidal Rotation. This is the motion of a rigid body constrained to rotate about a fixed axis which does not pass through its mass center. Such a motion is called a *noncentroidal rotation.* The mass center G of the body moves along a circle of radius $\bar{r}$ centered at the point O, where the axis of rotation intersects the plane of reference (Fig. 16.19). Denoting, respectively, by $\boldsymbol{\omega}$ and $\boldsymbol{\alpha}$ the angular velocity and the angular acceleration of the line OG, we obtain the following expressions for the tangential and normal components of the acceleration of G:

$$\bar{a}_t = \bar{r}\alpha \qquad \bar{a}_n = \bar{r}\omega^2 \tag{16.14}$$

Since line OG belongs to the body, its angular velocity $\boldsymbol{\omega}$ and its angular acceleration $\boldsymbol{\alpha}$ also represent the angular velocity and the angular acceleration of the body in its motion relative to G. Equations (16.14) define, therefore, the kinematic relation existing between the motion of the mass center G and the motion of the body about G. They should be used to eliminate $\bar{a}_t$ and $\bar{a}_n$ from the equations obtained by applying D'Alembert's principle (Fig. 16.20) or the method of dynamic equilibrium (Fig. 16.21).

An interesting relation may be obtained by equating the moments about the fixed point O of the forces and vectors shown respectively in parts *a* and *b* of Fig. 16.20. We write

$$+\circlearrowleft \ \Sigma M_O = \bar{I}\alpha + (m\bar{r}\alpha)\bar{r} = (\bar{I} + m\bar{r}^2)\alpha$$

But, according to the parallel-axis theorem, we have $\bar{I} + m\bar{r}^2 = I_O$, where I_O denotes the moment of inertia of the rigid body about the fixed axis. We write, therefore,

$$\Sigma M_O = I_O\alpha \tag{16.15}$$

While formula (16.15) expresses an important relation between the sum of the moments of the external forces about the fixed point O and the product $I_O\alpha$, it should be clearly understood that this formula *does not mean* that the system of the external forces is equivalent to a couple of moment $I_O\alpha$. The system of the effective forces, and thus the system of the external forces, reduces to a couple only when O coincides with G, that is, *only when the rotation is centroidal* (Sec. 16.3). In the more general case of noncentroidal rotation, the system of the external forces does not reduce to a couple.

A particular case of noncentroidal rotation is of special interest: the case of *uniform rotation*, in which the angular velocity ω is constant. Since α is zero, the inertia couple in Fig. 16.21 vanishes and the inertia vector reduces to its normal component. This component (also called *centrifugal force*) represents the tendency of the rigid body to break away from the axis of rotation.

Rolling Motion. Another important case of plane motion is the motion of a disk or wheel rolling on a plane surface. If the disk is constrained to roll without sliding, the acceleration $\bar{\mathbf{a}}$ of its mass center G and its angular acceleration α are not independent. Assuming the disk to be balanced, so that its mass center and its geometric center coincide, we first write that the displacement $\bar{s}$ of G corresponding to a rotation of θ radians of the disk is $\bar{s} = r\theta$, where r is the radius of the disk. Differentiating this relation twice, we write

$$\bar{a} = r\alpha \tag{16.16}$$

Recalling that the system of the effective forces in plane motion reduces to a vector $m\bar{\mathbf{a}}$ and a couple $\bar{I}\alpha$, we find that, in the particular case of the rolling motion of a balanced disk, the effective forces reduce to a vector of magnitude $mr\alpha$ attached at G and to a couple of moment $\bar{I}\alpha$. We may thus express that the external forces are equivalent to the vector and couple shown in Fig. 16.22.

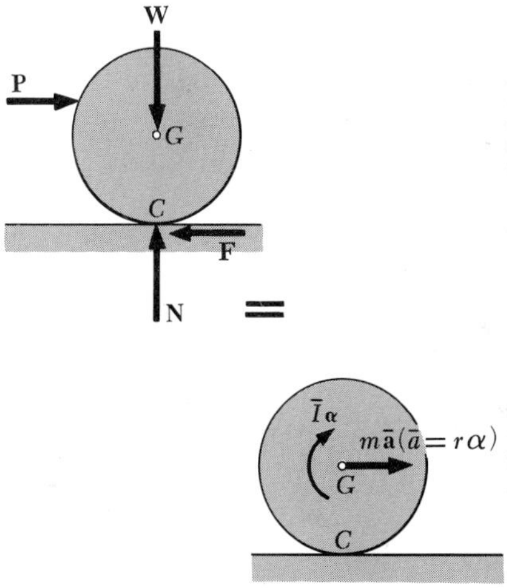

FIG. 16.22

Considering the vector and couple of opposite sense, we may also express that the disk is in dynamic equilibrium under the action of the external forces and of the inertia vector and inertia couple shown in Fig. 16.23. If the applied force **P** is known, appropriate equilibrium equations may be used to determine the components **F** and **N** of the reaction of the ground and the angular acceleration α of the disk. The magnitude of the acceleration $\bar{\mathbf{a}}$ of the mass center G may then be obtained from the relation (16.16).

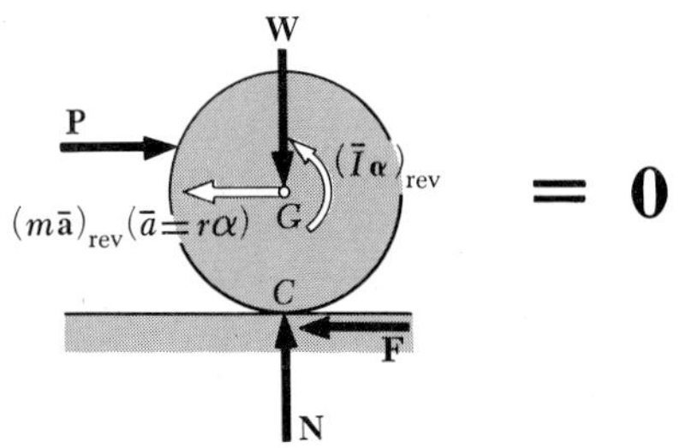

FIG. 16.23

When a disk *rolls without sliding*, there is no relative motion between the point of the disk which is in contact with the ground and the ground itself. As far as the computation of the friction force **F** is concerned, a rolling disk may thus be compared with a block at rest on a surface. The magnitude F of the friction force may have any value, as long as it does not exceed the maximum value $F_m = \mu_s N$, where μ_s is the coefficient of static friction and N the magnitude of the normal force. In the case of a rolling disk, the magnitude F of the friction force should therefore be determined independently of N by solving the equations obtained from Fig. 16.22 or Fig. 16.23.

When *sliding is impending*, the friction force reaches its maximum value $F_m = \mu_s N$ and may be obtained from N.

When the disk *rolls and slides* at the same time, a relative motion exists between the point of the disk which is in contact with the ground and the ground itself, and the force of friction has the magnitude $F_k = \mu_k N$, where μ_k is the coefficient of kinetic friction. In this case, however, the motion of the mass center G of the disk and the rotation of the disk about G are independent, and $\bar{a}$ is not equal to $r\alpha$. The motion of the disk is then of the type analyzed in Sec. 16.7.

These three different cases may be summarized as follows:

Rolling, no sliding:	$F \leq \mu_s N$	$\bar{a} = r\alpha$
Rolling, sliding impending:	$F = \mu_s N$	$\bar{a} = r\alpha$
Rolling and sliding:	$F = \mu_k N$	$\bar{a}$ *and* α *independent*

When it is not known whether a disk slides or not, it should first be assumed that the disk rolls without sliding. If F is found smaller than, or equal to, $\mu_s N$, the assumption is proved correct. If F is found larger than $\mu_s N$, the assumption is incorrect and the problem should be started again, assuming rolling and sliding.

When a disk is *unbalanced*, i.e., when its mass center G does not coincide with its geometric center O, the relation (16.16) does not hold between $\bar{a}$ and α. A similar relation will hold, however, between the magnitude a_O of the acceleration of the geometric center and the angular acceleration α,

$$a_O = r\alpha \tag{16.17}$$

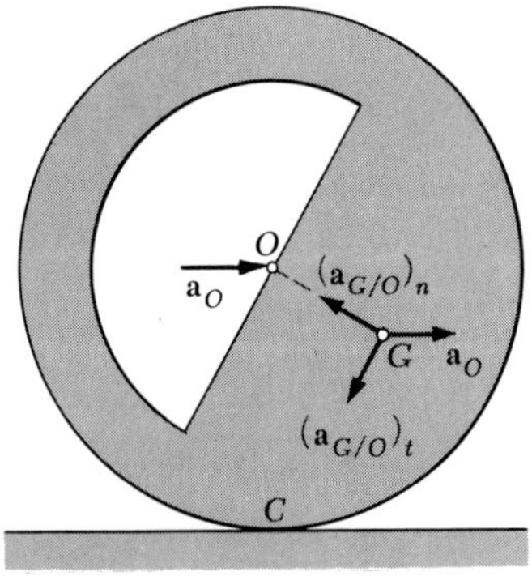

FIG. 16.24

To determine $\bar{a}$ in terms of the angular acceleration α and the angular velocity ω of the disk, we may use the relative-acceleration formula,

$$\begin{aligned}\bar{\mathbf{a}} = \mathbf{a}_G &= \mathbf{a}_O + \mathbf{a}_{G/O} \\ &= \mathbf{a}_O + (\mathbf{a}_{G/O})_t + (\mathbf{a}_{G/O})_n\end{aligned} \tag{16.18}$$

where the three component accelerations obtained have the directions indicated in Fig. 16.24 and the magnitudes $a_O = r\alpha$, $(a_{G/O})_t = (OG)\alpha$, and $(a_{G/O})_n = (OG)\omega^2$.

SAMPLE PROBLEM 16.7

At the instant shown, the lever AB rotates with a counterclockwise angular velocity of 10 radians/sec and with a clockwise angular acceleration of 50 radians/sec². Knowing that the lever weighs 30 lb and that its centroidal radius of gyration is 0.80 ft, determine (*a*) the tangential force exerted on the gear at A, (*b*) the components of the reaction at the shaft O.

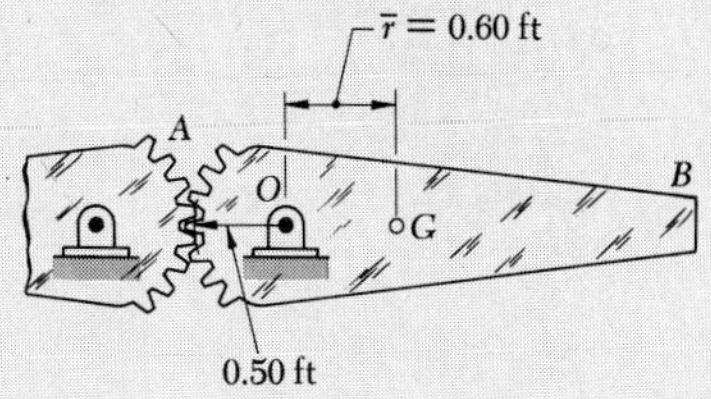

Acceleration of G. Since the lever rotates about O, we write

$$\bar{a}_n = \bar{r}\omega^2 = (0.60)(10^2) = 60 \text{ ft/sec}^2$$

$$\bar{a}_t = \bar{r}\alpha = (0.60)(50) = 30 \text{ ft/sec}^2$$

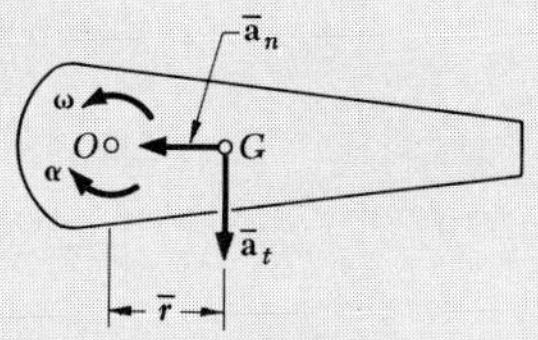

Dynamic Equilibrium. A free-body diagram of the lever is drawn, showing all external forces, the two components of the inertia vector $(m\bar{\mathbf{a}}_n)_{rev}$ and $(m\bar{\mathbf{a}}_t)_{rev}$, and the inertia couple $(\bar{I}\boldsymbol{\alpha})_{rev}$. Since the accelerations are known, we compute the magnitudes

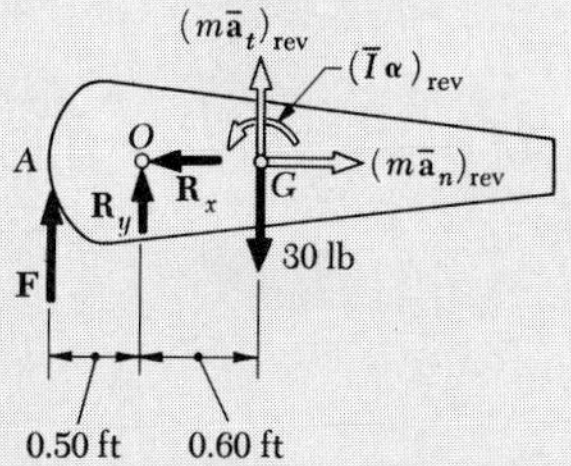

$$m\bar{a}_n = \frac{30}{32.2}(60) = 55.9 \text{ lb}$$

$$m\bar{a}_t = \frac{30}{32.2}(30) = 27.9 \text{ lb}$$

$$\bar{I}\alpha = m\bar{k}^2\alpha = \frac{30}{32.2}(0.80)^2(50) = 29.8 \text{ lb-ft}$$

We write the following equations of dynamic equilibrium:

$+\circlearrowleft \Sigma M_O = 0$:

$$-F(0.50 \text{ ft}) + m\bar{a}_t(0.60 \text{ ft}) + \bar{I}\alpha - (30 \text{ lb})(0.60 \text{ ft}) = 0$$

$$-0.50F + (27.9)(0.60) + 29.8 - 18 = 0$$

$$F = +57.1 \text{ lb} \qquad \mathbf{F} = 57.1 \text{ lb}\uparrow \blacktriangleleft$$

$\xrightarrow{+} \Sigma F_x = 0$: $\quad -R_x + m\bar{a}_n = 0 \qquad -R_x + 55.9 \text{ lb} = 0$

$$R_x = +55.9 \text{ lb} \qquad \mathbf{R}_x = 55.9 \text{ lb} \leftarrow \blacktriangleleft$$

$+\uparrow \Sigma F_y = 0$: $\quad +F + R_y - 30 \text{ lb} + m\bar{a}_t = 0$

$$+57.1 \text{ lb} + R_y - 30 \text{ lb} + 27.9 \text{ lb} = 0$$

$$R_y = -55.0 \text{ lb} \qquad \mathbf{R}_y = 55.0 \text{ lb}\downarrow \blacktriangleleft$$

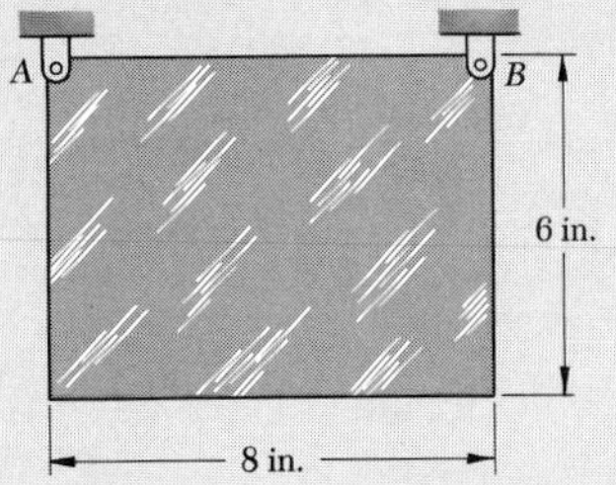

SAMPLE PROBLEM 16.8

A rectangular plate, 6 by 8 in., weighs 60 lb and is suspended from two pins A and B. If pin B is suddenly removed, determine (*a*) the angular acceleration of the plate, (*b*) the components of the reactions at pin A, immediately after pin B has been removed.

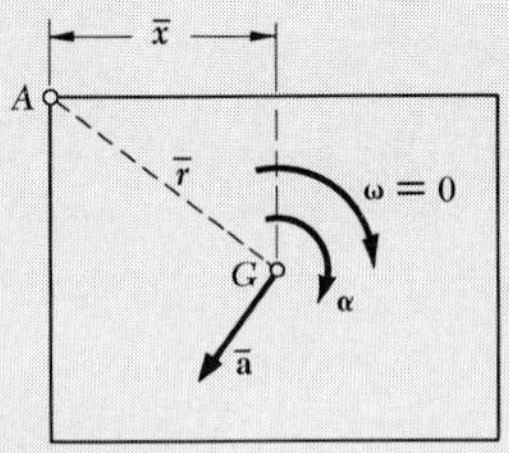

a. **Angular Acceleration.** We observe that as the plate rotates about point A, its mass center G describes a circle of radius $\bar{r}$ with center at A.

Since the plate is released from rest ($\omega = 0$), the normal component of the acceleration of G is zero. The magnitude of the acceleration $\bar{\mathbf{a}}$ of the mass center G is thus $\bar{a} = \bar{r}\alpha$. We draw a free-body diagram of the plate, showing all external forces, the inertia vector $(m\bar{\mathbf{a}})_{\text{rev}}$, and the inertia couple $(\bar{I}\boldsymbol{\alpha})_{\text{rev}}$.

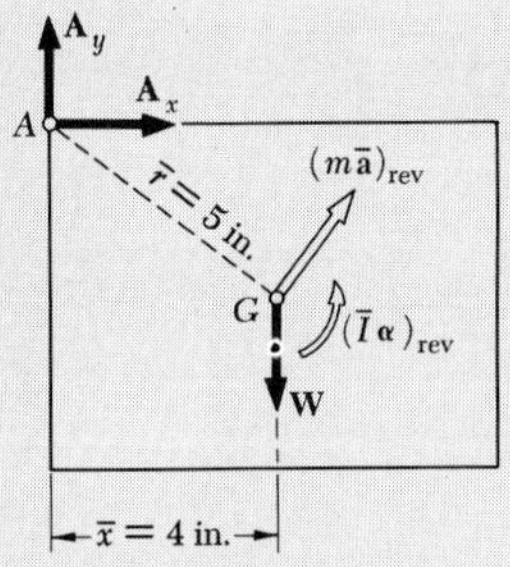

Dynamic Equilibrium

$+\circlearrowright \Sigma M_A = 0$: $\quad (m\bar{a})\bar{r} + \bar{I}\alpha - W\bar{x} = 0$

Since $\bar{a} = r\alpha$, we have

$$m(\bar{r}\alpha)\bar{r} + \bar{I}\alpha - W\bar{x} = 0$$

$$\alpha = \frac{W\bar{x}}{\dfrac{W}{g}\bar{r}^2 + \bar{I}} \qquad (1)$$

The centroidal moment of inertia of the plate is

$$\bar{I} = \frac{m}{12}(a^2 + b^2) = \frac{60}{(12)(32.2)}[(\tfrac{8}{12})^2 + (\tfrac{6}{12})^2] = 0.1078 \text{ lb-ft-sec}^2$$

Substituting this value of $\bar{I}$ together with $W = 60$ lb, $\bar{r} = 5$ in., and $\bar{x} =$ 4 in. into Eq. (1), we obtain

$$\alpha = +46.3 \text{ radians/sec}^2 \qquad \boldsymbol{\alpha} = 46.3 \text{ radians/sec}^2 \circlearrowright \blacktriangleleft$$

b. **Reaction at** A. Using the computed value of α, we determine the magnitude of the inertia vector attached at G,

$$m\bar{a} = m\bar{r}\alpha = \frac{60}{32.2}\frac{5}{12}(46.3) = 36.0 \text{ lb}$$

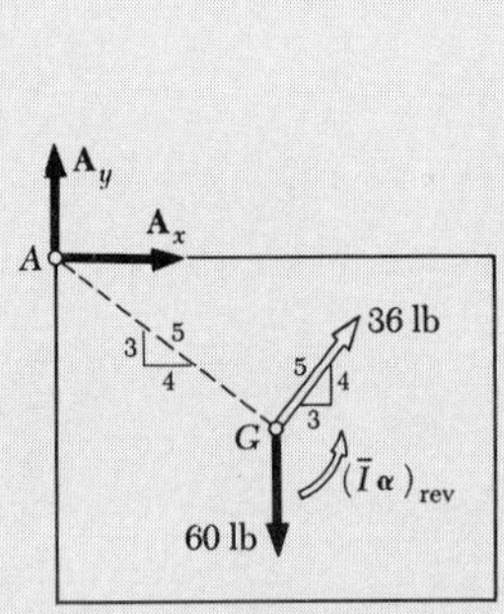

Showing this result on the free-body diagram, we then write

$\xrightarrow{+} \Sigma F_x = 0$: $\quad A_x + \tfrac{3}{5}(36 \text{ lb}) = 0$

$A_x = -21.6$ lb $\qquad \mathbf{A}_x = 21.6 \text{ lb} \leftarrow \blacktriangleleft$

$+\uparrow \Sigma F_y = 0$: $\quad A_y + \tfrac{4}{5}(36 \text{ lb}) - 60 \text{ lb} = 0$

$A_y = +31.2$ lb $\qquad \mathbf{A}_y = 31.2 \text{ lb} \uparrow \blacktriangleleft$

The inertia couple $(\bar{I}\boldsymbol{\alpha})_{\text{rev}}$ is not involved in the last two equations; nevertheless, it should be indicated on the free-body diagram.

SAMPLE PROBLEM 16.9

A sphere of radius r and weight W is released with no initial velocity on the incline and rolls without slipping. Determine (a) the minimum value of the coefficient of friction compatible with the rolling motion, (b) the velocity of the center G of the sphere after the sphere has rolled 10 ft, (c) the velocity of G if the sphere were to move 10 ft down a frictionless 30° incline.

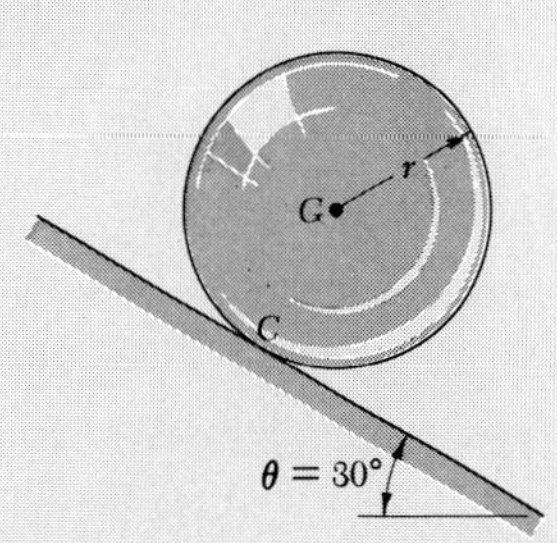

a. **Minimum μ for Rolling Motion.** A free-body diagram of the sphere is drawn showing all external forces, the inertia vector $(m\bar{\mathbf{a}})_{\text{rev}}$, and the inertia couple $(\bar{I}\alpha)_{\text{rev}}$. Since the sphere rolls without sliding, we have $\bar{a} = r\alpha$.

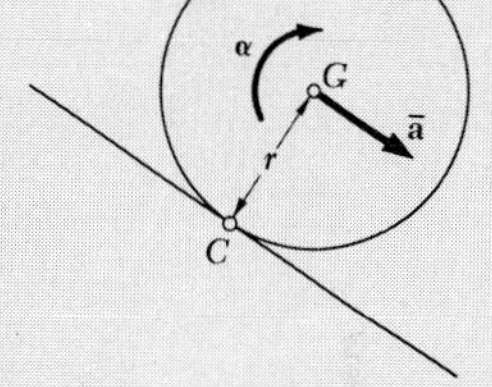

Dynamic Equilibrium

$$+\circlearrowleft \Sigma M_C = 0: \qquad (m\bar{a})r + \bar{I}\alpha - (W \sin\theta)r = 0$$
$$(mr\alpha)r + \bar{I}\alpha - (W\sin\theta)r = 0$$

Noting that $m = W/g$ and $\bar{I} = \frac{2}{5}mr^2$, we write

$$\left(\frac{W}{g}r\alpha\right)r + \frac{2}{5}\frac{W}{g}r^2\alpha - (W\sin\theta)r = 0 \qquad \alpha = +\frac{5g\sin\theta}{7r}$$

$$\bar{a} = r\alpha = \frac{5g\sin\theta}{7} = \frac{5g\sin 30^\circ}{7} = +11.50 \text{ ft/sec}^2$$

$$+\searrow \Sigma F_x = 0: \qquad W\sin\theta - m\bar{a} - F = 0$$

$$W\sin\theta - \frac{W}{g}\frac{5g\sin\theta}{7} - F = 0$$

$$F = +\tfrac{2}{7}W\sin\theta = \tfrac{2}{7}W\sin 30^\circ \qquad \mathbf{F} = 0.143\,W \measuredangle 30^\circ$$

$$+\nearrow \Sigma F_y = 0: \qquad N - W\cos\theta = 0$$

$$N = W\cos\theta = 0.866W \qquad \mathbf{N} = 0.866W \measuredangle 60^\circ$$

$$\mu_{\min} = \frac{F}{N} = \frac{0.143\,W}{0.866\,W} \qquad \mu_{\min} = 0.165 \blacktriangleleft$$

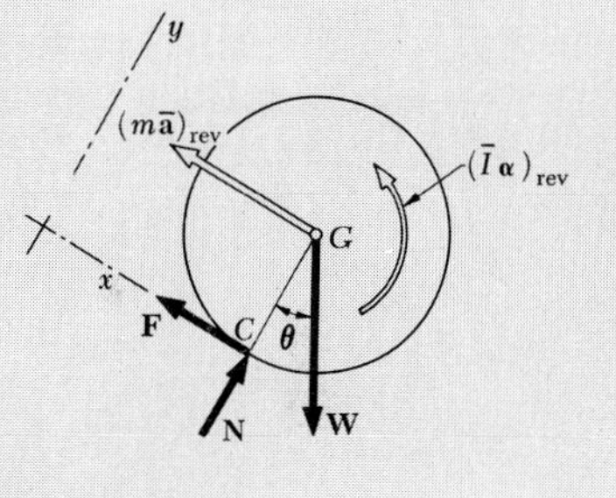

b. **Velocity of Rolling Sphere.** We have uniformly accelerated motion,

$$\bar{v}_0 = 0 \qquad \bar{a} = 11.50 \text{ ft/sec}^2 \qquad \bar{s} = 10 \text{ ft} \qquad \bar{s}_0 = 0$$
$$\bar{v}^2 = \bar{v}_0^2 + 2\bar{a}(\bar{s} - \bar{s}_0) \qquad \bar{v}^2 = 0 + (2)(11.50)(10)$$
$$\bar{v} = 15.17 \text{ ft/sec} \qquad \bar{\mathbf{v}} = 15.17 \text{ ft/sec} \measuredangle 30^\circ \blacktriangleleft$$

c. **Velocity of Sliding Sphere.** Assuming now no friction, we have $F = 0$ and obtain

$$+\circlearrowleft \Sigma M_G = 0: \qquad \bar{I}\alpha = 0 \qquad \alpha = 0$$
$$+\searrow \Sigma F_x = 0: \qquad W\sin 30^\circ - m\bar{a} = 0 \qquad 0.50W - \frac{W}{g}\bar{a} = 0$$
$$\bar{a} = 16.1 \text{ ft/sec}^2 \qquad \bar{\mathbf{a}} = 16.1 \text{ ft/sec}^2 \measuredangle 30^\circ$$

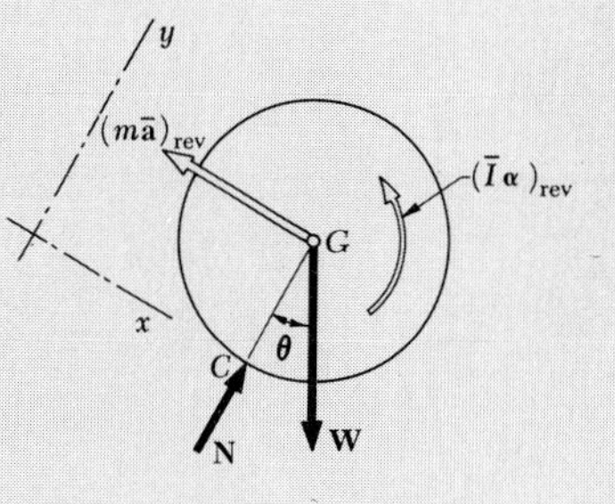

Substituting $\bar{a} = 16.1 \text{ ft/sec}^2$ into the equations for uniformly accelerated motion, we obtain

$$\bar{v}^2 = \bar{v}_0^2 + 2\bar{a}(\bar{s} - \bar{s}_0) \qquad \bar{v}^2 = 0 + (2)(16.1)(10)$$
$$\bar{v} = 17.95 \text{ ft/sec} \qquad \bar{\mathbf{v}} = 17.95 \text{ ft/sec} \measuredangle 30^\circ \blacktriangleleft$$

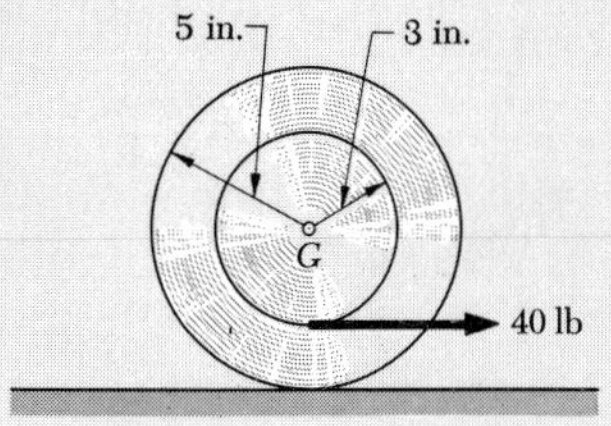

SAMPLE PROBLEM 16.10

A cord is wrapped around the inner drum of a wheel and pulled horizontally with a force of 40 lb. The wheel weighs 100 lb and has a radius of gyration of 3.5 in. Knowing that $\mu_s = 0.20$ and $\mu_k = 0.15$, determine the acceleration of G and the angular acceleration of the wheel.

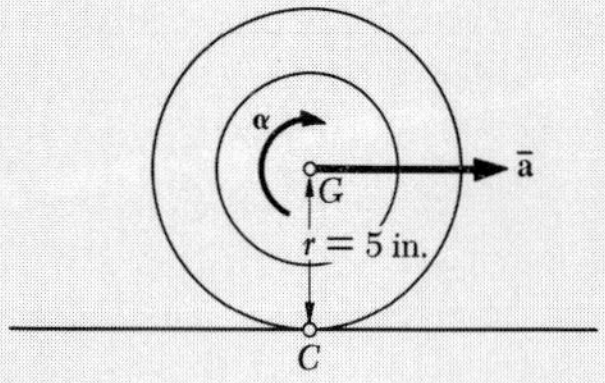

a. **Assume Rolling without Sliding.** In this case, we have

$$\bar{a} = r\alpha = \tfrac{5}{12}\alpha$$

By comparing the friction force obtained with the maximum friction force, we shall determine whether this assumption is justified. The mass and moment of inertia of the wheel are

$$m = \frac{100}{32.2} = 3.11 \text{ lb-sec}^2/\text{ft}$$

$$\bar{I} = m\bar{k}^2 = \frac{100}{32.2}\left(\frac{3.5}{12}\right)^2 = 0.264 \text{ lb-ft-sec}^2$$

Dynamic Equilibrium

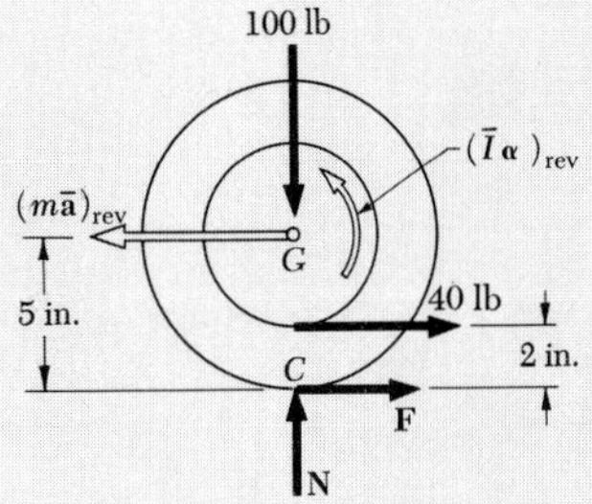

$$+\circlearrowright \Sigma M_C = 0: \quad \bar{I}\alpha + m\bar{a}(\tfrac{5}{12}) - (40)(\tfrac{2}{12}) = 0$$

$$0.264\alpha + (3.11)(\tfrac{5}{12}\alpha)(\tfrac{5}{12}) - 6.67 = 0$$

$$\alpha = +8.30 \text{ radians/sec}^2 \qquad \bar{a} = r\alpha = (\tfrac{5}{12})(8.30) = 3.46 \text{ ft/sec}^2$$

$$\overset{+}{\rightarrow} \Sigma F_x = 0: \quad F + 40 - m\bar{a} = 0$$

$$F + 40 - (3.11)(3.46) = 0$$

$$F = -29.3 \text{ lb} \qquad \mathbf{F} = 29.3 \text{ lb} \leftarrow$$

$$+\uparrow \Sigma F_y = 0: \quad N - 100 = 0 \qquad \mathbf{N} = 100 \text{ lb} \uparrow$$

Maximum Available Friction Force

$$F_{max} = \mu_s N = (0.20)(100) = 20 \text{ lb}$$

Since $F > F_{max}$, the assumed motion is impossible.

b. **Rolling and Sliding.** Since the wheel must roll and slide at the same time, we draw a new free-body diagram, where $\bar{a}$ and α are independent and where

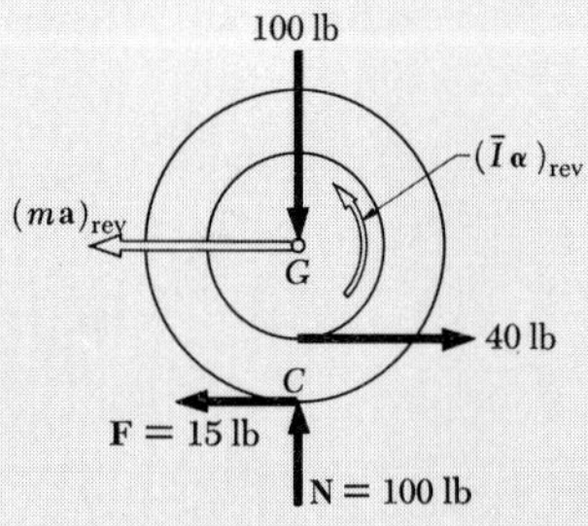

$$F = F_k = \mu_k N = (0.15)(100) = 15 \text{ lb}$$

From the computation of part *a*, it appears that **F** should be directed to the left.

$$\overset{+}{\rightarrow} \Sigma F_x = 0: \quad 40 - 15 - 3.11\bar{a} = 0$$

$$\bar{a} = +8.04 \text{ ft/sec}^2 \qquad \bar{\mathbf{a}} = 8.04 \text{ ft/sec}^2 \rightarrow ◀$$

$$+\circlearrowright \Sigma M_G = 0: \quad -(15)(\tfrac{5}{12}) + (40)(\tfrac{3}{12}) + 0.264\alpha = 0$$

$$\alpha = -14.2 \text{ radians/sec}^2 \qquad \alpha = 14.2 \text{ radians/sec}^2 \circlearrowleft ◀$$

SAMPLE PROBLEM 16.11

The extremities of a 4-ft rod, weighing 50 lb, may move freely and with no friction along two straight tracks as shown. If the rod is released with no velocity from the position shown, determine (*a*) the angular acceleration of the rod, (*b*) the reactions at *A* and *B*.

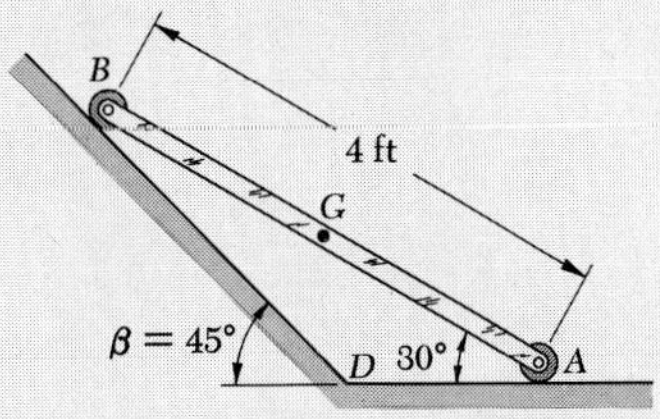

Kinematics of Motion. Since the motion is constrained, the acceleration of *G* must be related to the angular acceleration $\boldsymbol{\alpha}$. To obtain this relation, we shall first determine the magnitude of the acceleration $\mathbf{a}_A$ of point *A* in terms of α; assuming $\boldsymbol{\alpha}$ directed counterclockwise and noting that $a_{B/A} = 4\alpha$, we write

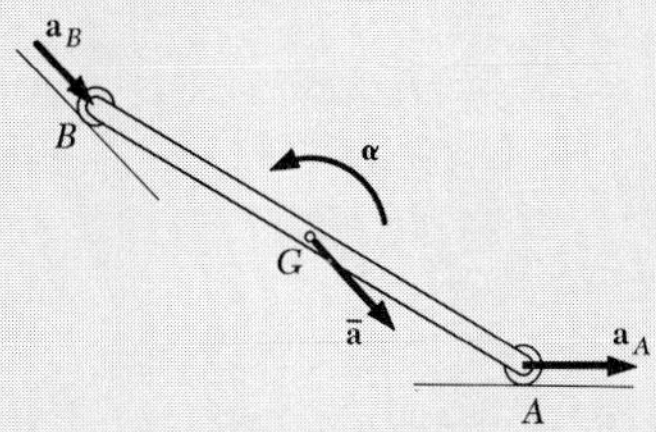

$$\mathbf{a}_B = \mathbf{a}_A + \mathbf{a}_{B/A}$$
$$[a_B \searrow 45°] = [a_A \rightarrow] + [4\alpha \swarrow 60°]$$

Noting that $\phi = 75°$ and using the law of sines, we obtain

$$a_A = 5.46\alpha \qquad a_B = 4.90\alpha$$

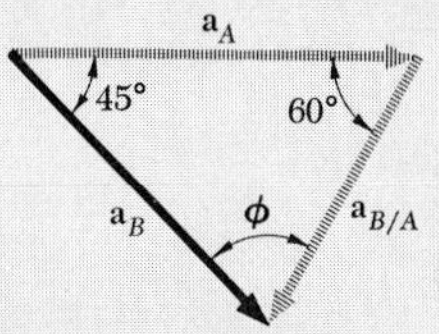

The acceleration of *G* is now obtained by writing

$$\bar{\mathbf{a}} = \mathbf{a}_G = \mathbf{a}_A + \mathbf{a}_{G/A}$$
$$\bar{\mathbf{a}} = [5.46\alpha \rightarrow] + [2\alpha \swarrow 60°]$$

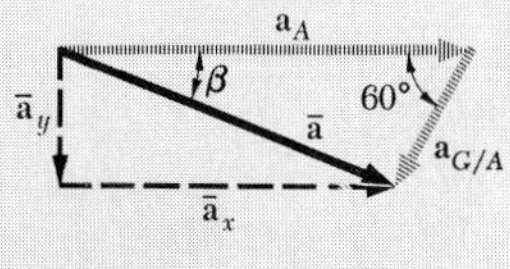

Resolving $\bar{\mathbf{a}}$ into *x* and *y* components, we obtain

$$\bar{a}_x = 5.46\alpha - 2\alpha\cos 60° = 4.46\alpha \qquad \bar{\mathbf{a}}_x = 4.46\alpha \rightarrow$$
$$\bar{a}_y = -2\alpha\sin 60° = -1.732\alpha \qquad \bar{\mathbf{a}}_y = 1.732\alpha \downarrow$$

Kinetics of Motion. We draw the free-body diagram of the rod, showing its weight, the reactions at *A* and *B*, the components of the inertia vector $(m\bar{\mathbf{a}}_x)_{\text{rev}}$ and $(m\bar{\mathbf{a}}_y)_{\text{rev}}$, and the inertia couple $(\bar{I}\boldsymbol{\alpha})_{\text{rev}}$.

$$\bar{I} = \frac{1}{12}ml^2 = \frac{1}{12}\frac{50}{32.2}(4)^2 = 2.07 \text{ lb-ft-sec}^2$$

$$\bar{I}\alpha = 2.07\alpha \qquad (\bar{I}\boldsymbol{\alpha})_{\text{rev}} = 2.07\alpha \curvearrowright$$

$$m\bar{a}_x = \frac{50}{32.2}(4.46\alpha) = 6.93\alpha \qquad (m\mathbf{a}_x)_{\text{rev}} = 6.93\alpha \leftarrow$$

$$m\bar{a}_y = \frac{50}{32.2}(1.732\alpha) = 2.69\alpha \qquad (m\mathbf{a}_y)_{\text{rev}} = 2.69\alpha \uparrow$$

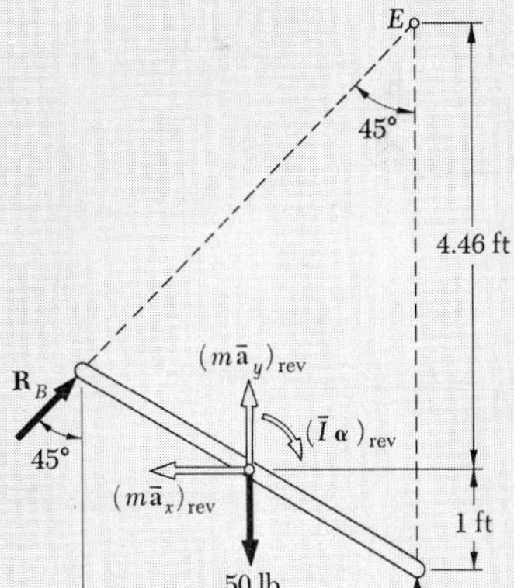

$+\circlearrowleft \Sigma M_E = 0$:
$$(50)(1.732) - (6.93\alpha)(4.46) - (2.69\alpha)(1.732) - 2.07\alpha = 0$$
$$\alpha = +2.30 \text{ radians/sec}^2 \qquad \alpha = 2.30 \text{ radians/sec}^2 \circlearrowleft \blacktriangleleft$$

Using the computed value of α and writing $\Sigma F_x = 0$ and $\Sigma F_y = 0$, we obtain

$$\mathbf{R}_A = 27.9 \text{ lb} \uparrow \qquad \mathbf{R}_B = 22.5 \text{ lb} \measuredangle 45° \blacktriangleleft$$

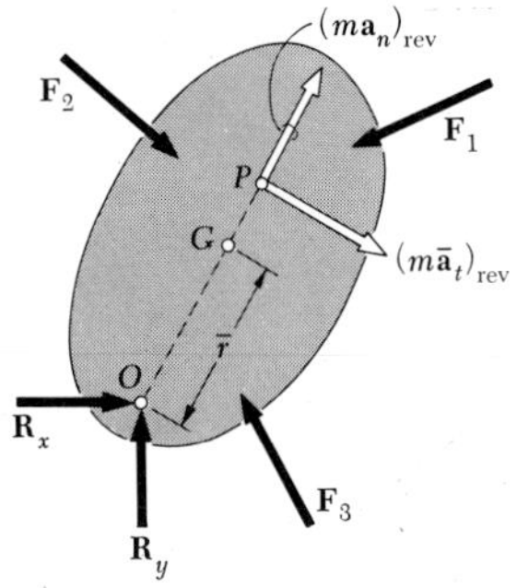

FIG. P 16.63

PROBLEMS

16.63. Show that the inertia couple $(\bar{I}\alpha)_{rev}$ of Fig. 16.21 may be eliminated by attaching the inertia vectors at a point P called the *center of percussion*, located on line OG at a distance $GP = \bar{k}^2/\bar{r}$ from the mass center of the body.

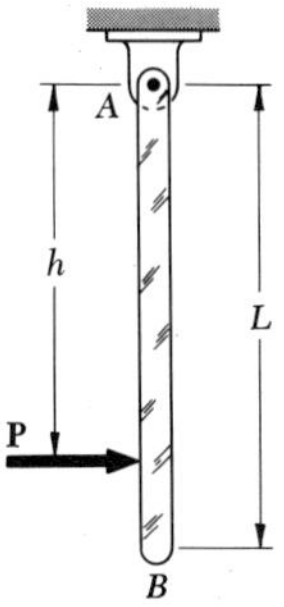

FIG. P 16.64

16.64. A uniform slender rod, of length $L = 48$ in. and weight $W = 16$ lb, hangs freely from a hinge at A. A horizontal force $\mathbf{P}$ of magnitude 30 lb is applied as shown. For $h = 48$ in., determine (a) the angular acceleration of the rod, (b) the components of the reaction at A.

16.65. In Prob. 16.64, determine (a) the distance h for which the horizontal component of the reaction at A is zero, (b) the corresponding angular acceleration of the rod.

16.66. In Prob. 16.64, determine the range of values of h for which the magnitude of the *total* reaction at A does not exceed 20 lb.

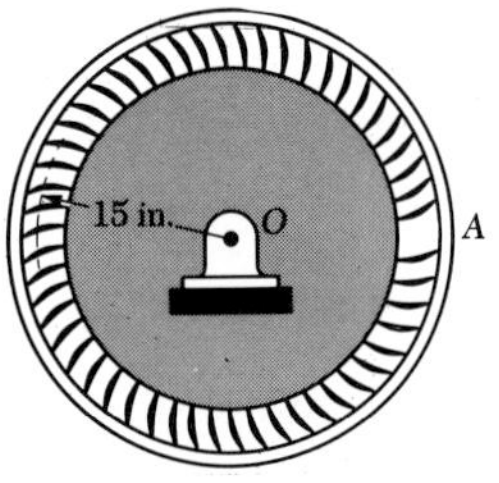

FIG. P 16.67

16.67. A turbine disk weighing 155 lb rotates at a constant speed of 9,600 rpm; the mass center of the disk coincides with the center of rotation O. Determine the reaction at O after a single vane at A, weighing 1.50 oz, becomes loose and is thrown off.

16.68. A 3,220-lb flywheel, of 4-ft diameter, is mounted on a fixed horizontal shaft. When the wheel rotates at a constant speed of 1,200 rpm, it exerts on the shaft a force varying from 12,580 lb upward to 19,020 lb downward. Determine the distance from the center of the shaft to the mass center of the flywheel.

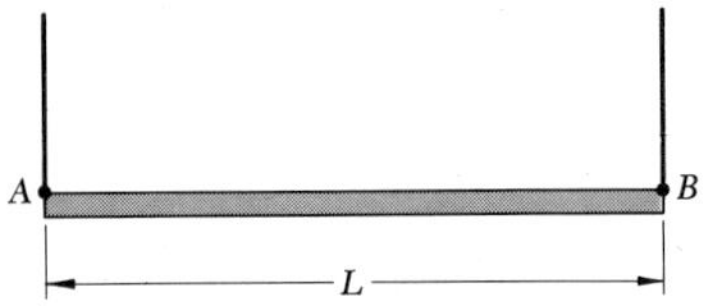

FIG. P 16.69

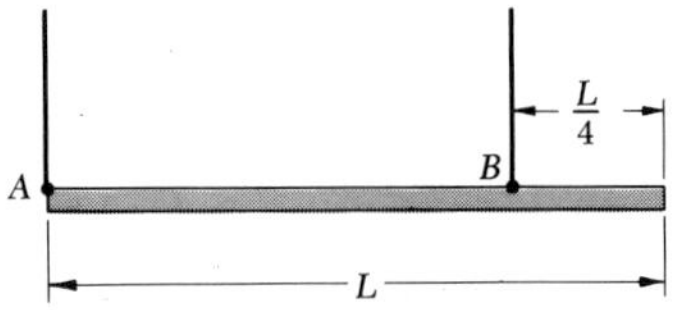

FIG. P 16.70

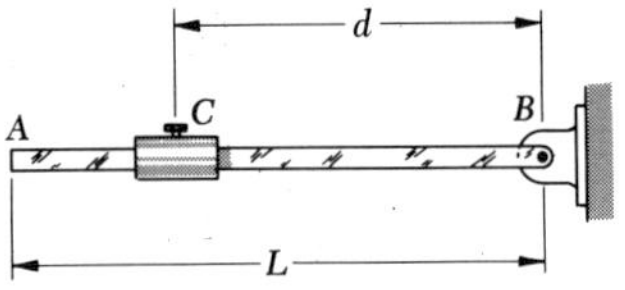

FIG. P 16.71 AND P 16.72

16.69 and 16.70. A uniform slender beam of length L, weighing w lb/ft, is suspended from two cables as shown. If the cable at A suddenly breaks, determine (a) the tension in the cable at B, (b) the acceleration of end A.

16.71. A collar C of weight W_C is rigidly attached to a uniform slender rod AB of length L and weight W. If the rod is released from rest in the position shown, determine the ratio d/L for which the reaction at B is independent of W_C.

***16.72.** A collar C of weight 2 lb is rigidly attached to a uniform slender rod AB of weight 12 lb and length $L = 20$ in. If the rod is released from rest in the position shown, determine the distance d for which the angular acceleration of the rod is maximum.

16.73. After being released, the plate of Sample Prob. 16.8 is allowed to swing through 90°. Knowing that at that instant the angular velocity of the plate is 4.82 radians/sec, determine (a) the angular acceleration of the plate, (b) the components of the reaction at A.

16.74. Two rods, each of weight 4 lb/ft, are welded together and rotate about A. In the position shown, the angular velocity of the rods is 5 radians/sec clockwise. Determine (*a*) the angular acceleration of the rods, (*b*) the components of the reaction at A.

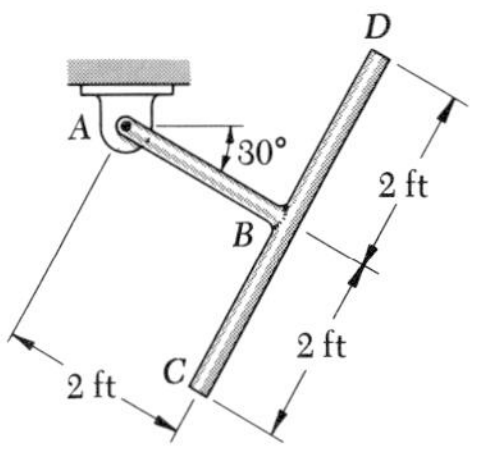

FIG. P 16.74

***16.75.** A uniform slender rod AB, of length $L = 4$ ft and weight 10 lb, is held in the position shown by three wires. If $\theta = 60°$, determine the tension in wires AC and BC immediately after wire AD has been cut.

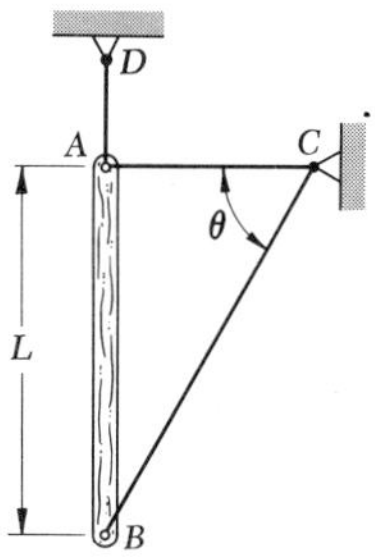

FIG. P 16.75

16.76. One end of a homogeneous rod of weight W rests on a rough horizontal surface. The rod is maintained at an angle $\beta = 60°$ by means of a string attached to its other end. The string is suddenly cut. Assuming that the friction between end A and the surface is large enough to prevent sliding, determine (*a*) the angular acceleration of the rod just after the string is cut, (*b*) the normal reaction and the friction force at A, (*c*) the minimum value of μ compatible with the described motion.

***16.77.** Knowing that the coefficient of friction between the rod and the floor is 0.30, determine the range of values of β for which the rod *will* slip immediately after the string at B is cut.

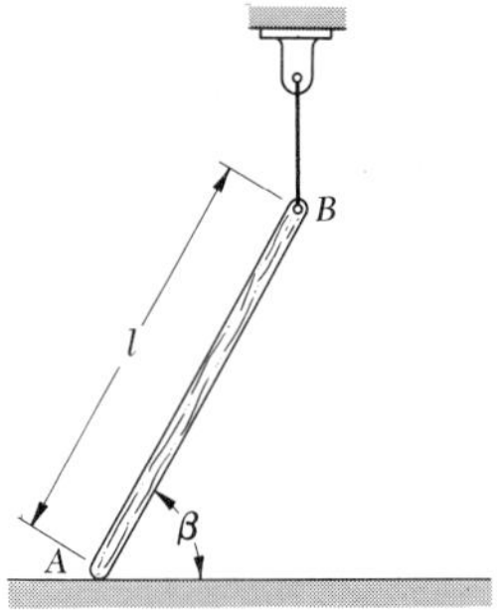

FIG. P 16.76 AND P 16.77

16.78. Derive the equation $\Sigma M_C = I_C\alpha$ for the rolling disk of Fig. 16.22, where ΣM_C represents the sum of the moments of the external forces about the instantaneous center C and I_C the moment of inertia of the disk about C.

16.79. Show that, in the case of an unbalanced disk, the equation derived in Prob. 16.78 is valid only when the mass center G, the geometric center O, and the instantaneous center C happen to lie in a straight line.

16.80. A cylinder of weight W and radius r rolls down an incline. Denoting by μ the coefficient of friction between the cylinder and the incline, determine the largest angle of inclination β for which no slipping will occur.

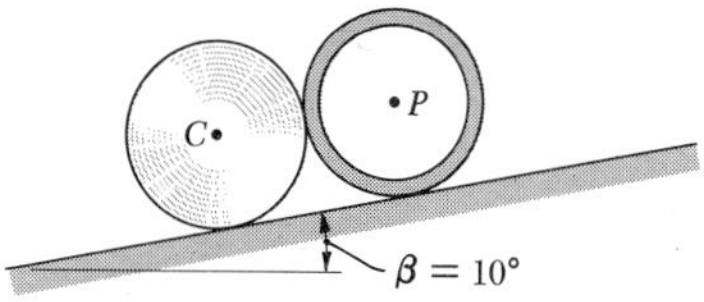

FIG. P 16.81

16.81. A cylinder C and a section of pipe P are in contact when they are released from rest. Knowing that both the cylinder and the pipe roll without slipping, determine the clear distance between them after 3 sec.

16.82. A flywheel is rigidly attached to a shaft of $1\frac{1}{2}$-in. radius which may roll along parallel rails as shown. When released from rest, the system rolls 16 ft in 40 sec. Determine the centroidal radius of gyration of the system.

16.83. A flywheel of centroidal radius of gyration $\bar{k}$ is rigidly attached to a shaft of radius r which may roll along parallel rails. Denoting by μ the coefficient of friction between the shaft and the rails, derive an expression for the largest angle of inclination β for which no slipping will occur.

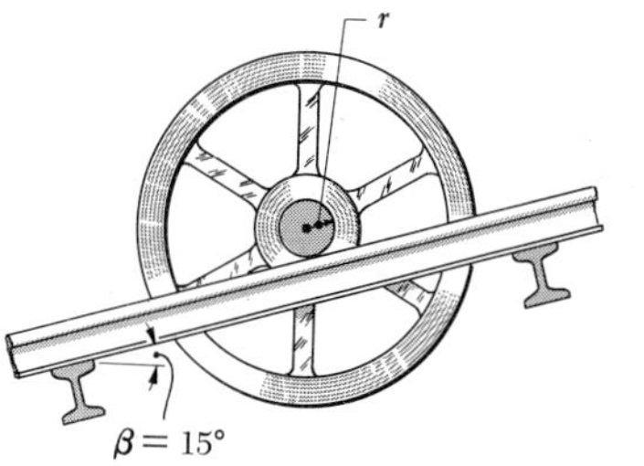

FIG. P 16.82 AND P 16.83

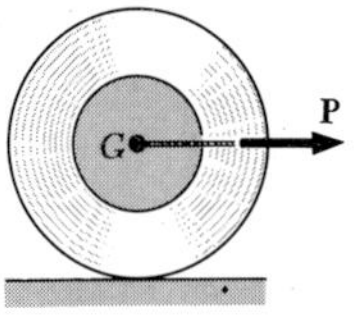

FIG. P 16.84 AND P 16.88

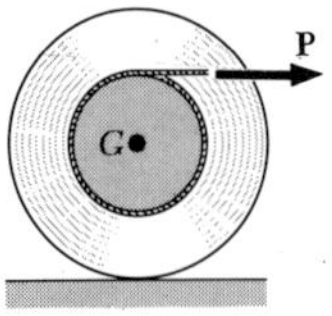

FIG. P 16.85 AND P 16.89

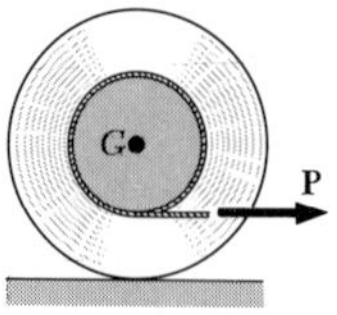

FIG. P 16.86 AND P 16.90

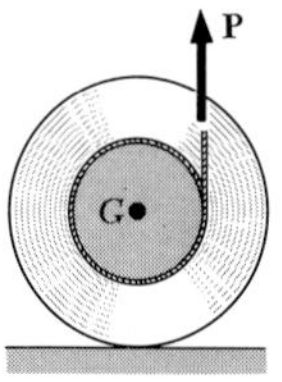

FIG. P 16.87 AND P 16.91

16.84 through 16.87. A drum of 6-in. radius is attached to a disk of 12-in. radius. The disk and drum have a total weight of 8 lb and a radius of gyration of 9 in. A cord is attached as shown and pulled with a force **P** of magnitude 4 lb. Knowing that the disk rolls without sliding, determine (*a*) the angular acceleration of the disk and the acceleration of *G*, (*b*) the minimum value of the coefficient of friction compatible with this motion.

16.88 through 16.91. A drum of 6-in. radius is attached to a disk of 12-in. radius. The disk and drum have a total weight of 8 lb and a radius of gyration of 9 in. A cord is attached as shown and pulled with a force **P** of magnitude 4 lb. Knowing that $\mu = 0.20$, determine (*a*) whether or not the disk slides, (*b*) the angular acceleration of the disk and the acceleration of *G*.

16.92. Find the magnitude of the maximum force **P** which may be applied to the disk of Prob. 16.91 if the disk is to roll without sliding.

16.93. The cord attached to the drum of Prob. 16.87 is pulled to the right in a direction forming an angle β with the horizontal and with a force **P** of magnitude 4 lb. Determine the range of values of β for which the disk (*a*) rolls to the right, (*b*) rolls to the left. Assume that μ is large enough to prevent sliding.

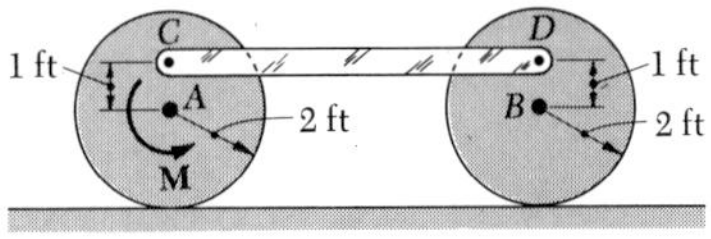

FIG. P 16.94

16.94. Two disks *A* and *B*, weighing 20 lb each, are connected by a rod *CD* of negligible weight. A couple **M** of moment 15 lb-ft is applied to disk *A*. Knowing that the disks roll without sliding, determine (*a*) the acceleration of the center of each disk, (*b*) the minimum value of μ for each disk compatible with the motion described.

16.95. Solve Prob. 16.94 assuming that the disks have rotated through 180° so that points *C* and *D* are directly below points *A* and *B* respectively.

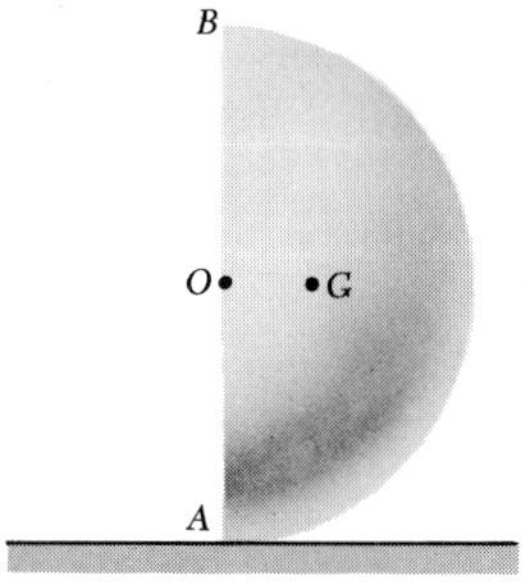

FIG. P 16.96

16.96. A hemisphere of weight *W* and radius *r* is released from rest in the position shown. Determine (*a*) the minimum value of μ for which the hemisphere starts to roll without sliding, (*b*) the corresponding acceleration of point *B*. (*Hint.* Note that $OG = \frac{3}{8}r$ and that, by the parallel-axis theorem, $\bar{I} = \frac{2}{5}mr^2 - m(OG)^2$.)

16.97. Solve Prob. 16.96, considering a half cylinder instead of a hemisphere. (*Hint.* Note that $OG = 4r/3\pi$ and that $\bar{I} = \frac{1}{2}mr^2 - m(OG)^2$.)

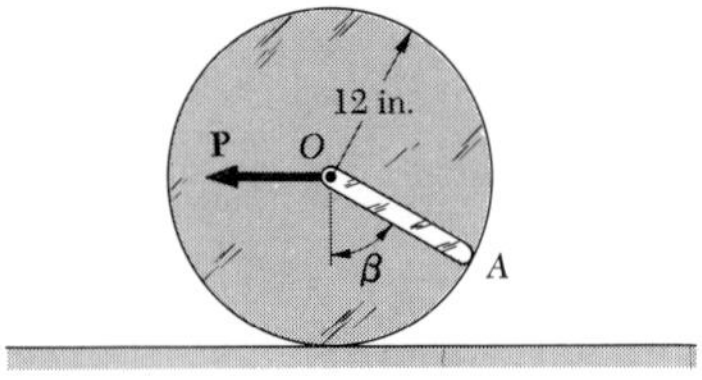

FIG. P 16.98

16.98. A slender rod *OA* of weight 10 lb is rigidly attached to a 10-lb disk as shown. At the instant when $\beta = 90°$, the center *O* of the disk has a velocity of 3 ft/sec and an acceleration of 4 ft/sec² both directed to the left. Knowing that the disk rolls without sliding, determine the magnitude of the force **P** applied to the disk.

16.99. Solve Prob. 16.98 assuming $\beta = 270°$.

16.100. Ends A and B of a 10-lb slender rod are attached to collars which slide without friction along the rods shown. A horizontal force **P** is applied to collar A, causing the rod to start from rest with a clockwise angular acceleration of 3 radians/sec^2. Neglecting the weight of the collars, determine (*a*) the required magnitude of **P**, (*b*) the reactions at A and B.

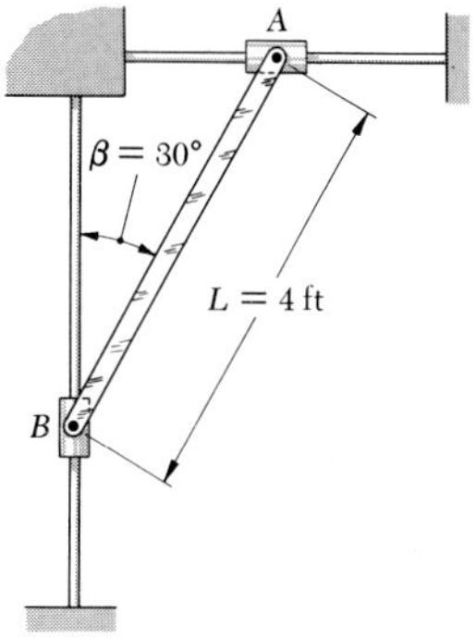

FIG. P 16.100

16.101. Solve Prob. 16.100 assuming that at the instant considered the angular velocity of the rod is 2 radians/sec counterclockwise.

16.102. The motion of the rod of Sample Prob. 16.11 is to be controlled by a horizontal force **P** applied at A. If at the instant shown the angular velocity of the rod is 3 radians/sec clockwise and the angular acceleration of the rod is 2 radians/sec^2 counterclockwise, determine the required magnitude and sense of the force **P**.

16.103. Two uniform rods AB and BC, each of length $L = 2$ ft, are welded together at B to form a rigid body of total weight 12 lb. A horizontal force **P** is applied at C, causing point C to start from rest with an acceleration of 10 ft/sec^2 to the left. Neglecting the effect of friction at A and at C, determine (*a*) the required magnitude of **P**, (*b*) the reactions at A and at C.

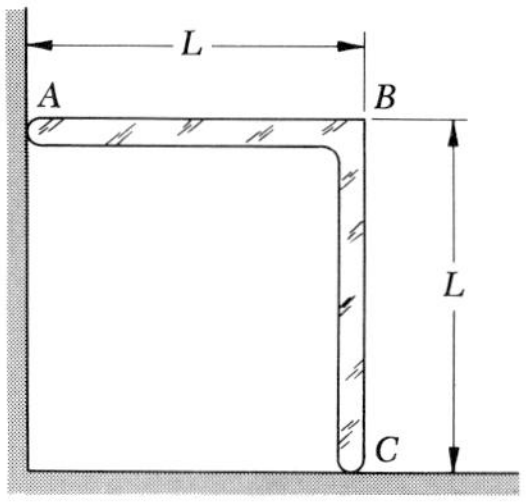

FIG. P 16.103 AND P 16.104

16.104. Two rods AB and BC, each of weight W and length L, are welded together at B and released from rest in the position shown. Neglecting the effect of friction at A and C, determine (*a*) the angular acceleration of the system, (*b*) the reactions at A and at C.

16.105. The rod of Prob. 16.100 is released from rest in the position shown. Determine (*a*) the angular acceleration of the rod, (*b*) the reactions at A and B.

16.106. A 50-lb sign is held in place by the three cables shown. Determine the tension in cables BD and CE immediately after the cable AD has been cut.

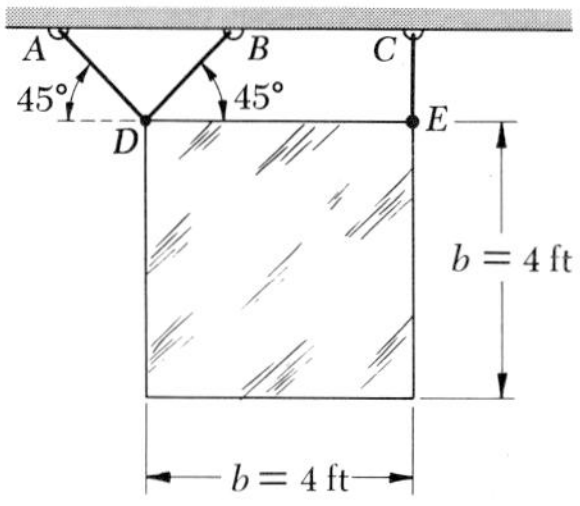

FIG. P 16.106 AND P 16.107

16.107. A 50-lb sign is held in place by the three cables shown. Determine the tension in cables AD and CE immediately after cable BD has been cut.

16.108. An 8-ft steel beam weighing 200 lb is being temporarily held in the position shown when the cable attached at B breaks. Determine the reaction at A immediately after the cable breaks, assuming that μ is zero at A.

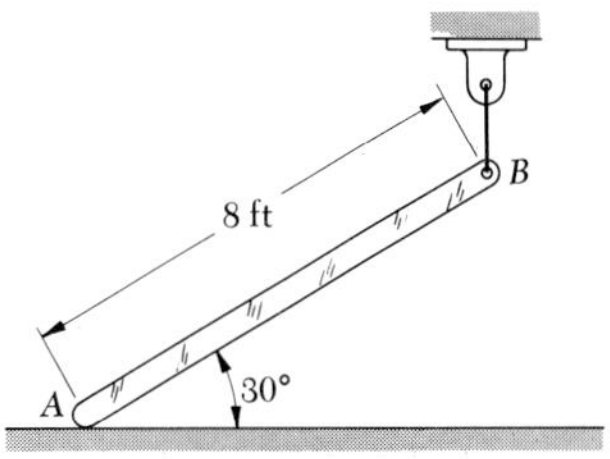

FIG. P 16.108

***16.109.** Solve Prob. 16.108 assuming that $\mu = 0.30$ between end A and the horizontal surface.

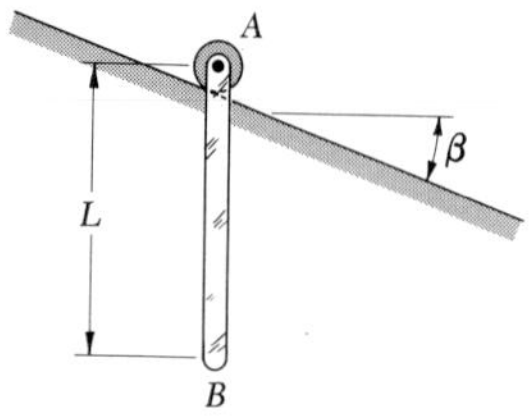

FIG. P 16.110 AND P 16.111

*16.110. A uniform rod *AB*, of weight $W = 5$ lb and length $L = 4$ ft, is released from rest in the position shown. Knowing that $\beta = 30°$, determine the values immediately after release of (*a*) the angular acceleration of the rod, (*b*) the acceleration of end *A*, (*c*) the reaction at *A*. Neglect the weight and friction of the roller at *A*.

*16.111. A uniform slender rod of length *L* is released from rest in the position shown. Derive an expression for (*a*) the angular acceleration of the rod, (*b*) the acceleration of end *A*, (*c*) the reaction at *A*, immediately after release. Neglect the weight and friction of the roller at *A*.

16.112. Show that, for a rigid body in plane motion, the equation $\Sigma M_A = I_A\alpha$, where ΣM_A represents the sum of the moments of the external forces about point *A* and I_A the moment of inertia of the body about the same point *A*, is verified *if and only if* one of the following conditions is satisfied: (*a*) *A* is the mass center of the body, (*b*) *A* has zero acceleration, (*c*) the acceleration of *A* is directed along a line joining point *A* and the mass center *G*.

16.113. A 6-lb rod *AB* is attached to the disk shown which rotates about *O* with a constant clockwise angular velocity of 10 radians/sec. Determine the forces exerted on the rod at *A* and *B* when (*a*) $\beta = 0$, (*b*) $\beta = 180°$.

16.114. Solve Prob. 16.113 when $\beta = 90°$.

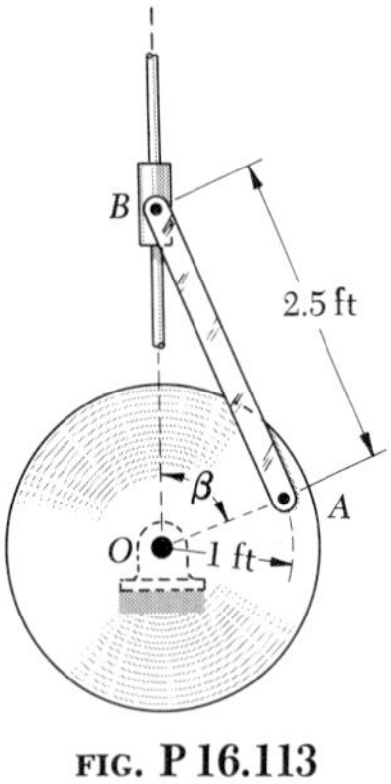

FIG. P 16.113

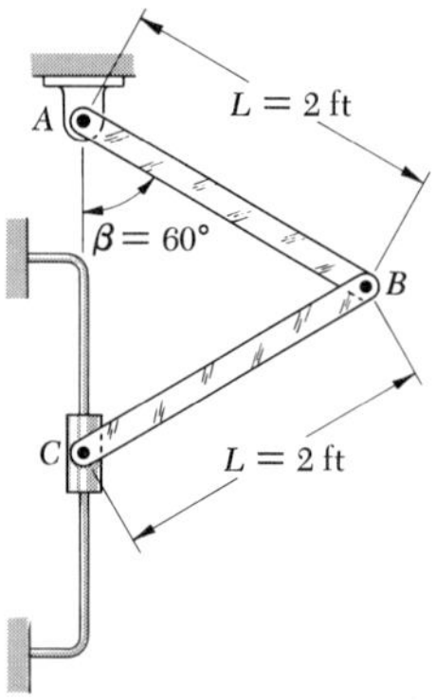

FIG. P 16.115 AND P 16.116

16.115. Each of the two bars shown is 2 ft long and weighs 10 lb. A vertical and variable force **P** is applied at *C*, causing point *C* to move up at a constant speed of 30 ft/sec. Determine the magnitude of **P** for the position shown.

16.116. The two bars *AB* and *BC* are released from rest in the position shown. Each bar is 2 ft long and weighs 10 lb. Determine the angular acceleration of each bar and the reactions at *A* and *C* immediately after release.

16.117. Two rods *AB* and *BC*, each of weight *W* and length $2r$, are connected as shown to a disk which is made to rotate in a vertical plane at a constant angular velocity ω_0. For the position shown, determine (*a*) the components of the forces exerted at *A* and *B* on rod *AB*, (*b*) the reaction at *C*.

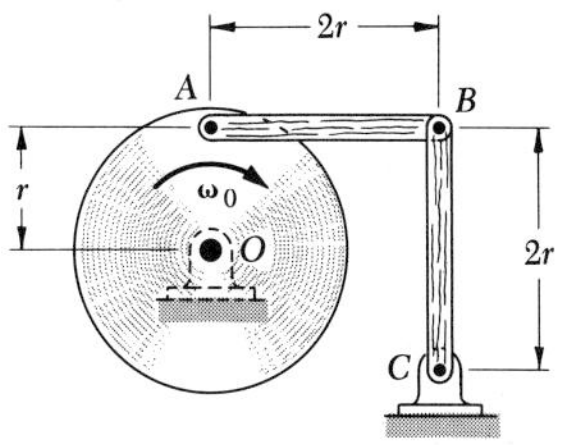

FIG. P 16.117

16.118. A 2-ft rod *AB* of weight 10 lb is attached to a 1-ft-radius disk of weight 10 lb as shown. When the system is at rest, a 20-lb force is applied at *B*. Knowing that the disk rolls without sliding, determine (*a*) the angular accelerations of the disk and of the rod, (*b*) the force exerted on the disk at *A*.

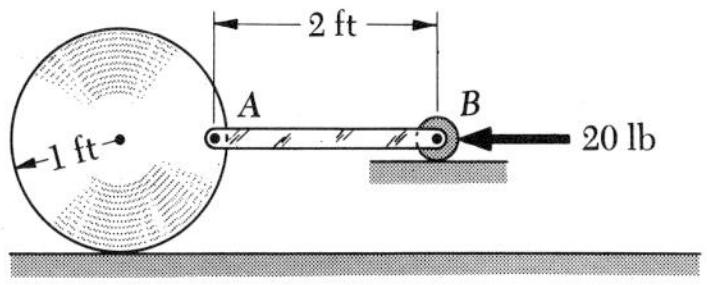

FIG. P 16.118

***16.119.** A section of pipe rests on a plate. The plate is then given a constant acceleration **a** directed to the right. Assuming that the pipe rolls on the plate, determine (*a*) the acceleration of the pipe, (*b*) the distance through which the plate will move before the pipe reaches end *A*.

***16.120.** Solve Prob. 16.119 assuming that the pipe is replaced (*a*) by a solid cylinder, (*b*) by a sphere.

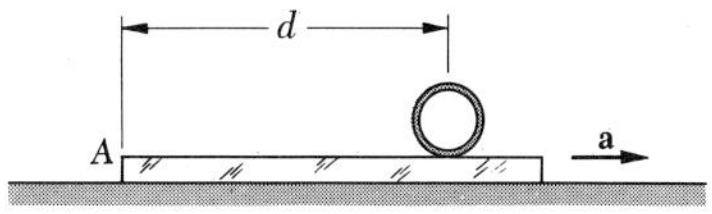

FIG. P 16.119

***16.121.** Identical cylinders of weight *W* and radius *r* are pushed by a series of moving arms. The coefficient of friction between all surfaces is μ. Denoting by *a* the magnitude of the acceleration of the arms, derive an expression for (*a*) the maximum allowable value of *a* if each cylinder is to roll without sliding, (*b*) the minimum allowable value of *a* if each cylinder is to move to the right without rotating.

***16.122.** Identical cylinders of weight 5 lb and radius 2 in. are pushed by a series of arms as shown. The coefficient of friction between all surfaces is 0.20. Determine the horizontal component of the force exerted on each cylinder when the acceleration of the cylinders is (*a*) 5 ft/sec^2 to the right, (*b*) 10 ft/sec^2 to the right.

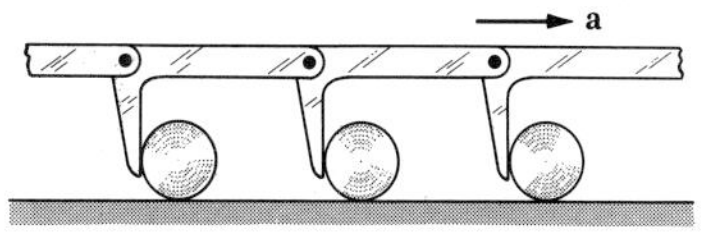

FIG. P 16.121 AND P 16.122

***16.123.** Two slender uniform bars *AB* and *BC* hang freely as shown. Each bar is of length $L = 2$ ft and weighs 5 lb. A horizontal force **P** of magnitude 3 lb is applied at *C*. Determine the angular acceleration of each bar.

***16.124.** Solve Prob. 16.123 assuming that the 3-lb force is applied at point *B*.

***16.125.** Two identical uniform bars *AB* and *BC* hang freely as shown. A horizontal force **P** is applied at a distance *h* below *A*. Determine the distance *h* for which the two bars start to move as if they formed a single rigid body. (*Hint.* The angular accelerations of the bars must be equal.)

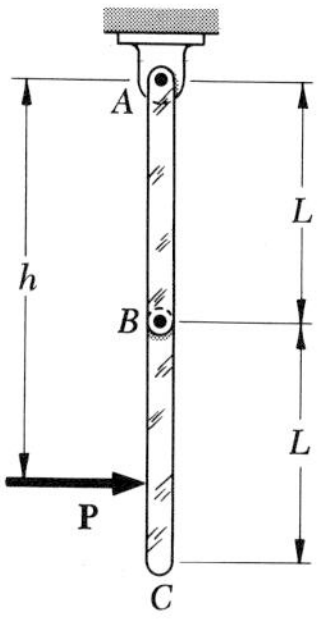

FIG. P 16.123 AND P 16.125

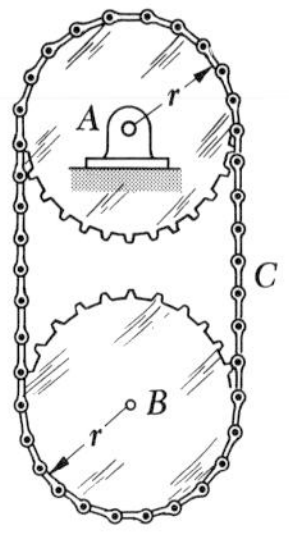

FIG. P 16.126

*16.126. Two disks of weight W and radius r are connected by a continuous chain belt as shown. The pin C is suddenly removed. Determine the value, immediately after the removal of C, (*a*) of the angular acceleration of each disk, (*b*) of the tension in the left-hand portion of the belt, (*c*) of the acceleration of point B.

*16.127. Two uniform bars AB and BC are connected by a pin at B and are held in a horizontal position by three wires as shown. Each bar is of length $L = 2$ ft and weighs 5 lb. The wires attached at D and B are cut simultaneously; determine at that instant (*a*) the angular acceleration of each bar, (*b*) the accelerations of points A and B, (*c*) the tension in the remaining wire attached at C.

*16.128. Two identical uniform bars AB and BC are held in a horizontal position by three wires as shown. The wires attached at B and C are cut simultaneously; determine the distance d for which the two bars start to move as if they formed a single rigid body. (*Hint.* The angular accelerations of the bars must be equal.)

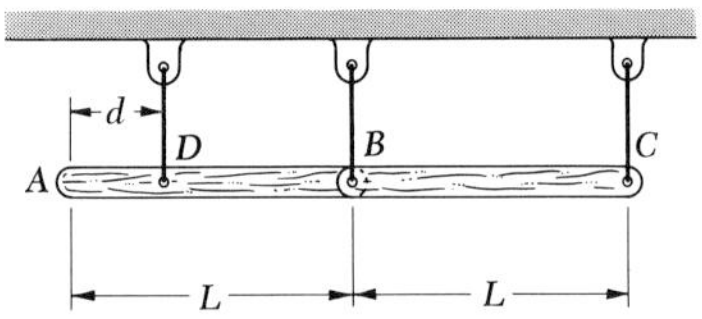

FIG. P 16.127 AND P 16.128

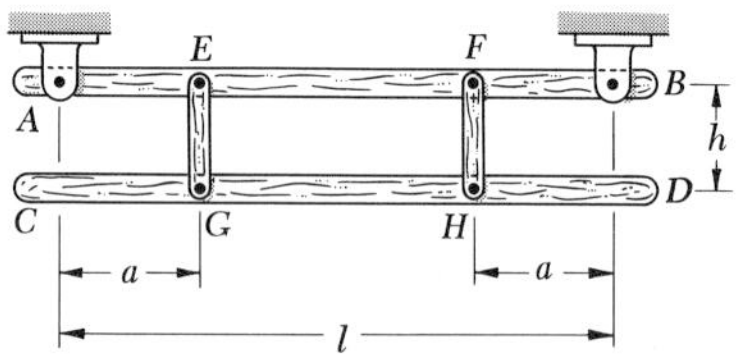

FIG. P 16.129

*16.129. Two uniform slender rods AB and CD, each of weight W and length l, are connected by two weightless links EG and FH. If the pin support at B is suddenly removed, determine (*a*) the angular acceleration of each rod, (*b*) the accelerations of points B and D.

*16.130. Solve Prob. 16.129 assuming that the connections at E, F, G, and H are welded so that no relative rotation can occur between the rods and the links.

*16.131. Solve Prob. 16.129 assuming that the two vertical links are replaced by a single vertical link connecting the centers of rods AB and CD.

*16.132. Draw the shear and bending-moment diagrams for the beam of Prob. 16.69 immediately after cable A breaks.

*16.133. (*a*) Determine the magnitude and the location of the maximum bending moment in the rod of Prob. 16.64. (*b*) Show that the answer to part *a* is independent of the weight W of the rod.

***16.134.** In Prob. 16.104, draw the shear and bending-moment diagrams for rod *AB* immediately after the rods have been released.

***16.135.** In Prob. 16.104, draw the shear and bending-moment diagrams for rod *BC* immediately after the rods have been released.

16.9. Rotation of a Three-dimensional Body about a Fixed Axis. The rigid bodies considered in the preceding sections were assumed to be symmetrical with respect to the reference plane used to describe their motion. While such an assumption considerably simplifies the derivations involved, it also limits the range of application of the results obtained. One of the most important types of motion which *cannot* be analyzed directly by the methods considered so far is the rotation about a fixed axis of an unsymmetrical three-dimensional body.

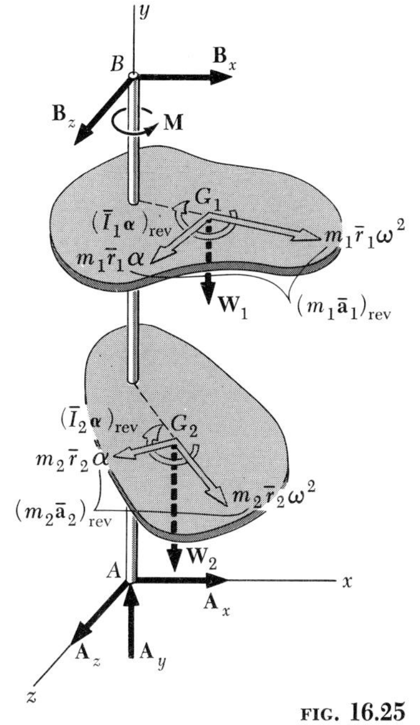

FIG. 16.25

We may, however, examine the particular case when the rotating body consists of several parallel slabs rigidly connected to a perpendicular shaft which is supported in bearings at *A* and *B* (Fig. 16.25). Using the method of dynamic equilibrium to analyze this problem, we note that, since each slab rotates in its own plane, we may apply to each slab the inertia vectors and inertia couple associated with the noncentroidal rotation of a slab (Sec. 16.8). Having thus reduced the problem to a problem of statics, we may use the methods of Chap. 4, Statics of Rigid Bodies in Three Dimensions, to obtain the necessary equilibrium equations. Summing components along and moments about each of the three coordinate axes, we write

$$\Sigma F_x = 0 \qquad \Sigma F_y = 0 \qquad \Sigma F_z = 0$$
$$\Sigma M_x = 0 \qquad \Sigma M_y = 0 \qquad \Sigma M_z = 0 \qquad (16.19)$$
(including inertia vectors and inertia couples)

It should be noted that this method may also be used when the bodies attached to the shaft are three-dimensional, *as long as each body is symmetrical with respect to a plane perpendicular to the shaft.*

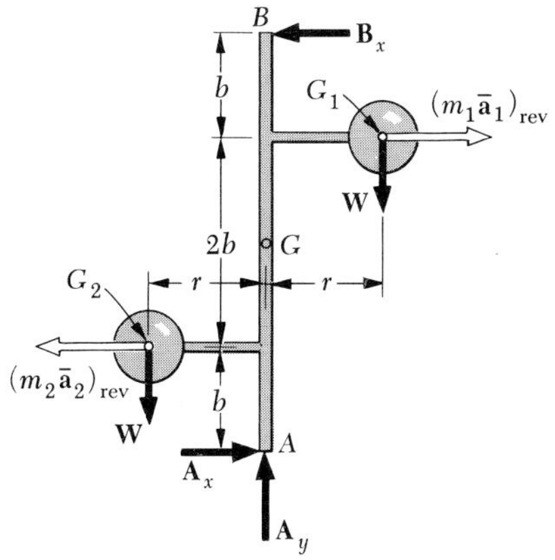

FIG. 16.26

As an example, we shall consider a shaft held in bearings at *A* and *B* and supporting two equal spheres of weight *W* (Fig. 16.26). We first observe that, when the system is at rest, the shaft exerts no lateral thrust on its supports since the center of gravity *G* of the system is located directly above *A*. We have $A_x = B_x = 0$ and $A_y = 2W$, and the system is said to be *statically balanced.* Assuming now that the shaft rotates at a constant angular velocity ω, we attach to each sphere an inertia vector of magnitude $(W/g)r\omega^2$, also called a centrifugal force. The two centrifugal forces form a couple of moment $2b(W/g)r\omega^2$; summing moments about A and B, we find that the horizontal components of the bearing reactions are $A_x = B_x = \frac{1}{2}(W/g)r\omega^2$. Although the system is statically balanced, it is clearly *not dynamically balanced.* A system which is not dynamically balanced will have a tendency to tear away from its bearings when rotating at high speed, as indicated by the values obtained for the bearing reactions. Moreover, since the bearing reactions are contained in the plane defined by the shaft and the centers of the spheres, they rotate with the shaft and cause the system to vibrate. *Rotating systems should therefore be dynamically as well as statically balanced.* This may be done by rearranging the distribution of mass around the shaft, or by adding corrective masses, until the system of the centrifugal forces becomes equivalent to zero (see Sample Prob. 16.12).

In the general case of the rotation about a fixed axis of an unsymmetrical three-dimensional body, a typical element of mass should be isolated and the appropriate inertia vector should be attached to the element. The resultant of the elementary inertia vectors may then be obtained by integration. While this approach is successfully used in Sample Prob. 16.13, it will lead, in general, to fairly involved computations. Other methods, beyond the scope of this chapter, may then be preferred. The approach indicated here shows clearly, however, that when a rigid body does not possess a plane of symmetry perpendicular to the axis of rotation, the resultant of the inertia vectors *should not be expected to pass through the mass center of the body.*

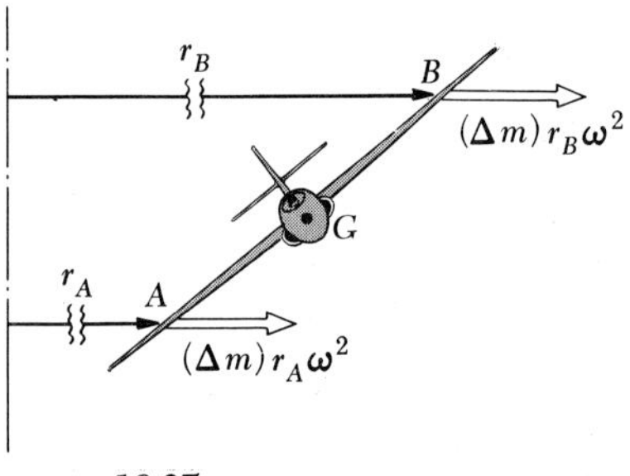

FIG. 16.27

Consider, for example, an airplane making a turn of radius $\bar{r}$ in the banked position shown in Fig. 16.27. Since two symmetrical wing elements A and B are not at the same distance from the axis of rotation, the centrifugal forces associated with A and B are not equal. The resultant of the centrifugal forces corresponding to the various elements of the airplane, therefore, will not pass through the mass center G of the airplane (Fig. 16.28). However, since the difference between the magnitudes of the centrifugal forces corresponding to A and B is relatively small, the distance from G to the resultant centrifugal force is also relatively small. It is therefore customary in such problems, and in problems dealing with the motion of cars along banked highway curves, to neglect the effect of the nonsymmetry of the three-dimensional body on the position of the resultant centrifugal force.

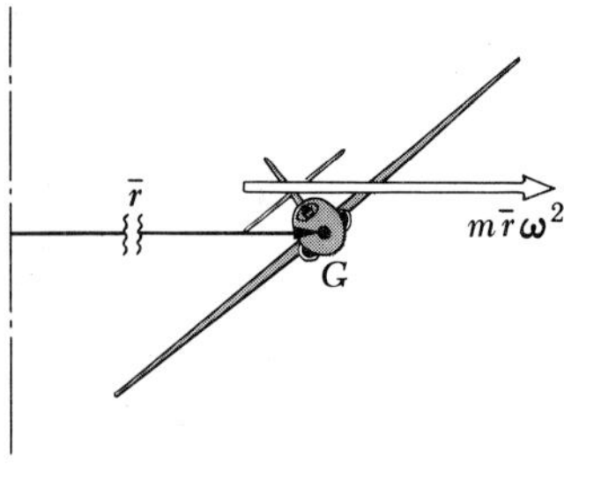

FIG. 16.28

SAMPLE PROBLEM 16.12

Two 4-in. rods A and B, each weighing 3 lb, are attached to a shaft which rotates at a constant speed of 1,200 rpm. Disks C and D are attached to the same shaft at the bearings. (*a*) Determine the dynamic reactions at the bearings. (*b*) If the system is to be dynamically balanced by attaching corrective weights to disks C and D at points 6 in. from the axis of rotation, determine the required weights and their location on the disks.

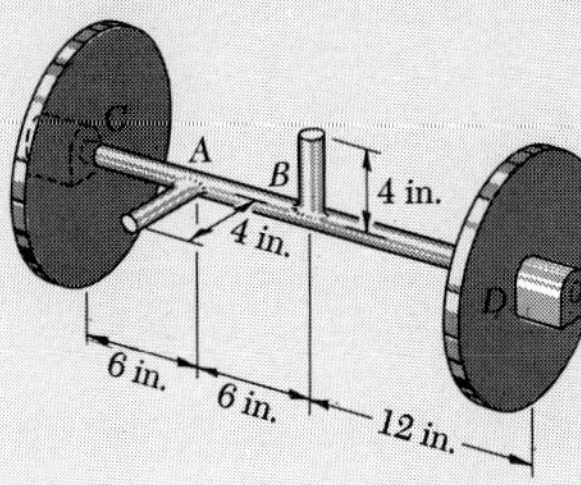

a. **Dynamic Equilibrium.** The system rotates at constant angular velocity $\omega = 1{,}200$ rpm $= 125.6$ radians/sec. Thus $\alpha = 0$, and all accelerations are directed toward the axis of rotation. Since each rod is in plane motion, we attach an inertia vector $(m\bar{\mathbf{a}})_{\text{rev}}$ of magnitude $m\bar{r}\omega^2$ at its mass center,

$$m\bar{r}\omega^2 = \frac{3}{32.2}\,\frac{2}{12}\,(125.6)^2 = 245\text{ lb}$$

Considering only dynamic reactions and inertia vectors, we draw the free-body diagram for the shaft. The equations of dynamic equilibrium are

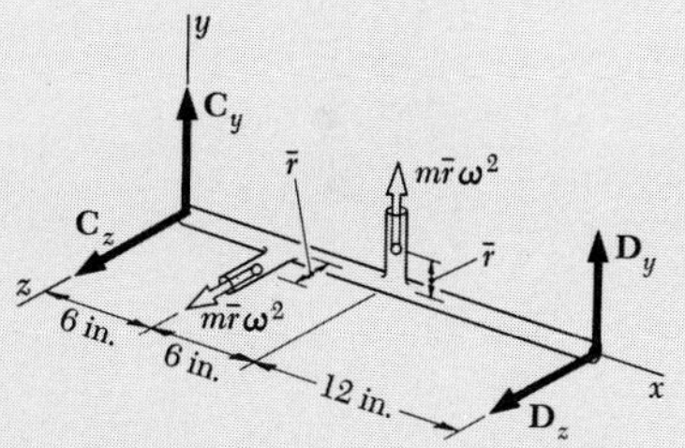

$$\begin{aligned}
+\circlearrowleft \Sigma M_y = 0: &\quad -(245\text{ lb})(6\text{ in.}) - D_z(24\text{ in.}) = 0\\
&\quad D_z = -61.3\text{ lb}\\
+\circlearrowleft \Sigma M_z = 0: &\quad (245\text{ lb})(12\text{ in.}) + D_y(24\text{ in.}) = 0\\
&\quad D_y = -122.5\text{ lb}\\
\Sigma F_y = 0: &\quad C_y + D_y + 245\text{ lb} = 0\\
&\quad C_y = -122.5\text{ lb}\\
\Sigma F_z = 0: &\quad C_z + D_z + 245\text{ lb} = 0\\
&\quad C_z = -183.7\text{ lb}
\end{aligned}$$

The dynamic reactions at the bearings C and D are

$$\mathbf{C} = 221\text{ lb} \measuredangle 33.7^\circ \quad ◄$$
$$\mathbf{D} = 137.0\text{ lb} \measuredangle 63.4^\circ \quad ◄$$

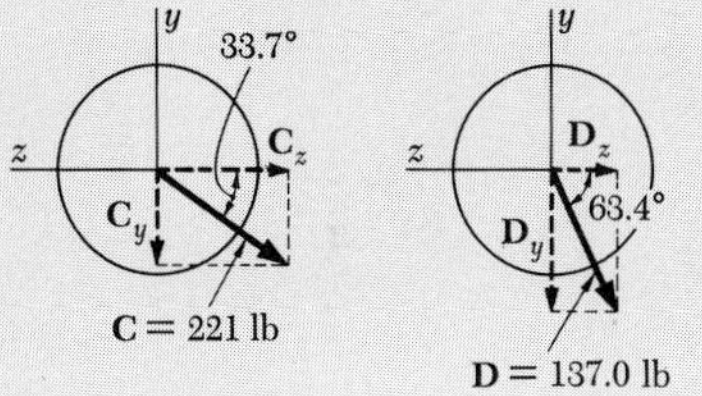

b. **Corrective Weights.** The disks C and D are located at the supports. Thus, the corrective weights should be attached so that the additional centrifugal forces they introduce will *replace* the dynamic reactions determined above.

Disk C. Since $\bar{r} = 6$ in., we write

$$m_C\bar{r}\omega^2 = 221\text{ lb}$$

$$\frac{W_C}{32.2}\,\frac{6}{12}\,(125.6)^2 = 221\text{ lb} \qquad W_C = 0.902\text{ lb} \quad ◄$$

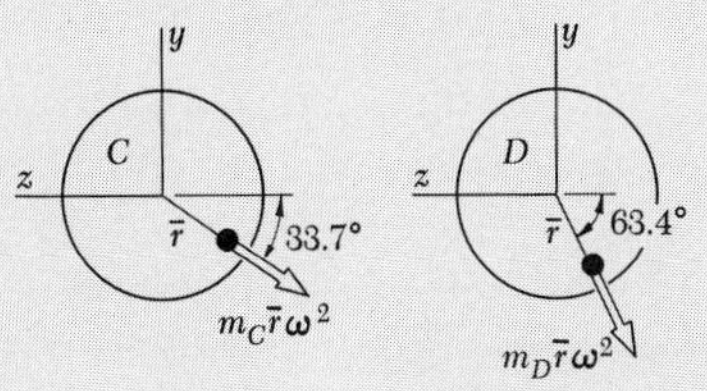

Disk D

$$m_D\bar{r}\omega^2 = 137.0\text{ lb}$$

$$\frac{W_D}{32.2}\,\frac{6}{12}\,(125.6)^2 = 137.0\text{ lb} \qquad W_D = 0.559\text{ lb} \quad ◄$$

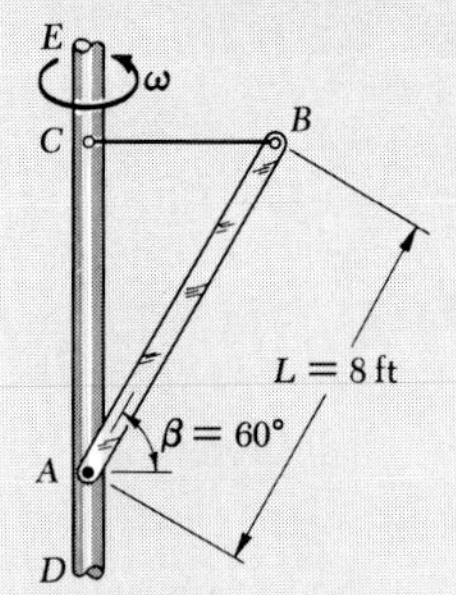

SAMPLE PROBLEM 16.13

A slender rod AB of length $L = 8$ ft and weight $W = 40$ lb is pinned at A to a vertical axle DE which rotates with a constant angular velocity $\omega = 15$ radians/sec. The rod is maintained in position by means of a wire BC attached to the axle and to the end B of the rod. Determine the tension in the wire BC.

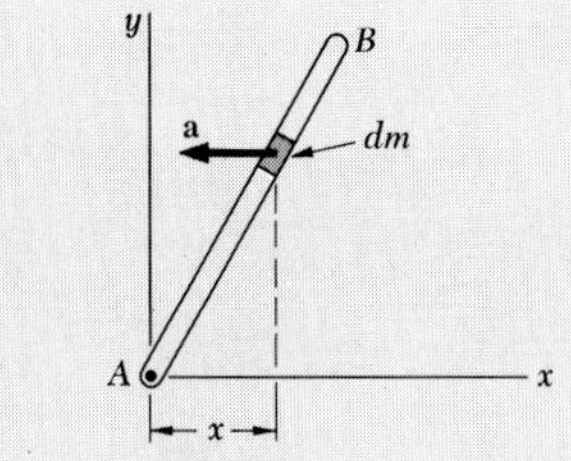

Kinematics of Motion. Choosing a coordinate system with origin at point A, we observe that each element of the rod moves in a horizontal circle of radius x. Each differential element of the rod dm is thus in plane motion and has an acceleration of magnitude $a = x\omega^2$ directed horizontally toward the y axis.

Dynamic Equilibrium. We draw the free-body diagram of the rod AB showing the external forces and elementary inertia vectors $(\mathbf{a}\,dm)_{\text{rev}}$.

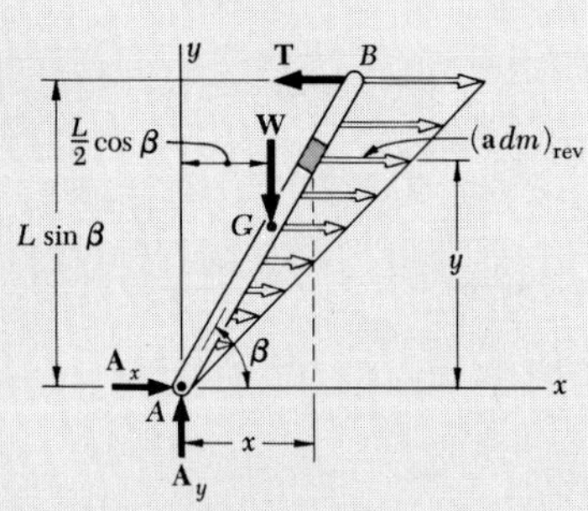

$$+\circlearrowright \Sigma M_A = 0: \qquad T(L \sin \beta) - W(\tfrac{1}{2}L \cos \beta) - \int y(a\,dm) = 0 \qquad (1)$$

We shall now evaluate the integral separately.

$$y = l \sin \beta \qquad a = x\omega^2 = (l \cos \beta)\omega^2 \qquad dm = \frac{m}{L}dl$$

Substituting these expressions into the integral and integrating from $l = 0$ to $l = L$, we obtain

$$\int y(a\,dm) = \int_0^L (l \sin \beta)(l \cos \beta)\omega^2 \left(\frac{m}{L}dl\right)$$

$$= \frac{m\omega^2}{L} \sin \beta \cos \beta \int_0^L l^2 dl = \tfrac{1}{3}mL^2\omega^2 \sin \beta \cos \beta \qquad (2)$$

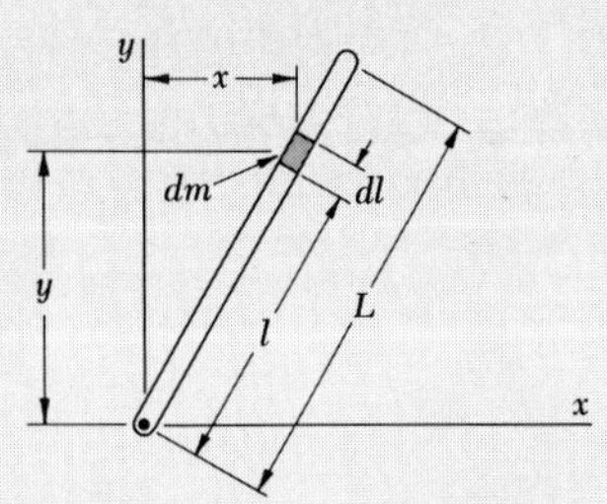

Substituting this expression into (1), we have

$$T(L \sin \beta) - W(\tfrac{1}{2}L \cos \beta) - \tfrac{1}{3}mL^2\omega^2 \sin \beta \cos \beta = 0$$

$$T = \tfrac{1}{2}W \cot \beta + \frac{1}{3}\frac{W}{g}L\omega^2 \cos \beta \quad ◄ \qquad (3)$$

For the rod considered, we have $W = 40$ lb, $L = 8$ ft, $\beta = 60°$, and $\omega = 15$ radians/sec. Substituting these values into (3), we obtain

$$T = 384 \text{ lb} \quad ◄$$

Note. The resultant of the elementary inertia vectors $(\mathbf{a}\,dm)_{\text{rev}}$ does not pass through the mass center of the rod. To show this, we first determine the magnitude of the resultant.

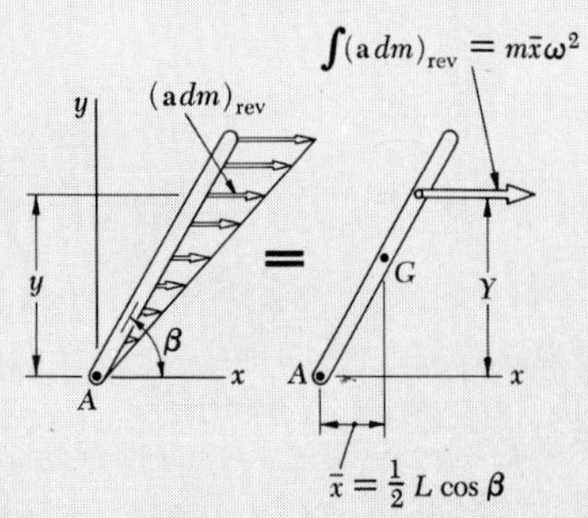

$$\int a\,dm = \int_0^L (l \cos \beta)\omega^2 \left(\frac{m}{L}dl\right) = \tfrac{1}{2}mL\omega^2 \cos \beta = m\bar{x}\omega^2 \qquad (4)$$

But the resultant is equivalent to the elementary inertia vectors:

$$+\circlearrowleft \Sigma M_A = \Sigma M_A: \qquad \int y(a\,dm) = Y \int a\,dm \qquad (5)$$

Substituting into (5) the expressions found in (2) and (4), we obtain

$$\tfrac{1}{3}mL^2\omega^2 \sin \beta \cos \beta = Y(\tfrac{1}{2}mL\omega^2 \cos \beta)$$

$$Y = \tfrac{2}{3}L \sin \beta$$

PROBLEMS

16.136. The mass center of a loaded freight car is located 7 ft above the rails. Knowing that the gage is 4 ft $8\frac{1}{2}$ in. (distance between rails), determine the speed at which the car will overturn while rounding an unbanked curve of 1,500-ft radius.

16.137. Solve Prob. 16.136 assuming that the rails are superelevated so that the outer rail is 3 in. higher than the inner rail.

16.138. The mass center of a 3,000-lb automobile is 2 ft above the ground and the transverse distance between the wheels is 5 ft. The automobile travels around an unbanked highway curve of 250-ft radius at a speed of 45 mph. Determine (*a*) the vertical component of the reaction at each wheel, (*b*) the minimum value of μ between the tires and the pavement if the automobile is not to skid.

16.139. The automobile described in Prob. 16.138 takes a turn of 250-ft radius on a highway banked at 15°. Determine the maximum safe velocity with regard to overturning.

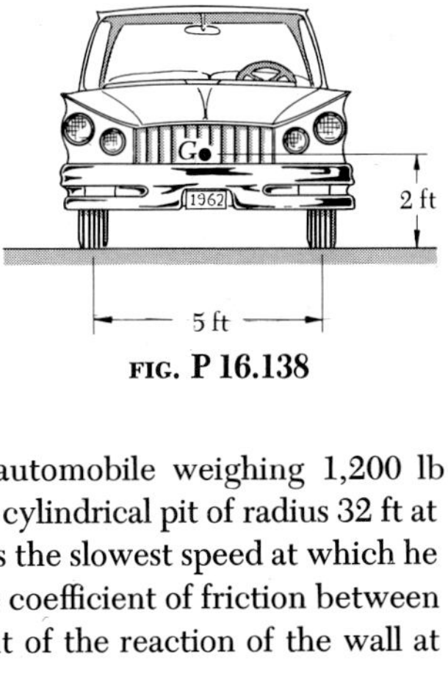

FIG. P 16.138

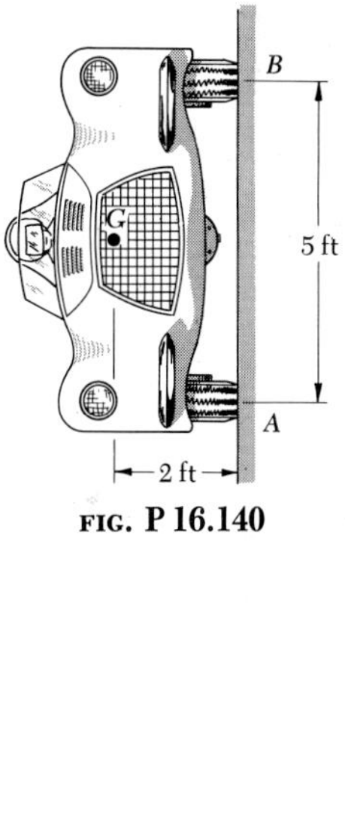

FIG. P 16.140

16.140. A daredevil drives a small automobile weighing 1,200 lb (driver included) on the vertical wall of a cylindrical pit of radius 32 ft at a speed of 30 mph. Knowing that this is the slowest speed at which he can perform this stunt, determine (*a*) the coefficient of friction between tires and wall, (*b*) the normal component of the reaction of the wall at each wheel.

16.141. If the coefficient of friction between the wall and the tires of the automobile of Prob. 16.140 is 0.40, determine (*a*) the lowest safe speed at which the stunt can be performed, (*b*) the normal component of the reaction of the wall at each wheel.

16.142. A daredevil rides a motorcycle at 40 mph inside a vertical cylindrical wall. Assuming that the mass center of the driver and motorcycle travel in a circle of radius 30 ft, determine (*a*) the angle β at which the motorcycle is inclined to the horizontal, (*b*) the minimum safe value of μ.

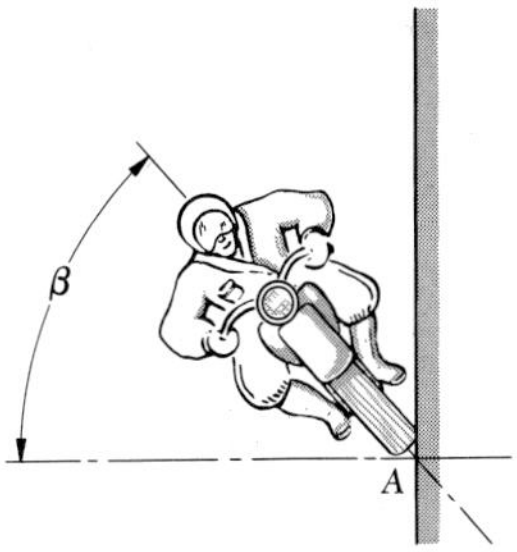

FIG. P 16.142

16.143. A motorcyclist drives around an unbanked curve at a speed of 45 mph. Assuming that the mass center of driver and motorcycle travels in a circle of radius 150 ft, determine (*a*) the angle between the plane of the motorcycle and the vertical, (*b*) the minimum safe value of μ.

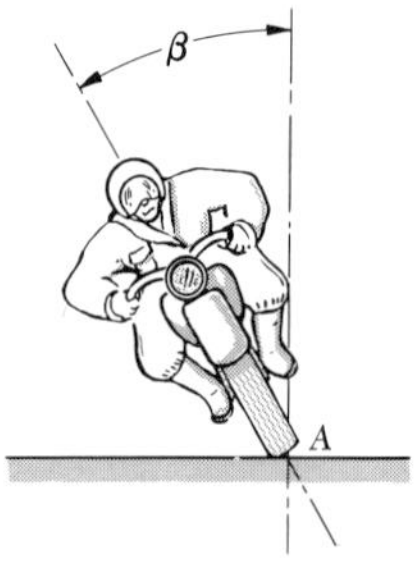

FIG. P 16.143

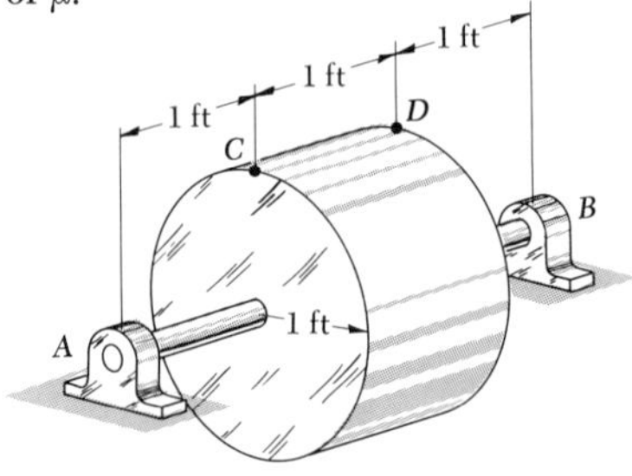

FIG. P 16.144

16.144. It has been found that the rotor shown will be in perfect balance (statically and dynamically) if a 2-oz weight is attached at point *C*. However, the 2-oz weight is mistakenly attached at point *D*. Determine the resulting dynamic bearing reactions at *A* and *B* for a speed of 3,600 rpm.

16.145. In Prob. 16.144, determine the dynamic bearing reactions at *A* and *B* for a speed of 3,600 rpm before the 2-oz weight was attached to the rotor.

16.146. Solve Sample Prob. 16.12 assuming that rod *B* is removed.

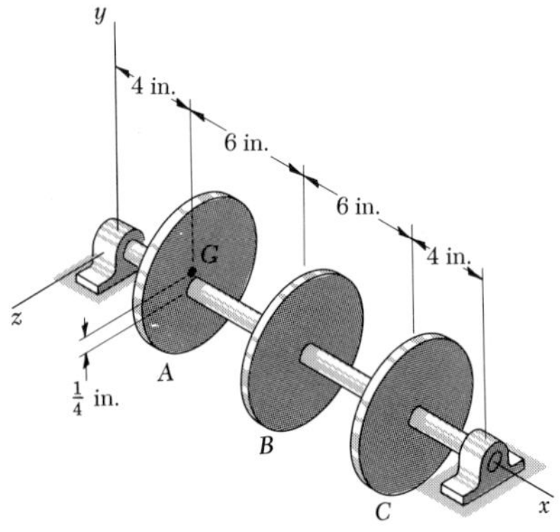

FIG. P 16.148

16.147. The shaft of Sample Prob. 16.12 is to be balanced by drilling holes in disks *C* and *D* rather than by adding weights to the disks. Knowing that each disk is 1 in. thick and is made of steel, determine the point on each disk where a $2\frac{1}{2}$-in.-diameter hole should be drilled to balance the shaft. Specific weight of steel = 490 lb/ft^3.

16.148. Three 25-lb rotor disks are attached to a shaft which rotates at 720 rpm. Disk *A* is attached eccentrically so that its mass center is $\frac{1}{4}$ in. from the axis of rotation, while disks *B* and *C* are attached so that their mass centers coincide with the axis of rotation. Where should 2-lb weights be bolted to disks *B* and *C* to balance the system dynamically?

16.149. The shaft of Prob. 16.148 is to be balanced dynamically by purposely attaching disks *B* and *C* eccentrically to the shaft rather than by adding weights to these disks. Determine the position of the mass centers of disks *B* and *C*.

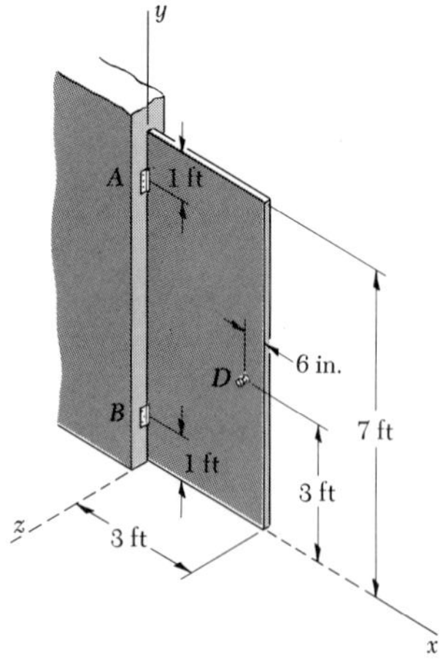

FIG. P 16.150

16.150. A door is made of a solid homogeneous panel 3 by 7 ft, weighing 80 lb. A man pushes on the knob *D* with a 10-lb force directed perpendicularly to the door. Determine (*a*) the angular acceleration of the door, (*b*) the horizontal components of the reactions at the hinges.

16.151. Locate the point on the face of the door of Prob. 16.150 at which a 10-lb force may be applied perpendicularly to the door without affecting the horizontal components of the reactions at the hinges.

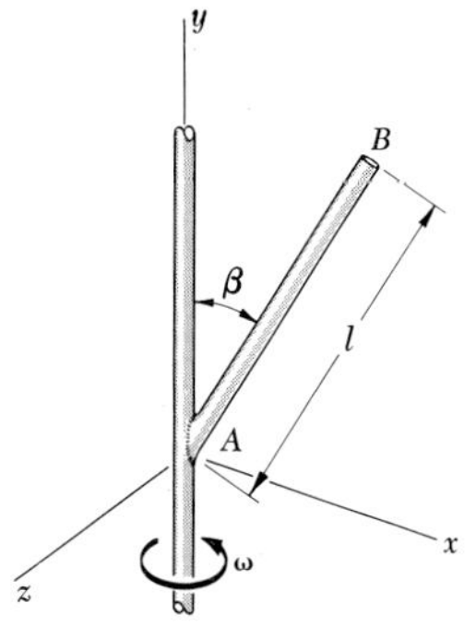

FIG. P 16.152 AND P 16.153

16.152. Rod AB is of length $l = 2$ ft and of weight $W = 10$ lb; it is welded to the vertical shaft, which rotates with a constant velocity of 60 rpm. Determine the moment of the couple exerted by the rod on the shaft if $\beta = 60°$.

16.153. One end of a slender rod of length l and weight W is welded to a vertical rotating shaft. Knowing that the shaft rotates with a constant angular velocity ω, determine the reaction at end A of the rod.

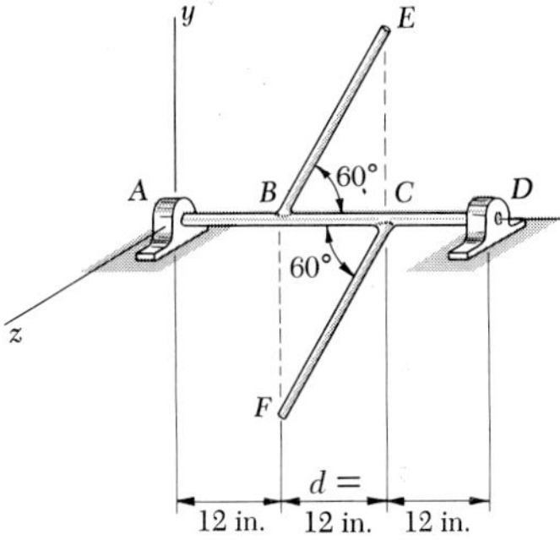

FIG. P 16.156

16.154. For the rod of Prob. 16.152, determine (*a*) the angle β for which the moment of the couple exerted by the rod on the shaft is maximum, (*b*) the corresponding moment of the couple.

16.155. For the rod of Prob. 16.153, derive the relation between β, g, and l which must be satisfied when the moment exerted by the rod on the shaft is maximum.

16.156. Two 24-in. rods BE and CF, each weighing 10 lb, are attached to the shaft AD which rotates at a constant speed of 30 radians/sec. Knowing that the two rods and the shaft lie in the same plane, determine the dynamic reactions at A and D.

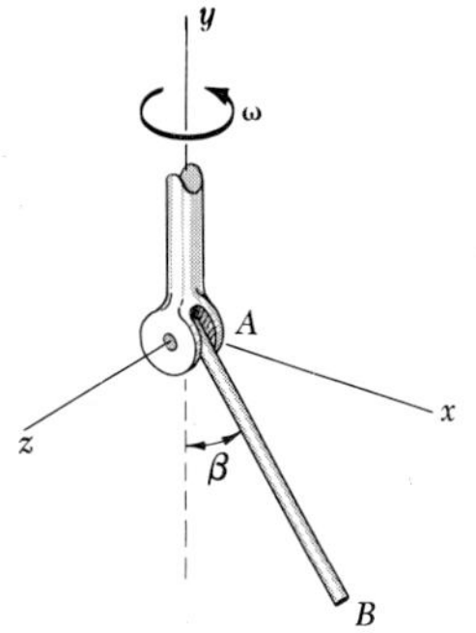

FIG. P 16.158 AND P 16.159

16.157. In Prob. 16.156, determine the distance d between points B and C for which the system is dynamically balanced. (The rods BE and CF are still to be 24 in. long and to form angles of 60° with the shaft AD.)

16.158. A 2-ft uniform rod AB is attached at A to the pin of a clevis which rotates with a constant angular velocity ω. Determine (*a*) the angle β that the rod forms with the vertical when $\omega = 10$ radians/sec, (*b*) the maximum value of ω for which the rod will remain vertical.

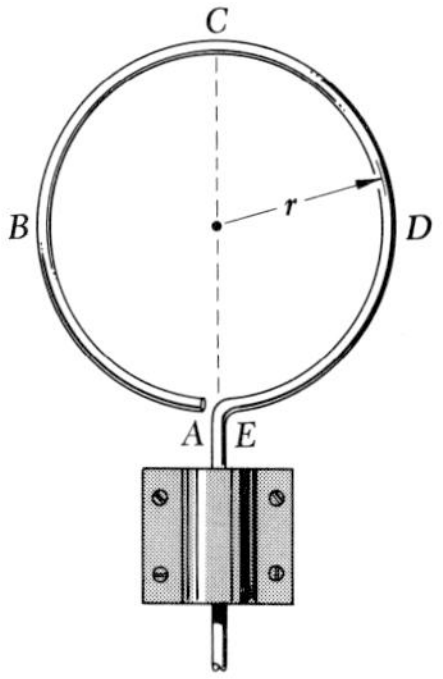

FIG. P 16.160

16.159. A uniform rod AB of length l and weight w lb/ft is attached to the pin of a clevis which rotates with a constant angular velocity ω. Derive an expression (*a*) for the angle β that the rod forms with the vertical, (*b*) for the maximum value of ω for which the rod will remain vertical.

16.160. A thin homogeneous wire, of weight w lb/ft and in the shape of a circle of radius r, is made to rotate about a vertical shaft with a constant angular velocity ω. Determine the bending moment in the wire (*a*) at point C, (*b*) at point E, (*c*) at point B. (Neglect the effect of gravity.)

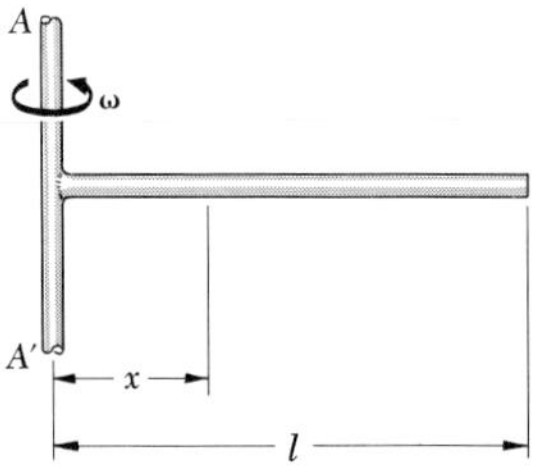

FIG. P 16.161

REVIEW PROBLEMS

16.161. A uniform slender rod of length l, weighing w lb/ft, rotates about a vertical axis AA' at a constant angular velocity ω. Determine the tension in the bar at a distance x from the axis of rotation.

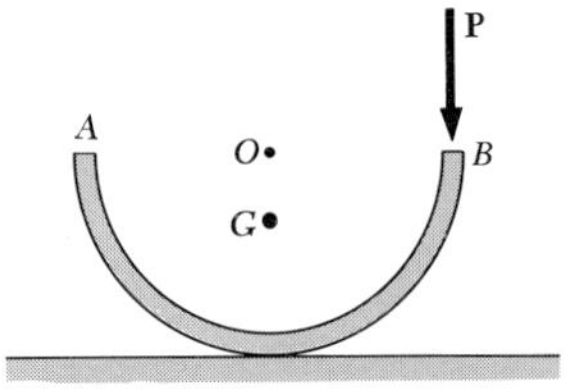

FIG. P 16.162

16.162. A half section of pipe of weight W and radius r rests on a rough horizontal surface. A vertical force **P** is applied as shown. Assuming that the section rolls without sliding, derive an expression (*a*) for its angular acceleration, (*b*) for the minimum value of μ compatible with this motion. (*Hint.* Note that $OG = 2r/\pi$ and that, by the parallel-axis theorem, $\bar{I} = mr^2 - m(OG)^2$.)

16.163. Solve Prob. 16.162 assuming that the force **P** is applied at B and is directed horizontally to the right.

16.164. A block B of weight W is attached to a cord wrapped around a cylinder of the same weight W and of radius r. The cylinder rolls without sliding on a horizontal surface. Determine the components of the accelerations of the center A of the cylinder and of the block B immediately after the system has been released from rest if (*a*) the block hangs freely, (*b*) the motion of the block is guided by a rigid member DAE, frictionless and of negligible weight, which is hinged to the cylinder at A.

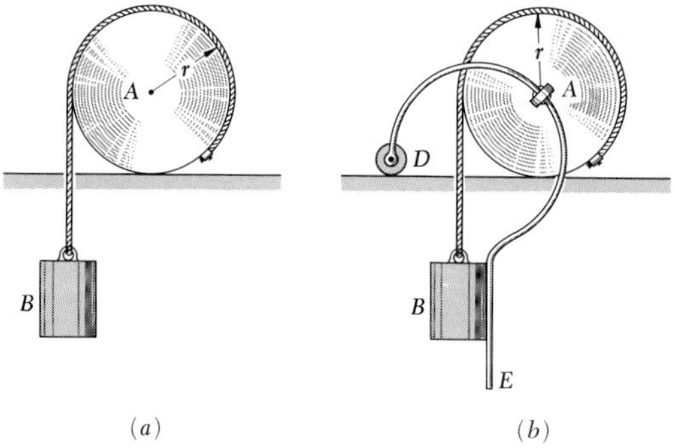

FIG. P 16.164

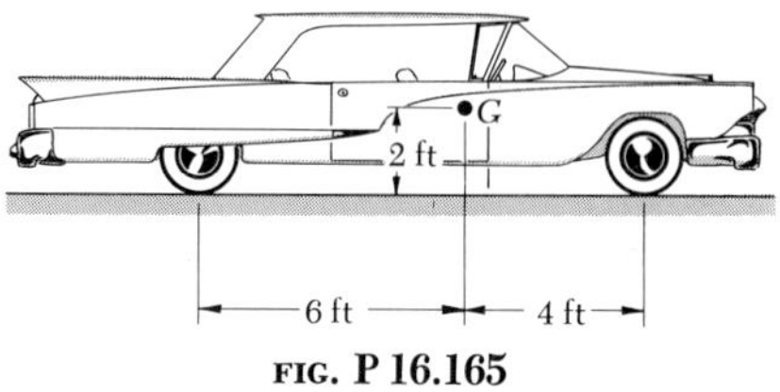

FIG. P 16.165

16.165. Knowing that the coefficient of friction between the tires and road is 0.75 for the car shown, determine the maximum possible acceleration on a level road, assuming (*a*) four-wheel drive, (*b*) conventional rear-wheel drive, (*c*) front-wheel drive.

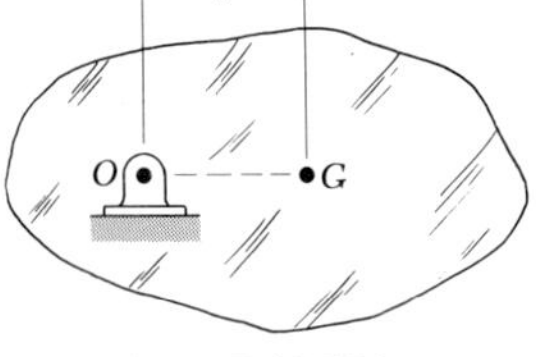

FIG. P 16.166

16.166. A body of weight W and centroidal radius of gyration $\bar{k}$ can rotate freely about a shaft O located at a distance $\bar{r}$ from its mass center G. If the body is released from rest in the position shown, determine (*a*) the distance $\bar{r}$ for which the angular acceleration of the body is maximum, (*b*) the corresponding vertical component of the reaction at O.

16.167. The flanged wheel shown rolls to the right with a constant velocity of 4 ft/sec. The rod AB is 4 ft long and weighs 10 lb. Knowing that point A slides without friction on the horizontal surface, determine the reaction at A (a) when $\beta = 0$, (b) when $\beta = 180°$.

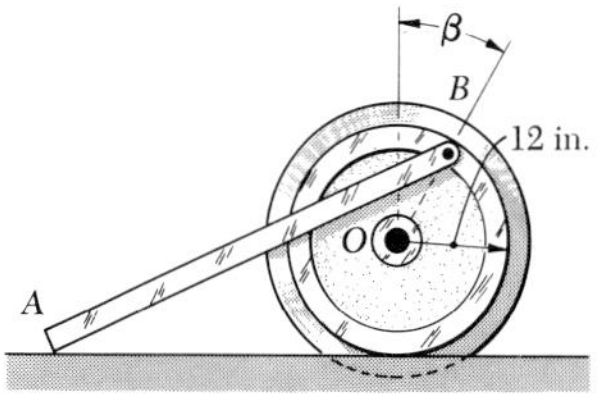

FIG. P 16.167

***16.168.** Solve Prob. 16.167 for the position $\beta = 90°$.

16.169. The rim of a flywheel weighs 9,000 lb and has a mean radius of 3 ft. As the flywheel rotates at a constant angular velocity of 300 rpm, radial forces are exerted on the rim by the spokes and internal forces are developed within the rim. Neglecting the weight of the spokes, determine (a) the internal forces in the rim, assuming the radial forces exerted by the spokes to be zero, (b) the radial force exerted by each spoke, assuming the tangential forces in the rim to be zero.

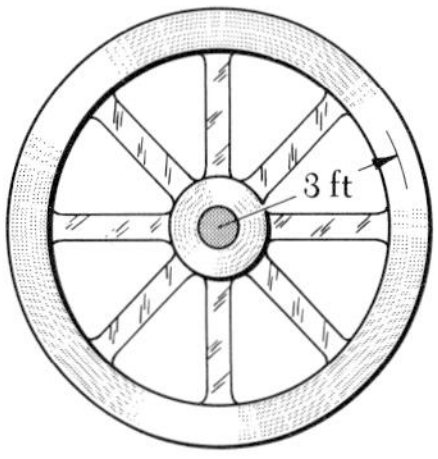

FIG. P 16.169

16.170. A section of pipe, of weight 100 lb and radius 1 ft, rests on two corners as shown. Assuming that μ between the corners and the pipe is sufficient to prevent sliding, determine (a) the angular acceleration of the pipe just after corner B is removed, (b) the corresponding magnitude of the reaction at A.

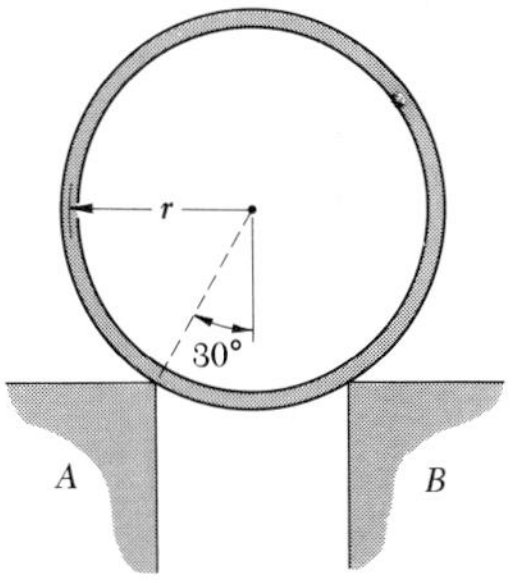

FIG. P 16.170

***16.171.** A slender rod AB of weight w lb/ft is placed inside a shallow drum of radius r which rotates at a constant angular velocity ω about a vertical shaft through O. (a) Determine the ratio L/r for which the maximum bending moment in the rod is as large as possible. (b) Derive an expression for the corresponding value of the maximum bending moment.

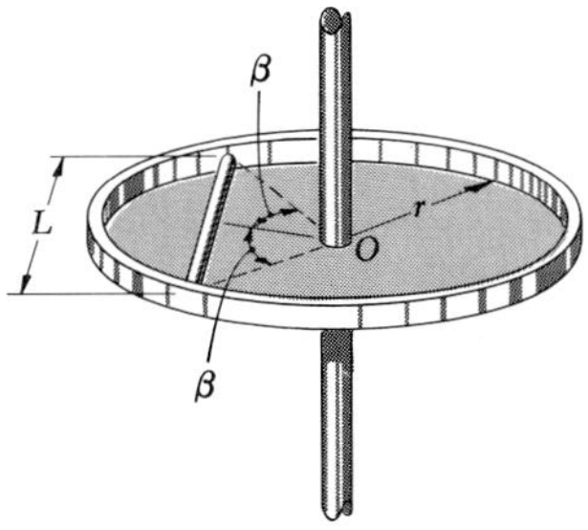

FIG. P 16.171

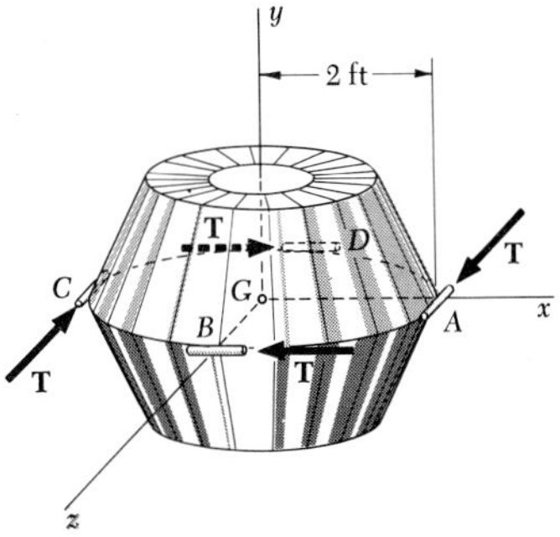

FIG. P 16.172

16.172. A space satellite weighs 100 lb and has a radius of gyration of 1.50 ft with respect to the y axis. The orientation of the satellite is changed by firing four small rockets A, B, C, and D which are equally spaced around the perimeter of the satellite. While being fired, each rocket produces a thrust $\mathbf{T}$ of magnitude 2 lb directed as shown. Determine the angular acceleration of the satellite and the acceleration of the mass center G (a) when all four rockets are fired, (b) when all rockets except rocket D are fired.

17. KINETICS OF RIGID BODIES: WORK AND ENERGY

17.1. Principle of Work and Energy for a Rigid Body. In this chapter, the principle of work and energy will be used to analyze the motion of rigid bodies and of systems of rigid bodies. As was pointed out in Chap. 13, the method of work and energy is particularly well adapted to the solution of problems involving velocities and displacements. Its main advantage resides in the fact that the work of forces and the kinetic energy of particles are scalar quantities.

Consider a rigid body of mass m, and let P be a particle of the body, of mass Δm. The kinetic energy of this particle is $\Delta T = \frac{1}{2}(\Delta m)v^2$, where v is the speed of the particle. Consider now a displacement of the rigid body during which the particle P moves from a position P_1 to a position P_2, and denote by $\Delta U_{1\to2}$ the work of all the forces acting on P during the displacement. We recall from Sec. 13.3 that the principle of work and energy for a particle states that

$$\Delta T_1 + \Delta U_{1\to2} = \Delta T_2$$

where ΔT_1 = kinetic energy of the particle at P_1
ΔT_2 = kinetic energy of the particle at P_2

Similar relations may be written for all the particles forming the body. Adding the kinetic energy of all the particles, and the work of all the forces involved, we write

$$T_1 + U_{1\to2} = T_2 \tag{17.1}$$

where T_1, T_2 = initial and final values of total kinetic energy of the particles forming the rigid body
$U_{1\to2}$ = work of all forces acting on the various particles of the body

The total kinetic energy

$$T = \Sigma\tfrac{1}{2}(\Delta m)v^2 \tag{17.2}$$

is obtained by adding positive scalar quantities and is itself a positive scalar quantity. We shall see later how T may be determined for various types of motion of a rigid body.

The expression $U_{1\to2}$ in (17.1) represents the work of all the forces acting on the various particles of the body, whether these forces are internal or external. However, as we shall see presently, the total work of the internal forces holding together the particles of a rigid body is zero. Consider two particles A and B of a rigid body and the two equal and opposite forces **F** and **F′** they exert on each other (Fig. 17.1). While, in general, the displacements $d\mathbf{r}$ and $d\mathbf{r}'$ of the two particles are different, the components of these displacements along AB must be equal; otherwise, the particles would not remain at the same distance from each other, and the body would not be rigid. Therefore, the work of **F** is equal in magnitude and opposite in sign to the work of **F′**, and their sum is zero. Thus, the total work of the internal forces acting on the particles of a rigid body is zero, and *the expression* $U_{1\to2}$ *in Eq.* (17.1) *reduces to the work of the external forces* acting on the body during the displacement considered.

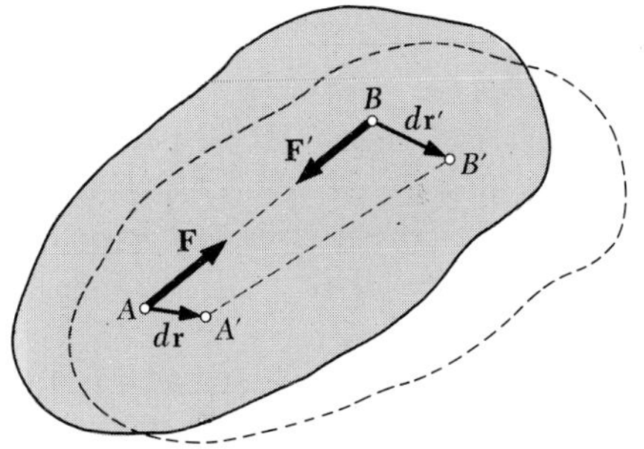

FIG. 17.1

17.2. Work of Forces Acting on a Rigid Body. We saw in Sec. 13.2 that the work of a force **F** during a displacement of its point of application from A_1 ($s = s_1$) to A_2 ($s = s_2$) is

$$U_{1\to2} = \int_{s_1}^{s_2} (F \cos \alpha)\, ds \qquad (17.3)$$

where F is the magnitude of the force **F**, and α the angle that **F** forms at any given instant with the direction of motion of its point of application.

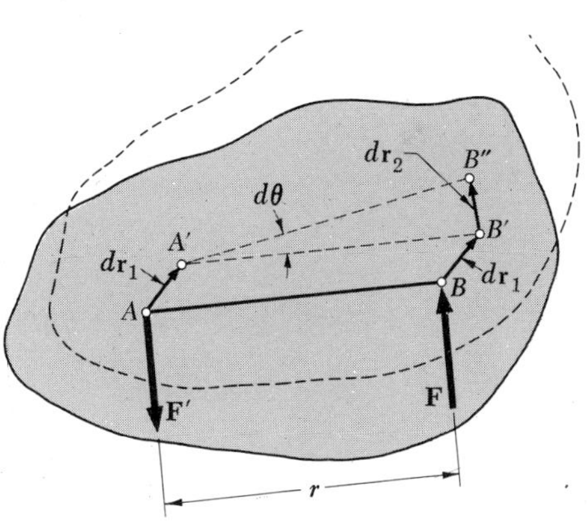

FIG. 17.2

In computing the work of the external forces acting on a rigid body, it is often convenient to determine the work of a couple without considering separately the work of each of the two forces forming the couple. Consider the two forces **F** and **F′** forming a couple of moment $M = Fr$ and acting on a rigid body (Fig. 17.2). Any small displacement of the rigid body bringing A and B, respectively, into A' and B'' may be divided into two parts, one in which points A and B undergo equal displacements $d\mathbf{r}_1$, the other in which A' remains fixed while B' moves into B'' through a displacement $d\mathbf{r}_2$ of magnitude $ds_2 = r\, d\theta$. In the first part of the motion, the work of **F** is equal in magnitude and opposite in sign to the work of **F′**, and their sum is zero. In the second part of the motion, only force **F** works, and its work is $dU = F\, ds_2 = Fr\, d\theta = M\, d\theta$. Thus, the work of a couple of moment M acting on a rigid body is

$$dU = M\, d\theta \qquad (17.4)$$

where $d\theta$ is the small angle expressed in radians through which the body rotates. We again note that work should be expressed in units obtained by multiplying units of force by units of length. The work of the couple during a finite rotation of the rigid body is obtained by integrating both members of (17.4) from the initial value θ_1 of the angle θ to its final value θ_2. We write

$$U_{1\to 2} = \int_{\theta_1}^{\theta_2} M\, d\theta \tag{17.5}$$

When the moment M of the couple is constant, formula (17.5) reduces to

$$U_{1\to 2} = M(\theta_2 - \theta_1) \tag{17.6}$$

It was pointed out in Sec. 13.2 that a number of forces encountered in problems of kinetics *do no work.* They are forces applied to fixed points or acting in a direction perpendicular to the displacement of their point of application. Among the forces which do no work the following have been listed: the reaction at a smooth pin when the body supported rotates about the pin, the reaction at a smooth frictionless surface when the body in contact moves along the surface, the weight of a body when its center of gravity moves horizontally. We should also indicate now that, *when a rigid body rolls without sliding on a fixed surface, the friction force* **F** *at the point of contact C does no work.* The velocity $\mathbf{v}_C$ of the point of contact C is zero, and the work of the friction force **F** during a small displacement of the rigid body is $dU = F\, ds_C = F(v_C\, dt) = 0$.

17.3. Kinetic Energy in Translation. Consider a rigid body in translation. Since, at a given instant, all the particles of the body have the same velocity as the mass center, we may substitute $v = \bar{v}$ in (17.2). We thus obtain the following expression for the kinetic energy of a rigid body in translation:

$$T = \Sigma \tfrac{1}{2}(\Delta m)\bar{v}^2 = \tfrac{1}{2}(\Sigma\, \Delta m)\bar{v}^2$$

$$T = \tfrac{1}{2}m\bar{v}^2 \tag{17.7}$$

This expression should be entered in formula (17.1) when the method of work and energy is used to analyze the motion of a rigid body in translation (either rectilinear or curvilinear).

We note that the expression obtained in (17.7) represents the kinetic energy of a particle of mass m moving with the velocity $\bar{\mathbf{v}}$ of the mass center. The approach used in Chap. 13, where bodies as large as automobiles or trains were considered as single particles, is therefore correct as long as the bodies considered are in translation.

17.4. Kinetic Energy in Rotation. Consider a rigid body rotating about a fixed axis intersecting the reference plane at O (Fig. 17.3). If the angular velocity of the body at a given instant is ω (radians/sec), the speed of a particle P located at a distance r from the axis of rotation is $v = r\omega$ at that instant. Substituting for v into (17.2), we obtain the following expression for the kinetic energy of the body:

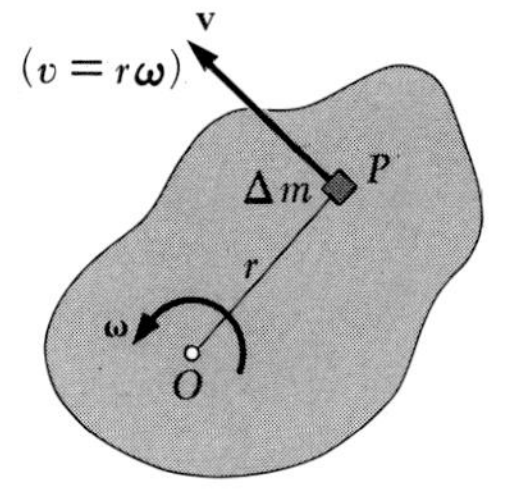

FIG. 17.3

$$T = \Sigma \tfrac{1}{2}(\Delta m)(r\omega)^2 = \tfrac{1}{2}\omega^2 \Sigma r^2 \, \Delta m$$

Replacing the sum $\Sigma r^2 \, \Delta m$ by the integral $\int r^2 \, dm$, and noting that this integral represents the moment of inertia I_O of the rigid body about the axis of rotation, we write

$$T = \tfrac{1}{2} I_O \omega^2 \tag{17.8}$$

This expression should be entered in formula (17.1) when the method of work and energy is used to analyze the motion of a rigid body rotating about a fixed axis.

We note that formula (17.8) is valid with respect to any fixed axis of rotation, whether or not this axis passes through the mass center of the body. Moreover, the result obtained is not limited to the rotation of plane slabs or to the rotation of bodies which are symmetrical with respect to the reference plane. Formula (17.8) may be applied to the rotation of any rigid body about a fixed axis, regardless of the shape of the body or of the location of the axis of rotation.

17.5. Systems of Rigid Bodies. When a problem involves several rigid bodies, each rigid body may be considered separately and the principle of work and energy may be applied to each body. Adding the kinetic energies of all the particles and considering the work of all the forces involved, we may also write the equation of work and energy for the entire system. We have

$$T_1 + U_{1\to2} = T_2 \tag{17.9}$$

where T represents the arithmetic sum of the kinetic energies of the rigid bodies forming the system (all terms are positive) and $U_{1\to2}$ the work of all the forces acting on the various bodies, whether these forces are *internal* or *external* from the point of view of the system as a whole.

The method of work and energy is particularly useful in solving problems involving pin-connected members, or blocks and pulleys connected by inextensible cords, or meshed gears. In all these cases, the internal forces occur by pairs of equal and opposite forces, and the points of application of the forces in each pair *move through equal distances* during a small displacement of the system. As a result, the work of the internal forces is zero, and $U_{1\to2}$ reduces to the work of the *forces external to the system.*

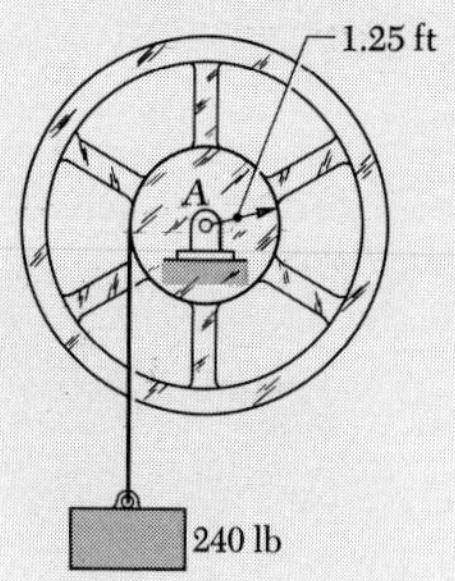

SAMPLE PROBLEM 17.1

A 240-lb block is suspended from an inextensible cable which is wrapped around a drum of 1.25-ft radius rigidly attached to a flywheel. The drum and flywheel have a combined centroidal moment of inertia $\bar{I}$ = 10.5 lb-ft-sec². At the instant shown, the velocity of the block is 6 ft/sec directed downward. Knowing that the bearing at A is poorly lubricated and that the bearing friction is equivalent to a couple **M** of moment 60 lb-ft, determine the velocity of the block after it has moved 4 ft downward.

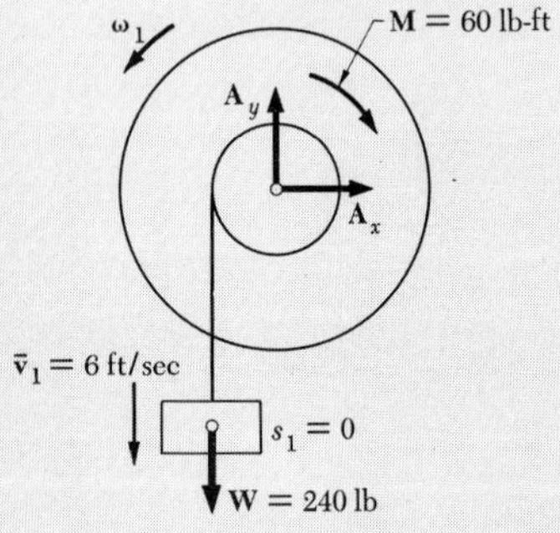

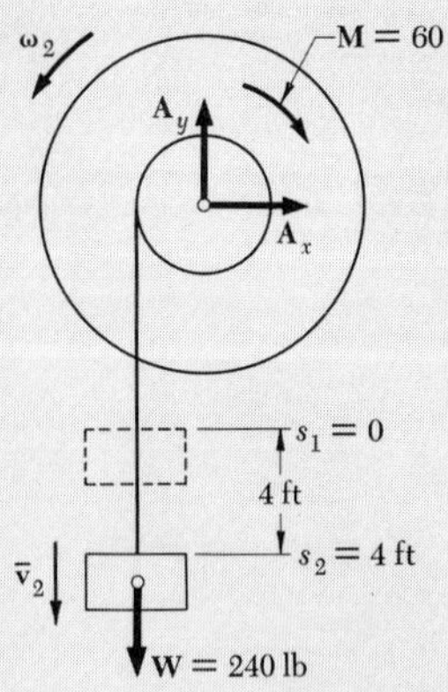

Solution. We consider the system formed by the flywheel and the block. Since the cable is inextensible, the work done by the internal forces exerted by the cable cancels. The initial and final positions of the system and the external forces acting on the system are as shown.

Kinetic Energy. *Position 1.* We have

$$\bar{v}_1 = 6 \text{ ft/sec} \qquad \omega_1 = \frac{\bar{v}_1}{r} = \frac{6}{1.25} = 4.80 \text{ radians/sec}$$

$$T_1 = \tfrac{1}{2}m\bar{v}_1^2 + \tfrac{1}{2}\bar{I}\omega_1^2$$
$$= \frac{1}{2}\frac{240}{g}(6)^2 + (\tfrac{1}{2})(10.5)(4.80)^2 = 255 \text{ ft-lb}$$

Position 2. Noting that $\omega_2 = \bar{v}_2/1.25$, we write

$$T_2 = \tfrac{1}{2}m\bar{v}_2^2 + \tfrac{1}{2}\bar{I}\omega_2^2$$
$$= \frac{1}{2}\frac{240}{g}(\bar{v}_2)^2 + (\tfrac{1}{2})(10.5)\left(\frac{\bar{v}_2}{1.25}\right)^2 = 7.09\bar{v}_2^2$$

Work. During the motion, only the weight **W** of the block and the friction couple **M** do work. Noting that **W** does positive work and that the friction couple **M** does negative work, we write

$$s_1 = 0 \qquad s_2 = 4 \text{ ft}$$
$$\theta_1 = 0 \qquad \theta_2 = \frac{s_2}{r} = 3.20 \text{ radians}$$

$$U_{1\to2} = W(s_2 - s_1) - M(\theta_2 - \theta_1)$$
$$= (240 \text{ lb})(4 \text{ ft}) - (60 \text{ lb-ft})(3.20 \text{ radians})$$
$$= 768 \text{ ft-lb}$$

Principle of Work and Energy

$$T_1 + U_{1\to2} = T_2$$
$$255 \text{ ft-lb} + 768 \text{ ft-lb} = 7.09\bar{v}_2^2$$
$$\bar{v}_2 = 12.01 \text{ ft/sec} \qquad \bar{\mathbf{v}}_2 = 12.01 \text{ ft/sec} \downarrow$$ ◄

SAMPLE PROBLEM 17.2

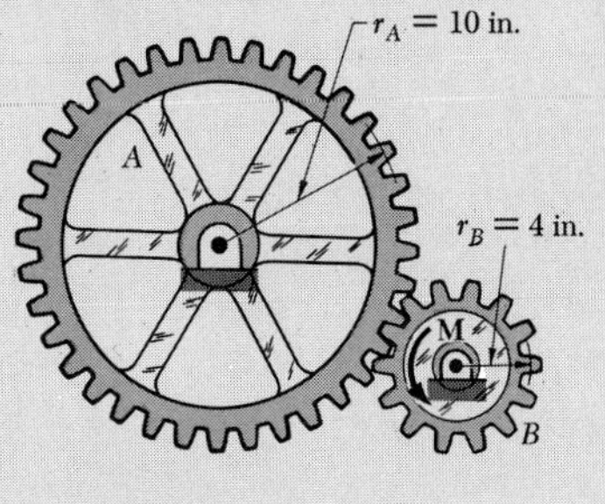

Gear A weighs 20 lb and has a radius of gyration of 9 in., while gear B weighs 5 lb and has a radius of gyration of 3 in. The system is at rest when a couple **M** of moment 4 lb-ft is applied to gear B. Neglecting friction, determine (*a*) the number of revolutions executed by gear B before its angular velocity reaches 600 rpm, (*b*) the tangential force which gear B exerts on gear A.

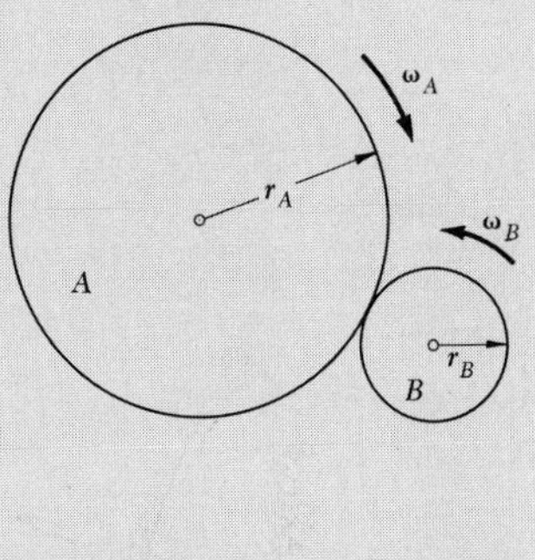

Motion of Entire System. Noting that the peripheral speeds of the gears are equal, we write

$$r_A\omega_A = r_B\omega_B \qquad \omega_A = \omega_B\frac{r_B}{r_A} = \omega_B\frac{4\text{ in.}}{10\text{ in.}} = 0.40\omega_B$$

For $\omega_B = 600$ rpm, we have

$$\omega_B = 62.8 \text{ radians/sec} \qquad \omega_A = 0.40\omega_B = 25.1 \text{ radians/sec}$$

$$\bar{I}_A = m_A\bar{k}_A^2 = \frac{20}{g}\left(\frac{9}{12}\right)^2 = 0.349 \text{ lb-ft-sec}^2$$

$$\bar{I}_B = m_B\bar{k}_B^2 = \frac{5}{g}\left(\frac{3}{12}\right)^2 = 0.00970 \text{ lb-ft-sec}^2$$

Kinetic Energy. Since the system is initially at rest, $T_1 = 0$. Adding the kinetic energies of the two gears when $\omega_B = 600$ rpm, we obtain

$$T_2 = \tfrac{1}{2}\bar{I}_A\omega_A^2 + \tfrac{1}{2}\bar{I}_B\omega_B^2$$
$$= (\tfrac{1}{2})(0.349)(25.1)^2 + (\tfrac{1}{2})(0.00970)(62.8)^2 = 129.1 \text{ ft-lb}$$

Work. Denoting by θ_B the angular displacement of gear B, we have

$$U_{1\to2} = M\theta_B = (4 \text{ lb-ft})\theta_B$$

Principle of Work and Energy

$$T_1 + U_{1\to2} = T_2 \qquad 0 + 4\theta_B = 129.1 \text{ ft-lb}$$
$$\theta_B = 32.3 \text{ radians} \qquad\qquad \theta_B = 5.14 \text{ rev} \blacktriangleleft$$

Motion of Gear A. *Kinetic Energy.* Initially, gear A is at rest, $T_1 = 0$. When $\omega_B = 600$ rpm, the kinetic energy of gear A is

$$T_2 = \tfrac{1}{2}\bar{I}_A\omega_A^2 = (\tfrac{1}{2})(0.349)(25.1)^2 = 109.9 \text{ ft-lb}$$

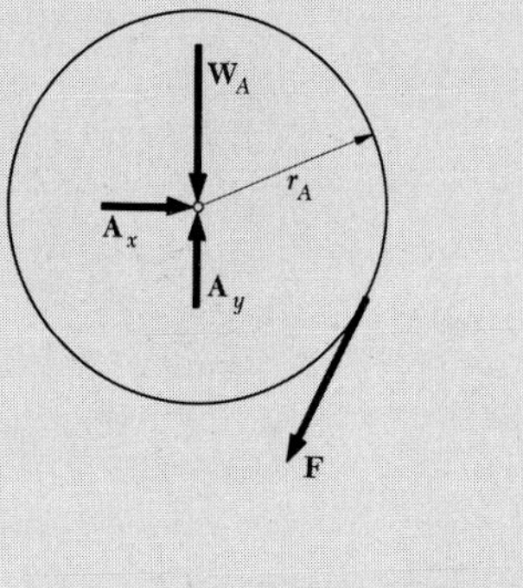

Work. The forces acting on gear A are as shown. The tangential force **F** does work equal to the product of its magnitude and of the length $\theta_A r_A$ described by the point of contact. Since $\theta_A r_A = \theta_B r_B$, we have

$$U_{1\to2} = F(\theta_B r_B) = F(32.3 \text{ radians})(\tfrac{4}{12} \text{ ft})$$

Principle of Work and Energy

$$T_1 + U_{1\to2} = T_2 \qquad 0 + F(32.3)(\tfrac{4}{12}) = 109.9$$
$$F = +10.21 \text{ lb} \qquad\qquad \mathbf{F} = 10.21 \text{ lb} \swarrow \blacktriangleleft$$

PROBLEMS

17.1. A large flywheel weighs 6,000 lb and has a radius of gyration of 36 in. It is observed that 1,500 revolutions are required for the flywheel to coast from an angular velocity of 300 rpm to rest. Determine the average moment of the couple due to kinetic friction in the bearings.

17.2. At a time when the rotor of an electric motor is rotating at 1,800 rpm, the load and power are cut off and the rotor coasts to rest. The rotor weighs 150 lb and has a radius of gyration of 6 in. If the kinetic friction of the rotor produces a couple of moment 5 lb-in., how many revolutions will the rotor execute before stopping?

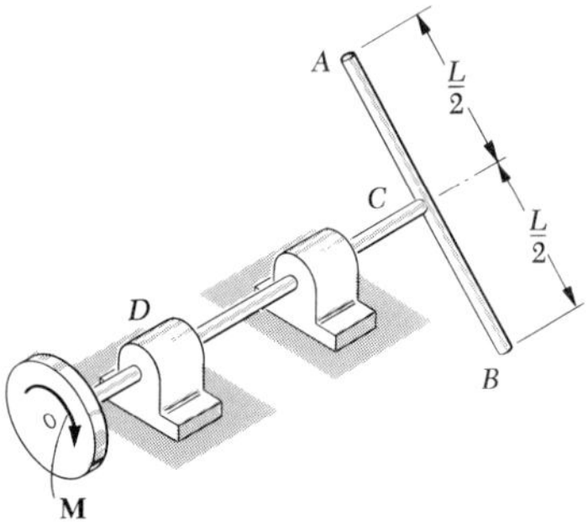

FIG. P 17.3 AND P 17.4

17.3. A 12-in.-diameter disk weighing 8 lb and a rod of length L weighing 2 lb/ft are attached to the shaft CD as shown. A couple **M** of moment 4 lb-ft is applied to the disk when the system is at rest. Determine the length L of rod AB if the angular velocity of the system is to be 300 rpm after two complete revolutions.

17.4. A rod AB weighing w lb/ft is to be attached to a shaft and disk as shown. A couple **M** of constant magnitude is applied to the disk when the system is at rest; after the system has executed one complete revolution the couple is removed. Denoting by I_0 the moment of inertia of the shaft and disk about the axis of rotation, derive an expression for the length L which results in the largest final speed of point A.

17.5. The flywheel of a small punch rotates at 180 rpm. It is known that 1,000 ft-lb of work must be done each time a hole is punched. It is desired that the speed of the flywheel after one punching be not less than 90 per cent of the original speed of 180 rpm. (*a*) Determine the required moment of inertia of the flywheel. (*b*) If a constant 25-lb-ft couple is applied to the shaft of the flywheel, determine the number of revolutions which must occur between each punching, knowing that the speed is to be 180 rpm at the start of each punching.

17.6. The flywheel of a punching machine weighs 600 lb and has a radius of gyration of 24 in. Each punching operation requires 2,000 ft-lb of work. (*a*) Knowing that the speed of the flywheel is 300 rpm just before a punching, determine the speed immediately after the punching. (*b*) If a constant 20-lb-ft couple is applied to the shaft of the flywheel, determine the number of revolutions executed before the speed is again 300 rpm.

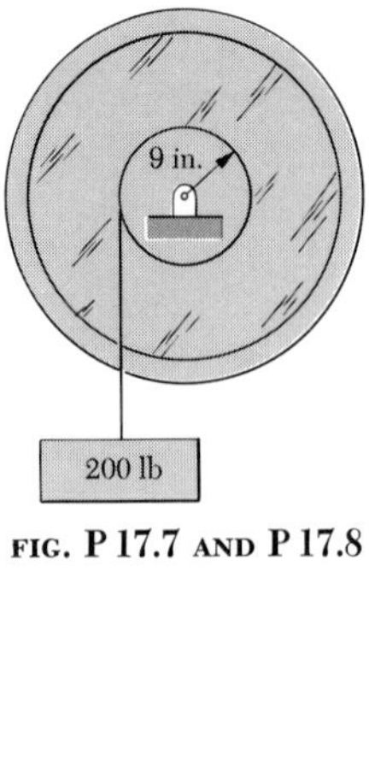

FIG. P 17.7 AND P 17.8

17.7. The flywheel of a small hoisting engine has a radius of gyration of 2 ft and weighs 800 lb. When the speed of the 200-lb load is 6 ft/sec upward, the power is cut off. Neglecting bearing friction, determine how far the load will rise before coming to rest.

17.8. The flywheel of a small hoisting engine has a radius of gyration of 2 ft and weighs 800 lb. When the speed of the 200-lb load is 6 ft/sec upward, the power is cut off. Knowing that the load rises 15 ft before coming to rest, determine the moment of the bearing-friction couple exerted on the shaft.

17.9. Using the principle of work and energy, solve Prob. 16.32.

17.10. Using the principle of work and energy, solve Prob. 16.34*c*.

17.11. Two blocks are attached to a double pulley of weight 200 lb and radius of gyration 2.5 ft as shown. If the system is released with no initial velocity, how far will the 100-lb block rise before coming to rest? What is the energy loss when the 200-lb block strikes the floor?

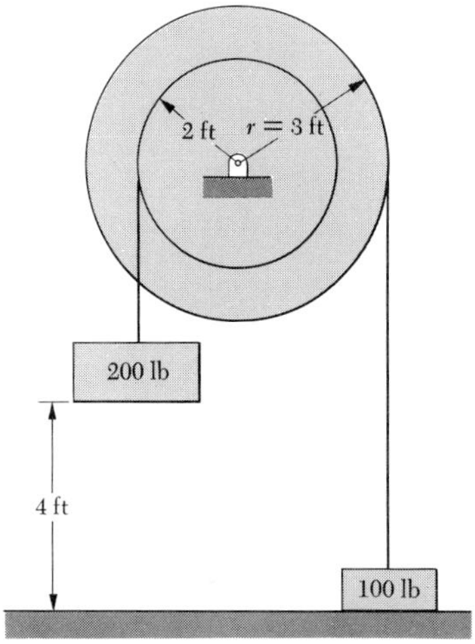

FIG. P 17.11

17.12. Solve Prob. 17.11 assuming that the weight of the pulley is increased to 400 lb.

17.13. In Prob. 17.11 determine the weight of the pulley for which the 100-lb block will rise 7.50 ft before coming to rest.

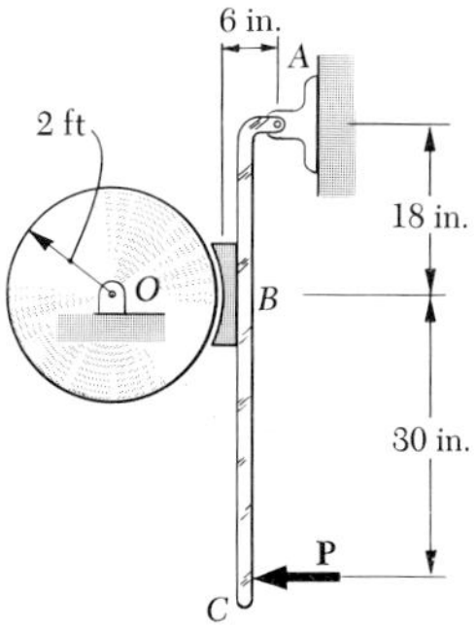

FIG. 17.14

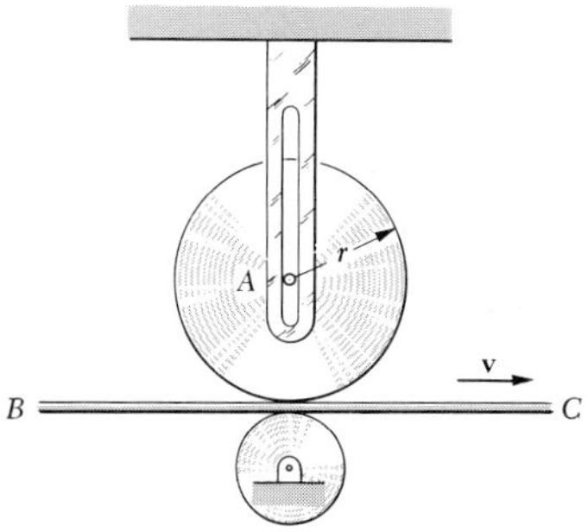

FIG. P 17.15 AND P 17.16

17.14. The flywheel shown consists of a disk which weighs 400 lb. The coefficient of friction between the brake shoe and the disk is 0.25. Determine the magnitude of the force **P** required to bring the flywheel to rest in 30 revolutions if the initial angular velocity is (*a*) 600 rpm clockwise, (*b*) 600 rpm counterclockwise.

17.15. A disk of constant thickness and initially at rest is placed in contact with the belt *BC*, which moves with a constant velocity v. Denoting by μ the coefficient of friction between the disk and the belt, derive an expression for the number of revolutions executed by the disk before it reaches a constant angular velocity.

17.16. Disk *A*, of weight 10 lb and radius $r = 6$ in., is at rest when it is placed in contact with belt *BC*, which moves to the right with a constant speed $v = 40$ ft/sec. Knowing that $\mu = 0.20$ between the disk and the belt, determine the number of revolutions executed by the disk before it reaches a constant angular velocity.

17.17. Using the principle of work and energy, solve Prob. 16.35.

17.18. Gears A and B weigh 20 lb each and have a radius of gyration of 9 in.; gear C weighs 5 lb and has a radius of gyration of 3 in. A couple **M** of moment 100 lb-in. is applied to gear C. Determine (a) the number of revolutions required for the angular velocity of gear A to increase from 60 to 660 rpm, (b) the tangential force acting on gear A.

17.19. Solve Prob. 17.18 assuming that the 100-lb-in. couple is applied to gear A.

17.20. Solve Sample Prob. 17.2 assuming that the 4-lb-ft couple is applied to gear A.

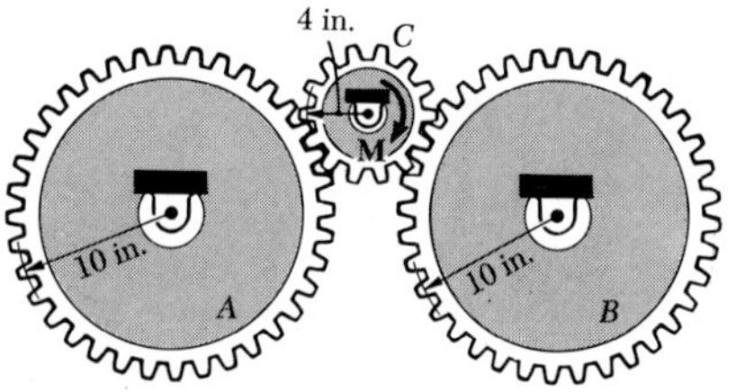

FIG. P 17.18

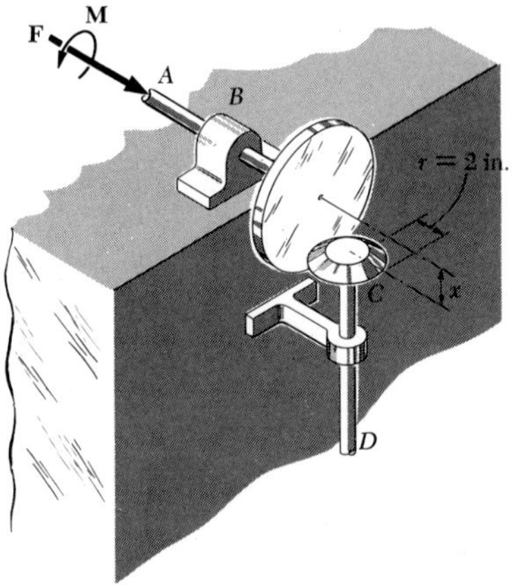

FIG. P 17.21

17.21. Shafts AB and CD are connected by a friction disk and wheel as shown. The moment of inertia of the friction disk and its shaft AB is 0.50 lb-ft-sec^2, and the moment of inertia of the wheel and its shaft CD is 0.30 lb-ft-sec^2. The system is initially at rest when a couple **M** of constant moment 12 lb-ft is applied to shaft AB for 20 revolutions. Assuming no slipping occurs, determine the resulting angular velocity of each shaft when $x = 1.5$ in.

17.22. The mechanism of Prob. 17.21 is set so that $x = 3$ in.; the initial angular velocity of shaft CD is 500 rpm. It is desired to increase this velocity to 600 rpm in 3 revolutions of shaft CD. Determine the moment of the couple **M** which must be applied to shaft AB.

17.23. In Prob. 17.21, a couple **M** of constant moment 12 lb-ft is applied to shaft AB for 20 revolutions. Knowing that the system is initially at rest, determine the setting x if the angular velocity of shaft CD is to reach 700 rpm.

17.6. Kinetic Energy in Plane Motion. Consider a rigid body in plane motion. We saw in Sec. 15.7 that at any given instant the velocities of the various particles of the body are the same as if the body were rotating about an axis perpendicular to the reference plane, called the *instantaneous axis of rotation.* We may therefore use the results obtained in Sec. 17.4 to express at any instant the kinetic energy of a rigid body in plane motion. Recalling that the instantaneous axis of rotation intersects the reference plane at a point C called the *instantaneous center of rotation* (Fig. 17.4a), we denote by I_C the moment of inertia of the body about the instantaneous axis. If the body has an angular velocity ω at the instant considered, its kinetic energy is therefore

$$T = \tfrac{1}{2}I_C\omega^2 \tag{17.10}$$

But we know from the parallel-axis theorem (Sec. 9.11) that $I_C = m\bar{r}^2 + \bar{I}$, where $\bar{I}$ is the moment of inertia of the body about a centroidal axis perpendicular to the reference plane and $\bar{r}$ the distance from the instantaneous center C to the mass center G. Substituting for I_C into (17.10), we write

$$T = \tfrac{1}{2}\,(m\bar{r}^2 + \bar{I})\,\omega^2 = \tfrac{1}{2}\,m\,(\bar{r}\omega)^2 + \tfrac{1}{2}\,\bar{I}\,\omega^2$$

or, since $\bar{r}\omega$ represents the magnitude $\bar{v}$ of the velocity of the mass center,

$$T = \tfrac{1}{2}m\bar{v}^2 + \tfrac{1}{2}\bar{I}\omega^2 \tag{17.11}$$

Either of the expressions (17.10) and (17.11) may be entered in formula (17.1) when the method of work and energy is used to analyze the plane motion of a rigid body.

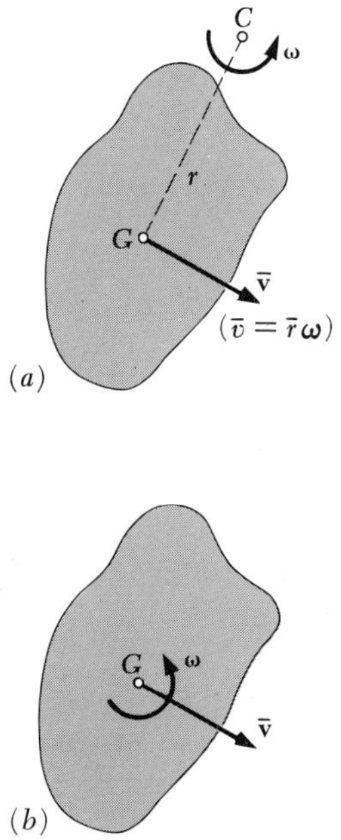

FIG. 17.4

We note that the expression given for the kinetic energy in (17.11) is separated into two distinct parts: (1) the kinetic energy $\frac{1}{2}m\bar{v}^2$ corresponding to the motion of the mass center G, and (2) the kinetic energy $\frac{1}{2}\bar{I}\omega^2$ corresponding to the rotation of the body about G (Fig. 17.4b). This formula thus conforms to the unified approach we have used so far, and we shall apply it in preference to (17.10) in the Sample Problems of this chapter.

We also note that the results obtained in this section are not limited to the motion of plane slabs or to the motion of bodies which are symmetrical with respect to the reference plane. They may be applied to the study of the plane motion of any rigid body, regardless of its shape.

17.7. Conservation of Energy. We saw in Sec. 13.6 that the work of conservative forces, such as the weight of a body or the force exerted by a spring, may be expressed as a change in potential energy. When a rigid body, or a system of rigid bodies, moves under the action of conservative forces, the principle of work and energy stated in Sec. 17.1 may be expressed in a modified form. Substituting for $U_{1\to2}$ from (13.17) into (17.1), we write

$$T_1 + V_1 = T_2 + V_2 \tag{17.12}$$

Formula (17.12) indicates that, when a rigid body, or a system of rigid bodies, moves under the action of conservative forces, *the sum of the kinetic energy and of the potential energy of the system remains constant.* It should be noted that, in the case of the plane motion of a rigid body, the kinetic energy of the body should include both the *translational* term $\frac{1}{2}m\bar{v}^2$ and the *rotational* term $\frac{1}{2}\bar{I}\omega^2$.

As an example of application of the principle of conservation of energy, we shall consider a slender rod AB, of length l and mass m, whose extremities are connected to blocks of negligible mass sliding along horizontal and vertical tracks. We assume that the rod is released with no initial velocity from a horizontal position (Fig. 17.5*a*), and we wish to determine its angular velocity after it has rotated through an angle θ (Fig. 17.5*b*).

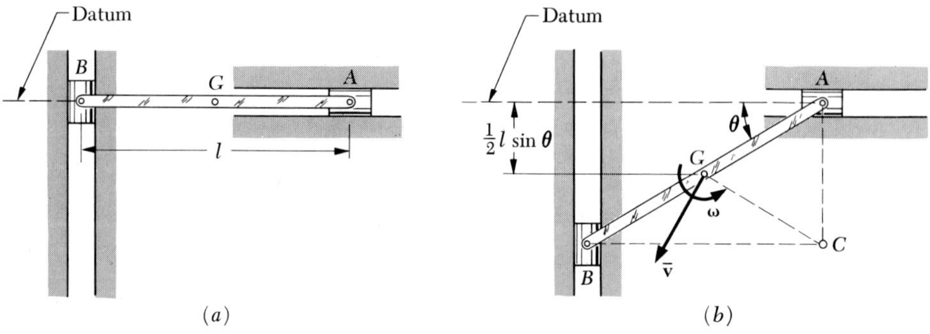

FIG. 17.5

Since the initial velocity is zero, we have $T_1 = 0$. Measuring the potential energy from the level of the horizontal track, we write $V_1 = 0$. After the rod has rotated through θ, the center of gravity G of the rod is at a distance $\frac{1}{2}l \sin \theta$ below the reference level and we have

$$V_2 = -\tfrac{1}{2}Wl \sin \theta = -\tfrac{1}{2}mgl \sin \theta$$

Observing that, in this position, the instantaneous center of the rod is located at C, and that $CG = \frac{1}{2}l$, we write $\bar{v}_2 = \frac{1}{2}l\omega$ and obtain

$$T_2 = \tfrac{1}{2}m\bar{v}_2^2 + \tfrac{1}{2}\bar{I}\omega_2^2 = \tfrac{1}{2}m(\tfrac{1}{2}l\omega)^2 + \tfrac{1}{2}(\tfrac{1}{12}ml^2)\omega^2$$
$$= \frac{1}{2}\frac{ml^2}{3}\omega^2$$

Applying the principle of conservation of energy, we write

$$T_1 + V_1 = T_2 + V_2$$
$$0 = \frac{1}{2}\frac{ml^2}{3}\omega^2 - \tfrac{1}{2}mgl\sin\theta$$
$$\omega = \left(\frac{3g}{l}\sin\theta\right)^{\frac{1}{2}}$$

We recall that the advantages of the method of work and energy, as well as its shortcomings, were indicated in Sec. 13.4. In this connection, we wish to mention that the method of work and energy must be supplemented by the method of dynamic equilibrium when reactions at fixed axles, at rollers, or at sliding blocks are to be determined. For example, in order to compute the reactions at the extremities A and B of the rod of Fig. 17.5*b*, a free-body diagram of the rod should be drawn, including all actual forces, as well as the inertia vector and the inertia couple. The angular velocity ω of the rod, however, is determined by the method of work and energy before the equations of dynamic equilibrium are solved for the reactions. The complete analysis of the motion of the rod and of the forces exerted on the rod requires, therefore, the combined use of the methods of work and energy and of dynamic equilibrium.

17.8. Power. *Power* was defined in Sec. 13.8 as the time rate at which work is done. In the case of a body acted upon by a force **F**, and moving with a velocity **v**, the power was expressed as follows [Eq. (13.20)]:

$$\text{Power} = \frac{dU}{dt} = \frac{(F\cos\alpha)\,ds}{dt} = (F\cos\alpha)v$$

where α is the angle between **F** and **v**. In the case of a rigid body acted upon by a couple **M** and rotating at an angular velocity ω, the power may be expressed in a similar way in terms of M and ω,

$$\text{Power} = \frac{dU}{dt} = \frac{M\,d\theta}{dt} = M\omega \qquad (17.13)$$

The various units used to measure power, such as the horsepower and the kilowatt, were defined in Sec. 13.8.

SAMPLE PROBLEM 17.3

A sphere, a cylinder, and a hoop are each released from rest on an incline. In each case, the weight is W and the radius is r. Determine the velocity of each body after it has rolled through a distance s.

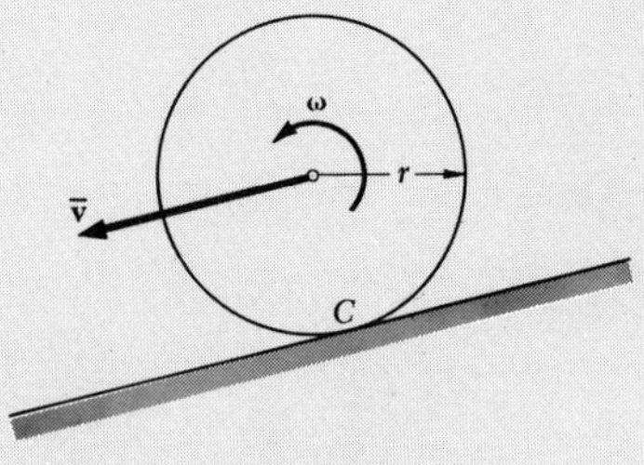

Solution. We shall first solve the problem in general terms and then find particular results for each body. We denote the centroidal moment of inertia by $\bar{I}$, the weight by W, and the radius by r.

Since each body rolls, the instantaneous center of rotation is located at C and we write

$$\omega = \frac{\bar{v}}{r}$$

Kinetic Energy

$$T_1 = 0$$

$$T_2 = \tfrac{1}{2}m\bar{v}^2 + \tfrac{1}{2}\bar{I}\omega^2$$

$$= \tfrac{1}{2}mv^2 + \tfrac{1}{2}\bar{I}\left(\frac{\bar{v}}{r}\right)^2 = \tfrac{1}{2}\left(m + \frac{\bar{I}}{r^2}\right)\bar{v}^2$$

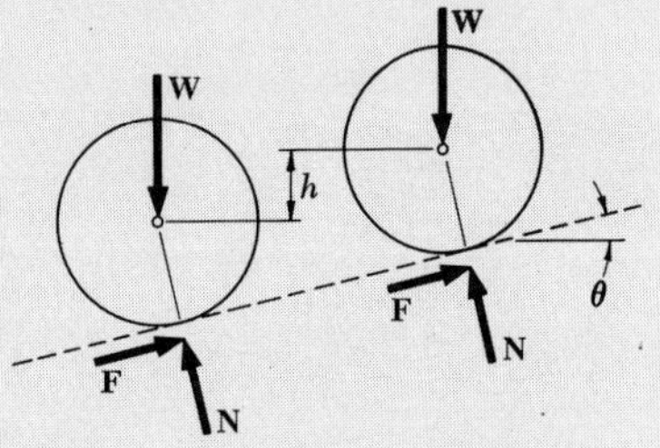

Work. Since the friction force **F** in rolling motion does no work, we have

$$U_{1\to 2} = Wh$$

Principle of Work and Energy

$$T_1 + U_{1\to 2} = T_2$$

$$0 + Wh = \tfrac{1}{2}\left(m + \frac{\bar{I}}{r^2}\right)\bar{v}^2 \qquad \bar{v}^2 = \frac{2Wh}{m + \bar{I}/r^2}$$

Noting that $W = mg$, we rearrange the result and obtain

$$\bar{v}^2 = \frac{2gh}{1 + \bar{I}/mr^2}$$

Velocities of Sphere, Cylinder, and Hoop. Introducing successively the particular expressions for $\bar{I}$, we obtain

Sphere:	$\bar{I} = \frac{2}{5}mr^2$	$\bar{v} = 0.845\sqrt{2gh}$
Cylinder:	$\bar{I} = \frac{1}{2}mr^2$	$\bar{v} = 0.817\sqrt{2gh}$
Hoop:	$\bar{I} = mr^2$	$\bar{v} = 0.707\sqrt{2gh}$

Remark. We may compare the results with the velocity attained by a frictionless block sliding through the same distance. The solution is identical to the above solution except that $\omega = 0$; we find $\bar{v} = \sqrt{2gh}$.

Comparing the results, we note that the velocity of the body is independent of both its weight and radius. However, the velocity does depend upon the quotient $\bar{I}/mr^2 = \bar{k}^2/r^2$, which measures the ratio of the rotational kinetic energy to the translational kinetic energy. Thus the hoop, which has the largest $\bar{k}$ for a given radius r, attains the smallest velocity, while the sliding block, which does not rotate, attains the largest velocity.

SAMPLE PROBLEM 17.4

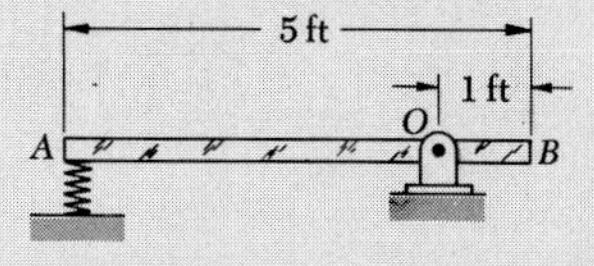

A 30-lb slender rod AB is 5 ft long and is pivoted about a point O which is 1 ft from end B. The other end is pressed against a spring of constant $k = 1{,}800$ lb/in. until the spring is compressed 1 in. The rod is then in a horizontal position. If the rod is released from this position, determine its angular velocity and the reaction at the pivot O as the rod passes through a vertical position.

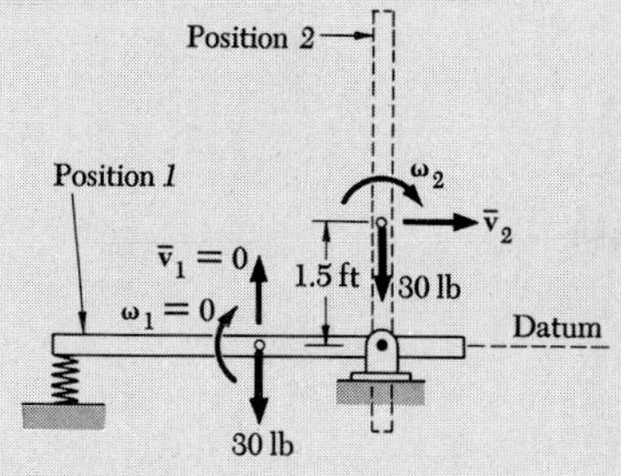

Position *1.* *Potential Energy.* Since the spring is compressed 1 in., we have $x_1 = 1$ in.

$$V_e = \tfrac{1}{2}kx_1^2 = \tfrac{1}{2}(1{,}800 \text{ lb/in.})(1 \text{ in.})^2 = 900 \text{ in.-lb}$$

Choosing the datum as shown, we have $V_g = 0$; therefore,

$$V_1 = V_e + V_g = 900 \text{ in.-lb} = 75 \text{ ft-lb}$$

Kinetic Energy. Since the velocity in position *1* is zero, we have $T_1 = 0$.

Position 2. *Potential Energy.* The elongation of the spring is zero, and we have $V_e = 0$. Since the center of gravity of the rod is now 1.5 ft above the datum,

$$V_g = (30 \text{ lb})(+1.5 \text{ ft}) = 45 \text{ ft-lb}$$
$$V_2 = V_e + V_g = 45 \text{ ft-lb}$$

Kinetic Energy. Denoting by ω_2 the angular velocity of the rod in position 2, we note that the rod rotates about O and write $\bar{v}_2 = \bar{r}\omega_2 = 1.5\omega_2$.

$$\bar{I} = \tfrac{1}{12}ml^2 = \frac{1}{12}\frac{30}{g}(5)^2 = 1.941 \text{ lb-ft-sec}^2$$

$$T_2 = \tfrac{1}{2}m\bar{v}_2^2 + \tfrac{1}{2}\bar{I}\omega_2^2 = \frac{1}{2}\frac{30}{g}(1.5\omega_2)^2 + (\tfrac{1}{2})(1.941)\omega_2^2 = 2.018\omega_2^2$$

Conservation of Energy

$$T_1 + V_1 = T_2 + V_2 \qquad 0 + 75 \text{ ft-lb} = 2.018\omega_2^2 + 45 \text{ ft-lb}$$

$$\omega_2 = 3.86 \text{ radians/sec} \circlearrowright \blacktriangleleft$$

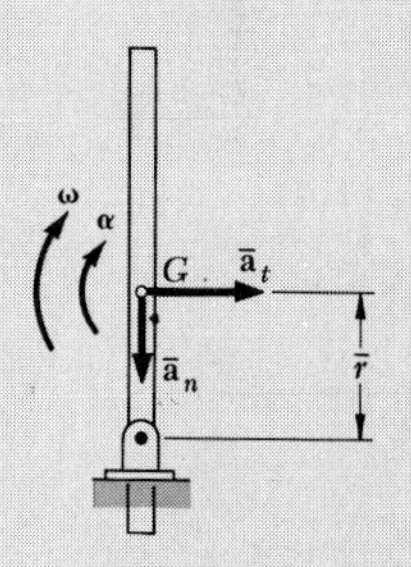

Dynamic Equilibrium in Position 2. Since $\omega_2 = 3.86$ radians/sec, the components of the acceleration of G as the rod passes through position 2 are

$$\bar{a}_n = \bar{r}\omega_2^2 = (1.5)(3.86)^2 = 22.3 \text{ ft/sec}^2 \qquad \bar{\mathbf{a}}_n = 22.3 \text{ ft/sec}^2 \downarrow$$
$$\bar{a}_t = \bar{r}\alpha \qquad \bar{\mathbf{a}}_t = \bar{r}\alpha \rightarrow$$

A free-body diagram of the rod is drawn, showing all external forces, the components $(m\mathbf{a}_n)_{\text{rev}}$ and $(m\mathbf{a}_t)_{\text{rev}}$ of the inertia vector attached at G, and the inertia couple $(\bar{I}\boldsymbol{\alpha})_{\text{rev}}$.

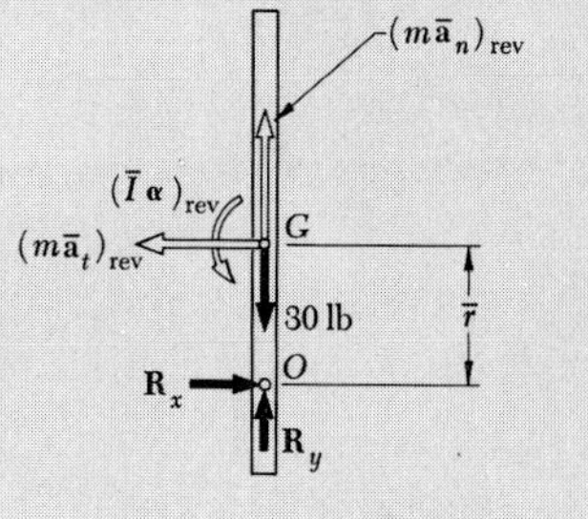

$$+\circlearrowleft \Sigma M_O = 0: \qquad \bar{I}\alpha + m(\bar{r}\alpha)\bar{r} = 0 \qquad \alpha = 0$$
$$\overset{+}{\rightarrow} \Sigma F_x = 0: \qquad -m(\bar{r}\alpha) + R_x = 0 \qquad R_x = 0$$
$$+\uparrow \Sigma F_y = 0: \qquad +m\bar{a}_n - 30 + R_y = 0$$
$$\frac{30}{g}(22.3) - 30 + R_y = 0$$
$$R_y = +9.22 \text{ lb} \qquad \mathbf{R} = 9.22 \text{ lb} \uparrow \blacktriangleleft$$

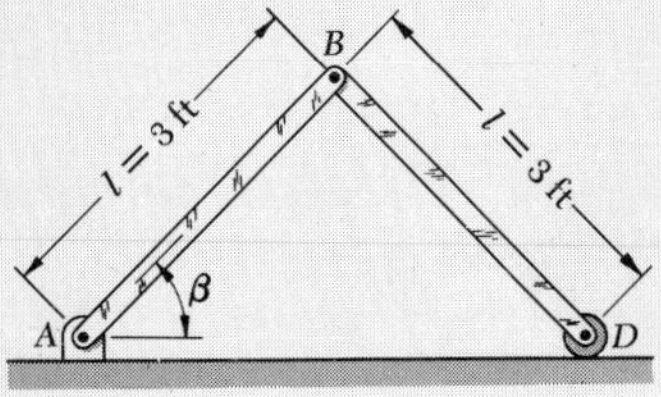

SAMPLE PROBLEM 17.5

Each of the two slender rods shown is 3 ft long and weighs 10 lb. If the system is released from rest when $\beta = 60°$, determine (*a*) the angular velocity of rod AB when $\beta = 20°$, (*b*) the velocity of point D at the same instant.

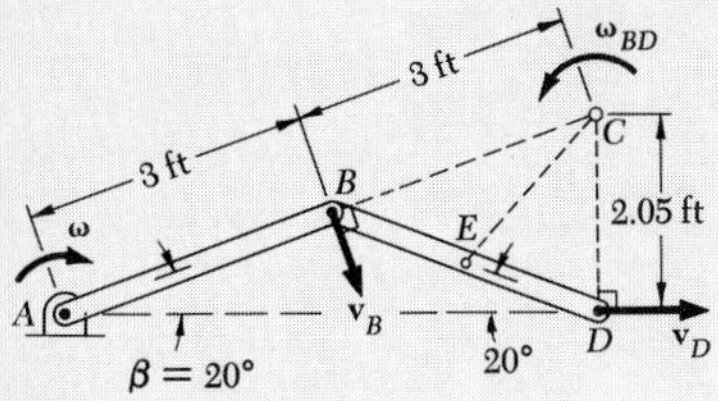

Kinematics of Motion When $\beta = 20°$. Since $\mathbf{v}_B$ is perpendicular to the rod AB and $\mathbf{v}_D$ is horizontal, the instantaneous center of rotation of rod BD is located at C. Considering the geometry of the figure, we obtain

$$BC = 3 \text{ ft} \qquad CD = 2(3 \text{ ft}) \sin 20° = 2.05 \text{ ft}$$

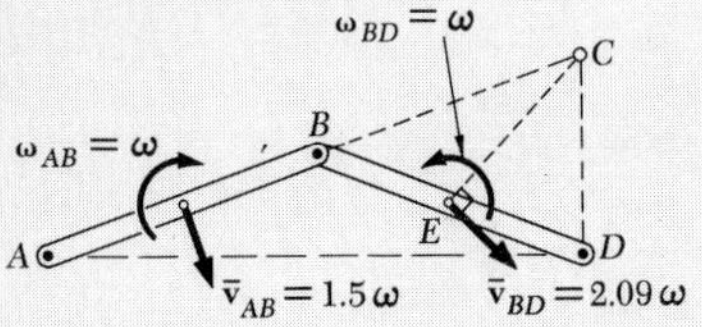

Solving the triangle CDE, where E is located at the mass center of rod BD, we find $EC = 2.09$ ft. Denoting by ω the angular velocity of rod AB, we have

$$\bar{v}_{AB} = (1.5 \text{ ft})\omega \qquad \bar{\mathbf{v}}_{AB} = 1.5\omega \searrow$$
$$v_B = (3 \text{ ft})\omega \qquad \mathbf{v}_B = 3\omega \searrow$$

Since rod BD seems to rotate about point C, we may write

$$v_B = (BC)\omega_{BD} \qquad (3 \text{ ft})\omega = (3 \text{ ft})\omega_{BD} \qquad \omega_{BD} = \omega \circlearrowleft$$
$$\bar{v}_{BD} = (EC)\omega_{BD} = 2.09\omega \qquad \bar{\mathbf{v}}_{BD} = 2.09\omega \searrow$$

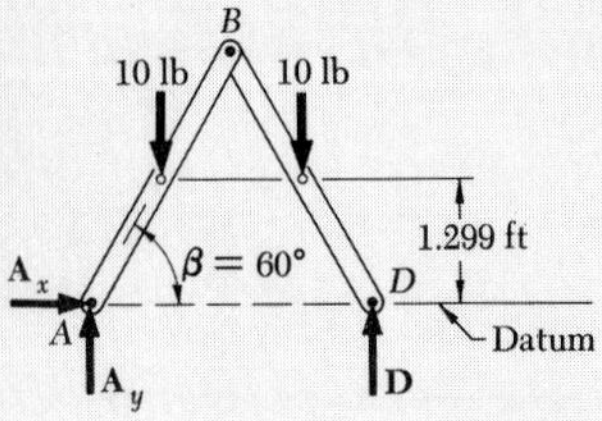

Position *1*

Position *1*. *Potential Energy.* Choosing the datum as shown, we have

$$V_1 = 2[(10 \text{ lb})(1.299 \text{ ft})] = 26.0 \text{ ft-lb}$$

Kinetic Energy. Since the system is at rest, $T_1 = 0$.

Position 2. *Potential Energy*

$$V_2 = 2[(10 \text{ lb})(0.513 \text{ ft})] = 10.26 \text{ ft-lb}$$

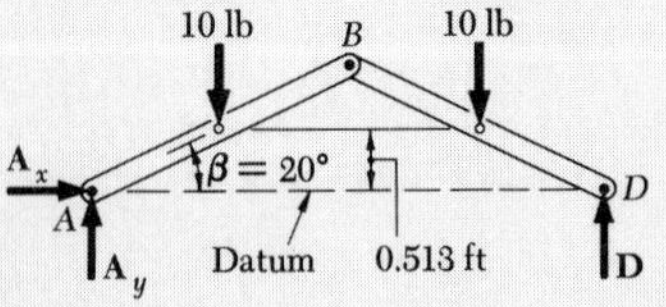

Position 2

Kinetic Energy

$$\bar{I}_{AB} = \bar{I}_{BD} = \tfrac{1}{12}ml^2 = \frac{1}{12}\frac{10}{g}(3)^2 = 0.233 \text{ lb-ft-sec}^2$$

$$T_2 = \tfrac{1}{2}m\bar{v}_{AB}^2 + \tfrac{1}{2}\bar{I}_{AB}\omega_{AB}^2 + \tfrac{1}{2}m\bar{v}_{BD}^2 + \tfrac{1}{2}\bar{I}_{BD}\omega_{BD}^2$$
$$= \frac{1}{2}\frac{10}{g}(1.5\omega)^2 + (\tfrac{1}{2})(0.233)\omega^2 + \frac{1}{2}\frac{10}{g}(2.09\omega)^2 + (\tfrac{1}{2})(0.233)\omega^2$$
$$= 1.261\omega^2$$

Conservation of Energy

$$T_1 + V_1 = T_2 + V_2 \qquad 0 + 26.0 \text{ ft-lb} = 1.261\omega^2 + 10.26 \text{ ft-lb}$$
$$\omega = 3.53 \text{ radians/sec} \qquad \omega_{AB} = 3.53 \text{ radians/sec} \circlearrowright \blacktriangleleft$$

Velocity of Point D

$$v_D = (CD)\omega = (2.05 \text{ ft})(3.53 \text{ radians/sec})$$
$$v_D = 7.24 \text{ ft/sec} \qquad \mathbf{v}_D = 7.24 \text{ ft/sec} \rightarrow \blacktriangleleft$$

PROBLEMS

17.24. A cord is wrapped around a cylinder of radius r and weight W as shown. If the cylinder is released from rest, determine the velocity of the center of the cylinder after it has moved through a distance s.

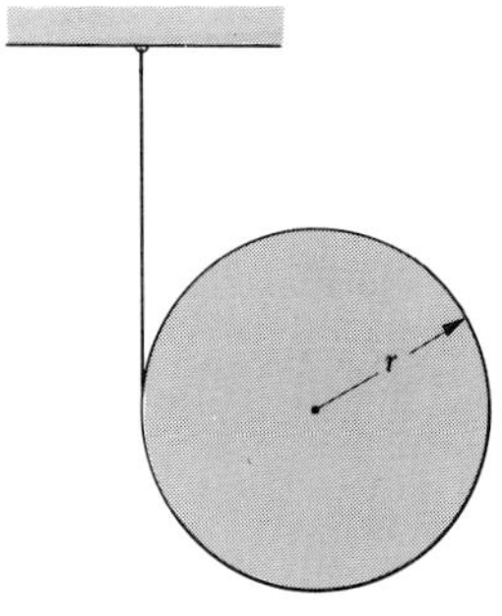

FIG. P 17.24

17.25. Solve Prob. 17.24 assuming that the cylinder is replaced by a hoop of weight W and radius r.

17.26. A flywheel is rigidly attached to a $1\frac{1}{2}$-in.-radius shaft which rolls without sliding along parallel rails. The system is released from rest and attains a speed of 6 in./sec after moving 75 in. along the rails. Determine the centroidal radius of gyration of the system.

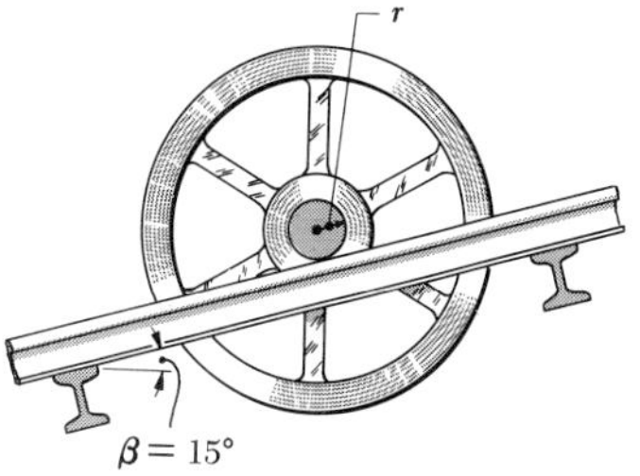

FIG. P 17.26

17.27. A sphere of weight W and radius r rolls without slipping inside a curved surface of radius R. Knowing that the sphere is released from rest in the position shown, derive an expression (*a*) for the linear velocity of the sphere when $\beta = 0$, (*b*) for the magnitude of the vertical reaction when $\beta = 0$.

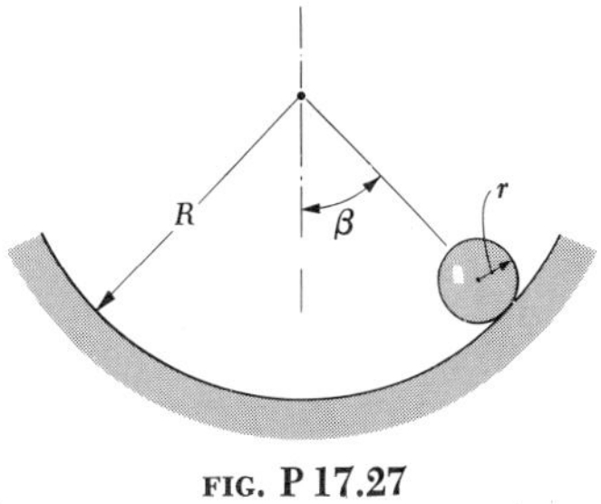

FIG. P 17.27

17.28. A hemisphere of weight W and radius r is released from rest in the position shown. Assuming that the hemisphere rolls without sliding, determine (*a*) the angular velocity of the hemisphere after it has rolled through 90°, (*b*) the normal reaction at the surface at the same instant. (*Hint.* Note that $GO = \frac{3}{8}r$ and that, by the parallel-axis theorem, $\bar{I} = \frac{2}{5}mr^2 - m(GO)^2$.)

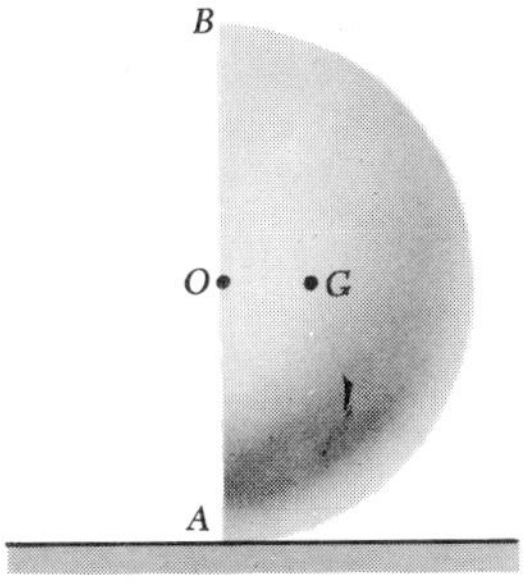

FIG. P 17.28

17.29. Solve Prob. 17.28 considering a half cylinder instead of a hemisphere. (*Hint.* Note that $GO = 4r/3\pi$ and that, by the parallel-axis theorem, $\bar{I} = \frac{1}{2}mr^2 - m(GO)^2$.)

17.30. A slender rod of length L and weight W is pivoted at one end as shown. It is released from rest in a horizontal position and swings freely. (*a*) Determine the angular velocity of the rod and the reaction at the pivot when $\theta = 90°$. (*b*) Solve part *a* for $W = 20$ lb and $L = 6$ ft.

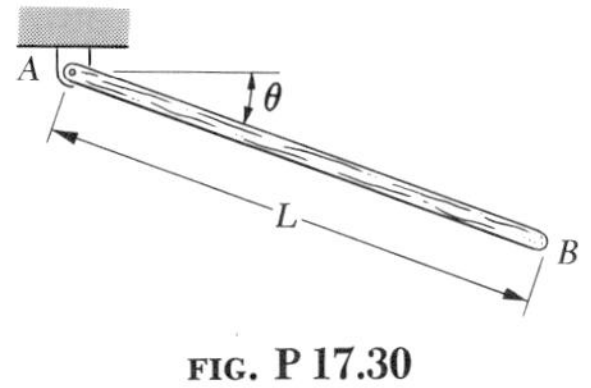

FIG. P 17.30

17.31. A 6- by 8-in. rectangular plate is suspended by two pins at A and B. The pin at B is removed and the plate swings about point A. Determine (*a*) the angular velocity of the plate after it has rotated through 90°, (*b*) the maximum angular velocity attained by the plate as it swings freely.

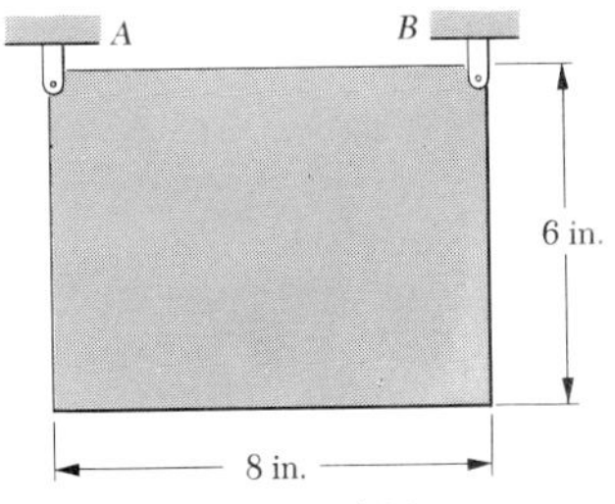

FIG. P 17.31

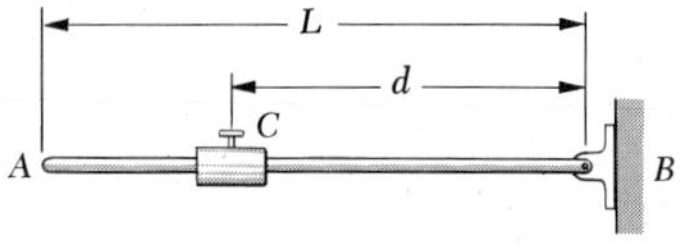

FIG. P 17.32 AND P 17.33

17.32. A collar of weight 2 lb is rigidly attached at a distance $d = 12$ in. from the end of a uniform slender rod AB. The rod weighs 6 lb and is of length $L = 24$ in. Knowing that the rod is released from rest in the position shown, determine the angular velocity of the rod after it has rotated through 90°.

***17.33.** A collar of weight 2 lb is rigidly attached to a slender rod AB of weight 6 lb and length $L = 24$ in. The rod is released from rest in the position shown. Determine the distance d for which the angular velocity of the rod is maximum after it has rotated through 90°.

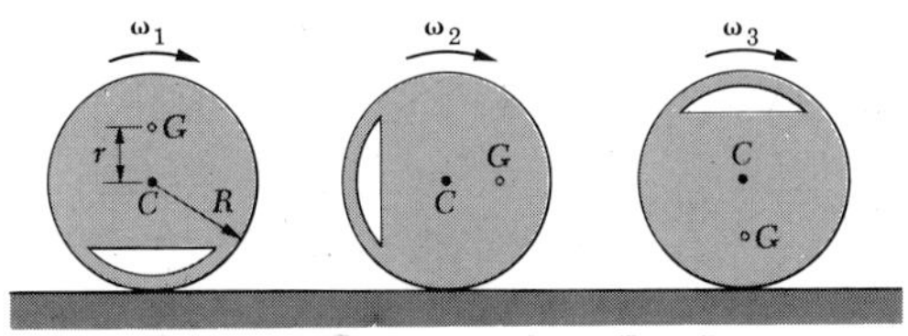

FIG. P 17.34 AND P 17.35

17.34. The mass center G of a wheel of radius R is located at a distance r from its geometric center C. The centroidal radius of gyration of the wheel is denoted by $\bar{k}$. As the wheel rolls freely and without sliding on a horizontal plane, its angular velocity is observed to vary. Denoting by ω_1, ω_2, and ω_3, respectively, the angular velocity of the wheel when G is directly above C, level with C, and directly below C, show that ω_1, ω_2, and ω_3 satisfy the relation

$$\frac{\omega_2^2 - \omega_1^2}{\omega_3^2 - \omega_2^2} = \frac{g/R + \omega_1^2}{g/R + \omega_3^2}$$

17.35. The mass center G of a 2-lb wheel of radius $R = 6$ in. is located at a distance $r = 2$ in. from its geometric center C. The centroidal radius of gyration of the wheel is $\bar{k} = 3$ in. As the wheel rolls without sliding, its angular velocity is observed to vary. Knowing that in position *1* the angular velocity is 10 radians/sec, determine the angular velocity of the wheel (*a*) in position 2, (*b*) in position 3.

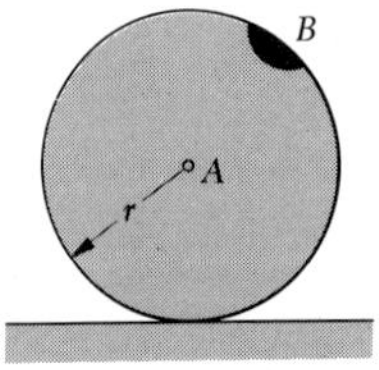

FIG. P 17.36

17.36. A weight W, of negligible dimensions, is attached at B to the rim of a disk of weight W and radius r. The disk rolls without sliding on a horizontal plane. Find the angular velocity ω_1 of the disk when B is directly above the center A in terms of g and r, knowing that the angular velocity of the disk is $3\omega_1$ when B is directly below A.

17.37. Solve Prob. 17.36 assuming that the disk is replaced by a hoop of weight W and radius r.

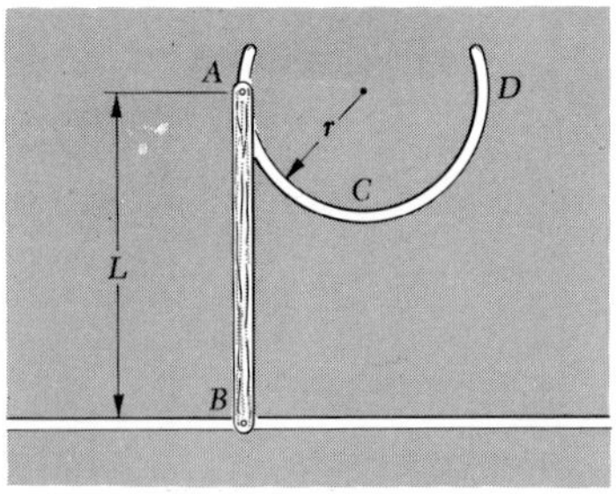

FIG. P 17.38

17.38. The motion of a slender rod of length L is guided by pins at A and B which slide freely in the slots shown. If end B is moved slightly to the right and then released, determine (*a*) the angular velocity of the rod and the velocity of the center of the rod as end A reaches point C, (*b*) the position in which the rod will come again to rest.

17.39. Solve Prob. 17.38 assuming that end B is moved slightly to the left and then released.

17.40. The motion of a 2-ft slender rod is guided by pins at A and B which slide freely in the slots shown. Knowing that the rod is released from rest when $\beta = 0$, determine the velocity of A and of B (a) when $\beta = 30°$, (b) when $\beta = 90°$.

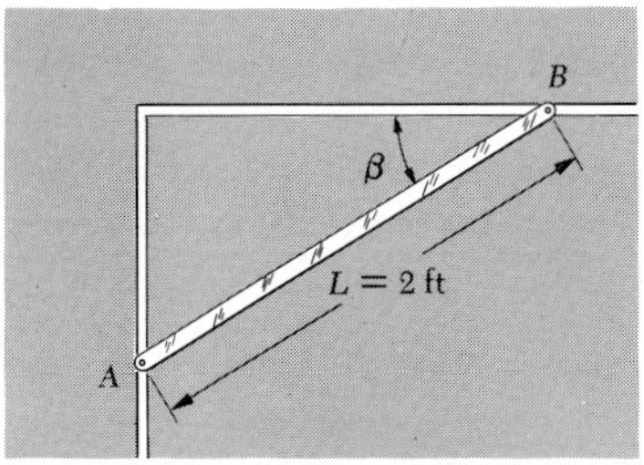

FIG. P 17.40

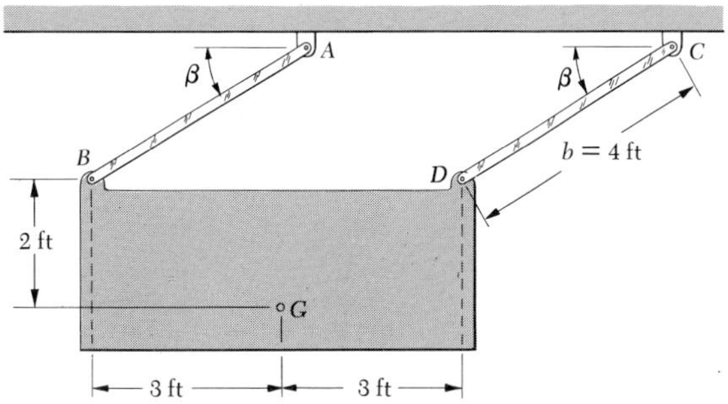

FIG. P 17.42

17.41. In Prob. 17.40, determine (a) the angle β for which the speed of end A is maximum, (b) the corresponding maximum speed of A.

17.42. A 200-lb bin is suspended from two rods AB and CD of negligible weight. The bin is released from rest in the position $\beta = 0$. As the bin passes through its lowest position, determine (a) the velocity of the bin, (b) the reactions at A and C. (c) Show that the answer to part b is independent of the length b of the rods.

17.43. Solve Prob. 17.42 assuming that each rod weighs 50 lb.

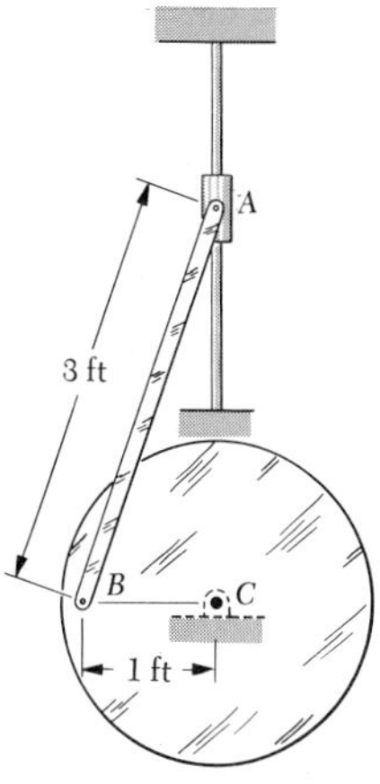

FIG. P 17.44

17.44. The connecting rod AB weighs 10 lb and is attached to a small collar of negligible weight at A and to a flywheel at B. The flywheel weighs 40 lb and has a radius of gyration of 9 in. Knowing that the angular velocity of the flywheel is 60 rpm clockwise in the position shown, determine the angular velocity of the flywheel (a) when B is directly above C, (b) when B is directly below C.

17.45. If in Prob. 17.44 the angular velocity of the flywheel is to be the same in the position shown and when point B is directly above C, determine its required angular velocity in the position shown.

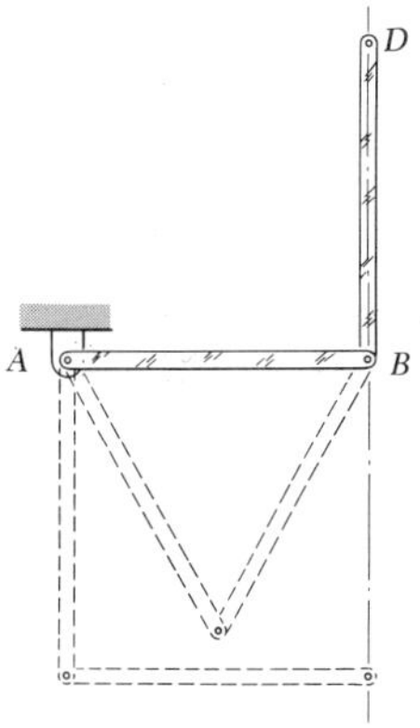

FIG. P 17.46

17.46. Each of the two rods shown is of length $L = 3$ ft and weighs $W = 5$ lb. Point D is constrained to move along a vertical line. If the system is released from rest when rod AB is horizontal, determine the velocity of points B and D as rod BD passes through a horizontal position.

17.47. In Prob. 17.46, determine the velocity of points B and D when points A and D are at the same elevation.

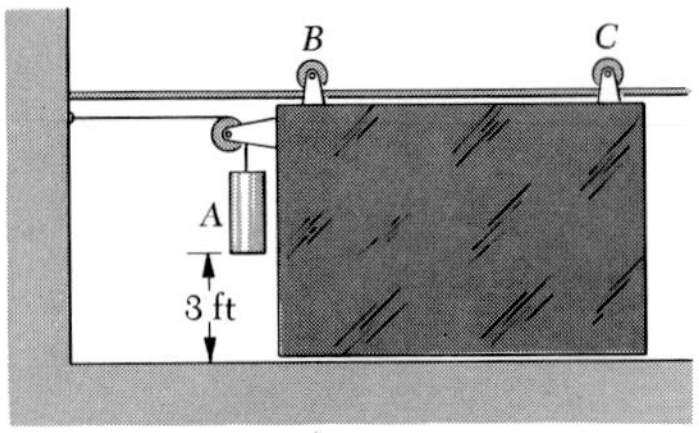

FIG. P 17.48

17.48. The motion of a 20-lb sliding panel is guided by rollers at B and C. The counterweight A weighs 15 lb and is attached to a cable as shown. If the system is released from rest in the position shown, determine the velocity of the counterweight as it strikes the ground. Neglect the effect of friction.

17.49. Determine the velocity of pin B as the rods of Sample Prob. 17.5 strike the horizontal surface.

17.50. A 2-ft rod AB of weight 10 lb is attached to a pin at A and to a spring of constant 6 lb/in. In the vertical position shown, the spring is unstretched and the angular velocity of the rod is 5 radians/sec clockwise. Determine the angular velocity of the rod after it has rotated through 90°.

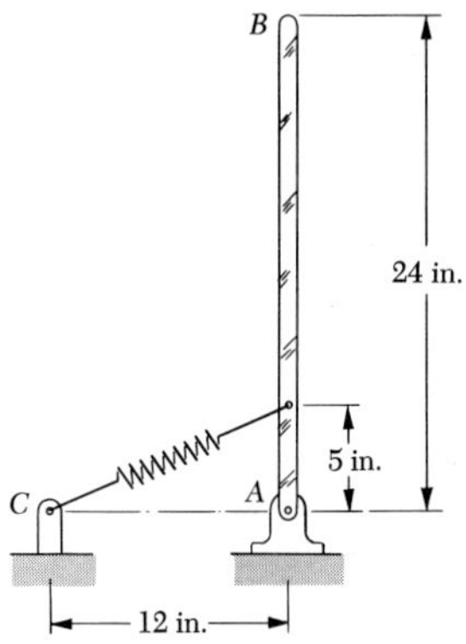

FIG. P 17.50

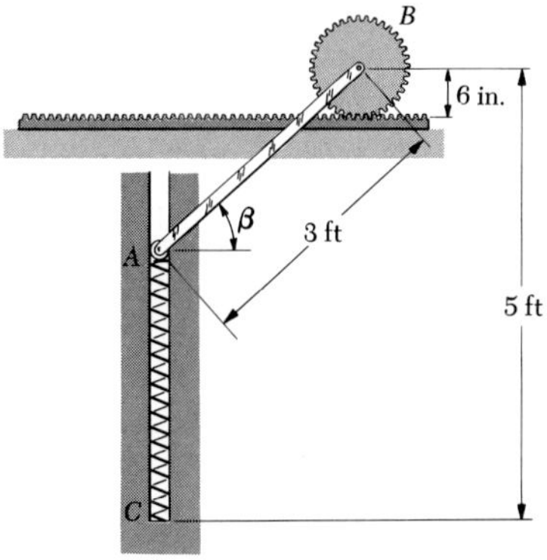

FIG. P 17.52

17.51. Solve Prob. 17.50 assuming that the rod rotates in a horizontal plane about a vertical axis (perpendicular to the page) through A.

17.52. Gear B weighs 10 lb and has a centroidal radius of gyration of 5 in. Rod AB weighs 8 lb and is attached to the gear at B and to a spring at A. The spring AC, of constant $k = 2$ lb/in., has an unstretched length of 18 in. If the system is released from rest when $\beta = 30°$, determine the velocity of point B when $\beta = 90°$.

17.53. The system of Prob. 17.52 is released from rest in the position shown. Determine the required initial value of β if the velocity of point B is to be 10 ft/sec when $\beta = 90°$.

17.54. Referring to Sample Prob. 16.3, determine the rate at which energy is being dissipated at the instant the brake is applied.

17.55. The motor shown runs a machine attached to the shaft at A. The motor develops 4 hp and runs at a constant speed of 300 rpm. Determine the moment of the couple exerted (*a*) by the shaft on pulley A, (*b*) by the motor on pulley B.

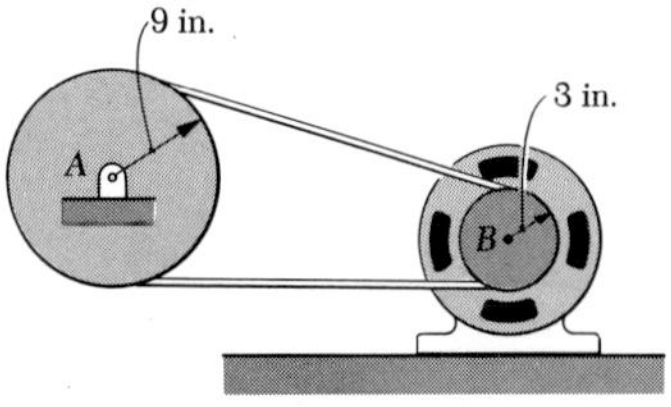

FIG. P 17.55

17.56. Knowing that the moment of the maximum allowable couple which may be applied to a shaft is 80 kip-in., determine the maximum horsepower which may be transmitted by the shaft (*a*) at 60 rpm, (*b*) at 300 rpm.

17.57. Determine the moment of the couple which must be exerted by a motor to develop $\frac{3}{4}$ hp at a speed of (*a*) 720 rpm, (*b*) 7,200 rpm.

REVIEW PROBLEMS

17.58. A rope of total weight 25 lb and total length 50 ft is wrapped around the drum of a hoist as shown. The drum and shaft weigh 40 lb and have a combined radius of gyration of 8 in. Knowing that a length $h = 10$ ft of rope hangs from the drum when the drum-shaft system is released from rest, determine the velocity of end *A* of the rope when $h = 40$ ft.

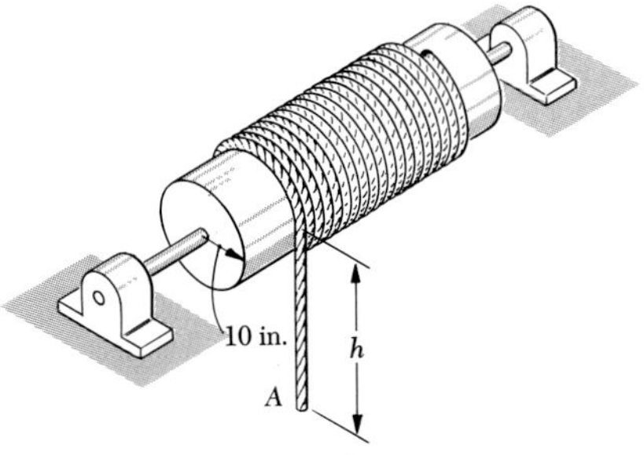

FIG. P 17.58

17.59. In Prob. 17.58, determine the velocity of end *A* of the rope after it has moved 20 ft, knowing that the system was released from rest when (*a*) $h = 5$ ft, (*b*) $h = 20$ ft.

17.60. Gear *B* weighs 4 lb and has a centroidal radius of gyration of 5 in. Rod *AB* is 12 in. long and weighs 3 lb. If the system is released from rest in the position shown, determine the velocity of point *B* after rod *AB* has rotated through 90°. Assume that gear *A* is fixed and cannot rotate.

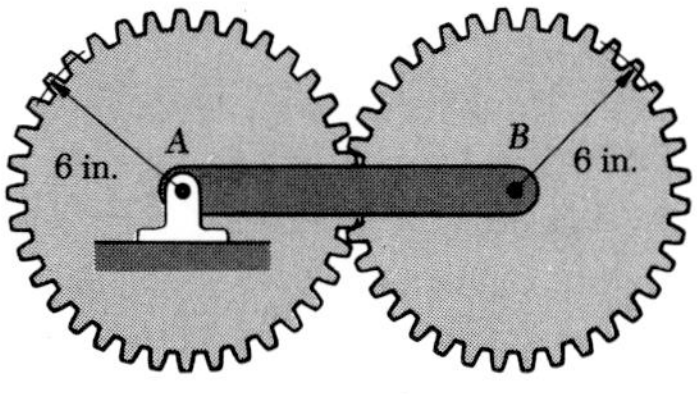

FIG. P 17.60

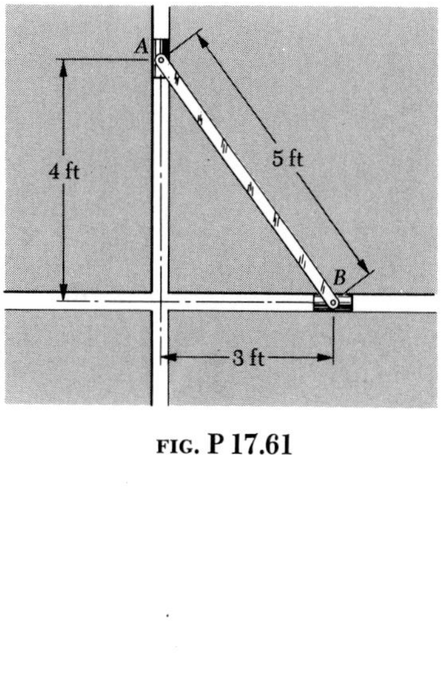

FIG. P 17.61

17.61. The ends of the 10-lb rod *AB* are attached to blocks which may slide without friction in the slots shown. If the rod is released from rest in the position shown, determine the velocities of blocks *A* and *B* after block *A* has moved (*a*) 1 ft, (*b*) 4 ft.

17.62. Solve Prob. 17.61 assuming that blocks *A* and *B* weigh 2 lb each.

17.63. A spring of constant *k* is attached to a pin located at a distance *r* from the center of a flywheel of moment of inertia $\bar{I}$. Knowing that in the position shown the tension in the spring is zero, determine the smallest initial angular velocity ω_0 which will permit continuous (although not uniform) rotation of the flywheel.

17.64. For the system of Prob. 17.63, determine the speed ω_0 so that the speed variation during each revolution will be limited to 2 per cent. Assume $\bar{I} = 15$ lb-ft-sec^2, $k = 100$ lb/in., $r = 2$ in.

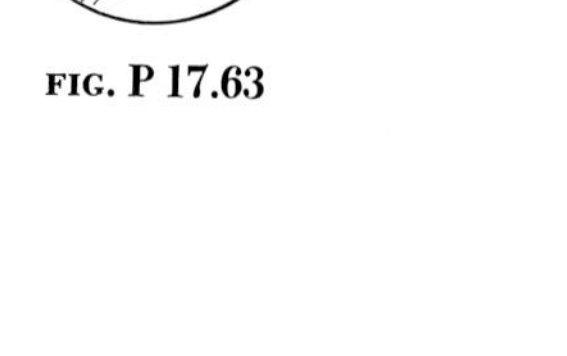

FIG. P 17.63

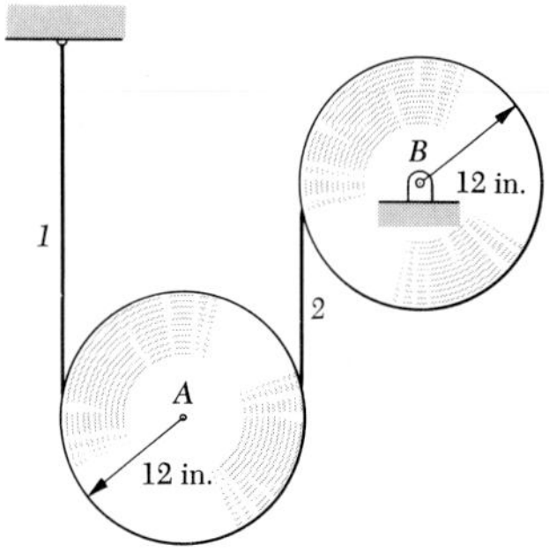

FIG. P 17.65 AND P 17.66

17.65. Two disks weighing 20 lb each are connected by a rope as shown. If the system is released from rest in the position shown, determine (*a*) the angular velocity of disk *B* after disk *A* has moved 10 ft, (*b*) the tension in portion 2 of the rope.

17.66. Two disks weighing 20 lb each are connected by a rope as shown. At the instant shown, the angular velocity of disk *B* is 10 radians/sec clockwise. Determine how far disk *A* will rise before the angular velocity of disk *B* is reduced to 2 radians/sec.

17.67. Two uniform rods, each of weight *W*, are attached to two gears as shown. The rods are released from rest in the position $\theta = 0$. Neglecting the mass of the gears, determine the angular velocity of the rods when (*a*) $\theta = 30°$, (*b*) $\theta = 45°$, (*c*) $\theta = 60°$.

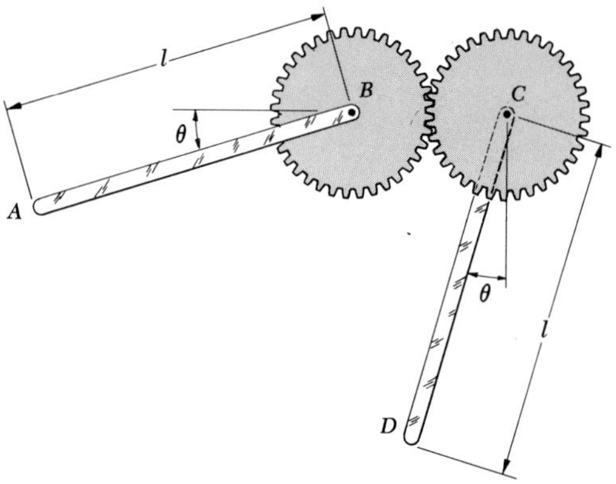

FIG. P 17.67

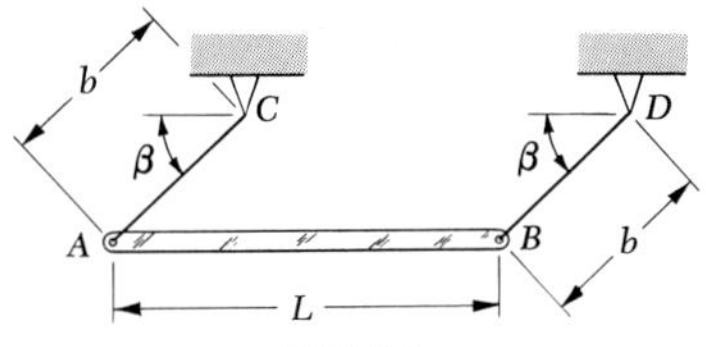

FIG. P 17.68

17.68. A uniform rod of length *L* and weight *W* is attached to two wires, each of length *b*. The rod is released from rest when $\beta = 0$ and swings to the position $\beta = 90°$ at which time wire *BD* suddenly breaks. Determine the tension in wire *AC* (*a*) immediately before wire *BD* breaks, (*b*) immediately after wire *BD* breaks.

***17.69.** In Prob. 17.68, draw the shear and bending-moment diagrams for rod *AB* (*a*) immediately before wire *BD* breaks, (*b*) immediately after wire *BD* breaks.

18. KINETICS OF RIGID BODIES: IMPULSE AND MOMENTUM

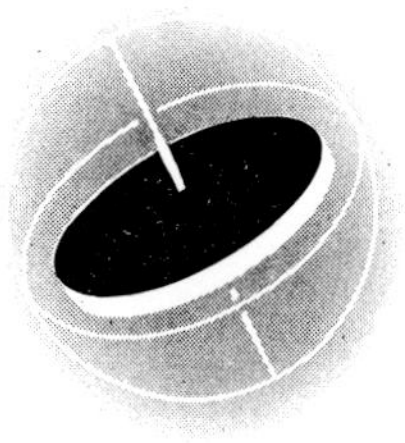

18.1. Principle of Impulse and Momentum for a Rigid Body. In this chapter, the principle of impulse and momentum will be used to analyze the motion of rigid bodies and of systems of rigid bodies. As was pointed out in Chap. 14, the method of impulse and momentum is particularly well adapted to the solution of problems involving time and velocities. Moreover, the principle of impulse and momentum provides the only practicable method for the solution of problems of impact.

Since a rigid body of mass m may be considered as made of a large number of particles of mass Δm, Eq. (14.31), which was derived in Sec. 14.10 for a system of particles, may now be used to analyze the motion of a rigid body. We write

$$\textbf{Syst Momenta}_1 + \textbf{Syst Ext Imp}_{1\rightarrow 2} = \textbf{Syst Momenta}_2 \qquad (18.1)$$

This equation relates the three systems of vectors shown in Fig. 18.1. It expresses that the system formed by the momenta of the particles of the rigid body at time t_1 and the system of the impulses of the external forces applied to the body from t_1 to t_2 are together equivalent to the system formed by the momenta of the particles at time t_2.

We recall from Sec. 14.10 that, in the case of particles moving in the xy plane, three scalar equations are required to express the same relationship. The first two equations may be obtained by considering respectively the x and y components of the vectors shown in Fig. 18.1; they will relate the linear momenta of the particles and the linear impulses of the given forces in the x and y directions respectively. The third equation, which is obtained by computing the moments about O of the same vectors, will relate the angular momenta of the particles and the angular impulses of the forces.

Before we may conveniently apply the principle of impulse and momentum to the study of the plane motion of a rigid body,

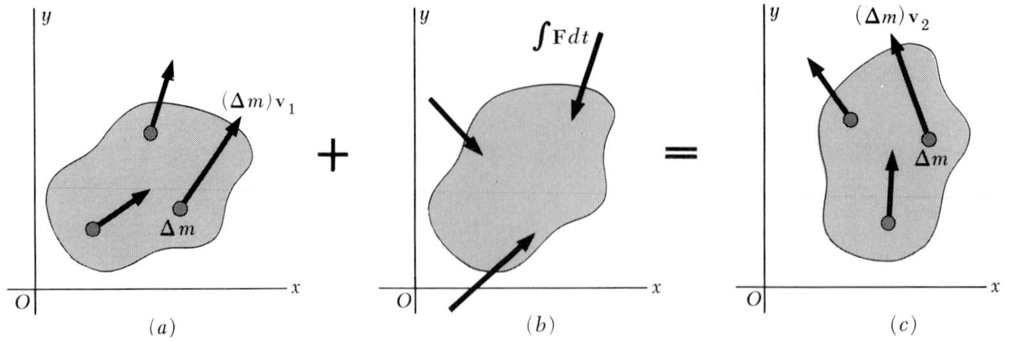

FIG. 18.1

we must learn to express more simply the systems of vectors representing the momenta of the particles forming the rigid body. This is the object of the next section.

18.2. Momentum of a Rigid Body in Plane Motion. We shall see in this section that the system of the momenta of the particles forming a rigid body may be replaced at any given instant by an equivalent system consisting of a *momentum vector* attached at the mass center of the body and a *momentum couple*. This reduction of the system of momenta to a vector and a couple is similar to the reduction of the system of effective forces described in Chap. 16. While the method involved is quite general, our present analysis will be limited to the plane motion of rigid slabs and of rigid bodies which are symmetrical with respect to the reference plane.†

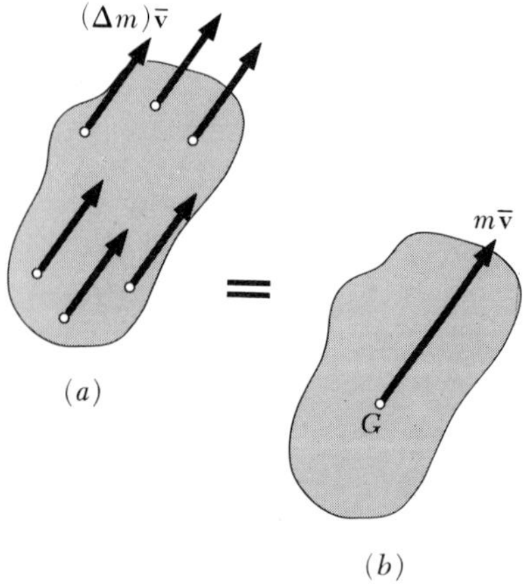

FIG. 18.2

Translation. Consider first the case of a rigid body in translation. Since each particle, at any given instant, has the same velocity $\overline{\mathbf{v}}$ as the mass center G of the body, we find by a reasoning similar to that used in Sec. 16.2 that *the system of the momenta* of the particles forming the body *is equivalent to a single momentum vector $m\overline{\mathbf{v}}$ attached at the mass center G* (Fig. 18.2). This vector is the *linear momentum* of the body.

Centroidal Rotation. When a rigid body rotates about a fixed centroidal axis perpendicular to the reference plane, the velocity $\mathbf{v}$ of any given particle of the body is perpendicular to the line joining the particle to the axis of rotation and has a magnitude $v = r\omega$, where r is the distance of the particle from the axis and ω the angular velocity of the body at the instant considered. The momentum of each particle is thus represented by a vector $(\Delta m)\mathbf{v}$ of magnitude $(\Delta m)r\omega$ and directed as shown in Fig. 18.3*a*. A derivation similar to that used in Sec. 16.3 shows that, if the body is symmetrical with respect to the reference plane, *the system of the momenta* of the particles forming the body *is equivalent to a single momentum couple.*

The moment of the momentum couple is obtained by summing the moments about G of the elementary momenta

† Or, more generally, to the motion of rigid bodies which have a principal axis of inertia perpendicular to the reference plane.

$(\Delta m)\mathbf{v}$. The sum obtained is denoted by h_G and referred to as the *angular momentum* of the body about the axis through G. We have

$$+\circlearrowleft \; h_G = \Sigma r(\Delta m)r\omega = \omega\Sigma r^2(\Delta m)$$

Since $\Sigma r^2(\Delta m)$ represents the centroidal moment of inertia $\bar{I}$ of the body, we write

$$h_G = \bar{I}\omega \tag{18.2}$$

Recalling from Sec. 15.3 that the angular velocity of a rigid body rotating about a fixed axis may be represented by a vector $\boldsymbol{\omega}$ of magnitude ω directed along that axis, we note that the momentum couple may be represented by a couple vector $\bar{I}\boldsymbol{\omega}$ of magnitude $\bar{I}\omega$ directed along the axis of rotation. We therefore conclude that, in the case of the centroidal rotation of a rigid body symmetrical with respect to the reference plane, *the system of the momenta* of the particles of the body *is equivalent to a momentum couple* $\bar{I}\boldsymbol{\omega}$, where $\boldsymbol{\omega}$ denotes the angular velocity of the body (Fig. 18.3*b*).

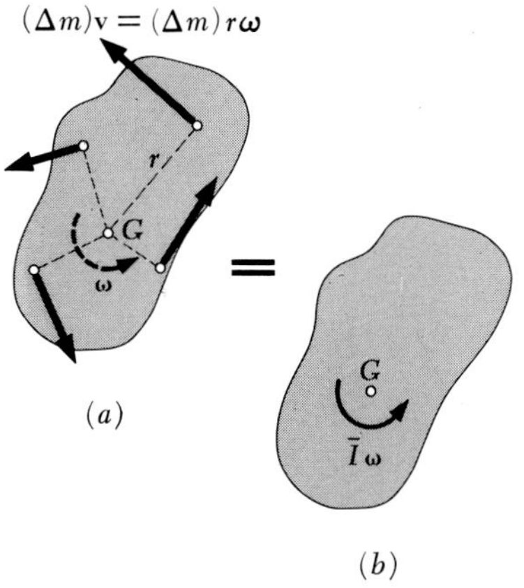

FIG. 18.3

General Plane Motion. In the general case of the plane motion of a rigid body, the velocity of any given particle P of the body may be resolved into the velocity $\bar{\mathbf{v}}$ of the mass center G and the relative velocity $\mathbf{v}_{P/G}$ (of magnitude $v_{P/G} = r\omega$) of P with respect to G. The momentum of each particle may thus be resolved into the vectors $(\Delta m)\bar{\mathbf{v}}$ and $(\Delta m)\mathbf{v}_{P/G}$ shown in Fig. 18.4*a*. Recalling the results obtained above in the particular cases of translation and centroidal rotation, we find that the vectors $(\Delta m)\bar{\mathbf{v}}$ may be replaced by their resultant $m\bar{\mathbf{v}}$ attached at G and that the vectors $(\Delta m)\mathbf{v}_{P/G}$ reduce to the couple $\bar{I}\boldsymbol{\omega}$. While this vector and this couple may in turn be replaced by a single vector,† it is generally found more convenient to represent the system of momenta by the momentum vector $m\bar{\mathbf{v}}$ attached at G and the momentum couple $\bar{I}\boldsymbol{\omega}$ (Fig. 18.4*b*). The momentum vector is associated with the translation of the body with G and represents the *linear momentum* of the body. The momentum couple corresponds to the rotation of the body about G and its moment $\bar{I}\omega$ represents the *angular momentum* h_G *of the body about an axis through G.* Recalling the definition given in Sec. 14.10 for the angular momentum of a system of particles, we note that the angular momentum h_A of the body about an axis through an arbitrary point A may be obtained by adding algebraically the moment about A of the momentum vector $m\bar{\mathbf{v}}$ and the moment $\bar{I}\omega$ of the momentum couple.‡

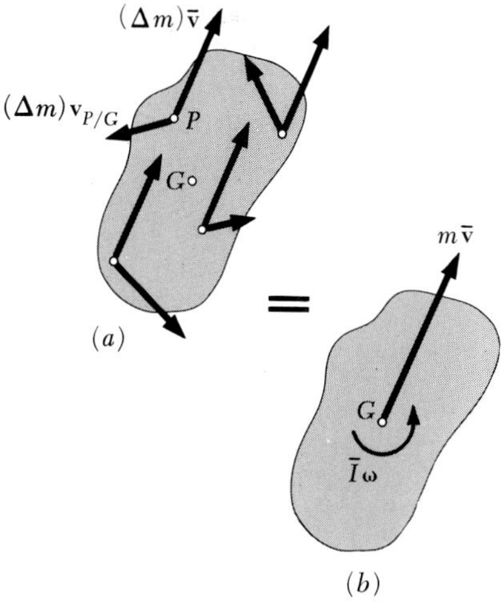

FIG. 18.4

† See Probs. 18.9 and 18.10.

‡ Note that, in general, h_A is *not* equal to $I_A\omega$ (see Prob. 18.11).

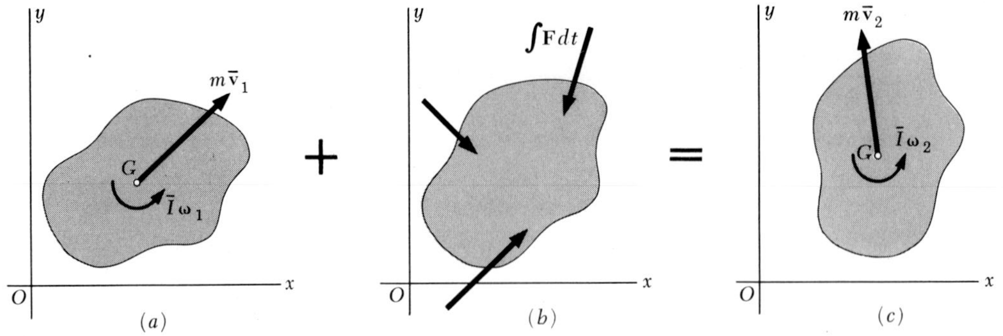

FIG. 18.5

18.3. Application of the Principle of Impulse and Momentum to the Analysis of the Plane Motion of a Rigid Body. We saw in the preceding section that, in the most general case of the plane motion of a rigid body, the system of the momenta of the particles of the body reduces to a vector $m\bar{\mathbf{v}}$ attached at G and a couple $\bar{I}\omega$. Replacing the system of momenta in parts a and c of Fig. 18.1 by the equivalent momentum vector and momentum couple, we obtain the three diagrams shown in Fig. 18.5. This figure expresses graphically, in the case of the plane motion of a rigid body, the fundamental relation

$$\textbf{Syst Momenta}_1 + \textbf{Syst Ext Imp}_{1\to 2} = \textbf{Syst Momenta}_2 \quad (18.1)$$

Three equations of motion may be derived from Fig. 18.5. Two equations are obtained by summing and equating the x and y *components* of the momenta and impulses, and the third by summing and equating the *moments* of these vectors *about any given point.* The coordinate axes may be chosen fixed in space, or they may be allowed to move with the mass center of the body while maintaining a fixed direction. In either case, the point about which moments are taken should keep the same position relative to the coordinate axes during the interval of time considered.

In deriving the three equations of motion for a rigid body, care should be taken not to add indiscriminately linear and angular momenta. Confusion will be avoided if it is kept in mind that $m\bar{v}_x$ and $m\bar{v}_y$ represent the *components of a vector*, namely, the linear momentum vector $m\bar{\mathbf{v}}$, while $\bar{I}\omega$ represents the *moment of a couple*, namely, the momentum couple $\bar{I}\omega$. Thus the angular momentum $\bar{I}\omega$ should be added only to the *moment* of the linear momentum $m\bar{\mathbf{v}}$, never to this vector itself nor to its components. All quantities involved will then be expressed in the same units, namely, lb-ft-sec.

As an example, we shall consider the motion of a wheel of radius r, mass m, and centroidal moment of inertia $\bar{I}$, which rolls down an incline without sliding. Assuming that the initial angular velocity ω_1 of the wheel is known, we propose to determine its angular velocity ω_2, after a time interval t, and the

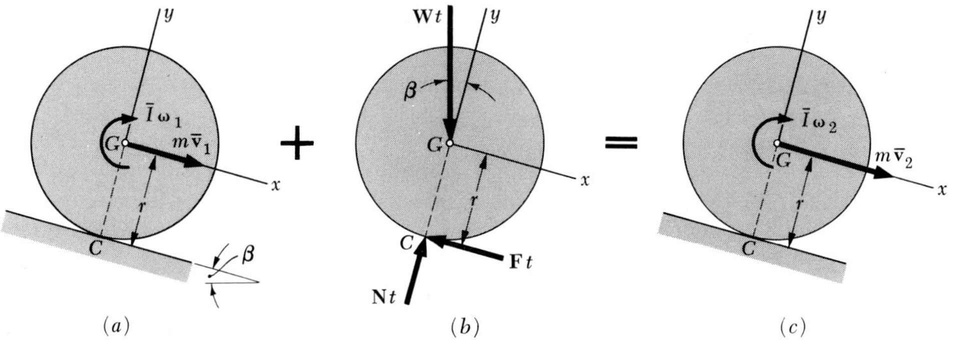

FIG. 18.6

values of the components F and N of the reaction of the incline.

The system of momenta at times t_1 and t_2 are shown, respectively, in parts *a* and *c* of Fig. 18.6. They are represented in both cases by a vector $m\bar{\mathbf{v}}$ attached at the center G of the wheel and a couple $\bar{I}\omega$. Choosing coordinate axes centered at G with the x and y axes parallel and perpendicular, respectively, to the incline, we note that the lines of action of the forces **W**, **F**, and **N** remain fixed with respect to the coordinate axes. Since these forces are also constant in magnitude, their impulses will be represented by the vectors $\mathbf{W}t$, $\mathbf{F}t$, and $\mathbf{N}t$ shown in part *b* of Fig. 18.6. Denoting by β the angle the incline forms with the horizontal, we add and equate successively the x components, y components, and moments about C (positive clockwise) of the momenta and impulses shown in Fig. 18.6. We write

$+\searrow$ x components:

$$m\bar{v}_1 - Ft + Wt \sin \beta = m\bar{v}_2 \tag{18.3}$$

$+\nearrow$ y components:

$$Nt - Wt \cos \beta = 0 \tag{18.4}$$

$+\circlearrowright$ moments about C:

$$\bar{I}\omega_1 + m\bar{v}_1 r + (Wt \sin \beta)r = \bar{I}\omega_2 + m\bar{v}_2 r \tag{18.5}$$

We note that all quantities involved in Eqs. (18.3) and (18.4) are expressed in the same units, namely, lb-sec. Since, in Eq. (18.5), the magnitudes of the linear impulse $\mathbf{W}t \sin \beta$ and of the linear momenta $m\bar{\mathbf{v}}_1$ and $m\bar{\mathbf{v}}_2$ are multiplied by the radius r, all quantities involved in that equation are also expressed in the same units, namely, lb-ft-sec. Observing that $\bar{v} = r\omega$, we write

$$mr\omega_1 - Ft + Wt \sin \beta = mr\omega_2 \tag{18.3'}$$
$$Nt - Wt \cos \beta = 0 \tag{18.4'}$$
$$(\bar{I} + mr^2)\omega_1 + (Wt \sin \beta)r = (\bar{I} + mr^2)\omega_2 \tag{18.5'}$$

Equation (18.5′) may be solved for ω_2 and Eq. (18.4′) for N; Eq. (18.3′) may be solved for F after substituting for ω_2.

Noncentroidal Rotation. In this particular case of plane motion, the magnitude of the velocity of the mass center of the body is $\bar{v} = \bar{r}\omega$, where $\bar{r}$ represents the distance from the mass center to the fixed axis of rotation and ω the angular velocity of the body at the instant considered; the magnitude of the momentum vector attached at G is thus $m\bar{v} = m\bar{r}\omega$. Summing the moments about O of the momentum vector and momentum couple (Fig. 18.7) and using the parallel-axis theorem for moments of inertia, we find that the angular momentum of the body about O is

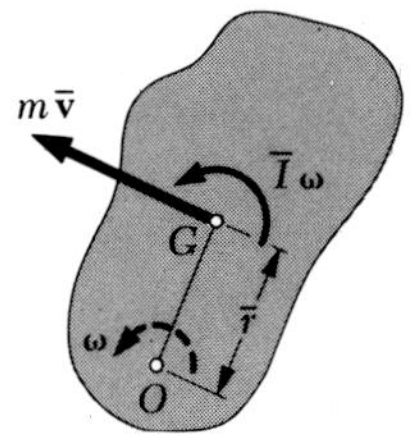

FIG. 18.7

$$\bar{I}\omega + (m\bar{r}\omega)\bar{r} = (\bar{I} + m\bar{r}^2)\omega = I_O\omega \qquad (18.6)$$

Equating the moments about O of the momenta and impulses in (18.1), we write

$$I_O\omega_1 + \Sigma \int_{t_1}^{t_2} M_O\, dt = I_O\omega_2 \qquad (18.7)$$

In the general case of plane motion of a rigid body, formula (18.6) may be used to express the angular momentum of the body with respect to the instantaneous axis of rotation. Equation (18.7) may also be used with respect to the instantaneous axis of rotation under certain conditions of symmetry. We check, for example, that Eq. (18.5′) in the example given above could have been obtained by applying formula (18.7) about C. It is recommended, however, that all problems of plane motion be solved by the general method described earlier in this section.

18.4. Systems of Rigid Bodies. The motion of several connected rigid bodies may be analyzed by applying the principle of impulse and momentum to each body separately (see Sample Prob. 18.1).

However, in solving problems involving no more than three unknowns (including the impulses of unknown reactions), it is often found more convenient to apply the principle of impulse and momentum to the system as a whole. We write

Syst Momenta$_1$ + Syst Ext Imp$_{1\to 2}$ = Syst Momenta$_2$ (18.1)

and draw the three corresponding momentum and impulse diagrams for the entire system of connected bodies. The diagrams of momenta should include a momentum vector, a momentum couple, or both, for each moving part of the system. Impulses of forces internal to the system, such as tensions in connecting cables, may be omitted from the impulse diagram (see Sample Prob. 18.2). Here again, care should be taken not to add indiscriminately linear and angular momenta; each equation should be checked to make sure that consistent units have been used.

SAMPLE PROBLEM 18.1

Gear A weighs 20 lb and has a radius of gyration of 9 in., while gear B weighs 5 lb and has a radius of gyration of 3 in. The system is at rest when a couple **M** of moment 4 lb-ft is applied to gear B. Neglecting friction, determine (*a*) the time required for the angular velocity of gear B to reach 600 rpm, (*b*) the tangential force which gear B exerts on gear A. These gears have been previously considered in Sample Prob. 17.2.

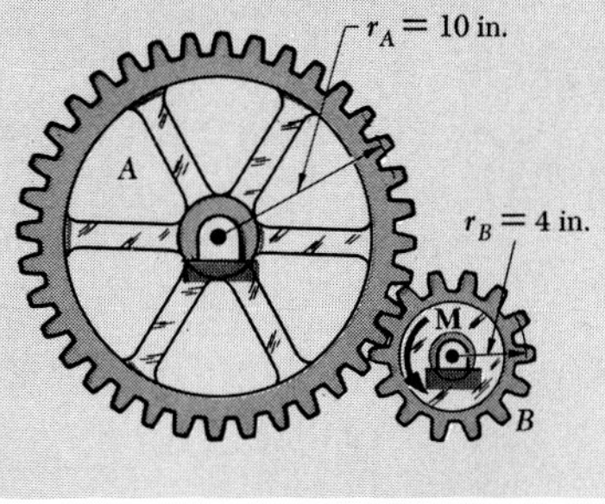

Solution. We apply the principle of impulse and momentum to each gear separately. Since all forces and the couple are constant, their impulses are obtained by multiplying them by the unknown time t. We recall from Sample Prob. 17.2 that the centroidal moments of inertia and the final angular velocities are

$$\bar{I}_A = 0.349 \text{ lb-ft-sec}^2 \qquad \bar{I}_B = 0.00970 \text{ lb-ft-sec}^2$$
$$(\omega_A)_2 = 25.1 \text{ radians/sec} \qquad (\omega_B)_2 = 62.8 \text{ radians/sec}$$

Principle of Impulse and Momentum for Gear A. The systems of initial momenta, impulses, and final momenta are shown in three separate sketches.

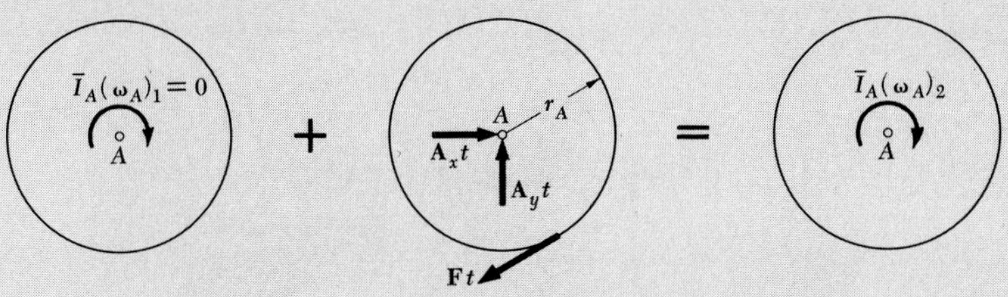

Syst Momenta$_1$ + Syst Ext Imp$_{1\to 2}$ = Syst Momenta$_2$

+↻ moments about A: $\quad 0 - Ftr_A = -\bar{I}_A(\omega_A)_2$

$$Ft(\tfrac{10}{12}) = (0.349)(25.1)$$
$$Ft = 10.51 \text{ lb-sec}$$

Principle of Impulse and Momentum for Gear B

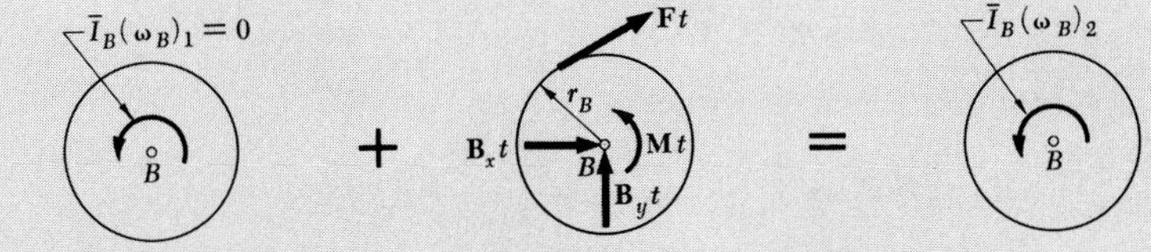

Syst Momenta$_1$ + Syst Ext Imp$_{1\to 2}$ = Syst Momenta$_2$

+↻ moments about B: $\quad 0 + Mt - Ftr_B = \bar{I}_B(\omega_B)_2$

$$+4t - (10.51)(\tfrac{4}{12}) = (0.00970)(62.8)$$
$$t = 1.028 \text{ sec} \quad ◄$$

Recalling that $Ft = 10.51$ lb-sec, we write

$$F(1.028 \text{ sec}) = 10.51 \text{ lb-sec}$$
$$F = +10.22 \text{ lb}$$

Thus, the force exerted by gear B on gear A is

$$\mathbf{F} = 10.22 \text{ lb} \swarrow \quad ◄$$

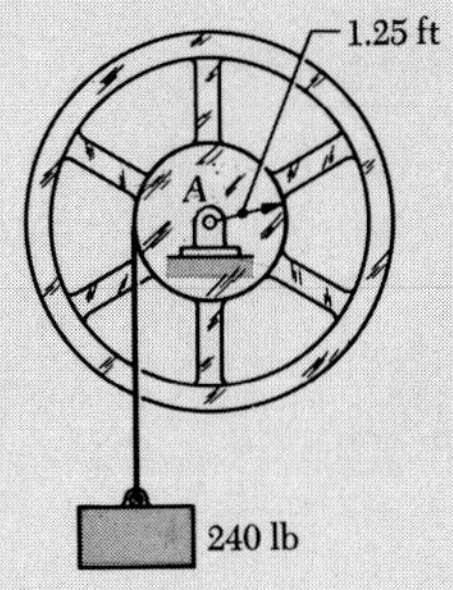

SAMPLE PROBLEM 18.2

A 240-lb block is suspended from an inextensible cable which is wrapped around a drum of radius 1.25 ft rigidly attached to a flywheel. The drum and flywheel have a combined moment of inertia $\bar{I} = 10.5$ lb-ft-sec^2. At the instant shown, the velocity of the block is 6 ft/sec directed downward. Knowing that the bearing at A is poorly lubricated and that the bearing friction is equivalent to a couple **M** of moment 60 lb-ft, determine the velocity of the block 2 sec later.

Solution. We consider the system formed by the flywheel and the block. Forces external to this system consist of the weight **W** of the flywheel, the weight **W** of the block, the reaction **A**, and the friction couple **M**. Since the magnitude and the line of action of each force are constant, the impulse of each force is equal to the product of the force and of the time interval t. Likewise, since the friction couple is constant, its angular impulse is **M**t.

Principle of Impulse and Momentum. The systems of initial momenta, impulses, and final momenta are shown in three separate sketches.

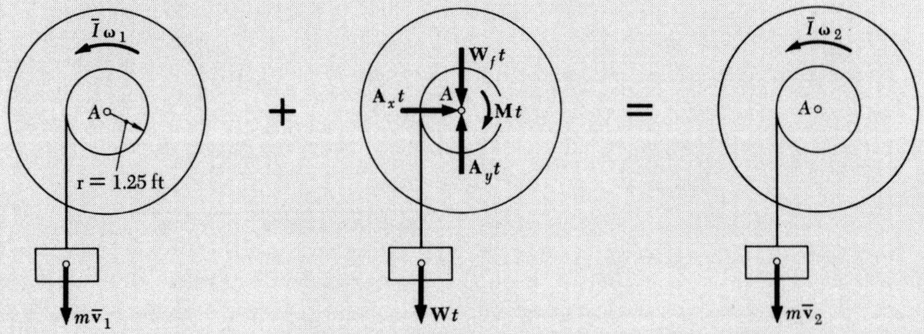

$$\textbf{Syst Momenta}_1 + \textbf{Syst Ext Imp}_{1\to 2} = \textbf{Syst Momenta}_2$$

$+\circlearrowright$ moments about A: $\quad \bar{I}\omega_1 + m\bar{v}_1 r + Wtr - Mt = \bar{I}\omega_2 + m\bar{v}_2 r$

We note that $\bar{v} = r\omega$ and write

$$\bar{v}_1 = 6 \text{ ft/sec} \qquad \omega_1 = \frac{\bar{v}_1}{r} = \frac{6}{1.25} = 4.80 \text{ radians/sec}$$

$$\omega_2 = \frac{\bar{v}_2}{r} = \frac{\bar{v}_2}{1.25}$$

Substituting these expressions together with the known values of W, $\bar{I}$, r, M, and t into the above equation, we obtain

$$(10.5)(4.80) + \frac{240}{g}(6)(1.25) + (240)(2)(1.25) - (60)(2)$$
$$= (10.5)\frac{\bar{v}_2}{1.25} + \frac{240}{g}\bar{v}_2(1.25)$$

$$\bar{v}_2 = +33.1 \text{ ft/sec} \qquad \bar{\mathbf{v}}_2 = 33.1 \text{ ft/sec} \downarrow \blacktriangleleft$$

SAMPLE PROBLEM 18.3

A hoop of radius r and weight W is placed on a horizontal surface with no linear velocity but with a clockwise angular velocity ω_1. Denoting by μ the coefficient of friction between the hoop and the surface, determine (*a*) the time t_2 at which the hoop will start rolling without sliding, (*b*) the linear and angular velocities of the hoop at time t_2.

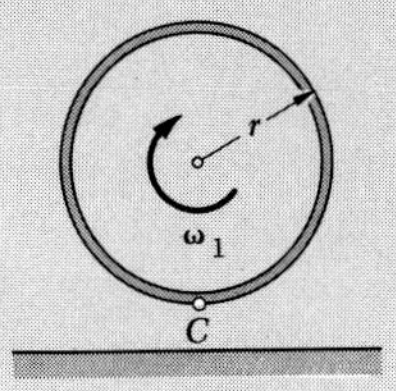

Solution. Since the entire mass, $m = W/g$, is located at a distance r from the center of the hoop, we write $\bar{I} = mr^2 = (W/g)r^2$. While the hoop is sliding relative to the surface, it is acted upon by the normal force **N**, the friction force **F**, and its weight **W**.

Principle of Impulse and Momentum. We apply the principle of impulse and momentum to the hoop from the time t_1 when it is placed on the surface until the time t_2 when it starts rolling without sliding.

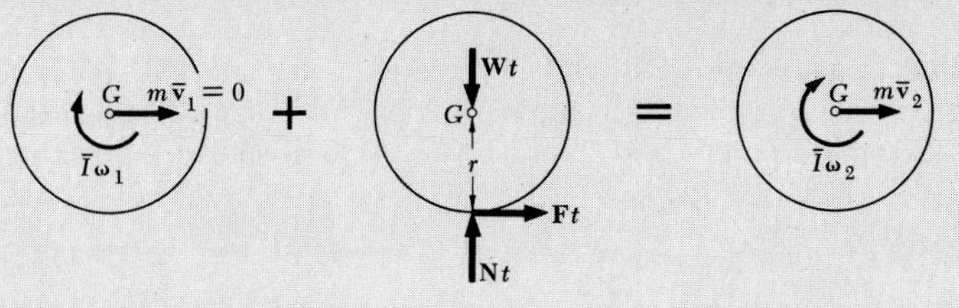

$$\textbf{Syst Momenta}_1 + \textbf{Syst Ext Imp}_{1\to 2} = \textbf{Syst Momenta}_2$$

$+\uparrow$ y components: $\quad Nt - Wt = 0 \qquad (1)$

$\xrightarrow{+}$ x components: $\quad Ft = m\bar{v}_2 \qquad (2)$

$+\circlearrowright$ moments about G: $\quad -\bar{I}\omega_1 + Ftr = -\bar{I}\omega_2 \qquad (3)$

From (1) we obtain $N = W$. For $t < t_2$, sliding occurs at point C and we have $F = \mu N = \mu W$. Substituting $F = \mu W$ into (2),

$$\mu Wt = \frac{W}{g}\bar{v}_2 \qquad \bar{v}_2 = \mu g t \qquad (4)$$

Substituting $F = \mu W$ into (3),

$$-\frac{W}{g}r^2\omega_1 + \mu Wtr = -\frac{W}{g}r^2\omega_2 \qquad \omega_2 = \omega_1 - \frac{\mu g}{r}t \qquad (5)$$

The hoop will start rolling without sliding when the velocity $\mathbf{v}_C$ of the point of contact is zero. At that time, $t = t_2$, point C becomes the instantaneous center of rotation, and we have $\bar{v}_2 = r\omega_2$. Substituting from (4) and (5), we write

$$\bar{v}_2 = r\omega_2 \qquad \mu g t_2 = r\left(\omega_1 - \frac{\mu g}{r}t_2\right) \qquad t_2 = \frac{r\omega_1}{2\mu g} \quad ◄$$

Substituting this expression for t_2 into (4),

$$\bar{v}_2 = \mu g t_2 = \mu g\frac{r\omega_1}{2\mu g} \qquad \bar{v}_2 = \tfrac{1}{2}r\omega_1 \qquad \bar{\mathbf{v}}_2 = \tfrac{1}{2}r\omega_1 \rightarrow \quad ◄$$

$$\omega_2 = \frac{\bar{v}_2}{r} \qquad \omega_2 = \tfrac{1}{2}\omega_1 \qquad \omega_2 = \tfrac{1}{2}\omega_1 \circlearrowright \quad ◄$$

PROBLEMS

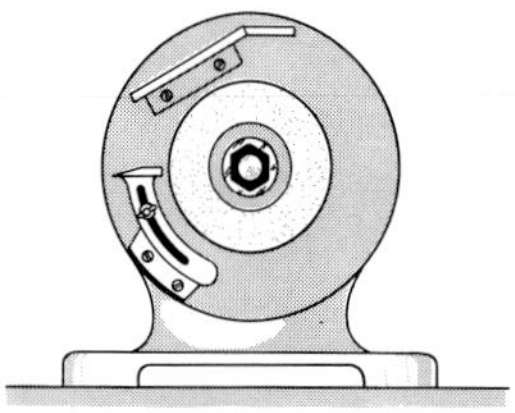

FIG. P 18.2

18.1. At a time when an electric motor is rotating at 1,200 rpm, the load and power are cut off and the rotor coasts to rest. The rotor weighs 75 lb and has a radius of gyration of 6 in. If the kinetic friction of the rotor produces a couple of moment equal to 6 lb-in., determine the time required for the rotor to coast to rest.

18.2. A small grinding wheel is attached to the shaft of an electric motor which has a rated speed of 3,600 rpm. When the power is turned off, the unit coasts to rest in 70 sec. The grinding wheel and rotor have a combined weight of 6 lb and a combined radius of gyration of 2 in. Determine the average moment of the couple due to kinetic friction in the bearings of the motor.

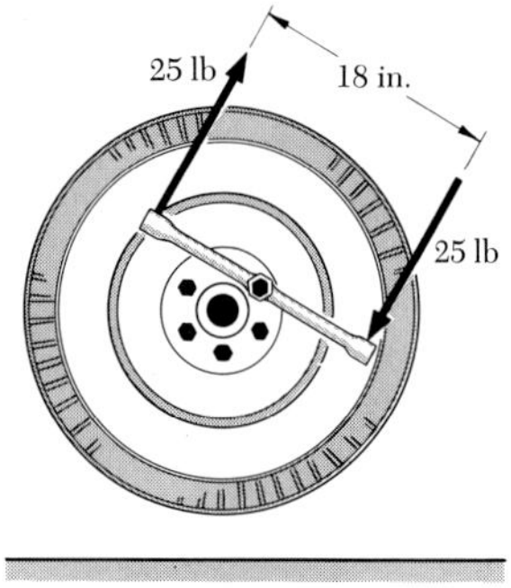

FIG. P 18.3

18.3. A bolt located 2 in. from the center of an automobile wheel is tightened by applying the couple shown for $\frac{1}{10}$ sec. Assuming that the wheel is free to rotate and is initially at rest, determine the resulting angular velocity of the wheel. The wheel weighs 45 lb and has a radius of gyration of 11 in.

18.4. A cylinder of radius r and weight W is placed with no initial velocity on a moving belt as shown. Denoting by μ the coefficient of friction at A and B, derive an expression for the time during which slippage occurs at B.

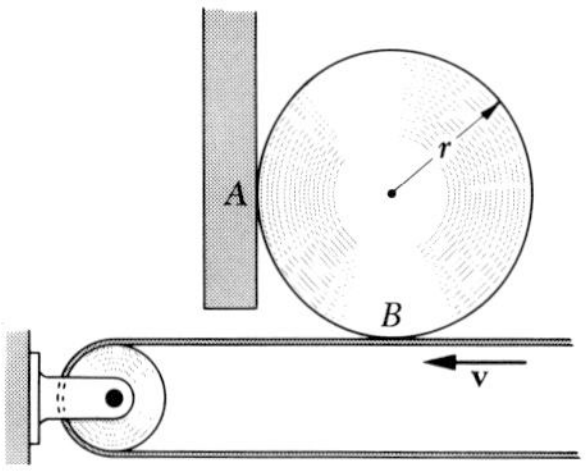

FIG. P 18.4

18.5. Using the principle of impulse and momentum, solve Prob. 16.34*b*.

18.6. Using the principle of impulse and momentum, solve Prob. 16.42*b*.

18.7. Using the principle of impulse and momentum, solve Prob. 16.43*b*.

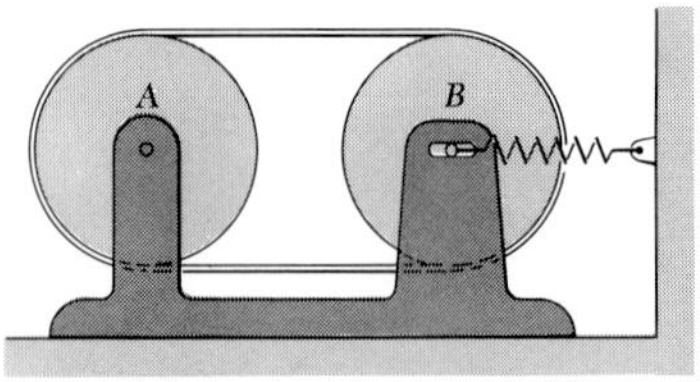

FIG. P 18.8

18.8. Two disks A and B are connected by a belt as shown. Each disk weighs 30 lb and has a radius of 1.5 ft. The shaft of disk B rests in a slotted bearing and is held by a spring which exerts a constant force of 15 lb. If a couple of moment 20 lb-ft is applied to disk A, determine (a) the time required for the disks to attain a speed of 600 rpm, (b) the tension in both portions of the belt, (c) the minimum coefficient of friction if no slipping is to occur.

18.9. Show that the system of momenta for a rigid body in plane motion reduces to a single vector, and express the distance from the mass center G to the line of action of this vector in terms of the centroidal radius of gyration $\bar{k}$ of the body, the magnitude $\bar{v}$ of the velocity of G, and the angular velocity ω.

18.10. Show that, when a body rotates about a fixed axis through O, the system of momenta of its particles is equivalent to a single vector of magnitude $m\bar{r}\omega$, perpendicular to the line OG, and applied to a point P on this line, called the *center of percussion*, at a distance $GP = \bar{k}^2/\bar{r}$ from the mass center of the body.

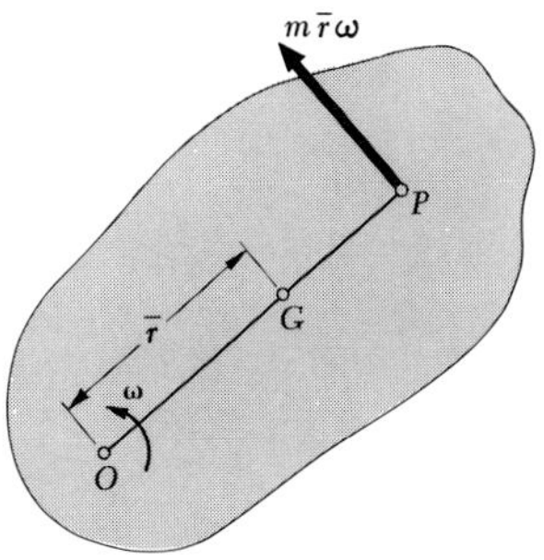

FIG. P 18.10

18.11. Show that the angular momentum of a rigid body about a point A is equal to $I_A\omega$, where ω is the angular velocity of the body at the instant considered and I_A the moment of inertia of the body about A, *if and only if* one of the following conditions is satisfied: (*a*) A is the mass center of the body, (*b*) A is the instantaneous center of rotation, (*c*) the velocity of A is directed along a line joining point A and the mass center G.

18.12. Consider a rigid slab initially at rest and subjected to an impulsive force **F** contained in the plane of the slab. We define the *center of percussion* P as the point of intersection of the line of action of **F** with the perpendicular drawn from G. (*a*) Show that the instantaneous center of rotation C of the slab is located on line GP at a distance $GC = \bar{k}^2/GP$ on the opposite side of G. (*b*) Show that, if the center of percussion were located at C, the instantaneous center of rotation would be located at P.

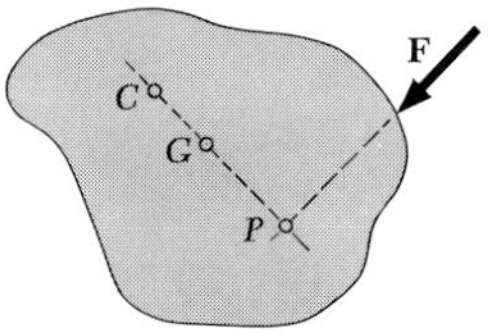

FIG. P 18.12

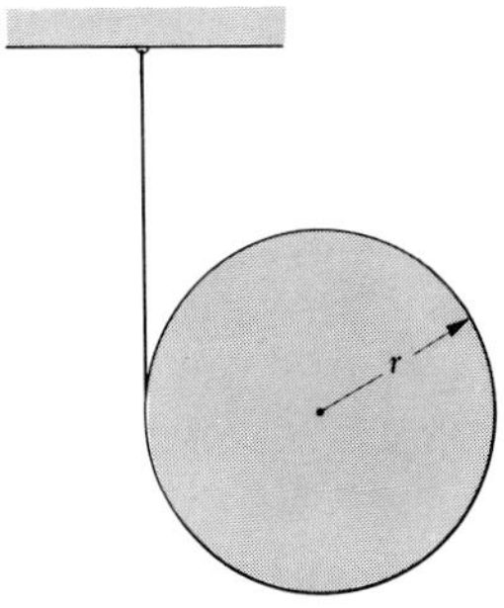

FIG. P 18.13

18.13. A cord is wrapped around a solid cylinder of radius r and weight W as shown. If the cylinder is released from rest at time $t = 0$, determine the velocity of the center of the cylinder at a time t.

18.14. Solve Prob. 18.13 assuming that the solid cylinder is replaced by a hollow cylinder of outside radius r, weight W, and centroidal radius of gyration $\bar{k}$.

18.15. Two disks, each of weight 12 lb and radius 6 in., which roll without slipping, are connected by a drum of radius r and of negligible weight. A rope is wrapped around the drum and is pulled horizontally with a force **P** of magnitude 8 lb. Knowing that $r = 3$ in. and that the disks are initially at rest, determine (*a*) the velocity of the center G after 3 sec, (*b*) the friction force required to prevent slipping.

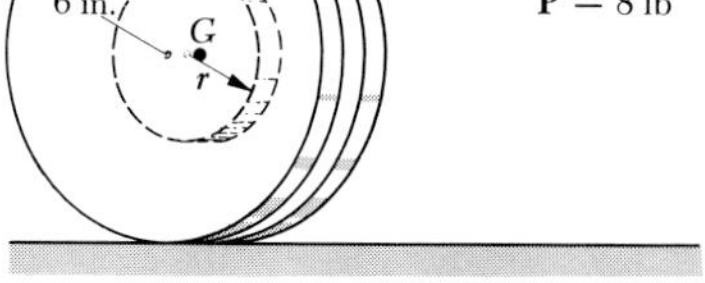

FIG. P 18.15

18.16. In Prob. 18.15, determine the required value of r and the corresponding velocity after 3 sec if the friction force is to be zero.

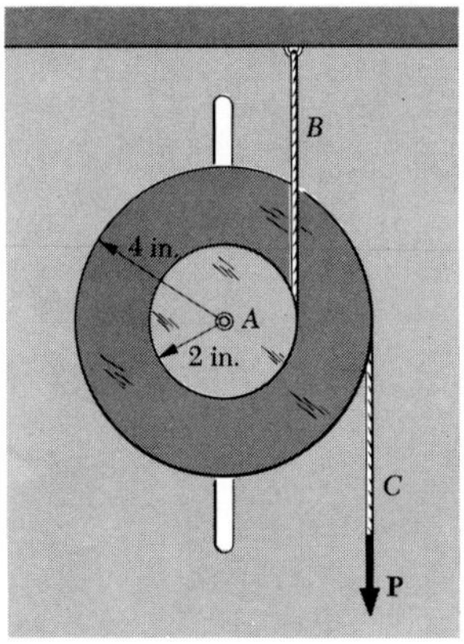

FIG. P 18.17

18.17. The double pulley shown weighs 6 lb and has a centroidal radius of gyration of 3 in. The 2-in.-radius inner pulley is rigidly attached to the 4-in.-radius outer pulley, and the motion of the center A is guided by a smooth pin at A which slides in a vertical slot. When the pulley is at rest, a force $\mathbf{P}$ of magnitude 8 lb is applied to cord C. Determine the velocity of the center of the pulley after 5 sec.

18.18. Solve Prob. 18.17 assuming that the force $\mathbf{P}$ is replaced by an 8-lb weight attached to cord C.

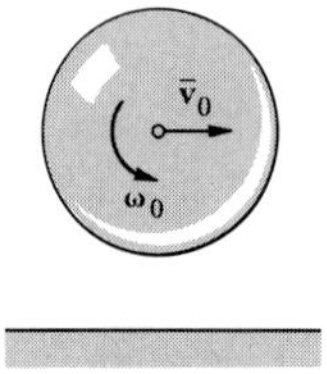

FIG. P 18.19

18.19. A sphere of weight W and radius r is projected along a rough horizontal surface with the initial velocities indicated. If the final velocity of the sphere is to be zero, express (*a*) the required ω_0 in terms of $\bar{v}_0$ and r, (*b*) the time required for the sphere to come to rest in terms of μ and $\bar{v}_0$.

18.20. In Prob. 18.19, assume $\omega_0 = 0$, and determine (*a*) the time at which the velocity of the sphere becomes constant, (*b*) the final velocity of the sphere.

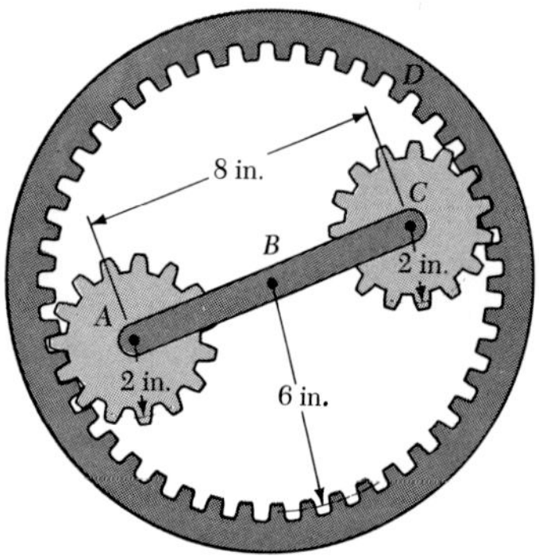

FIG. P 18.21

***18.21.** In the gear arrangement shown, the inner gears A and C are attached to the rod ABC which is free to rotate about B, while the outer gear D is fixed. Knowing that the system is initially at rest, determine the moment of the couple $\mathbf{M}$ which must be applied to rod ABC if 3 sec later the angular velocity of the rod is to be 300 rpm clockwise. Gears A and C weigh 3 lb each and may be considered as disks of radius 2 in.; rod ABC weighs 5 lb.

***18.22.** In the gear arrangement shown, gears A and C are attached to the rod ABC, which is free to rotate about B, while the inner gear B is fixed. Knowing that the system is at rest, determine the moment of the couple $\mathbf{M}$ which must be applied to rod ABC, if 3 sec later the angular velocity of the rod is to be 300 rpm clockwise. Gears A and C weigh 3 lb each and may be considered as disks of radius 2 in.; rod ABC weighs 5 lb.

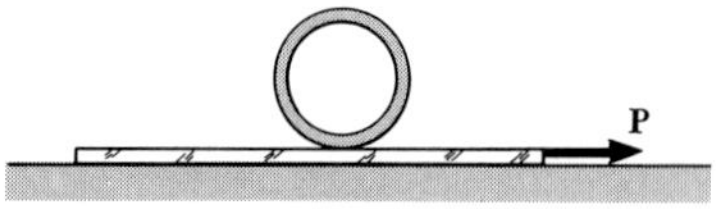

FIG. P 18.23

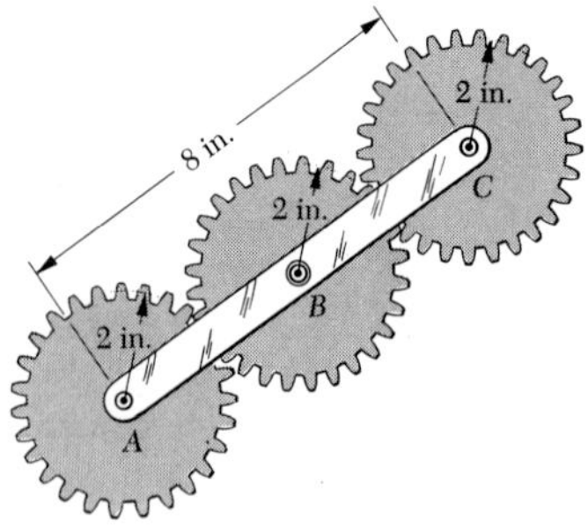

FIG. P 18.22

***18.23.** A 12-in.-diameter pipe weighing 40 lb rests on a 10-lb plate. The pipe and plate are initially at rest when a force $\mathbf{P}$ of magnitude 20 lb is applied for 0.50 sec. Knowing that $\mu = 0.20$ between the plate and *both* the pipe and the floor, determine the resulting velocities of the pipe and of the plate.

*18.24. Solve Prob. 18.23 assuming that the magnitude of the force **P** is 30 lb.

18.5. Conservation of Angular Momentum. We recall the fundamental equation of impulse and momentum for a rigid body or a system of rigid bodies moving under the action of given forces:

$$\textbf{Syst Momenta}_1 + \textbf{Syst Ext Imp}_{1\rightarrow 2} = \textbf{Syst Momenta}_2 \quad (18.1)$$

When no external force acts on the system or, more generally, when the system of the impulses of the external forces is equivalent to zero, Eq. (18.1) reduces to

$$\textbf{Syst Momenta}_1 = \textbf{Syst Momenta}_2 \qquad (18.8)$$

Summing and equating successively the x components, y components, and moments of the momenta in (18.8), we conclude that the total linear momentum of the system is conserved in any direction and that its total angular momentum is conserved about any point.

There are many engineering applications, however, in which *the linear momentum is not conserved,* yet in which *the angular momentum* h_O of the system about a given point O *is conserved:*

$$(h_O)_1 = (h_O)_2 \qquad (18.9)$$

Such cases occur when the lines of action of all external forces pass through O or, more generally, when the sum of the angular impulses of the external forces about O is zero.

Problems involving *conservation of angular momentum* about a point O may be solved by the general method of impulse and momentum, i.e., by drawing the three diagrams corresponding to the fundamental equation (18.1). Equation (18.9) is then obtained by summing and equating moments about O. Two additional equations may be written by summing and equating x and y components; these equations may be used to determine two unknown linear impulses, such as the impulses of the reaction components at a fixed point (Sample Prob. 18.4).

There are many nonengineering applications of conservation of angular momentum which are familiar to all of us. By bringing his arms together or by extending them, a skater may vary his moment of inertia $\bar{I}$ and thus spin more or less rapidly (since $\bar{I}\omega$ must remain constant). A skier performing a high jump has no control over his *total* angular momentum once he has left the ground. Yet by revolving his arms he may change the *distribution* of his angular momentum and thus keep his body vertical. A cat dropped with no initial angular momentum spins its tail in one sense and thus causes its body to rotate in the other sense, with the result that it lands on its paws.

18.6. Eccentric Impact. We saw in Chap. 14 that the method of impulse and momentum is the only practicable method for the solution of problems involving impulsive forces. Now we shall also find that, compared with the various problems considered in the preceding sections, problems involving impulsive forces are particularly well adapted to a solution by the method of impulse and momentum. The computation of linear impulses and angular impulses is quite simple, since, the time interval considered being very short, the bodies involved may be assumed to occupy the same position during that time interval.

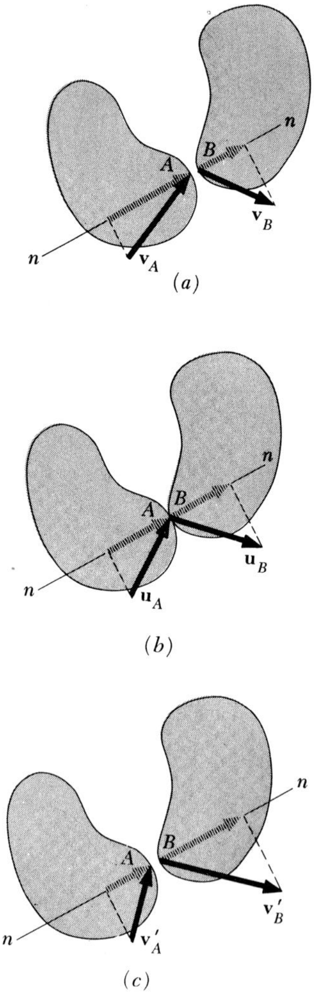

FIG. 18.8

In Secs. 14.5 to 14.7, we learned to solve problems of *central impact,* i.e., problems in which the mass centers of the two colliding bodies are located on the line of impact. We shall now analyze the *eccentric impact* of two rigid bodies. Consider two bodies which collide, and denote by $\mathbf{v}_A$ and $\mathbf{v}_B$ the velocities before impact *of the two points of contact* A and B (Fig. 18.8*a*). Under the impact, the two bodies will *deform* and, at the end of the period of deformation, their velocities $\mathbf{u}_A$ and $\mathbf{u}_B$ will have equal components along the line of impact nn (Fig. 18.8*b*). A period of *restitution* will then take place, at the end of which the points of contact will have velocities $\mathbf{v}'_A$ and $\mathbf{v}'_B$ (Fig. 18.8*c*). Assuming the bodies perfectly smooth, we find that the forces they exert on each other are directed along the line of impact. Denoting, respectively, by $\int P\,dt$ and $\int R\,dt$ the magnitude of the impulse of one of these forces during the period of deformation and during the period of restitution, we recall that the coefficient of restitution e is defined as the ratio

$$e = \frac{\int R\,dt}{\int P\,dt} \tag{18.10}$$

We propose to show that the relation established in Sec. 14.6 between the relative velocities of two particles before and after impact also holds between the components along the line of impact of the relative velocities of the two points of contact A and B. We propose to show, therefore, that

$$(v'_B)_n - (v'_A)_n = e[(v_A)_n - (v_B)_n] \tag{18.11}$$

We shall first assume that the motion of each of the two colliding bodies of Fig. 18.8 is unconstrained. Thus the only impulsive forces exerted on the bodies during the impact are applied at A and B respectively. Consider the body to which point A belongs and draw the three momentum and impulse diagrams corresponding to the period of deformation (Fig. 18.9).

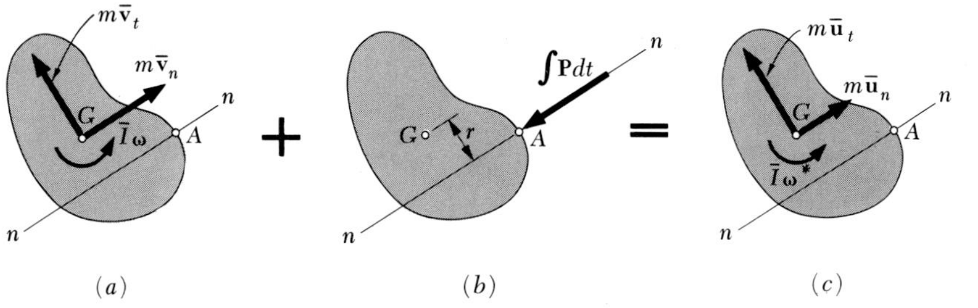

FIG. 18.9

We denote by $\bar{\mathbf{v}}$ and $\bar{\mathbf{u}}$, respectively, the velocity of the mass center at the beginning and at the end of the period of deformation, and by ω and ω^* the angular velocity of the body at the same instants. Summing and equating the components of the momenta and impulses along the line of impact nn, we write

$$m\bar{v}_n - \int P\, dt = m\bar{u}_n \tag{18.12}$$

Summing and equating the moments about G of the momenta and impulses, we also write

$$\bar{I}\omega - r\int P\, dt = \bar{I}\omega^* \tag{18.13}$$

where r represents the perpendicular distance from G to the line of impact. Considering now the period of restitution, we obtain in a similar way

$$m\bar{u}_n - \int R\, dt = m\bar{v}'_n \tag{18.14}$$

$$\bar{I}\omega^* - r\int R\, dt = \bar{I}\omega' \tag{18.15}$$

where $\bar{\mathbf{v}}'$ and ω' represent, respectively, the velocity of the mass center and the angular velocity of the body after impact. Solving (18.12) and (18.14) for the two impulses and substituting into (18.10), and then solving (18.13) and (18.15) for the same two impulses and substituting again into (18.10), we obtain the following two alternate expressions for the coefficient of restitution:

$$e = \frac{\bar{u}_n - \bar{v}'_n}{\bar{v}_n - \bar{u}_n} \qquad e = \frac{\omega^* - \omega'}{\omega - \omega^*} \tag{18.16}$$

Multiplying by r the numerator and denominator of the second expression obtained for e, and adding respectively to the numerator and denominator of the first expression, we have

$$e = \frac{\bar{u}_n + r\omega^* - (\bar{v}'_n + r\omega')}{\bar{v}_n + r\omega - (\bar{u}_n + r\omega^*)}$$

Observing that $\bar{v}_n + r\omega$ represents the component $(v_A)_n$ along nn of the velocity of the point of contact A and that, similarly, $\bar{u}_n + r\omega^*$ and $\bar{v}'_n + r\omega'$ represent, respectively, the components $(u_A)_n$ and $(v'_A)_n$, we write

$$e = \frac{(u_A)_n - (v'_A)_n}{(v_A)_n - (u_A)_n} \qquad (18.17)$$

The analysis of the motion of the second body leads to a similar expression for e in terms of the components along nn of the successive velocities of point B. Recalling that $(u_A)_n = (u_B)_n$, and eliminating these two velocity components by a manipulation similar to the one used in Sec. 14.6, we obtain relation (18.11).

If one or both of the colliding bodies is constrained to rotate about a fixed point O, as in the case of a compound pendulum (Fig. 18.10a), an impulsive reaction will be exerted at O (Fig. 18.10b). We shall verify that, while their derivation must be modified, Eqs. (18.17) and (18.11) remain valid. Applying formula (18.7) to the period of deformation and to the period of restitution, we write

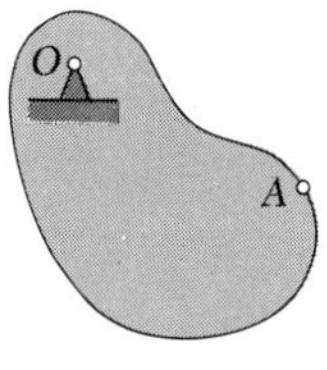

(a)

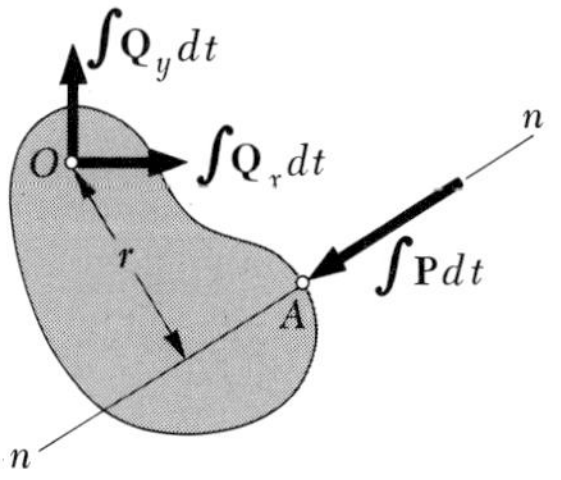

(b)

FIG. 18.10

$$I_O\omega - r\int P\,dt = I_O\omega^* \qquad (18.18)$$
$$I_O\omega^* - r\int R\,dt = I_O\omega' \qquad (18.19)$$

where r represents the perpendicular distance from the fixed point O to the line of impact. Solving (18.18) and (18.19) for the two impulses and substituting into (18.10), and then observing that $r\omega$, $r\omega^*$, and $r\omega'$ represent the components along nn of the successive velocities of point A, we write

$$e = \frac{\omega^* - \omega'}{\omega - \omega^*} = \frac{r\omega^* - r\omega'}{r\omega - r\omega^*} = \frac{(u_A)_n - (v'_A)_n}{(v_A)_n - (u_A)_n}$$

and check that Eq. (18.17) still holds. Thus Eq. (18.11) remains valid when one or both of the colliding bodies is constrained to rotate about a fixed point O.

In order to determine the velocities of the two colliding bodies after impact, relation (18.11) should be used in conjunction with one or several other equations obtained by applying the principle of impulse and momentum (Sample Prob. 18.5).

SAMPLE PROBLEM 18.4

A 0.125-lb bullet A is fired with an initial velocity of 1,500 ft/sec into a 50-lb wooden beam B which is suspended from a hinge at O. Knowing that the beam is initially at rest, determine (a) the angular velocity of the beam immediately after the bullet becomes embedded in the beam, (b) the impulsive reactions at the hinge, assuming that the bullet becomes embedded in 0.0002 sec.

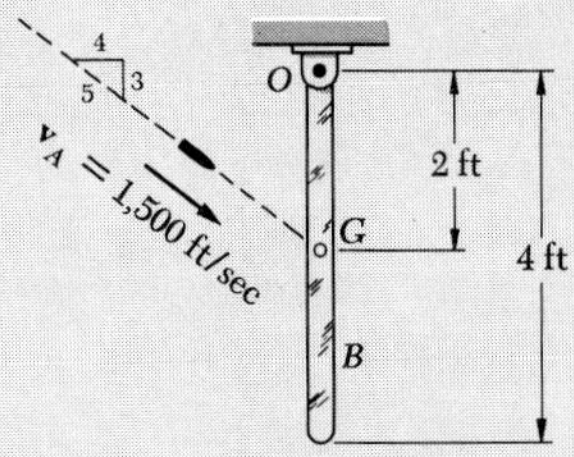

Solution. We consider the bullet and the beam as a single system. Since the time interval $\Delta t = 0.0002$ sec is very short, we neglect all nonimpulsive forces and consider only the external impulses $\mathbf{R}_x \, \Delta t$ and $\mathbf{R}_y \, \Delta t$.

Principle of Impulse and Momentum

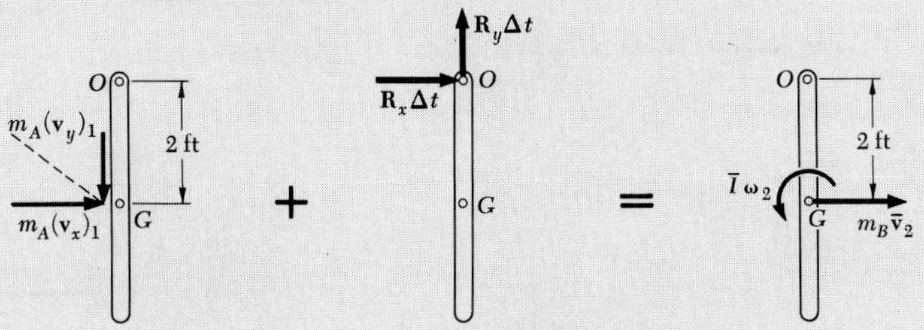

$$\textbf{Syst Momenta}_1 + \textbf{Syst Ext Imp}_{1\to 2} = \textbf{Syst Momenta}_2$$

$+\circlearrowleft$ moments about O: $\quad m_A(v_x)_1(2\text{ ft}) + 0 = \bar{I}\omega_2 + m_B\bar{v}_2(2\text{ ft}) \qquad (1)$

$\xrightarrow{+}$ x components: $\quad m_A(v_x)_1 + R_x\,\Delta t = m_B\bar{v}_2 \qquad (2)$

$+\uparrow$ y components: $\quad -m_A(v_y)_1 + R_y\,\Delta t = 0 \qquad (3)$

The components of the velocity of the bullet and the centroidal moment of inertia of the beam are

$$(v_x)_1 = \tfrac{4}{5}(1{,}500) = 1{,}200 \text{ ft/sec} \qquad (v_y)_1 = \tfrac{3}{5}(1{,}500) = 900 \text{ ft/sec}$$

$$\bar{I} = \tfrac{1}{12}ml^2 = \frac{1}{12}\frac{50}{g}(4)^2 = 2.07 \text{ lb-ft-sec}^2$$

Substituting these values into (1) and noting that $\bar{v}_2 = (2\text{ ft})\omega_2$, we obtain

$$\frac{0.125}{g}(1{,}200)(2) = 2.07\omega_2 + \frac{50}{g}(2\omega_2)(2)$$

$$\omega_2 = 1.125 \text{ radians/sec} \qquad \omega_2 = 1.125 \text{ radians/sec} \circlearrowleft \blacktriangleleft$$

Substituting $\bar{v}_2 = (2\text{ ft})(1.125\text{ radians/sec}) = 2.25$ ft/sec into (2), we solve Eqs. (2) and (3) for R_x and R_y, respectively.

$$\frac{0.125}{g}(1{,}200) + R_x(0.0002) = \frac{50}{g}(2.25)$$

$$R_x = -5{,}820 \text{ lb} \qquad \mathbf{R}_x = 5{,}820 \text{ lb} \leftarrow \blacktriangleleft$$

$$-\frac{0.125}{g}(900) + R_y(0.0002) = 0$$

$$R_y = +17{,}470 \text{ lb} \qquad \mathbf{R}_y = 17{,}470 \text{ lb} \uparrow \blacktriangleleft$$

SAMPLE PROBLEM 18.5

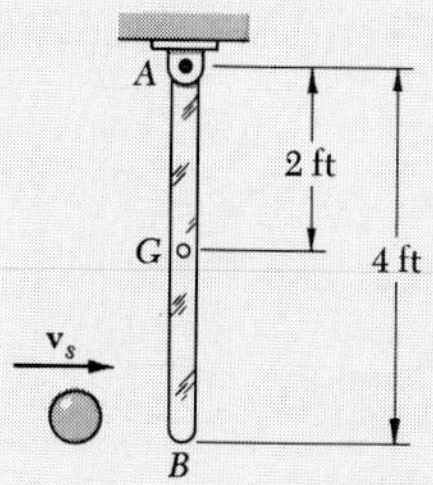

A 3-lb sphere moving horizontally to the right with an initial velocity of 20 ft/sec strikes the lower end of a 12-lb rigid rod AB. The rod is suspended from a hinge at A and is initially at rest. Knowing that the coefficient of restitution between the rod and sphere is 0.80, determine the angular velocity of the rod and the velocity of the sphere immediately after the impact.

Principle of Impulse and Momentum. We consider the rod and sphere as a single system and apply the principle of impulse and momentum during the impact. The only impulsive force external to this system is the impulsive reaction at A.

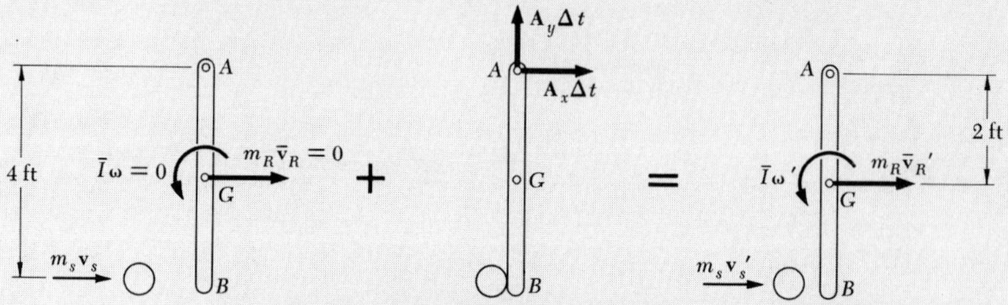

Syst Initial Momenta + Syst Ext Imp = Syst Final Momenta

+↺ moments about A: $m_s v_s(4\text{ ft}) = m_s v_s'(4\text{ ft}) + m_R\bar{v}_R'(2\text{ ft}) + \bar{I}\omega'$ (1)

Since the rod rotates about A, we have $\bar{v}_R' = \bar{r}\omega' = (2\text{ ft})\omega'$. Also,

$$\bar{I} = \frac{1}{12}\frac{12}{g}(4)^2 = 0.497 \text{ lb-ft-sec}^2$$

Substituting these values and the given data into Eq. (1), we have

$$\frac{3}{g}(20)(4) = \frac{3}{g}v_s'(4) + \frac{12}{g}(2\omega')(2) + 0.497\omega'$$

$$7.45 = 0.373v_s' + 1.988\omega' \qquad (2)$$

Coefficient of Restitution. Choosing positive to the right, we write

$$v_B' - v_s' = e(v_s - v_B)$$

Substituting $v_s = 20$ ft/sec, $v_B = 0$, and $e = 0.80$, we obtain

$$v_B' - v_s' = (0.80)(20 - 0) \qquad (3)$$

Again noting that the rod rotates about A, we write

$$v_B' = (4\text{ ft})\omega' \qquad (4)$$

Solving Eqs. (2) to (4) simultaneously, we obtain

$\omega' = +3.86$ radians/sec $\omega' = 3.86$ radians/sec ↺ ◄

$v_s' = -0.58$ ft/sec $\mathbf{v}_s' = 0.58$ ft/sec ← ◄

SAMPLE PROBLEM 18.6

A square package of side a and weight W moves down a conveyor belt A with a constant velocity $\bar{\mathbf{v}}_1$. At the end of the conveyor belt, the corner of the package strikes a rigid support at B. Assuming that the impact at B is perfectly plastic, derive an expression for the smallest magnitude of the velocity $\bar{\mathbf{v}}_1$ for which the package will rotate about B and reach conveyor belt C.

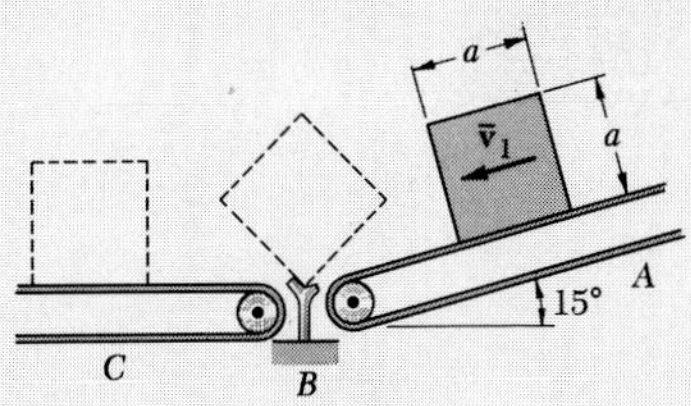

Principle of Impulse and Momentum. Since the impact between the package and the support is perfectly plastic, the package rotates about B during the impact. We apply the principle of impulse and momentum to the package and note that the only impulsive force external to the package is the impulsive reaction at B.

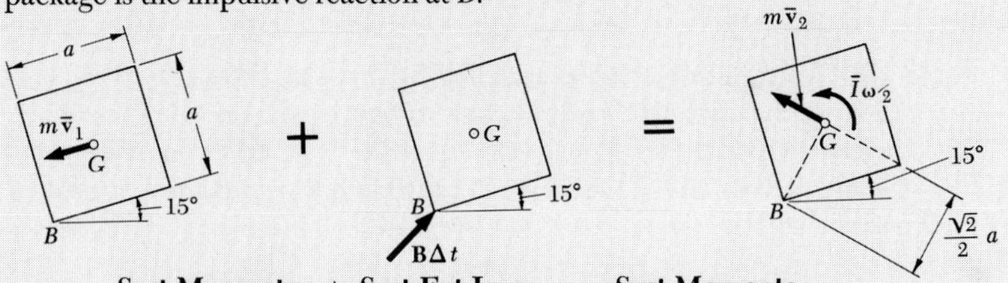

Syst Momenta$_1$ + Syst Ext Imp$_{1\to 2}$ = Syst Momenta$_2$

+↻ moments about B: $\quad (m\bar{v}_1)(\frac{1}{2}a) + 0 = (m\bar{v}_2)(\frac{1}{2}\sqrt{2}\,a) + \bar{I}\omega_2 \qquad (1)$

Since the package rotates about B, we have $\bar{v}_2 = (GB)\omega_2 = \frac{1}{2}\sqrt{2}\,a\omega_2$. We substitute this expression, together with $\bar{I} = \frac{1}{6}ma^2$, into Eq. (1):

$$(m\bar{v}_1)(\tfrac{1}{2}a) = m(\tfrac{1}{2}\sqrt{2}\,a\omega_2)(\tfrac{1}{2}\sqrt{2}\,a) + \tfrac{1}{6}ma^2\omega_2$$

$$\bar{v}_1 = \frac{4}{3}a\omega_2 \qquad (2)$$

Position 2

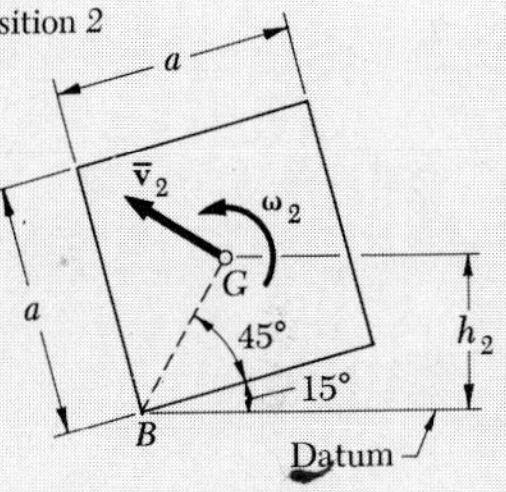

$GB = \frac{1}{2}\sqrt{2}a = 0.707a$
$h_2 = GB\sin(45° + 15°)$
$= 0.612\,a$

Principle of Conservation of Energy. We apply the principle of conservation of energy between position 2 and position 3.

Position 2. $V_2 = Wh_2$. Recalling that $\bar{v}_2 = \frac{1}{2}\sqrt{2}\,a\omega_2$, we write

$$T_2 = \tfrac{1}{2}m\bar{v}_2^2 + \tfrac{1}{2}\bar{I}\omega_2^2 = \tfrac{1}{2}m(\tfrac{1}{2}\sqrt{2}\,a\omega_2)^2 + \tfrac{1}{2}(\tfrac{1}{6}ma^2)\omega_2^2 = \tfrac{1}{3}ma^2\omega_2^2$$

Position 3. Since the package must reach conveyor belt B, it must pass through position 3 where G is directly above B. Also, since we wish to determine the smallest velocity for which the package will reach this position, we choose $\bar{v}_3 = \omega_3 = 0$. Therefore $T_3 = 0$ and $V_3 = Wh_3$.

Conservation of Energy $\qquad T_2 + V_2 = T_3 + V_3$

$$\tfrac{1}{3}ma^2\omega_2^2 + Wh_2 = 0 + Wh_3$$

$$\omega_2^2 = \frac{3W}{ma^2}(h_3 - h_2) = \frac{3g}{a^2}(h_3 - h_2) \qquad (3)$$

Position 3

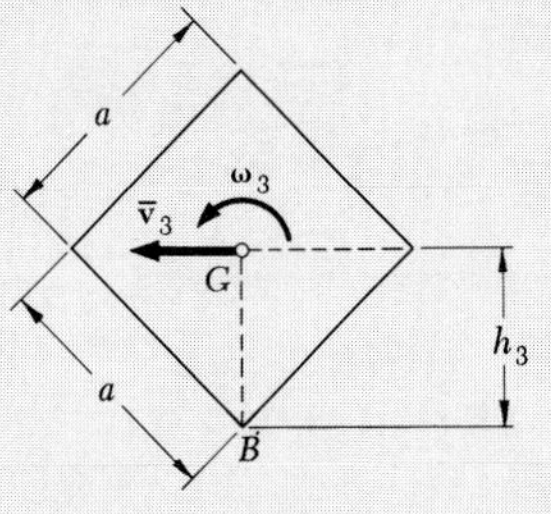

$h_3 = GB = 0.707a$

Substituting the computed values of h_2 and h_3 into Eq. (3), we obtain

$$\omega_2^2 = \frac{3g}{a^2}(0.707a - 0.612a) = \frac{3g}{a^2}(0.095a) \qquad \omega_2 = \sqrt{0.285g/a}$$

$$\bar{v}_1 = \frac{4}{3}a\omega_2 = \frac{4}{3}a\sqrt{0.285g/a} \qquad \bar{v}_1 = 0.713\sqrt{ga} \quad ◄$$

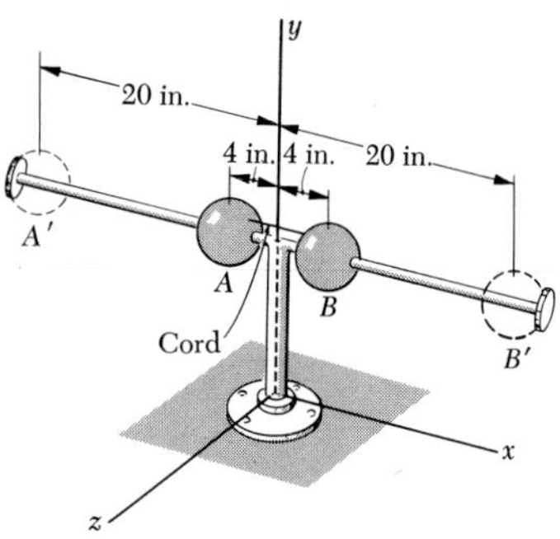

FIG. P 18.25

PROBLEMS

18.25. Two balls weighing 2 lb each are mounted at A and B on the horizontal rod $A'B'$, which rotates freely at 60 rpm about the vertical shaft. The balls are held in position by a cord which is suddenly cut. Knowing that the centroidal moment of inertia of the rod is 0.25 lb-ft-sec², determine the angular velocity of the rod after the balls have moved to positions A' and B'.

18.26. Solve Prob. 18.25 assuming that, after the cord is cut, ball B moves to position B' but that an obstruction prevents ball A from moving.

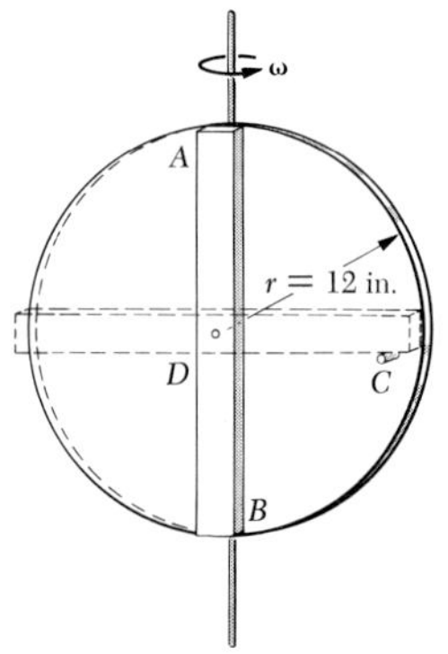

FIG. P 18.27

18.27. An 8-lb bar AB is attached by a pin at D to a 10-lb circular plate which may rotate freely about a vertical axis. Knowing that when the bar is vertical the angular velocity of the plate is 90 rpm, determine the angular velocity of the plate after the bar has swung into a horizontal position and has come to rest against pin C.

18.28. In the helicopter shown, a vertical tail propeller is used to prevent rotation of the cab as the speed of the main blades is changed. Assuming that the tail propeller is not operating, determine the final angular velocity of the cab after the speed of the main blades has been changed from 200 to 300 rpm. The speed of the main blades is measured relative to the cab, which has a centroidal moment of inertia of 800 lb-ft-sec². Each of the four main blades is assumed to be a 15-ft slender rod weighing 60 lb.

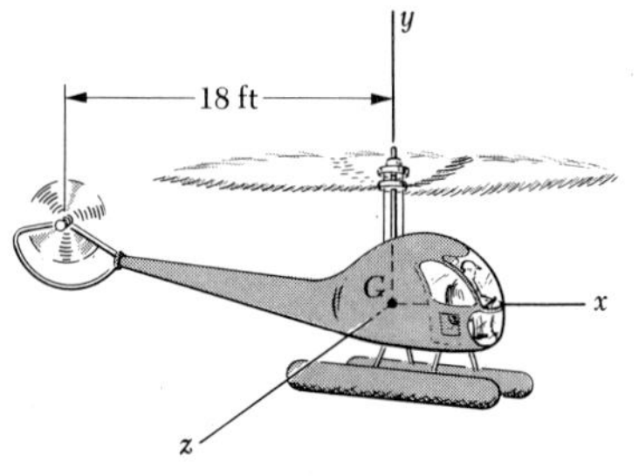

FIG. P 18.28

18.29. Assuming that the tail propeller in Prob. 18.28 is operating and that the angular velocity of the cab remains zero, determine the final horizontal velocity of the cab when the speed of the main blades is changed from 200 to 300 rpm. The cab weighs 1,500 lb and is initially at rest. Also determine the force exerted by the tail propeller if this change in speed takes places uniformly in 12 sec.

18.30. Two 10-lb disks and a small motor are mounted on a 15-lb rectangular platform which is free to rotate about a central vertical spindle. The normal operating speed of the motor is 180 rpm. If the motor is started when the system is at rest, determine the angular velocity of all elements of the system after the motor has attained its normal operating speed. Neglect the weight of the motor, and assume that the system is perfectly lubricated.

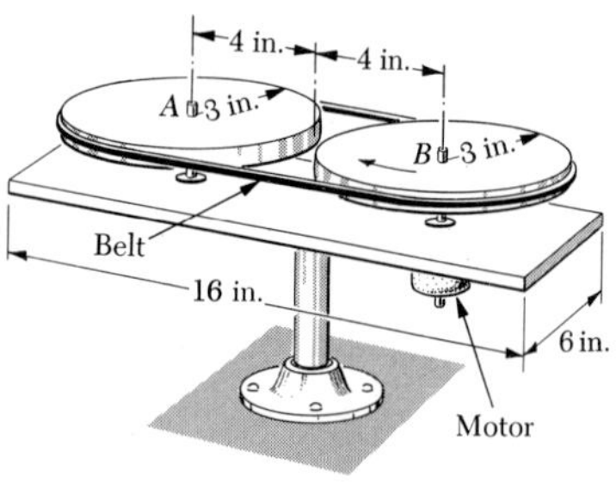

FIG. P 18.30

18.31. Solve Prob. 18.30 assuming (*a*) that the belt is removed, (*b*) that the belt is looped around the disks in a figure 8.

18.32. A slender tube weighing 4 lb rotates freely at 100 rpm about a vertical spindle as shown. A small ball weighing 1 lb is introduced in the tube at *A* with a very small velocity. Determine the angular velocity of the tube (*a*) just before the ball leaves the tube at *B*, (*b*) just after the ball has left the tube.

18.33. A slender tube weighing 4 lb rotates freely at 100 rpm about a vertical spindle as shown. A small ball weighing $\frac{1}{2}$ lb is introduced in the tube at *A* with a very small velocity; after this ball has left the tube at *B*, a second $\frac{1}{2}$-lb ball is introduced at *A*. Determine the angular velocity of the tube after the second ball has left the tube.

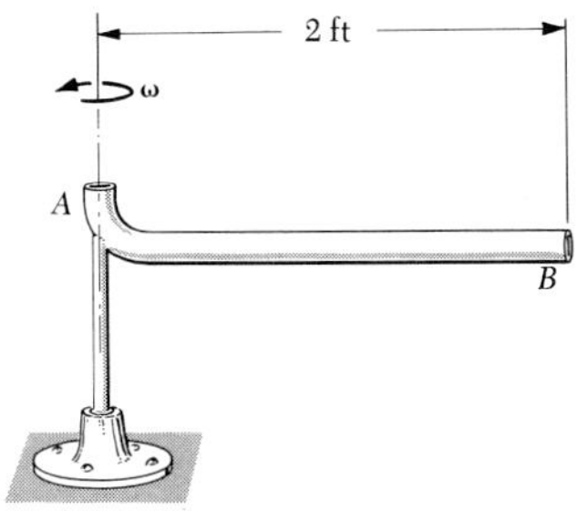

FIG. P 18.32 AND P 18.33

18.34. In Prob. 18.32, determine the radial and transverse components of the velocity of the ball as it leaves the tube at *B*.

18.35. In Prob. 18.27, determine the energy loss during the impact between the bar and pin *C*.

18.36. A bullet of mass *m* is fired with a horizontal velocity $\mathbf{v}_0$ and at a height $h = \frac{1}{2}R$ into a wooden disk of much larger mass *M* and radius *R*. The disk rests on a horizontal plane and the coefficient of friction between the disk and the plane is finite. (*a*) Determine the linear velocity $\mathbf{v}_1$ and the angular velocity ω_1 of the disk immediately after the bullet has penetrated the disk. (*b*) Describe the ensuing motion of the disk and determine its linear velocity after the motion has become uniform.

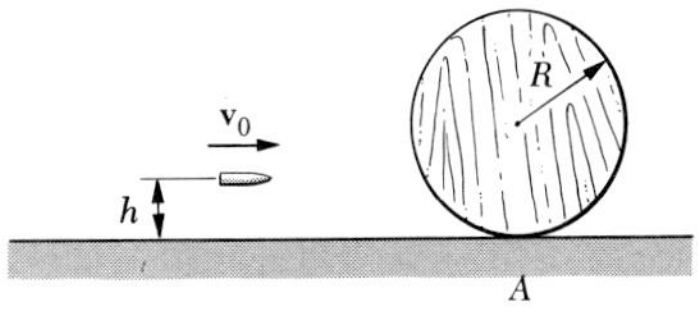

FIG. P 18.36

18.37. Determine the height *h* at which the bullet of Prob. 18.36 should be fired (*a*) if the disk is to roll without sliding immediately after impact, (*b*) if the disk is to slide without rolling immediately after impact.

18.38. Solve Prob. 18.36 assuming that the disk is fitted with a short spike at *A* which prevents it from slipping at the time of impact.

18.39. Knowing that $e = 0.70$ between the sphere and rod of Sample Prob. 18.5, determine the required weight of the rod if the velocity of the sphere after impact is to be zero. The weight of the sphere is unchanged.

18.40. Solve Sample Prob. 18.4 assuming that the bullet is fired so that its path forms the same angle with the horizontal but that it becomes embedded in the beam at its lower end.

18.41. A rigid rod of length *l* and weight *W* is released in the position shown. It is observed that the rod rebounds to a horizontal position after striking the vertical surface. (*a*) Determine the coefficient of restitution between the knob *K* and the surface. (*b*) Show that the same rebound may be expected for any position of the knob *K*.

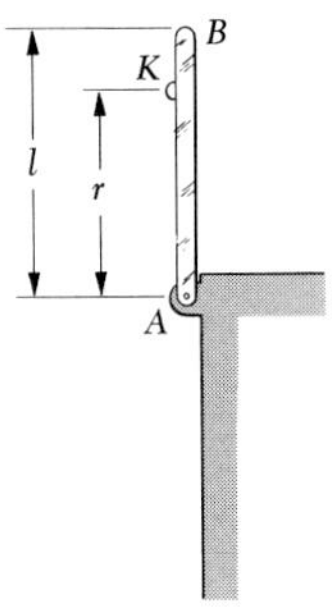

FIG. P 18.41

18.42. In Prob. 18.41, determine the required distance *r* from end *A* to knob *K* if, during the impact, the impulsive reaction at *A* is to be zero.

18.43. The plank CDE of weight W_P rests on top of a small pivot at D. A man A of weight W stands on the plank at end C; a second man B of the same weight W jumps from a height h and strikes the plank at E. Assuming perfectly plastic impact, determine the height to which man A will rise. (Assume that man A stands completely rigid.)

18.44. Solve Prob. 18.43 assuming that the impact between man B and the plank is perfectly elastic.

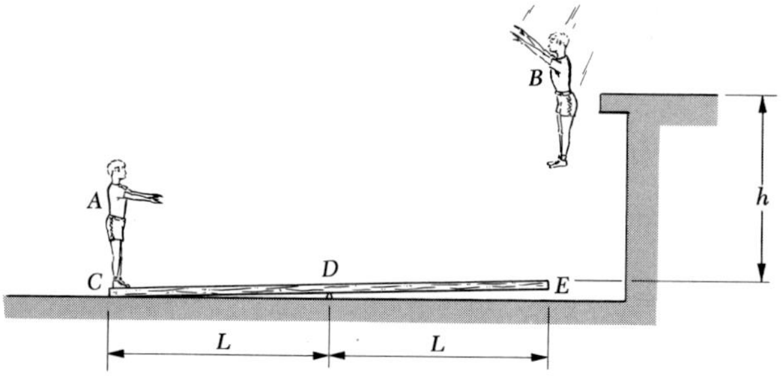

FIG. P 18.43

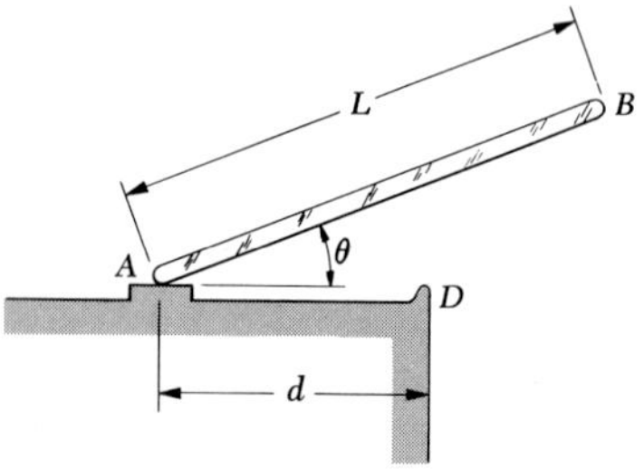

FIG. P 18.45

18.45. A slender rod of mass m and length L is released from rest in the position shown. The coefficient of friction is sufficient to prevent sliding at A. Assuming perfectly elastic impact ($e = 1$) at D, determine the distance d for which the rod will rebound with no angular velocity.

18.46. Assuming perfectly plastic impact ($e = 0$) at D in Prob. 18.45, determine the minimum value of d for which the rod will remain in contact with the ground at A and D after impact.

18.47. A uniformly loaded square crate is released from rest with its corner D directly above A; it rotates about A until its corner B strikes the floor, and then rotates about B. The floor is sufficiently rough to prevent slipping and the impact at B is perfectly plastic. Denoting by ω_0 the angular velocity of the crate immediately before B strikes the floor, find the angular velocity of the crate immediately after B strikes the floor. What fraction of the kinetic energy of the crate is lost during the impact?

18.48. In Prob. 18.47, determine the maximum value of the angle θ through which the crate will rotate after B strikes the floor.

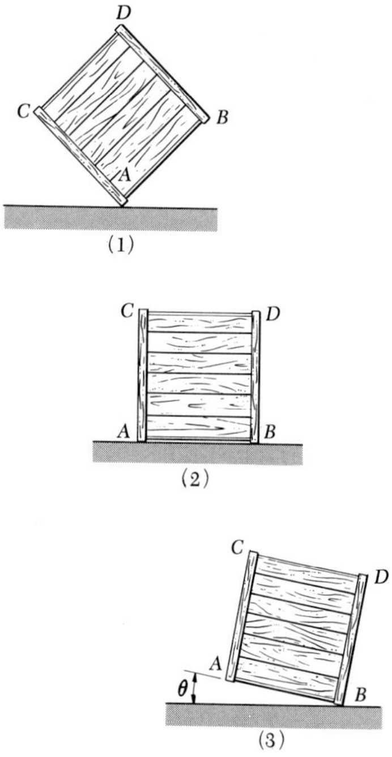

FIG. P 18.47

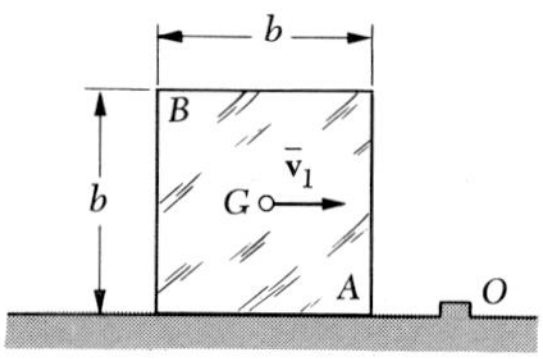

FIG. P 18.49

18.49. A square block of weight W moves along a smooth horizontal surface and strikes a small obstruction at O. Assuming that the impact between corner A and the obstruction O is perfectly *plastic*, determine the angular velocity of the block and the velocity of its mass center G immediately after the impact.

18.50. Solve Prob. 18.49 assuming that the impact between corner A and the obstruction O is perfectly *elastic*.

18.51. A uniform slender rod of length L is dropped onto rigid supports at A and B. Immediately before striking A the velocity of the rod is $\bar{\mathbf{v}}_1$. Since support B is slightly lower than support A, the rod strikes A before it strikes B. Assuming perfectly *plastic* impact at both A and B, determine the velocity of each of the extremities of the rod immediately after the rod (*a*) strikes support A, (*b*) strikes support B.

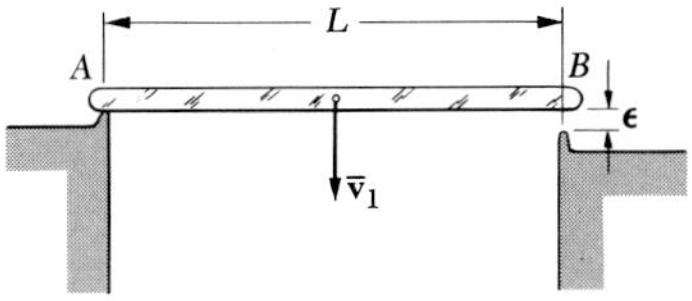

FIG. P 18.51

18.52. Solve Prob. 18.51 assuming that the impact at both A and B is perfectly *elastic*.

18.53. In Prob. 18.51, determine the impulse exerted on the rod (*a*) at A as the rod strikes the support at A, (*b*) at A as the rod strikes the support at B, (*c*) at B.

18.54. In Prob. 18.49, determine the line of action of the impulsive force exerted on the block by the obstruction at O.

18.55. A slender rod of weight W and length l is held in the position shown. Roller B is given a slight push to the right and moves along the horizontal plane, while roller A is constrained to move vertically. Determine the magnitudes of the impulses exerted on the rollers A and B as roller A strikes the ground. Assume perfectly plastic impact.

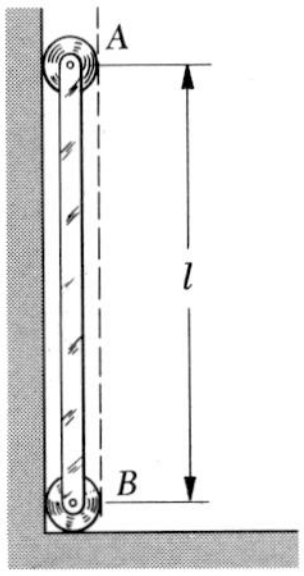

FIG. P 18.55

18.56. Solve Prob. 18.55 assuming that roller A is given a slight push to the right and describes a circular path, while roller B is maintained in a fixed position at the corner.

*18.7. Gyroscopes.

Our study of kinetics is limited to the plane motion of rigid bodies. The analysis of the general motion of a rigid body in space is indeed beyond the scope of this text. Among the problems which we shall *not* attempt to solve with the means at our disposal are those involving the general motion of a top or of a gyroscope. However, we shall consider in this section a particular case of gyroscopic motion which requires only a very limited knowledge of the motion of a rigid body in space and yet has many useful engineering applications.

A *gyroscope* consists of a body of revolution mounted on an axle which coincides with its geometric axis. Consider a gyroscope which spins at a very large rate ω about an axle AB directed along the z axis (Fig. 18.11). This motion may be represented by a vector $\boldsymbol{\omega}$ of magnitude equal to the *rate of spin*

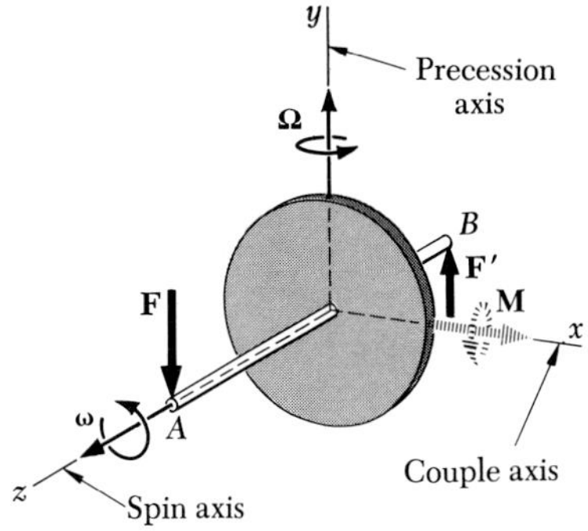

FIG. 18.11

ω of the gyroscope and directed along the *spin axis AB* in such a way that an observer located at the tip of the vector $\boldsymbol{\omega}$ will see the gyroscope rotate counterclockwise.

If we attempt to rotate the axle of the gyroscope about the x axis by applying two vertical forces **F** and **F′** at A and B, forming a couple of moment M, we find that the axle will resist the motion we try to impose and that *it will rotate about the y axis* with an angular velocity Ω. This motion of the gyroscope is called *precession;* it may be represented by a vector $\boldsymbol{\Omega}$ of magnitude equal to the *rate of precession* Ω of the gyroscope and directed along the y axis, or *precession axis*, in such a way that a man located at the tip of the vector will observe this motion as counterclockwise.

In order to explain this apparently odd behavior, we shall consider the gyroscope in two different positions and apply the principle of impulse and momentum. We first consider the gyroscope in its initial position at $t_1 = 0$. Denoting by $\bar{I}$ its centroidal moment of inertia, we find that the system of the momenta of its particles reduces to a couple of moment $\bar{I}\omega$ (Sec. 18.2). This momentum couple is contained in the xy plane and may therefore be represented by the couple vector $\bar{I}\boldsymbol{\omega}$ directed along the z axis (Fig. 18.12*a*). Next we consider the gyroscope at time $t_2 = \Delta t$, after its axle has rotated about the y axis through an angle $\Delta\phi$ as a result of our miscalculated effort. We may neglect the relatively small angular momentum of the gyroscope about the y axis and consider only the large momentum couple vector $\bar{I}\boldsymbol{\omega}'$ associated with the rotation of the gyroscope about its axle (Fig. 18.12*c*). The change in momentum during the time interval Δt is represented by the couple vector $\Delta(\bar{I}\boldsymbol{\omega})$. This couple vector has the same direction as the couple vector $\mathbf{M}\,\Delta t$, which represents the angular impulse of the couple formed by the two forces applied to the axle (Fig. 18.12*b*).

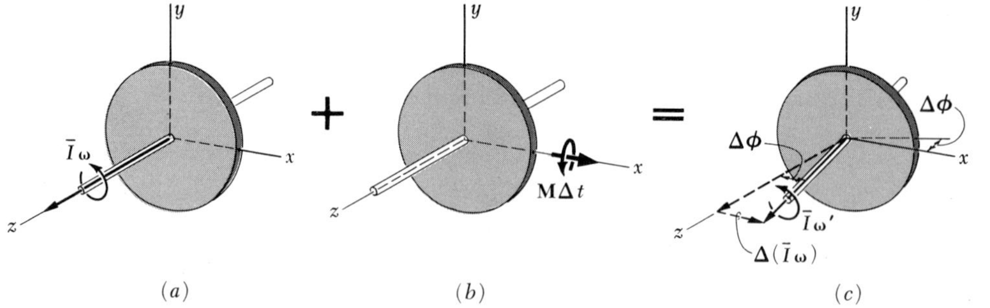

FIG. 18.12

Far from being strange, the behavior of the gyroscope is therefore entirely predictable. Noting that the couple vector $\Delta(\bar{I}\omega)$ has a magnitude equal to $\bar{I}\omega\Delta\phi$, we equate the angular impulse and the change in angular momentum and write

$$M\Delta t = \bar{I}\omega\Delta\phi$$

Dividing both members by Δt and letting Δt approach zero, we find that the moment M of the *gyroscopic couple* is equal to

$$M = \bar{I}\omega \frac{d\phi}{dt}$$

$$M = \bar{I}\omega\Omega \tag{18.20}$$

where ω = rate of spin
$\Omega = d\phi/dt$ = rate of precession of the axis of the gyroscope

We note that the spin axis, the couple axis (about which the force couple is applied), and the precession axis are at right angles to each other. The relative position of these axes may easily be found if we remember that the extremity of the vector couple $\bar{I}\omega$ representing the momentum of the gyroscope tends to move in the direction defined by the vector **M** representing the gyroscopic couple.

If the motion just described is maintained for an appreciable length of time, the gyroscope is said to be in *steady precession*. Steady precession may be obtained only if the axis of the applied couple is maintained perpendicular to the spin axis and to the precession axis.

We shall now consider another case of steady precession, in which the axis of the gyroscope forms with the precession axis an angle β different from 90° (Fig. 18.13). Neglecting again the angular momentum associated with the motion of precession, we observe that the change in momentum during a time interval Δt is represented by the vector $\Delta(\bar{I}\omega)$ of magnitude $\bar{I}\omega \sin\beta\,\Delta\phi$. Equating angular impulse and change in angular momentum, we write

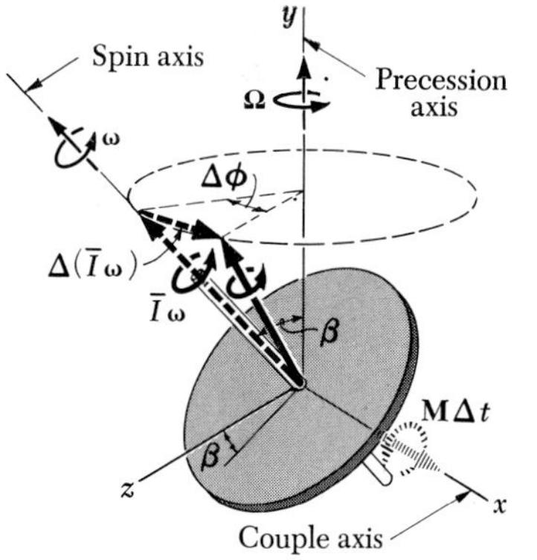

FIG. 18.13

$$M\,\Delta t = \bar{I}\omega \sin\beta\,\Delta\phi$$

and obtain

$$M = \bar{I}\omega\Omega \sin\beta \tag{18.21}$$

where Ω represents the rate of precession $d\phi/dt$. Thus, the motion described will be obtained if a couple of moment M satisfying Eq. (18.21) is applied about an axis which is maintained perpendicular to the spin axis and to the precession axis.

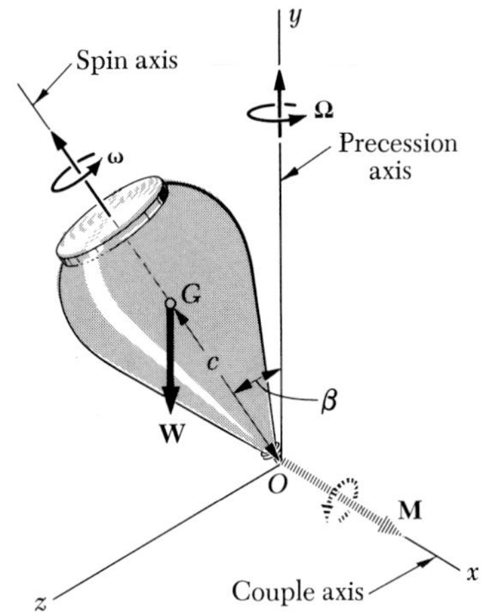

FIG. 18.14

An interesting example of gyroscopic motion is provided by a top supported at a fixed point O (Fig. 18.14). The weight **W** of the top and the normal component of the reaction at O form a couple of moment $M = Wc \sin \beta$. Assuming that the angle β the axis of the top forms with the vertical remains constant, we substitute for M in formula (18.21) and write

$$Wc = \bar{I}\omega\Omega \tag{18.22}$$

We should note that the result obtained is valid only for a very large rate of spin and that the top will just fall if it does not spin. Besides, the top will move in *steady* precession, at a constant rate Ω and with its axis forming a constant angle β with the vertical, only if it is given initially a rate of spin ω and a rate of precession Ω which satisfy Eq. (18.22). Otherwise, *the precession will be unsteady* and will be accompanied by variations in β, referred to as *nutation*. The study of the general case of motion of the top is a difficult one which requires a full knowledge of the motion of rigid bodies in space.†

A gyroscope mounted in a Cardan's suspension (Fig. 18.15) is free from any applied couple and thus will maintain a fixed direction with respect to a newtonian frame of reference. This was one of the facts used by the French physicist Jean Foucault (1819–1868) to prove that the earth rotates about its axis. The *gyrocompass* used to indicate the true north consists essentially of a gyroscope whose axis is maintained in a horizontal plane and oscillates symmetrically about the direction north-south. Other sensitive instruments based on gyroscopic motion include the inertial guidance systems of rockets, as well as the turn indicator, the artificial horizon, and the automatic pilot used on airplanes.

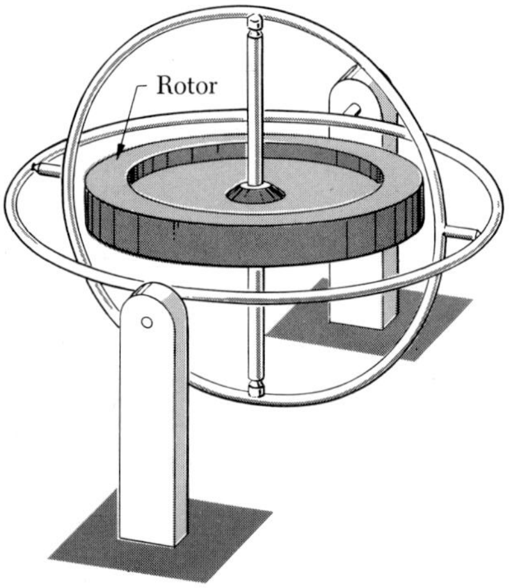

FIG. 18.15

Because of the relatively large couples required to change the orientation of their axles, gyroscopes are used as stabilizers in torpedoes and ships. Spinning bullets and shells remain tangent to their trajectory because of gyroscopic action. And a bicycle is easier to keep balanced at high speeds because of the stabilizing effect of its spinning wheels. However, gyroscopic action is not always welcome and must be taken into account in the design of bearings supporting rotating shafts subjected to forced precession. The reactions exerted by its propellers on an airplane which changes its direction of flight must also be taken into consideration and compensated for whenever possible.

† Cf. Synge and Griffith, "Principles of Mechanics," McGraw-Hill Book Company, Inc., sec. 14.2, or Becker, "Introduction to Theoretical Mechanics," McGraw-Hill Book Company, Inc., sec. 12.14.

SAMPLE PROBLEM 18.7

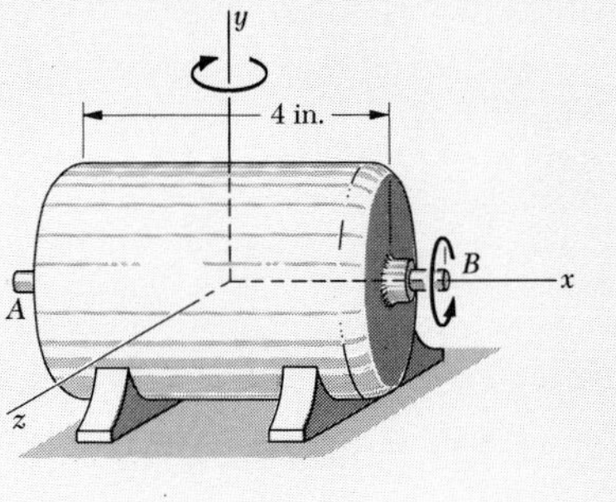

The rotor of an electric motor weighs 6 lb and has a radius of gyration of 2 in. The angular velocity of the rotor is 3,600 rpm counterclockwise as viewed from the positive x axis. Determine the reactions exerted by the bearings on the axle AB when the motor is rotated about the y axis clockwise as viewed from above and at a rate of 6 rpm.

Solution. During the time interval Δt, the momentum couple vector $\bar{I}\omega$ maintains a constant magnitude $\bar{I}\omega$ but is rotated in a horizontal plane through an angle $\Delta\phi$ into a new position $\bar{I}\omega'$. Thus, the change in angular momentum is represented by the vector $\Delta(\bar{I}\omega)$ parallel to the z axis and of magnitude $\bar{I}\omega\Delta\phi$.

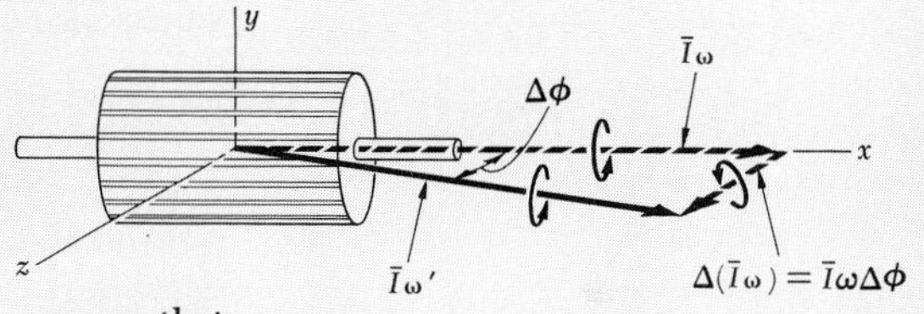

Denoting by $\mathbf{M}_z$ the couple applied about the z axis, we express that the angular impulse $\mathbf{M}_z\,\Delta t$ must equal the change in angular momentum.

$$M_z\,\Delta t = \bar{I}\omega\,\Delta\phi \qquad M_z = \bar{I}\omega\frac{\Delta\phi}{\Delta t}$$

Denoting by $\mathbf{\Omega}$ the angular velocity about the vertical y axis, we write $\Omega = \Delta\phi/\Delta t$ and obtain

$$M_z = \bar{I}\omega\Omega \tag{1}$$

Using the given data, we have

$$\omega = 3{,}600 \text{ rpm} = 377 \text{ radians/sec}$$
$$\Omega = 6 \text{ rpm} = 0.628 \text{ radian/sec}$$
$$\bar{I} = m\bar{k}^2 = \frac{6}{32.2}\left(\frac{2}{12}\right)^2 = 0.00518 \text{ lb-ft-sec}^2$$

Substituting these values into (1), we obtain the moment of the gyroscopic couple.

$$M_z = (0.00518)(377)(0.628) \qquad M_z = 1.226 \text{ lb-ft}$$

Reactions at A and B. The gyroscopic reactions $\mathbf{A}_g$ and $\mathbf{B}_g$ must be *equivalent* to the gyroscopic couple $\mathbf{M}_z$.

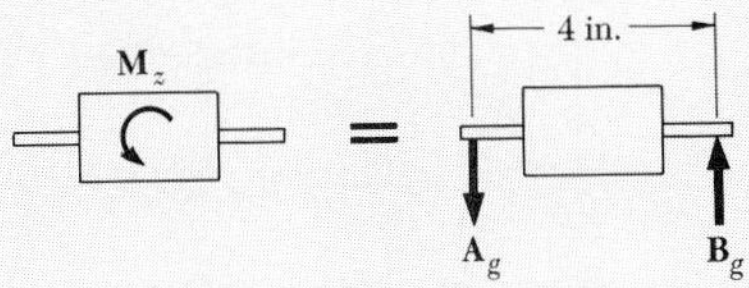

$$M_z = A_g(\tfrac{4}{12}\text{ ft})$$
$$1.226 = A_g(\tfrac{4}{12})$$
$$A_g = 3.68 \text{ lb} \qquad \mathbf{A}_g = 3.68 \text{ lb}\downarrow$$
$$B_g = 3.68 \text{ lb} \qquad \mathbf{B}_g = 3.68 \text{ lb}\uparrow$$

Since the static reactions are $\mathbf{A}_s = 3$ lb ↑ and $\mathbf{B}_s = 3$ lb ↑, the total reactions are

$$\mathbf{A} = 0.68 \text{ lb}\downarrow \qquad \mathbf{B} = 6.68 \text{ lb}\uparrow \;◀$$

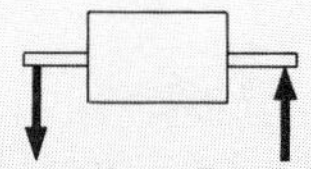

PROBLEMS

18.57. The major rotating elements of a given propeller-driven airplane rotate clockwise when viewed from behind. If the pilot turns the airplane to his right, determine in what direction the nose of the airplane will tend to move under the action of the gyroscopic couple exerted by the rotating elements.

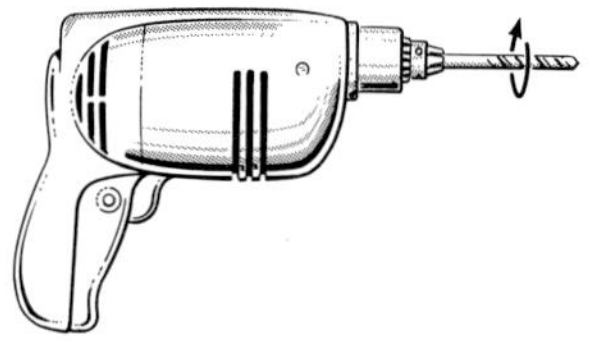

FIG. P 18.58

18.58. The main rotating parts of a hand drill rotate clockwise when viewed from behind. In what direction will the front end of the drill tend to move if the man holding the drill (*a*) rotates it clockwise in a horizontal plane, (*b*) tips it downward while maintaining it in the same vertical plane?

18.59. A three-bladed airplane propeller weighs 300 lb and has a radius of gyration of 3 ft. Knowing that the propeller rotates at 1,500 rpm, determine the moment of the couple applied by the propeller to its shaft when the airplane travels in a circular path of 1,200-ft radius at 350 mph.

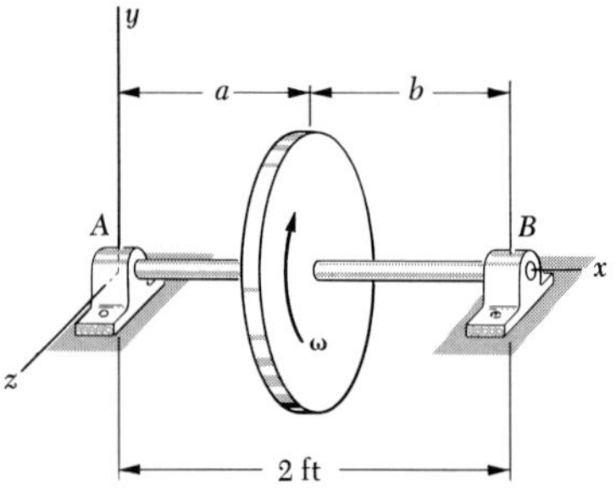

FIG. P 18.61

18.60. Each wheel of an automobile weighs 45 lb and has a radius of gyration of 11 in. The automobile travels around an unbanked curve of radius 600 ft at a speed of 60 mph. Knowing that each wheel is of 26-in. diameter and that the transverse distance between the wheels is 5 ft, determine the additional normal reaction at each outside wheel due to gyroscopic action.

18.61. The rotor of a given turbine may be approximated by a 50-lb disk of 12 in. radius. Knowing that the turbine rotates clockwise at 10,000 rpm as viewed from the positive x axis, determine the components due to gyroscopic action of the forces exerted by the bearings on axle AB if the instantaneous angular velocity of the turbine housing is 2 radians/sec clockwise as viewed from (*a*) the positive y axis, (*b*) the positive x axis.

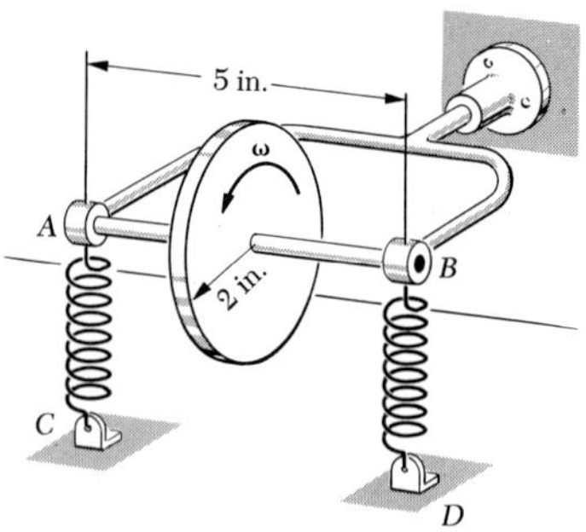

FIG. P 18.63

18.62. Solve Prob. 18.61 at an instant when the angular velocity of the turbine housing is 2 radians/sec clockwise as viewed from the positive z axis.

18.63. The essential structure of a certain type of aircraft turn indicator is shown. Springs AC and BD are initially stretched and exert equal vertical forces at A and B when the airplane is traveling in a straight path. Knowing that the disk weighs $\frac{1}{2}$ lb and spins at the rate of 10,000 rpm, determine the angle through which the yoke will rotate when the airplane executes a horizontal turn of radius 2,000 ft at a speed of 400 mph. The constant of each spring is 3 lb/in.

18.64. A toy top has a radius of gyration of 0.75 in. about its geometric axis and is set spinning at the rate of 1,600 rpm. Assuming steady precession, determine the rate of precession (*a*) for $\beta = 10°$, (*b*) for $\beta = 20°$.

18.65. A toy top having a radius of gyration of 0.75 in. with respect to its geometric axis is set in motion as shown. It is observed that the top precesses through two complete turns in 1 sec. Assuming steady precession, determine the rate at which the top spins about its geometric axis.

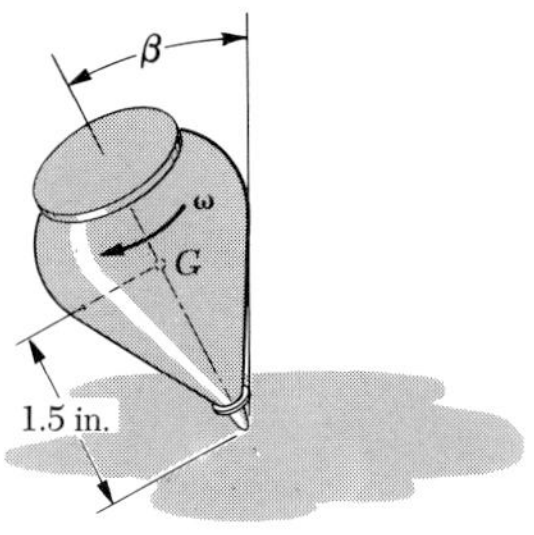

FIG. P 18.64 AND P 18.65

18.66. Two disks, each of weight 10 lb and radius 12 in., spin as shown at 1,200 rpm about the rod *AB*, which is attached to shaft *CD*. The entire system is made to rotate about the *z* axis with an angular velocity $\mathbf{\Omega}$ of 60 rpm. (*a*) Determine the reactions at *C* and *D* due to gyroscopic action as the system passes through the position shown. (*b*) Solve part *a* assuming that the direction of spin of disk *B* is reversed.

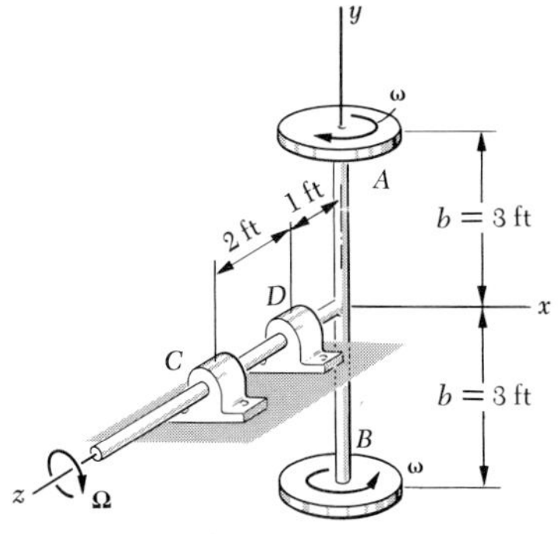

FIG. P 18.66

18.67. A right circular cone of height *h* and base radius *r* spins with an angular velocity ω about its geometric axis. The cone is of weight *W* and is supported by a ball-and-socket joint at *A*. Assuming steady precession, derive an expression for the angular velocity of precession (*a*) if $\beta = 60°$, (*b*) if $\beta = 120°$.

18.68. Solve Prob. 18.67 assuming that the ball-and-socket joint *A* is attached to an elevator which has an acceleration of magnitude *a* directed downward.

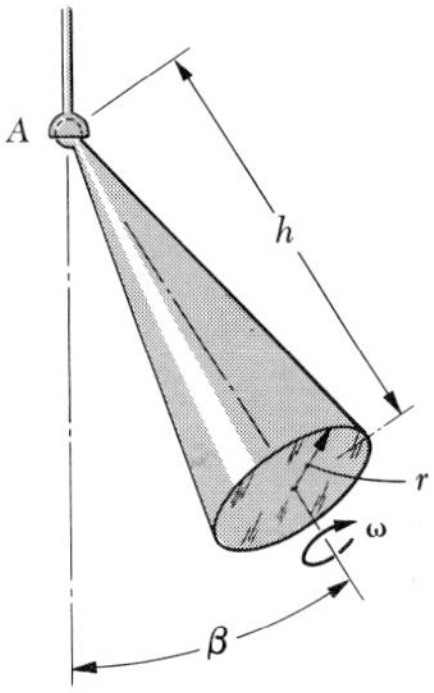

FIG. P 18.67

REVIEW PROBLEMS

18.69. A uniformly loaded rectangular crate is released from rest in the position shown. Assuming that the floor is sufficiently rough to prevent slipping and that the impact at *B* is perfectly plastic, determine the largest value of the ratio b/a for which corner *A* will remain in contact with the floor.

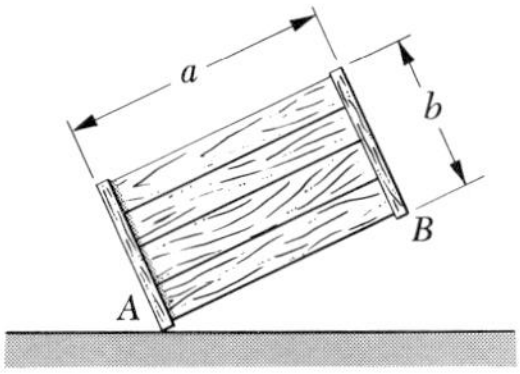

FIG. P 18.69

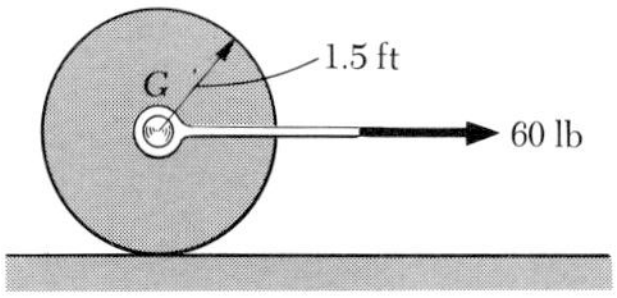

FIG. P 18.70

18.70. A 200-lb cylindrical roller is initially at rest and is acted upon by a 60-lb force as shown. Assuming that the body rolls without slipping, determine (*a*) the velocity of the center *G* after 6 sec, (*b*) the friction force required to prevent slipping.

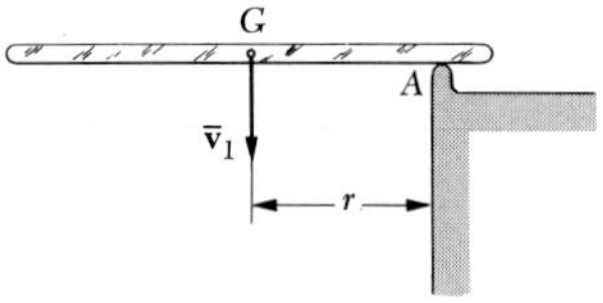

FIG. P 18.71

18.71. A slender rigid rod of mass m and with a centroidal radius of gyration $\bar{k}$ strikes a rigid pin at A with a vertical velocity of magnitude $\bar{v}_1$ and no angular velocity. Assuming that the impact is perfectly plastic, show that the magnitude of the velocity of G after impact is

$$\bar{v}_2 = \bar{v}_1 \frac{r^2}{r^2 + \bar{k}^2}$$

18.72. Assuming that in Prob. 18.71 the impact with pin A is perfectly elastic, $e = 1$, (*a*) show that the magnitude of the velocity of G after impact is

$$\bar{v}_2 = \bar{v}_1 \frac{r^2 - \bar{k}^2}{r^2 + \bar{k}^2}$$

(*b*) derive an expression for the angular velocity of the rod after impact.

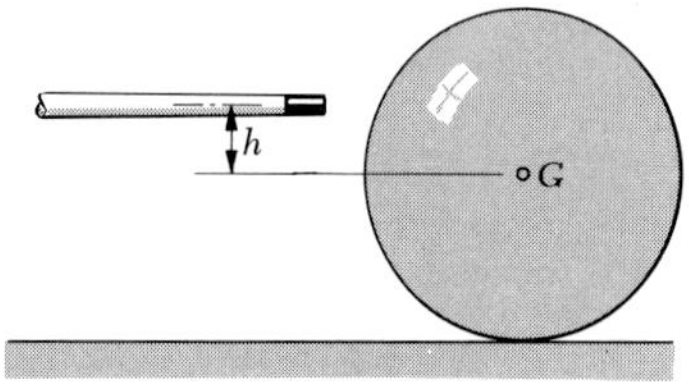

FIG. P 18.73

18.73. At what height h above its center G should a billiard ball of radius r be struck horizontally by a cue if the ball is to start rolling without sliding?

18.74. A slender rod of length l strikes a *smooth* floor at A with a vertical velocity $\bar{\mathbf{v}}_1$ and no angular velocity. Assuming that end A does not rebound, derive an expression (*a*) for the angular velocity of the rod immediately after impact, (*b*) for the corresponding velocity of end A of the rod.

18.75. Solve part *a* of Prob. 18.74 assuming that the distance d is zero so that end A strikes the corner C.

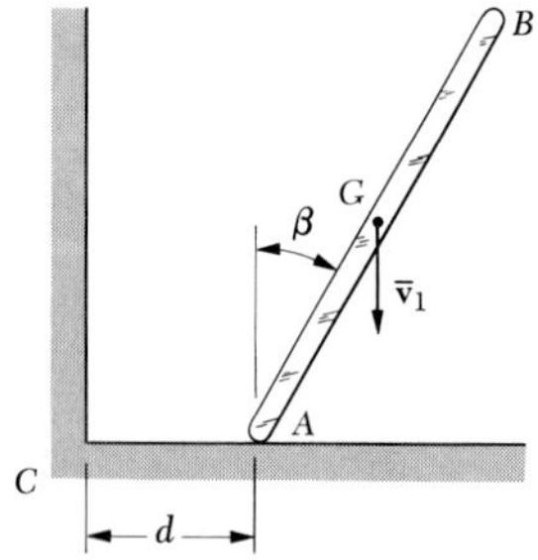

FIG. P 18.74

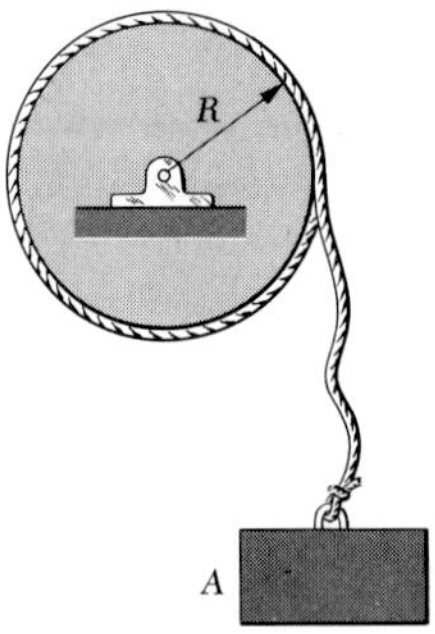

FIG. P 18.76

18.76. Block A of mass m is attached to a cord which is wrapped around a uniform disk of mass M. The block is released from rest and falls through a distance h before the cord becomes taut. Derive expressions for the velocity of the block and the angular velocity of the disk immediately after the impact. Assume that the impact is (*a*) perfectly plastic, (*b*) perfectly elastic.

18.77. The flywheel shown consists of a disk which weighs 400 lb. The coefficient of friction between the brake shoe and the disk is 0.25. Determine the magnitude of the force **P** required to bring the flywheel to rest in 8 sec if the initial angular velocity is (*a*) 600 rpm clockwise, (*b*) 600 rpm counterclockwise.

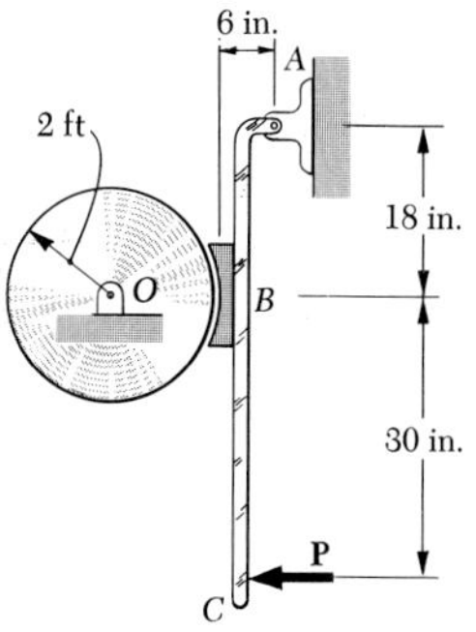

FIG. P 18.77

18.78. While moving forward at high speed, a motorcycle starts falling to the driver's right. Determine in what way the falling motion of the motorcycle is affected by the gyroscopic couple exerted by the rotating wheels.

18.79. Two identical slender rods swing freely from the pivots shown. Rod A is released from rest in a horizontal position and swings to a vertical position at which time the small knob K strikes rod B. If $h = \frac{1}{2}l$ and $e = \frac{1}{2}$, determine the angle through which rod B will swing.

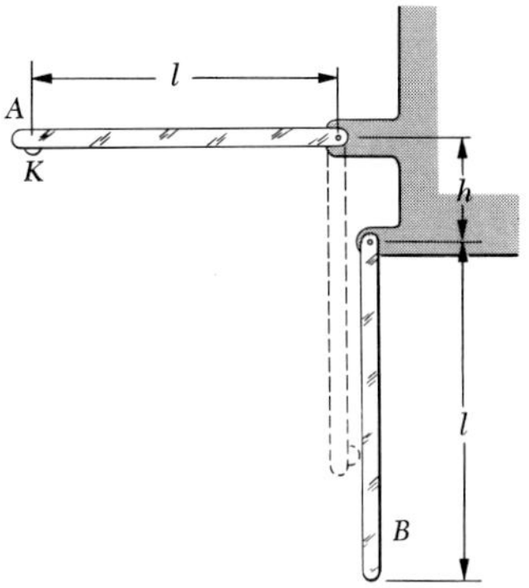

FIG. P 18.79

18.80. A space satellite of total weight 100 lb has a radius of gyration of 1.50 ft with respect to the y axis. The angular velocity of the satellite with respect to the x and z axes is zero while the angular velocity with respect to the y axis is 3 rpm. A rotor of weight 2 lb and radius of gyration 3 in. is mounted on an axis parallel to the y axis. The rotor is initially at rest with respect to the satellite and is then rotated at an angular velocity ω with respect to the satellite. Determine the required angular velocity ω if the corresponding angular velocity of the satellite is to be zero.

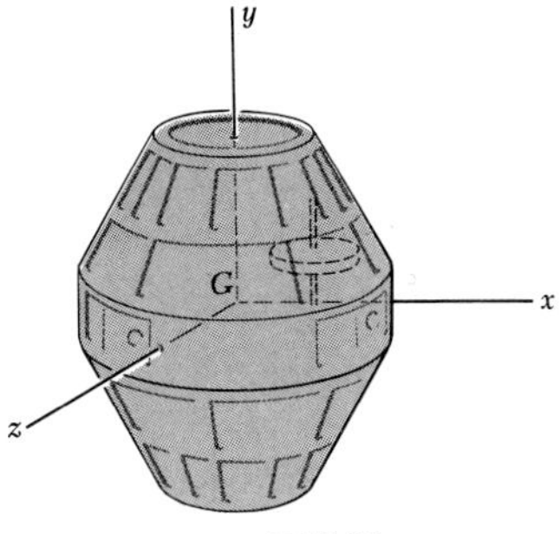

FIG. P 18.80

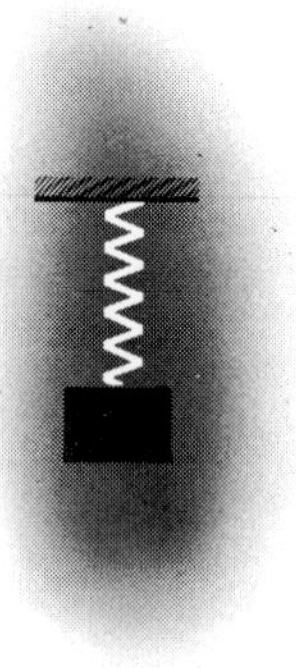

19. MECHANICAL VIBRATIONS

19.1. Introduction. A *mechanical vibration* is the motion of a particle or a body which oscillates about a position of equilibrium. Most vibrations in machines and structures are undesirable because of the increased stresses and energy losses which accompany them. They should therefore be eliminated or reduced as much as possible by appropriate design. The analysis of vibrations has become increasingly important in recent years owing to the current trend toward higher-speed machines and lighter structures. There is every reason to expect that this trend will continue and that an even greater need for vibration analysis will develop in the future.

The analysis of vibrations is a very extensive subject to which entire texts have been devoted.† We shall therefore limit our present study to the simpler types of vibrations, namely, the vibrations of a body or a system of bodies with one degree of freedom.

A mechanical vibration generally results when a system is displaced from a position of stable equilibrium. The system tends to return to this position under the action of restoring forces (either elastic forces, as in the case of a mass attached to a spring, or gravitational forces, as in the case of a pendulum). But the system generally reaches its original position with a certain acquired velocity which carries it beyond that position. Since the process can be repeated indefinitely, the system keeps moving back and forth across its position of equilibrium. The time interval required for the system to complete a full cycle of motion is called the *period* of the vibration. The number of cycles per unit time defines the *frequency*, and the maximum displacement of the system from its position of equilibrium is called the *amplitude* of the vibration.

† See, for example, Den Hartog, "Mechanical Vibrations," 4th ed., McGraw-Hill Book Company, Inc.

When the motion is maintained by the restoring forces only, the vibration is said to be a *free vibration* (Secs. 19.2 to 19.6). When a periodic force is applied to the system, the resulting motion is described as a *forced vibration* (Sec. 19.7). When the effects of friction may be neglected, the vibrations are said to be *undamped.* However, all vibrations are actually *damped* to some degree. If a free vibration is only slightly damped, its amplitude slowly decreases until, after a certain time, the motion comes to a stop. But damping may be large enough to prevent any true vibration; the system then slowly regains its original position (Sec. 19.8). A damped forced vibration is maintained as long as the periodic force which produces the vibration is applied. The amplitude of the vibration, however, is affected by the magnitude of the damping forces (Sec. 19.9).

VIBRATIONS WITHOUT DAMPING

19.2. Free Vibrations of Particles. Simple Harmonic Motion. Consider a body of mass m attached to a spring of constant k (Fig. 19.1*a*). Since, at the present time, we are concerned only with the motion of its mass center, we shall refer to this body as a particle. When the particle is in static equilibrium, the forces acting on it are its weight **W** and the force **T** exerted by the spring, of magnitude $T = k\delta_{st}$, where δ_{st} denotes the elongation of the spring. We have, therefore,

$$W = k\delta_{st} \tag{19.1}$$

Suppose now that the particle is displaced through a distance x_m from its equilibrium position and released with no initial velocity. If x_m has been chosen smaller than δ_{st}, the particle will move back and forth through its equilibrium position; a vibration of amplitude x_m has been generated. Note that the vibration may also be produced by imparting a certain initial velocity to the particle when it is in its equilibrium position $x = 0$ or, more generally, by starting the particle from any given position $x = x_0$ with a given initial velocity $\mathbf{v}_0$.

To analyze the vibration, we shall consider the particle in a position P at some arbitrary time t (Fig. 19.1*b*). Denoting by x the displacement OP measured from the equilibrium position O (positive downward), we note that the forces acting on the particle are its weight **W** and the force **T** exerted by the spring which, in this position, has a magnitude $T = k(\delta_{st} + x)$. Recalling (19.1), we find that the magnitude of the resultant **F** of the two forces (positive downward) is

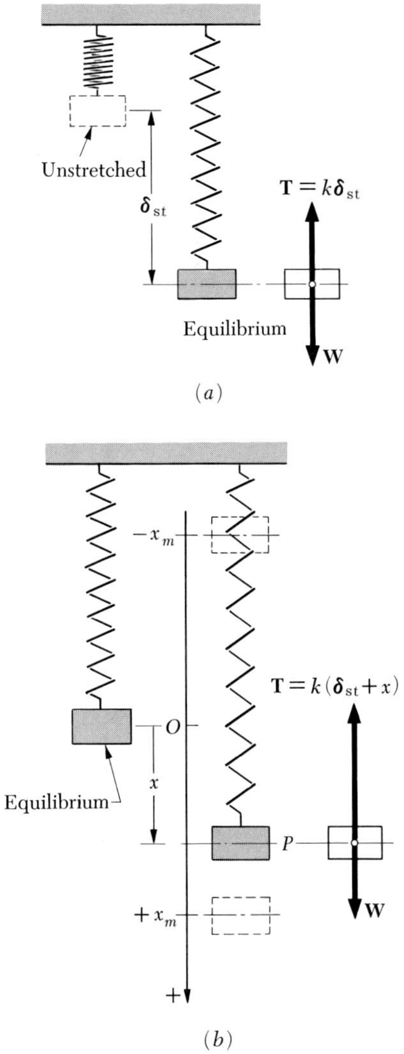

FIG. 19.1

$$F = W - k(\delta_{st} + x) = -kx \tag{19.2}$$

Thus the *resultant* of the forces exerted on the particle is proportional to the displacement *OP measured from the equilibrium position.* Recalling the sign convention, we note that **F** is always directed *toward* the equilibrium position *O*. Substituting for *F* into the fundamental equation $F = ma$ and recalling that $a = d^2x/dt^2$, we write

$$m\frac{d^2x}{dt^2} + kx = 0 \tag{19.3}$$

Note that the same sign convention should be used for the acceleration d^2x/dt^2 and for the displacement x, namely, positive downward.

Equation (19.3) is a linear differential equation of the second order. Setting

$$p^2 = \frac{k}{m} \tag{19.4}$$

we write (19.3) in the form

$$\frac{d^2x}{dt^2} + p^2x = 0 \tag{19.5}$$

The motion defined by Eq. (19.5) is called *simple harmonic motion.* It is characterized by the fact that *the acceleration is proportional to the displacement and of opposite direction.* We note that each of the functions $x_1 = \sin pt$ and $x_2 = \cos pt$ satisfies (19.5). These functions, therefore, constitute two *particular solutions* of the differential equation (19.5). As we shall see presently, the *general solution* of (19.5) may be obtained by multiplying the two particular solutions by arbitrary constants *A* and *B* and adding. We write

$$x = Ax_1 + Bx_2 = A \sin pt + B \cos pt \tag{19.6}$$

Differentiating, we obtain successively the velocity and acceleration at time *t*,

$$v = \frac{dx}{dt} = Ap \cos pt - Bp \sin pt \tag{19.7}$$

$$a = \frac{d^2x}{dt^2} = -Ap^2 \sin pt - Bp^2 \cos pt \tag{19.8}$$

Substituting from (19.6) and (19.8) into (19.5), we verify that the expression (19.6) provides a solution of the differential equation (19.5). Since this expression contains two arbitrary constants *A* and *B*, the solution obtained is the general solution of the differential equation. The values of the constants A and B depend upon the *initial conditions* of the motion. For example, we have $A = 0$ if the particle is displaced from its equilibrium position and released at $t = 0$ with no initial velocity, and we have $B = 0$ if P is started from O at $t = 0$ with a certain initial velocity. In general, substituting $t = 0$ and the initial values x_0 and v_0 of the displacement and velocity into (19.6) and (19.7), we find $A = v_0/p$ and $B = x_0$.

The expressions obtained for the displacement, velocity, and acceleration of a particle may be written in a more compact form if we observe that (19.6) expresses that the displacement $x = OP$ is the sum of the x components of two vectors of magnitude A and B, directed as shown in Fig. 19.2*a*. As t varies,

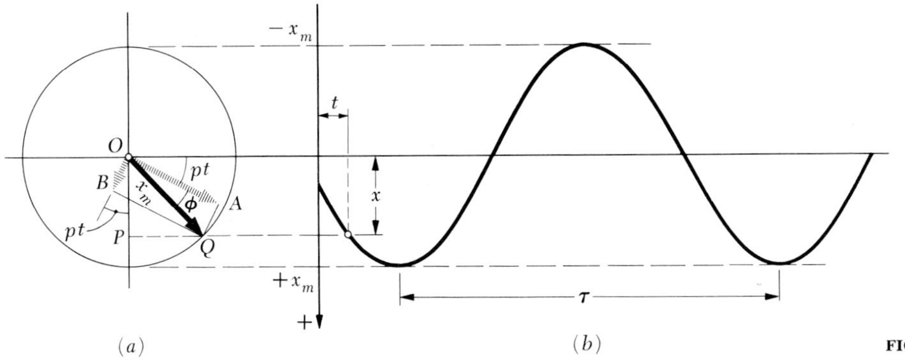

FIG. 19.2

both vectors rotate clockwise; we also note that the magnitude of their resultant $\overrightarrow{OQ}$ is equal to the maximum displacement x_m. The simple harmonic motion of P along the x axis may thus be obtained by projecting on this axis the motion of a point Q describing an *auxiliary circle* of radius x_m *with a constant angular velocity* p. Denoting by ϕ the angle formed by the vectors OQ and A, we write

$$OP = OQ \sin (pt + \phi) \tag{19.9}$$

which leads to new expressions for the displacement, velocity, and acceleration of P,

$$x = x_m \sin (pt + \phi) \tag{19.10}$$

$$v = \frac{dx}{dt} = x_m p \cos (pt + \phi) \tag{19.11}$$

$$a = \frac{d^2x}{dt^2} = -x_m p^2 \sin (pt + \phi) \tag{19.12}$$

The displacement-time curve is represented by a sine curve (Fig. 19.2*b*), and the maximum value x_m of the displacement is called the *amplitude* of the vibration. The angular velocity p of the point Q which describes the auxiliary circle is known as the *circular frequency* of the vibration and is measured in radians/sec, while the angle ϕ which defines the initial position of Q on the circle is called the *phase angle.* We note from Fig. 19.2 that a full *cycle* has been described after the angle pt has increased by 2π radians. The corresponding value of t, denoted by τ, is called the *period* of the vibration and is measured in seconds. The number of cycles described per unit of time is denoted by f and known as the *frequency* of the vibration. Frequencies are measured in cycles/sec (or cps, or sec^{-1}, since cycles are dimensionless units).

$$\text{Period} = \tau = \frac{2\pi}{p} \tag{19.13}$$

$$\text{Frequency} = f = \frac{1}{\tau} = \frac{p}{2\pi} \tag{19.14}$$

Recalling that p was defined in (19.4) in terms of the constant k of the spring and the mass m of the particle, we observe that the period and the frequency are independent of the initial conditions and of the amplitude of the vibration. Note that τ and f depend on the *mass* rather than on the *weight* of the particle and thus are independent of the value of g.

The velocity-time and acceleration-time curves may be represented by sine curves of the same period as the displacement-time curve, but with different phase angles. From (19.11) and (19.12), we note that the maximum values of the magnitudes of the velocity and acceleration are

$$v_m = x_m p \qquad a_m = x_m p^2 \tag{19.15}$$

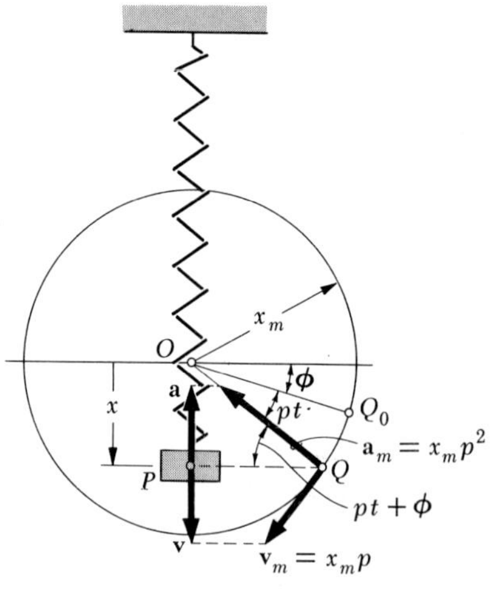

FIG. 19.3

Since the point Q describes the auxiliary circle, of radius x_m, at the constant angular velocity p, its velocity and acceleration are equal, respectively, to the expressions (19.15). Recalling Eqs. (19.11) and (19.12), we find, therefore, that the velocity and acceleration of P may be obtained at any instant by projecting on the x axis vectors of magnitudes $v_m = x_m p$ and $a_m = x_m p^2$ representing respectively the velocity and acceleration of Q at the same instant (Fig. 19.3).

The results obtained are not limited to the solution of the problem of a mass attached to a spring. They may be used to analyze the rectilinear motion of a particle *whenever the resultant* **F** *of the forces acting on the particle is proportional* *to the displacement x and directed toward O.* The fundamental equation of motion $F = ma$ may then be written in the form (19.5), which characterizes simple harmonic motion. Observing that the coefficient of x in (19.5) represents the square of the circular frequency p of the vibration, we easily obtain p and, after substitution into (19.13) and (19.14), the period τ and the frequency f of the vibration.

19.3. Simple Pendulum (Approximate Solution). Most of the vibrations encountered in engineering applications may be represented by a simple harmonic motion. Many others, although of a different type, may be *approximated* by a simple harmonic motion, provided that their amplitude remains small. Consider for example a *simple pendulum*, consisting of a bob of mass m attached to a cord of length l, which may oscillate in a vertical plane (Fig. 19.4*a*). At a given time t, the cord forms an angle θ with the vertical. The forces acting on the bob are its weight **W** and the force **T** exerted by the cord (Fig. 19.4*b*). Using tangential components (positive to the right) and observing that $a_t = l(d^2\theta/dt^2)$, we write

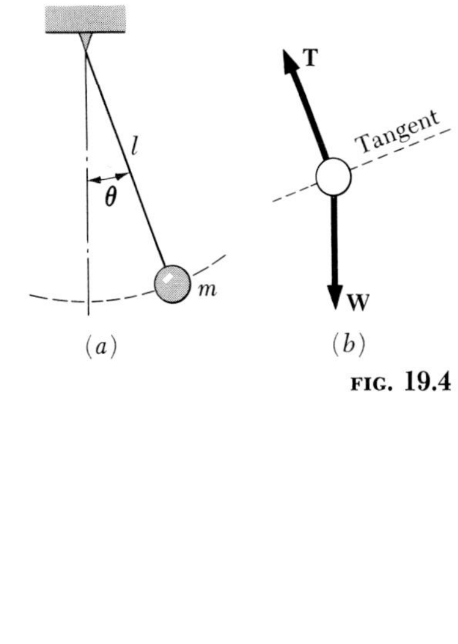

FIG. 19.4

$$F_t = ma_t: \qquad -W \sin\theta = ml\,\frac{d^2\theta}{dt^2}$$

Noting that $W = mg$ and dividing through by ml, we obtain

$$\frac{d^2\theta}{dt^2} + \frac{g}{l}\sin\theta = 0 \tag{19.16}$$

For oscillations of small amplitude, we may replace $\sin\theta$ by θ, expressed in radians, and write

$$\frac{d^2\theta}{dt^2} + \frac{g}{l}\theta = 0 \tag{19.17}$$

Comparison with (19.5) shows that the equation obtained is that of a simple harmonic motion and that the circular frequency p of the oscillations is equal to $(g/l)^{\frac{1}{2}}$. Substitution into (19.13) yields the period of the small oscillations of a pendulum of length l,

$$\tau = \frac{2\pi}{p} = 2\pi\sqrt{\frac{l}{g}} \tag{19.18}$$

***19.4. Simple Pendulum (Exact Solution).** Formula (19.18) is only approximate. To obtain an exact expression for the period of the oscillations of a simple pendulum, we must return to (19.16). Multiplying both terms by $2\,d\theta/dt$ and integrating from an initial position corresponding to the maximum deflection, i.e., $\theta = \theta_m$ and $d\theta/dt = 0$, we write

$$\left(\frac{d\theta}{dt}\right)^2 = \frac{2g}{l}(\cos\theta - \cos\theta_m)$$

Replacing $\cos\theta$ by $1 - 2\sin^2(\theta/2)$ and $\cos\theta_m$ by a similar expression, solving for dt, and integrating over a quarter period from $t = 0, \theta = 0$ to $t = \tau/4, \theta = \theta_m$, we have

$$\tau = 2\sqrt{\frac{l}{g}}\int_0^{\theta_m}\frac{d\theta}{\sqrt{\sin^2(\theta_m/2) - \sin^2(\theta/2)}}$$

The integral in the right-hand member is known as an *elliptic integral;* it cannot be expressed in terms of the usual algebraic or trigonometric functions. However, setting

$$\sin(\theta/2) = \sin(\theta_m/2)\sin\phi$$

we may write

$$\tau = 4\sqrt{\frac{l}{g}}\int_0^{\pi/2}\frac{d\phi}{\sqrt{1 - \sin^2(\theta_m/2)\sin^2\phi}} \tag{19.19}$$

where the integral obtained, commonly denoted by K, may be found in *tables of elliptic integrals* for various values of $\theta_m/2$.† In order to compare the result just obtained with that of the preceding section, we write (19.19) in the form

$$\tau = \frac{2K}{\pi}\left(2\pi\sqrt{\frac{l}{g}}\right) \tag{19.20}$$

Formula (19.20) shows that the actual value of the period of a simple pendulum may be obtained by multiplying the approximate value (19.18) by the correction factor $2K/\pi$. Values of the correction factor are given in Table 19.1 for various values

TABLE **19.1.** *Correction Factor for the Period of a Simple Pendulum*

θ_m	0°	10°	20°	30°	60°	90°	120°	150°	180°
K	1.571	1.574	1.583	1.598	1.686	1.854	2.157	2.768	∞
$2K/\pi$	1.000	1.002	1.008	1.017	1.073	1.180	1.373	1.762	∞

of the amplitude θ_m. We note that for ordinary engineering computations the correction factor may be omitted as long as the amplitude does not exceed 10°.

† See, for example, Dwight, "Table of Integrals and Other Mathematical Data," The Macmillan Company, p. 208, or Peirce, "A Short Table of Integrals," Ginn & Company, p.121.

SAMPLE PROBLEM 19.1

A 100-lb block moves between vertical guides as shown. The block is pulled 2 in. down from its equilibrium position and released. For each spring arrangement, determine the period of the vibration and the maximum velocity of the block.

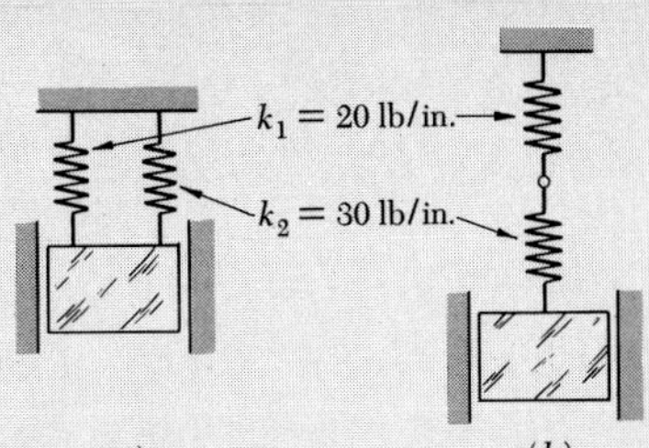

(a) (b)

a. **Springs Attached in Parallel.** We first determine the constant k of a single spring equivalent to the two springs *by finding the magnitude of the force* **P** required to cause a deflection of 1 in. Since for a deflection of 1 in. the forces exerted by the springs are, respectively, equal in magnitude to k_1 and k_2, we have

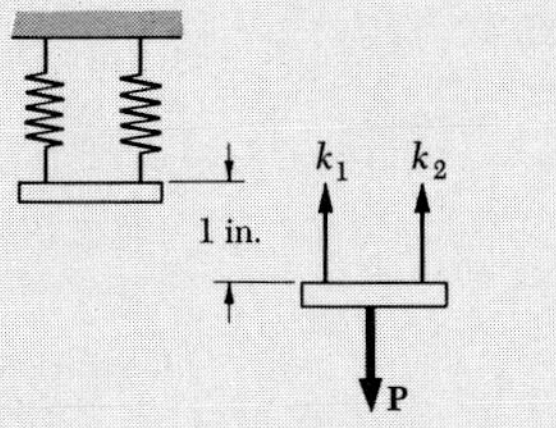

$$P = k_1 + k_2$$

The constant k of the single equivalent spring is

$$k = \frac{P}{1 \text{ in.}} = k_1 + k_2$$

$$k = 20 \text{ lb/in.} + 30 \text{ lb/in.} = 50 \text{ lb/in.} = 600 \text{ lb/ft}$$

Period of Vibration. Since $m = 100/g = 3.11$ lb-sec²/ft, Eq. (19.4) yields

$$p^2 = \frac{k}{m} = \frac{600}{3.11} \qquad p = 13.89 \text{ radians/sec}$$

$$\tau = \frac{2\pi}{p} \qquad \tau = 0.452 \text{ sec} \blacktriangleleft$$

Maximum Velocity

$$v_m = x_m p = (2 \text{ in.})(13.89 \text{ radians/sec})$$

$$\mathbf{v}_m = 27.8 \text{ in./sec} \updownarrow \blacktriangleleft$$

b. **Springs Attached in Series.** We first determine the constant k of a single spring equivalent to the two springs *by finding the total elongation* δ of the springs under a given static load. To facilitate the computation, a static load of magnitude $P = 60$ lb is used.

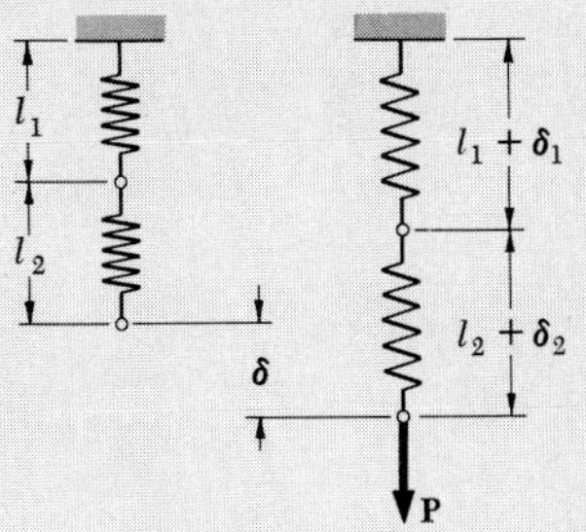

$$\delta = \delta_1 + \delta_2 = \frac{P}{k_1} + \frac{P}{k_2} = \frac{60}{20} + \frac{60}{30} = 5 \text{ in.}$$

$$k = \frac{P}{\delta} = \frac{60 \text{ lb}}{5 \text{ in.}} = 12 \text{ lb/in.} = 144 \text{ lb/ft}$$

Period of Vibration

$$p^2 = \frac{k}{m} = \frac{144}{3.11} \qquad p = 6.80 \text{ radians/sec}$$

$$\tau = \frac{2\pi}{p} \qquad \tau = 0.924 \text{ sec} \blacktriangleleft$$

Maximum Velocity

$$v_m = x_m p = (2 \text{ in.})(6.80 \text{ radians/sec})$$

$$\mathbf{v}_m = 13.60 \text{ in./sec} \updownarrow \blacktriangleleft$$

PROBLEMS

19.1. A particle is known to move with a simple harmonic motion. The maximum acceleration is 40 ft/sec^2, and the maximum velocity is 5 ft/sec. Determine the amplitude and the frequency of the motion.

19.2. A particle moves in simple harmonic motion with an amplitude of 4 in. and a period of 0.75 sec. Find the maximum velocity and the maximum acceleration.

19.3. Collar A of weight 8 lb rests on a spring of constant $k = 2$ lb/in. as shown. If the collar is depressed 2 in. and released, determine the period, the maximum velocity, and the maximum acceleration of the resulting motion.

19.4. Collar A of weight 8 lb rests on, but is not attached to, a spring as shown. The collar is to move in simple harmonic motion with an amplitude of 2 in. Determine (a) the largest permissible value of the spring constant k, (b) the corresponding frequency of the motion.

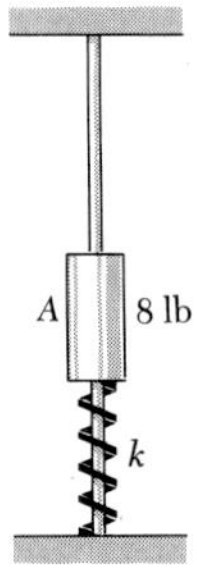

FIG. P 19.3 AND P 19.4

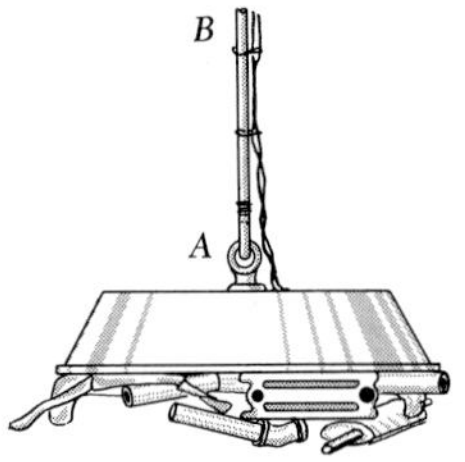

FIG. P 19.5

19.5. A 300-lb electromagnet is at rest and is holding 200 lb of scrap steel when the current is turned off and the steel is dropped. Knowing that the cable and the supporting crane have a total stiffness equivalent to a spring of constant 1,000 lb/in., determine (a) the frequency, the amplitude, and the maximum velocity of the resulting motion, (b) the minimum tension which will occur in the cable during the motion.

19.6. In Prob. 19.5, determine the largest weight of scrap steel which the electromagnet can hold and then drop, if the cable is to remain taut during the resulting motion. What is the corresponding frequency of the resulting motion?

19.7. In Prob. 19.3, determine the position, velocity, and acceleration of the collar 0.10 sec after it has been released.

19.8. In Prob. 19.3, determine (a) the time required for the collar to move 1 in. upward after it has been released from rest, (b) the corresponding velocity and acceleration of the collar.

19.9 and 19.10. A 100-lb block is supported by the spring arrangement shown. If the block is moved vertically downward and released, determine (*a*) the period and frequency of the resulting motion, (*b*) the maximum velocity and acceleration of the block if the amplitude of the motion is 3 in.

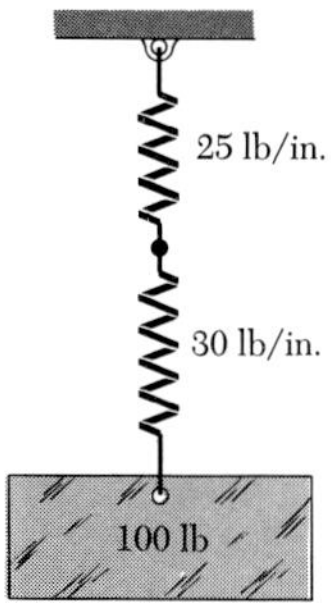

FIG. P 19.9

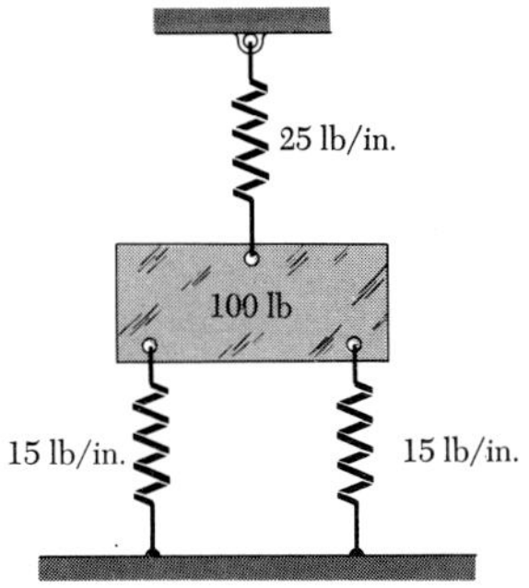

FIG. P 19.10

19.11. Denoting by δ_{st} the static deflection of a beam under a given weight, show that the frequency of vibration of the weight is

$$f = \frac{1}{2\pi}\sqrt{\frac{g}{\delta_{st}}}$$

Neglect the mass of the beam, and assume that the weight remains in contact with the beam.

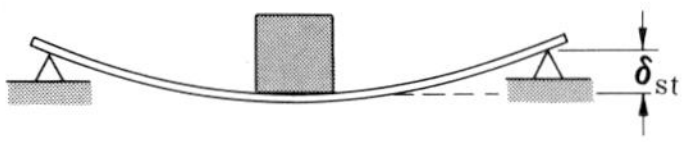

FIG. P 19.11

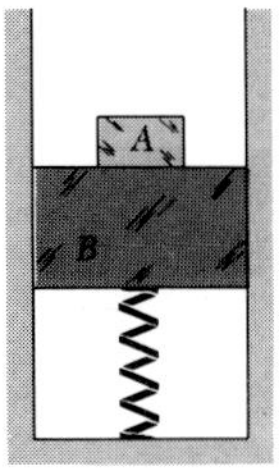

FIG. P 19.12

19.12. The period of vibration of the system shown is observed to be 0.80 sec. If block A is removed, the period is observed to be 0.70 sec. Knowing that block A weighs 1 lb, determine the weight of block B.

19.13. Determine the required length l of a simple pendulum if the period of small oscillations is to be 2 sec.

19.14. Determine the amplitude of a simple pendulum of length 4 ft if the maximum velocity of the bob is (*a*) 6 in./sec, (*b*) 12 in./sec.

19.15. A small bob is attached to a cord of length 4 ft and is released from rest when $\theta_A = 5°$. Knowing that $d = 2$ ft, determine (*a*) the time required for the bob to return to point A, (*b*) the amplitude θ_C.

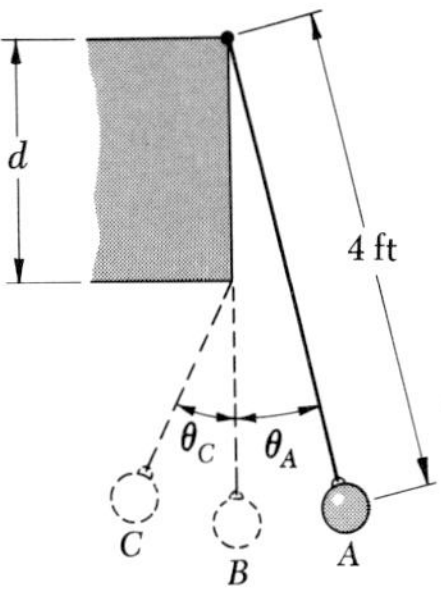

FIG. P 19.15

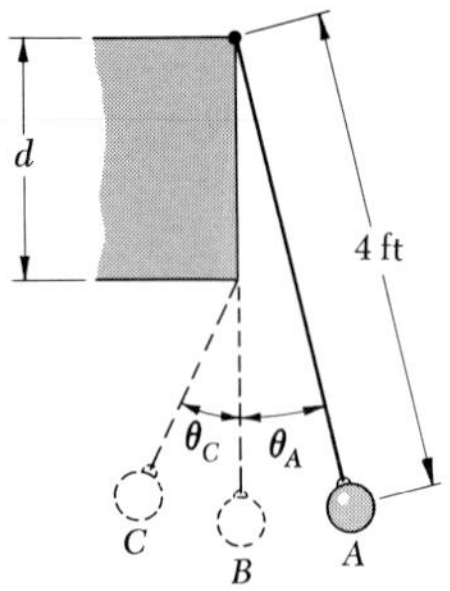

FIG. P 19.16

19.16. A small bob is attached to a cord of length 4 ft and released from rest at A when $\theta_A = 4°$. Determine the distance d for which the bob will return to point A in 2 sec.

19.17. A small weight W rests on a smooth horizontal surface and is attached to a taut string. Denoting by T the tension in the string, determine the period and frequency of small oscillations of the weight in a direction perpendicular to the string. Show that the longest period occurs when $a = b = \frac{1}{2}l$.

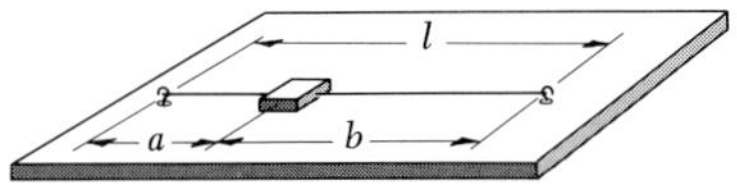

FIG. P 19.17

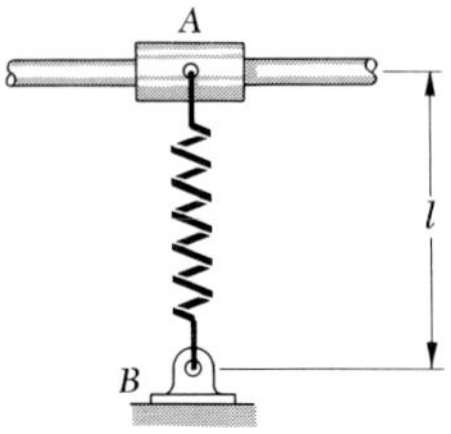

FIG. P 19.18

***19.18.** A collar of weight W slides without friction on a horizontal rod and is attached to a spring AB of constant k. (*a*) If the unstretched length of the spring is just equal to l, show that the collar does not execute simple harmonic motion even when the amplitude of the oscillations is small. (*b*) If the unstretched length of the spring is less than l, show that the motion may be approximated by a simple harmonic motion for small oscillations.

***19.19.** A particle is placed with no initial velocity on a smooth *plane* tangent to the surface of the earth. (*a*) Show that the particle will theoretically execute simple harmonic motion with a period of oscillation equal to that of a simple pendulum of length equal to the radius of the earth. (*b*) Knowing that the radius of the earth is 3,960 miles, compute the theoretical period of oscillation.

***19.20.** Using the data of Table 19.1, determine the period of a simple pendulum of length 48 in. (*a*) for small oscillations, (*b*) for oscillations of amplitude $\theta_m = 60°$, (*c*) for oscillations of amplitude $\theta_m = 120°$.

***19.21.** Expanding the integrand in (19.19) into a series of even powers of sin ϕ and integrating, show that the period of a simple pendulum of length l may be approximated by the formula

$$\tau = 2\pi\sqrt{\frac{l}{g}}\left(1 + \tfrac{1}{4}\sin^2\frac{\theta_m}{2}\right)$$

where θ_m is the amplitude of the oscillations.

*19.22. Using the formula given in Prob. 19.21, determine the amplitude θ_m for which the period of a simple pendulum is $\frac{1}{2}$ per cent longer than the period of the same pendulum for small oscillations.

*19.23. Using a table of elliptic integrals, determine the period of a simple pendulum of length $l = 36$ in. if the amplitude of the oscillations is $\theta_m = 40°$.

19.5. Free Vibrations of Rigid Bodies. The analysis of the vibrations of a rigid body or of a system of rigid bodies possessing a single degree of freedom is similar to the analysis of the vibrations of a particle. An appropriate variable, such as a distance x or an angle θ, is chosen to define the position of the body or system of bodies, and an equation relating this variable and its second derivative with respect to t is written. If the equation obtained is of the same form as (19.5), i.e., if we have

$$\frac{d^2x}{dt^2} + p^2x = 0 \qquad \text{or} \qquad \frac{d^2\theta}{dt^2} + p^2\theta = 0 \qquad (19.21)$$

the vibration considered is a simple harmonic motion. The period and frequency of the vibration may then be obtained by identifying p and substituting into (19.13) and (19.14).

In general, a simple way to obtain one of Eqs. (19.21) is to draw the free-body diagram of the system for an arbitrary value of the variable, including all external forces and all inertia vectors and couples, and to apply the method of dynamic equilibrium. We recall that our goal should be *the determination of the coefficient* of the variable x or θ, *not* the determination of the variable itself or of the derivatives d^2x/dt^2 or $d^2\theta/dt^2$. Setting this coefficient equal to p^2, we obtain the circular frequency p, from which τ and f may be determined.

The method we have outlined may be used to analyze vibrations which are truly represented by a simple harmonic motion, or vibrations of small amplitude which can be *approximated* by a simple harmonic motion. As an example, we shall determine the period of the small oscillations of a square plate of side $2b$ which is suspended from the mid-point O of one side (Fig. 19.5a). We consider the plate in an arbitrary position defined by the angle θ that the line OG forms with the vertical and draw its free-body diagram, including the weight $\mathbf{W}$ of the plate, the components $\mathbf{R}_x$ and $\mathbf{R}_y$ of the reaction at O, the components of the inertia vector, and the inertia couple (Fig. 19.5b). Since

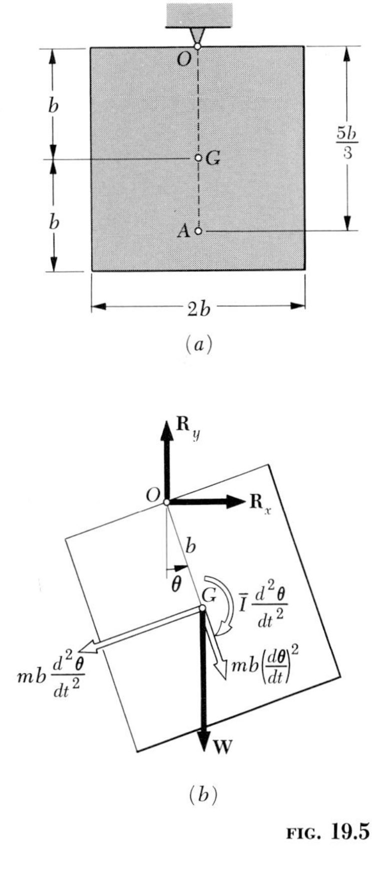

FIG. 19.5

the angular velocity and angular acceleration of the plate are equal, respectively, to $d\theta/dt$ and $d^2\theta/dt^2$, the normal and tangential components of the inertia vector are, respectively, $mb(d\theta/dt)^2$ and $mb(d^2\theta/dt^2)$, while the moment of the inertia couple is $\bar{I}(d^2\theta/dt^2)$. In previous applications of the method of dynamic equilibrium (Chap. 16), we tried whenever possible to assume the correct sense for the acceleration. Here, however, we should assume the same positive sense for θ and $d^2\theta/dt^2$ in order to obtain an equation of the form (19.21). Consequently, the angular acceleration $d^2\theta/dt^2$ will be assumed positive counterclockwise, even though this assumption is obviously unrealistic, and the inertia couple and the components of the inertia vector will be represented as indicated in Fig. 19.5*b*. Summing moments about O, we write

$$+\circlearrowleft \Sigma M_O = 0: \qquad \left(mb\frac{d^2\theta}{dt^2}\right)b + \bar{I}\frac{d^2\theta}{dt^2} + W(b\sin\theta) = 0$$

Noting that $\bar{I} = \frac{1}{12}m[(2b)^2 + (2b)^2] = \frac{2}{3}mb^2$ and $W = mg$, we obtain

$$\frac{d^2\theta}{dt^2} + \frac{3}{5}\frac{g}{b}\sin\theta = 0 \tag{19.22}$$

For oscillations of small amplitude, we may replace $\sin\theta$ by θ, expressed in radians, and write

$$\frac{d^2\theta}{dt^2} + \frac{3}{5}\frac{g}{b}\theta = 0 \tag{19.23}$$

Comparison with (19.21) shows that the equation obtained is that of a simple harmonic motion and that the circular frequency p of the oscillations is equal to $(3g/5b)^{\frac{1}{2}}$. Substituting into (19.13), we find that the period of the oscillations is

$$\tau = \frac{2\pi}{p} = 2\pi\sqrt{\frac{5b}{3g}} \tag{19.24}$$

The result obtained is valid only for oscillations of small amplitude. A more accurate description of the motion of the plate is obtained by comparing Eqs. (19.16) and (19.22). We note that the two equations are identical if we choose l equal to $5b/3$. This means that the plate will oscillate as a simple pendulum of length $l = 5b/3$, and the results of Sec. 19.4 may be used to correct the value of the period given in (19.24). The point A of the plate located on line OG at a distance $l = 5b/3$ from O is defined as the *center of oscillation* corresponding to O (Fig. 19.5*a*).

SAMPLE PROBLEM 19.2

A cylinder of weight W and radius r is suspended from a looped cord as shown. One end of the cord is attached directly to a rigid support, while the other end is attached to a spring of constant k. Determine the period and frequency of vibration of the cylinder.

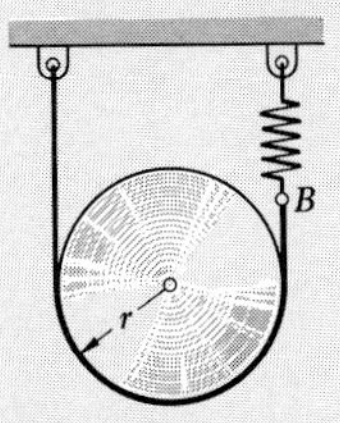

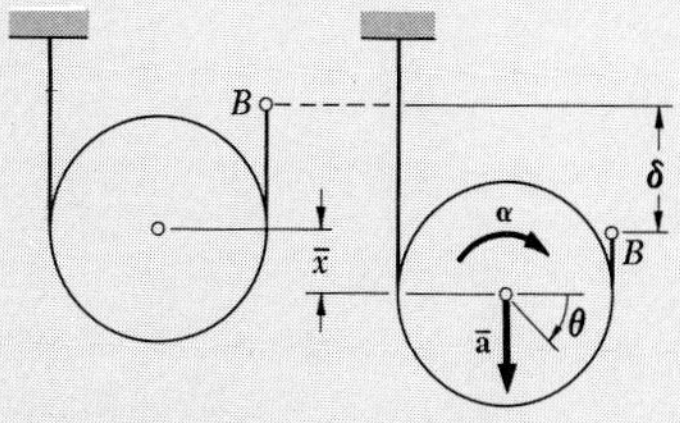

Kinematics of Motion. We express the linear displacement and the acceleration of the cylinder in terms of the angular displacement θ. Choosing the positive sense clockwise and measuring the displacements from the equilibrium position, we write

$$\bar{x} = r\theta \qquad \delta = 2\bar{x} = 2r\theta$$

$$\alpha = \frac{d^2\theta}{dt^2} \circlearrowright \qquad \bar{a} = r\alpha = r\frac{d^2\theta}{dt^2} \qquad \bar{\mathbf{a}} = r\frac{d^2\theta}{dt^2} \downarrow \tag{1}$$

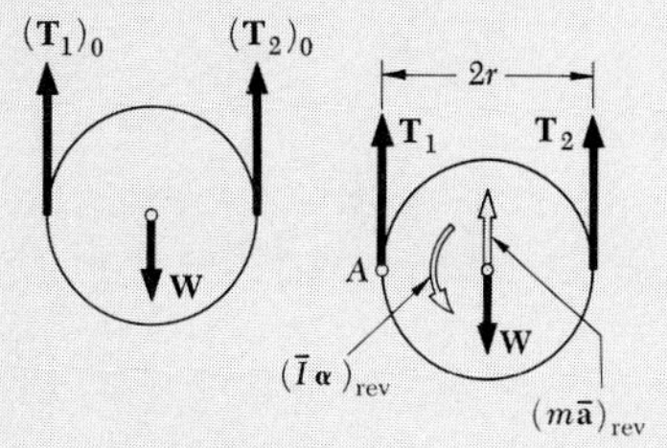

Dynamic Equilibrium. The cylinder is in dynamic equilibrium under the action of its weight $\mathbf{W}$, the forces $\mathbf{T}_1$ and $\mathbf{T}_2$ exerted by the cords, the inertia vector $(m\bar{\mathbf{a}})_{\text{rev}}$, and the inertia couple $(\bar{I}\boldsymbol{\alpha})_{\text{rev}}$. We write

$$+\circlearrowright \Sigma M_A = 0: \qquad T_2(2r) - Wr + m\bar{a}r + \bar{I}\alpha = 0 \tag{2}$$

Noting that, for an angular displacement θ, the magnitude of $\mathbf{T}_2$ is

$$T_2 = (T_2)_0 + k\delta = \frac{W}{2} + k\delta = \frac{W}{2} + k(2r\theta) \tag{3}$$

we substitute from (1) and (3) into (2) and write

$$(\tfrac{1}{2}W + 2kr\theta)(2r) - Wr + m\left(r\frac{d^2\theta}{dt^2}\right)r + \tfrac{1}{2}mr^2\frac{d^2\theta}{dt^2} = 0$$

$$\frac{d^2\theta}{dt^2} + \frac{8}{3}\frac{k}{m}\theta = 0$$

The motion is seen to be simple harmonic, and we have

$$p^2 = \frac{8}{3}\frac{k}{m} \qquad p = \sqrt{\frac{8}{3}\frac{k}{m}}$$

$$\tau = \frac{2\pi}{p} \qquad\qquad \tau = 2\pi\sqrt{\frac{3}{8}\frac{m}{k}} \blacktriangleleft$$

$$f = \frac{p}{2\pi} \qquad\qquad f = \frac{1}{2\pi}\sqrt{\frac{8}{3}\frac{k}{m}} \blacktriangleleft$$

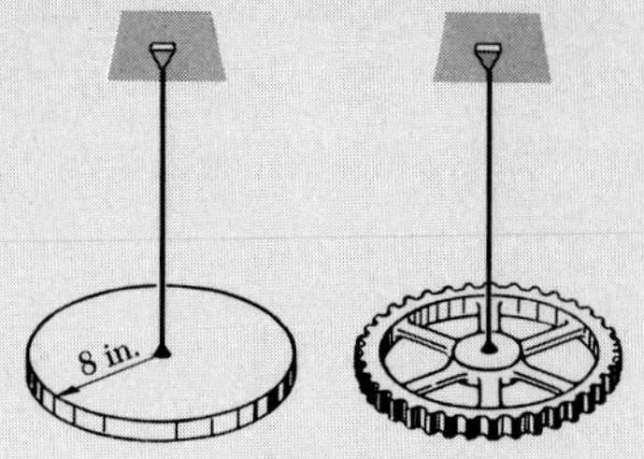

SAMPLE PROBLEM 19.3

A circular disk, weighing 20 lb and of radius 8 in., is suspended from a wire as shown. The disk is rotated (thus twisting the wire) and then released; the period of the torsional vibration is observed to be 1.13 sec. A gear is then suspended from the same wire, and the period of torsional vibration for the gear is observed to be 1.93 sec. Assuming that the moment of the couple exerted by the wire is proportional to the angle of twist, determine (*a*) the torsional spring constant of the wire, (*b*) the centroidal moment of inertia of the gear.

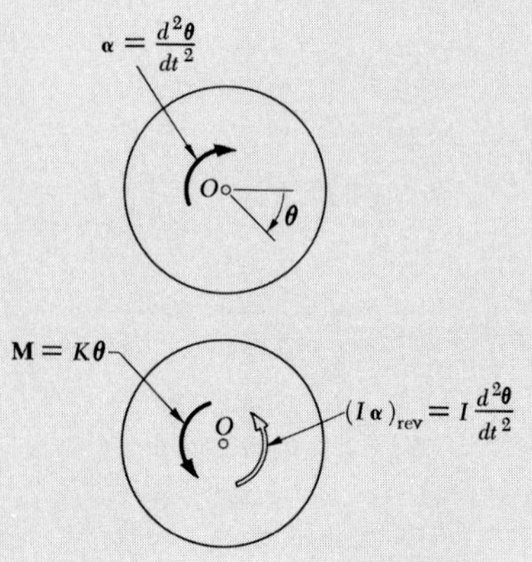

a. **Vibration of Disk.** Denoting by θ the angular displacement of the disk, we express that the moment of the couple exerted by the wire is $M = K\theta$, where K is the torsional spring constant of the wire. The disk is in dynamic equilibrium under the action of the couple **M** and the inertia couple $(I\alpha)_{rev}$.

$$+\circlearrowleft \Sigma M_O = 0: \qquad +K\theta + I\frac{d^2\theta}{dt^2} = 0 \qquad \frac{d^2\theta}{dt^2} + \frac{K}{I}\theta = 0$$

The motion is seen to be simple harmonic, and we have

$$p^2 = \frac{K}{I} \qquad p = \sqrt{\frac{K}{I}}$$

$$\tau = \frac{2\pi}{p} \qquad \tau = 2\pi\sqrt{\frac{I}{K}} \qquad (1)$$

For the disk, we have

$$\tau = 1.13 \text{ sec} \qquad I = \tfrac{1}{2}mr^2 = \frac{1}{2}\left(\frac{20}{32.2}\right)\left(\frac{8}{12}\right)^2 = 0.138 \text{ lb-ft-sec}^2$$

Substituting into (1), we obtain

$$1.13 = 2\pi\sqrt{\frac{0.138}{K}} \qquad K = 4.27 \text{ lb-ft/radian} \blacktriangleleft$$

b. **Vibration of Gear.** Since the period of vibration of the gear is 1.93 sec and $K = 4.27$ lb-ft/radian, Eq. (1) yields

$$1.93 = 2\pi\sqrt{\frac{I}{4.27}} \qquad I_{gear} = 0.403 \text{ lb-ft-sec}^2 \blacktriangleleft$$

Note. It is shown in mechanics of materials that the torsional spring constant of a cylindrical rod of length L is $K = L/JG$, where J is the polar moment of inertia of the circular cross-sectional area of the rod and G the shearing modulus of elasticity of the material.

PROBLEMS

19.24. A 600-lb flywheel has a diameter of 4 ft and a radius of gyration of 20 in. A belt is placed over the rim and attached to two springs, each of constant $k = 75$ lb/in. The initial tension in the belt is sufficient to prevent slipping. If the end C of the belt is pulled 1 in. to the right and released, determine (*a*) the period of vibration, (*b*) the maximum angular velocity of the flywheel.

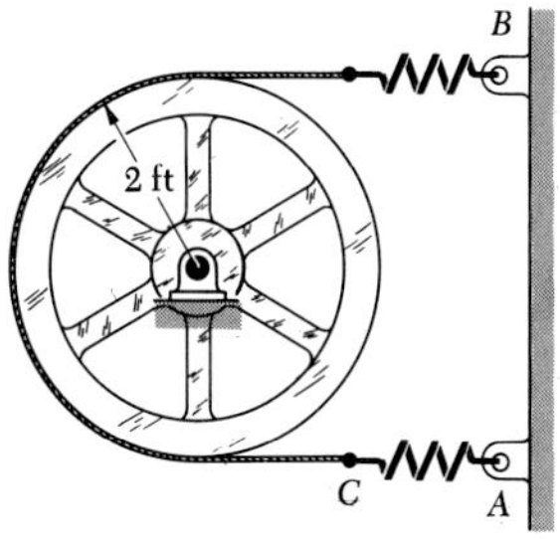

FIG. P 19.24

19.25. A disk is rigidly attached to a gear of radius r which may roll on the gear rack shown. The disk and gear have a total weight W and a combined radius of gyration $\bar{k}$. A spring of constant K is attached to the center of the gear. If the disk is released from rest when the tension in the spring is zero, derive an expression (*a*) for the amplitude and frequency of the resulting vibration, (*b*) for the maximum velocity of the center of the gear.

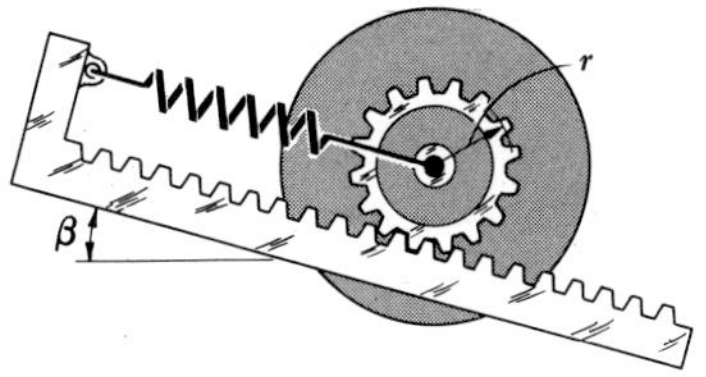

FIG. P 19.25

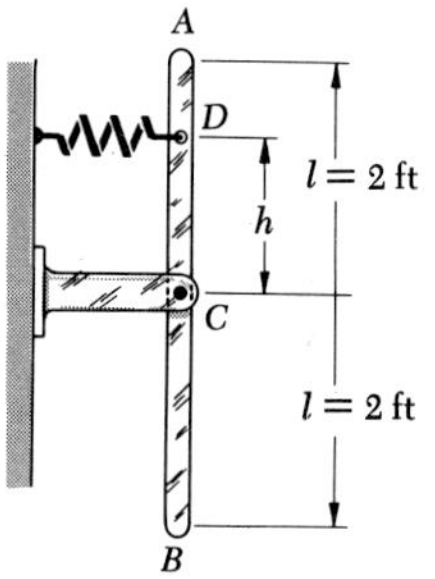

FIG. P 19.27

19.26. Solve Prob. 19.25 assuming $r = 3$ in., $\bar{k} = 4$ in., $W = 20$ lb, $K = 2$ lb/in., and $\beta = 30°$.

19.27. A 4-ft rod AB weighing 15 lb is attached to a hinge at its center C and to a spring of constant $k = 3$ lb/in. at D. Determine the distance h for which the period of vibration of the rod is 1 sec.

19.28 and 19.29. Two slender rods, each of weight W and length L, are welded together at B to form an L-shaped bracket. The bracket is supported in the horizontal plane by a hinge at B and by a spring of constant k as shown. If the spring is compressed by a small amount and released, determine the period of the resulting motion.

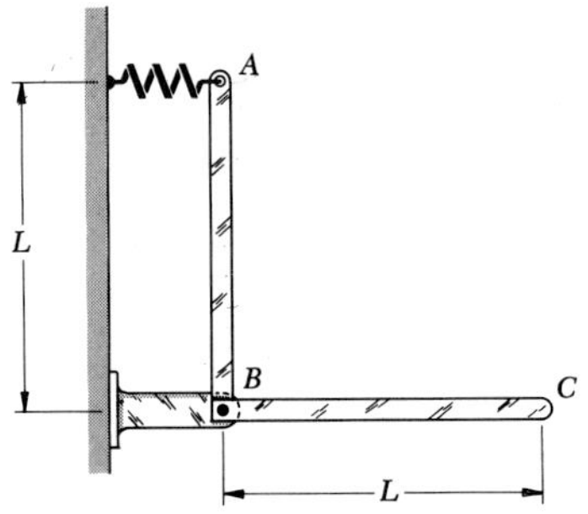

FIG. P 19.28

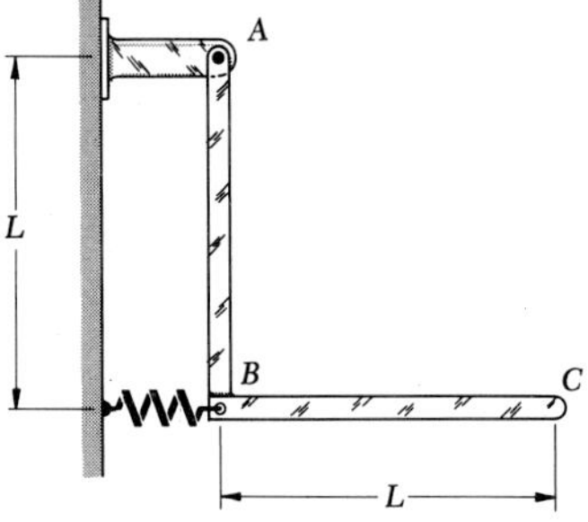

FIG. P 19.29

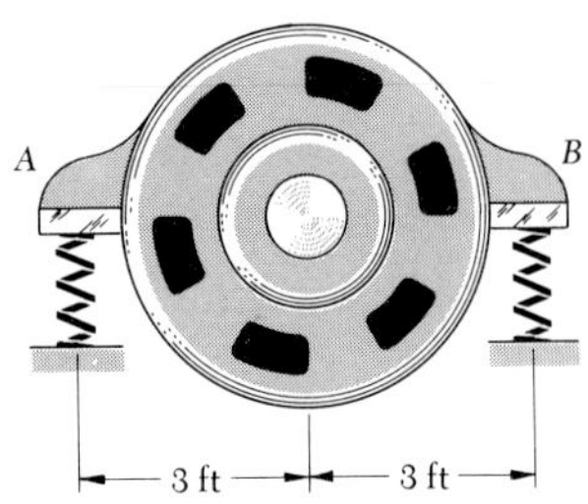

FIG. P 19.30

19.30. During the normal operation of a single-phase generator, the transmission of undesirable vibrations is prevented by four springs mounted as shown (two springs at A and two springs at B). Knowing that the stator of the generator weighs 400 lb and has a centroidal radius of gyration of 24 in., determine the required constant of each spring if the frequency of the free *angular* vibration of the stator is to be 15 cycles/sec.

19.31. The *rotor* of the generator of Prob. 19.30 weighs 300 lb and has a centroidal radius of gyration of 18 in. Knowing that the springs have been chosen so that the angular frequency of the *stator* alone is 15 cycles/sec, determine the frequency of the *angular* vibration of the generator if the bearings are frozen so that the rotor and stator move as a single rigid body.

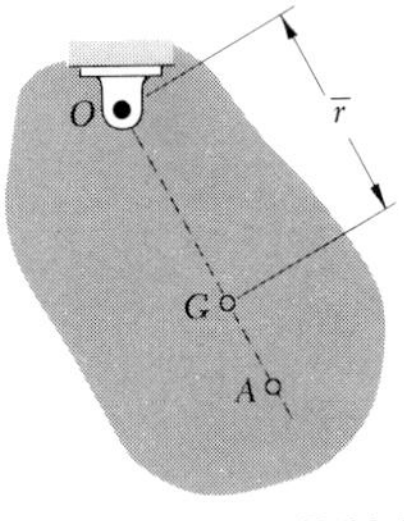

FIG. P 19.32 AND P 19.34

19.32. A *compound pendulum* is defined as a rigid body which oscillates about a fixed point O called the center of suspension. Show that the period of oscillation of a compound pendulum is equal to the period of a simple pendulum of length OA, where the distance from A to the mass center G is $GA = \bar{k}^2/\bar{r}$. Point A is defined as the center of oscillation and coincides with the center of percussion defined in Prob. 18.10.

19.33. Show that, if the compound pendulum of Prob. 19.32 is suspended from A instead of O, the period of oscillation is the same as before and the new center of oscillation is located at O.

19.34. A rigid body oscillates about a fixed point O. Show that the smallest period of oscillation occurs when the distance $\bar{r}$ from point O to the mass center G is equal to $\bar{k}$.

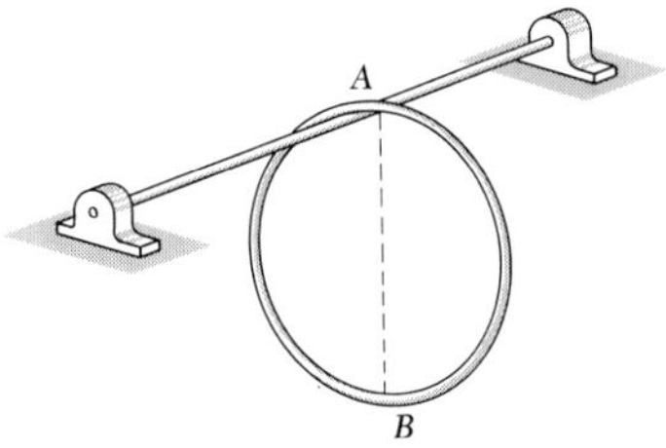

FIG. P 19.35

19.35. A thin hoop of radius r and weight W is suspended from a rough rod as shown. Determine the frequency of small oscillations of the hoop (*a*) in the plane of the hoop, (*b*) in a direction perpendicular to the plane of the hoop. Assume that μ is sufficiently large to prevent slipping at A.

19.36. Solve Prob. 19.35 assuming that a small collar of weight W is rigidly attached to the hoop at point B.

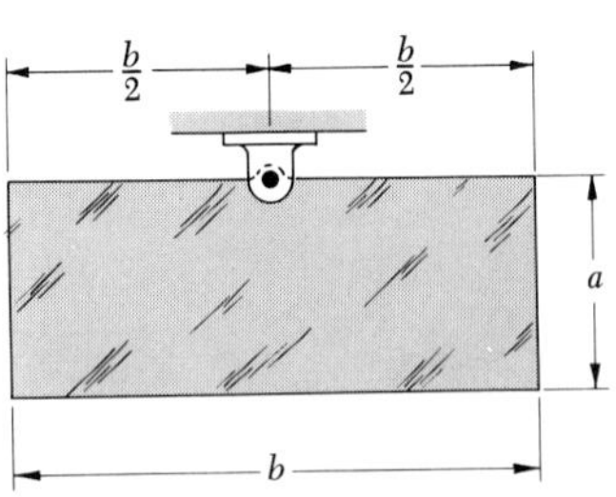

FIG. P 19.37 AND P 19.38

19.37. A homogeneous rectangular plate is suspended from a pin located at the mid-point of one edge as shown. Considering the dimension b constant, determine the ratio a/b for which the period of oscillation of the plate is minimum.

19.38. A homogeneous rectangular plate is suspended from a pin located at the mid-point of one edge as shown. Determine the ratio a/b for which the period of oscillation of the plate is the same as the period of a simple pendulum of length a.

19.39. The period of small oscillations about A of a connecting rod is observed to be 1.12 sec. Knowing that the distance r_a is 7.50 in., determine the centroidal radius of gyration of the connecting rod.

19.40. A connecting rod is supported by a knife-edge at point A; the period of small oscillations is observed to be 0.945 sec. The rod is then inverted and supported by a knife-edge at point B and the period of small oscillations is observed to be 0.850 sec. Knowing that $r_a + r_b =$ 11.50 in., determine (a) the location of the mass center G, (b) the centroidal radius of gyration $\bar{k}$.

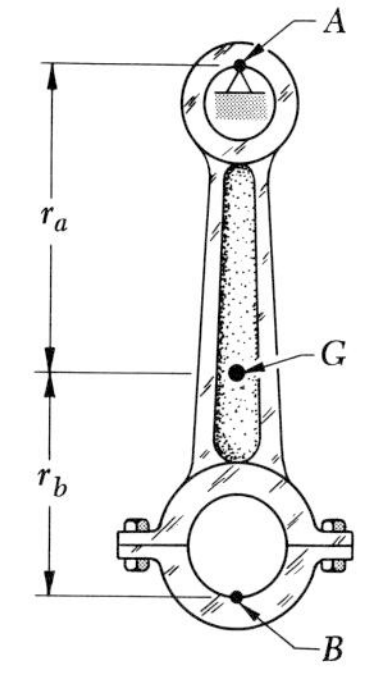

FIG. P 19.39 AND P 19.40

19.41. A slender bar of length L is attached by a smooth pin at A to a collar of negligible weight as shown. Assuming that the coefficient of friction between the collar and the horizontal rod is sufficient to prevent any movement of the collar, determine the period of small oscillations of the rod.

19.42. Solve Prob. 19.41 assuming that the coefficient of friction between the collar and the horizontal rod is zero.

19.43. Solve Prob. 19.35 assuming that $\mu = 0$.

19.44. A thin circular plate of radius r is suspended from three vertical wires of length h equally spaced around the perimeter of the plate. Determine the period of oscillation when (a) the plate is rotated through a small angle about a vertical axis passing through its mass center and released, (b) the plate is given a small horizontal translation and released.

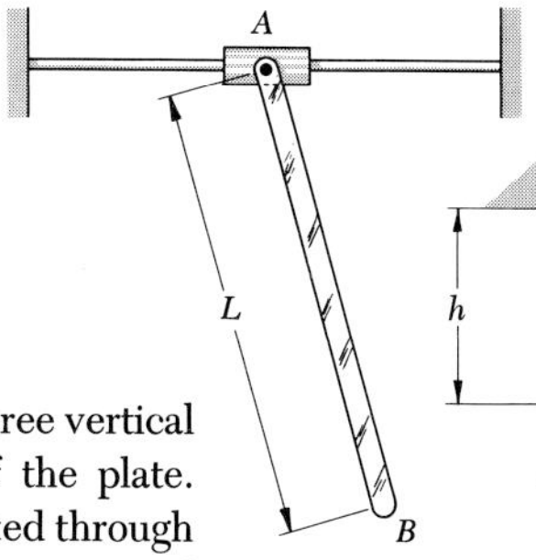

FIG. P 19.41

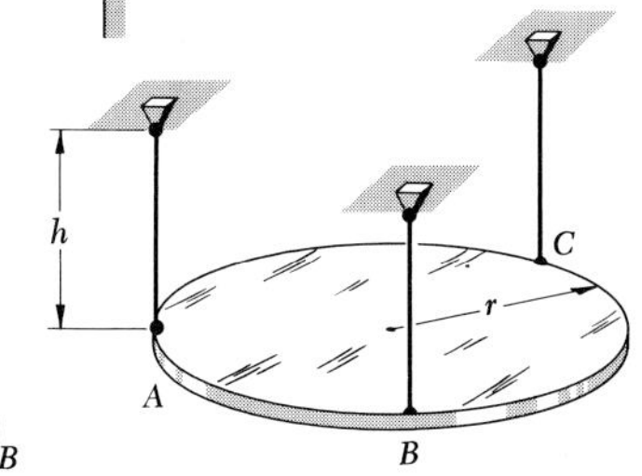

FIG. P 19.44

19.45. In Prob. 19.44, the points of attachment of the three vertical wires are changed so that they are *unequally* spaced around the perimeter of the plate. Show that this change does not affect the answers to either part a or b of Prob. 19.44, as long as the points A, B, and C are not on the same side of a given diameter of the plate.

19.46. An automobile wheel-and-tire assembly of total weight 47 lb is attached to a mounting plate of negligible weight which is suspended from a steel wire. The torsional spring constant of the wire is known to be $K = 0.40$ lb-in./radian. The wheel is rotated through 90° about the vertical and then released. Knowing that the period of oscillation is observed to be 30 sec, determine the centroidal mass moment of inertia and the centroidal radius of gyration of the wheel-and-tire assembly.

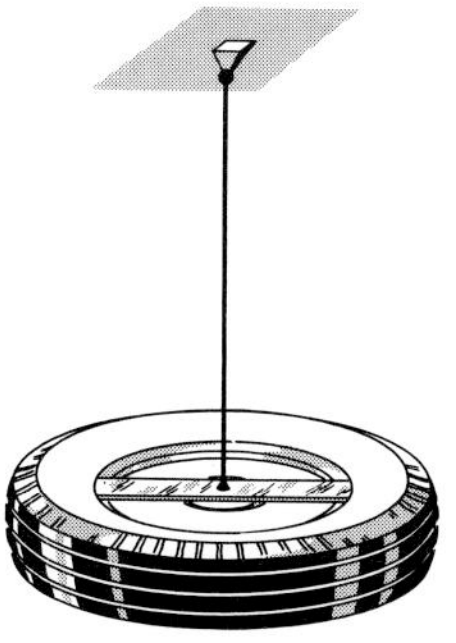

FIG. P 19.46

19.47. A disk of radius 12 in. weighing 20 lb is attached to a horizontal shaft which is rigidly held at B. It is known that the disk rotates through 5° when a 10-lb-ft static couple is applied to the disk. If the disk is rotated through 3° and then released, determine (a) the period of the resulting vibration, (b) the maximum angular velocity of the disk.

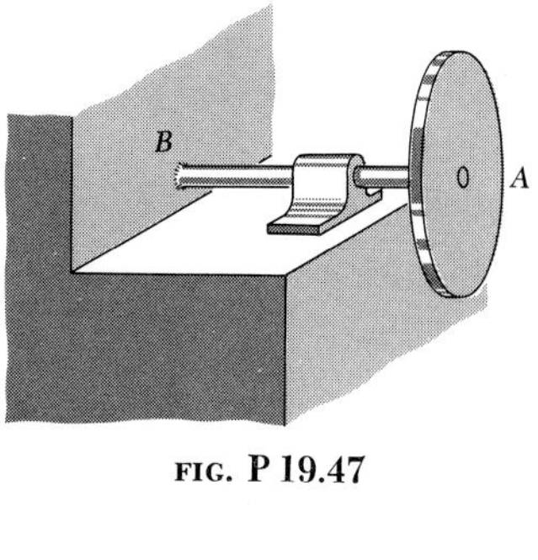

FIG. P 19.47

19.48. An instrument is rigidly bolted to the disk of Prob. 19.47. Knowing that the period of torsional vibration of the disk and instrument is 0.410 sec, determine the moment of inertia of the instrument with respect to the shaft AB.

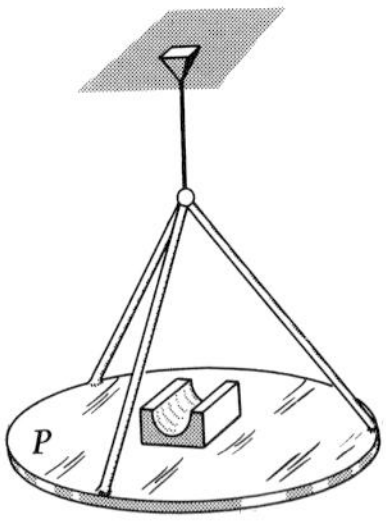

FIG. P 19.49

19.49. A torsion pendulum may be used to determine experimentally the moment of inertia of a given object. The horizontal platform P is held by several rigid bars which are connected to a vertical wire. The period of oscillation of the platform is found equal to τ_0 when the platform is empty and to τ_A when an object of known moment of inertia I_A is placed on the platform so that its mass center is directly above the center of the plate. (*a*) Show that the moment of inertia I_0 of the platform and its supports may be expressed as $I_0 = I_A\tau_0^2/(\tau_A^2 - \tau_0^2)$. (*b*) If a period of oscillation τ_B is observed when an object B of unknown moment of inertia I_B is placed on the platform, show that

$$I_B = I_A(\tau_B^2 - \tau_0^2)/(\tau_A^2 - \tau_0^2)$$

19.6. Application of the Principle of Conservation of Energy. We saw in Sec. 19.2 that, when a particle of mass m is in simple harmonic motion, the resultant $\mathbf{F}$ of the forces exerted on the particle has a magnitude proportional to the displacement x measured from the position of equilibrium O and is directed toward O; we wrote $F = -kx$. Referring to Sec. 13.6, we note that $\mathbf{F}$ is a *conservative force* and that the corresponding potential energy is $V = \frac{1}{2}kx^2$, where V is assumed equal to zero in the equilibrium position $x = 0$. Since the velocity of the particle is equal to dx/dt, its kinetic energy is $T = \frac{1}{2}m(dx/dt)^2$ and we may express that the total energy of the particle is conserved by writing

$$T + V = \text{constant} \qquad \tfrac{1}{2}m\left(\frac{dx}{dt}\right)^2 + \tfrac{1}{2}kx^2 = \text{constant}$$

Setting $p^2 = k/m$ as in (19.4), where p is the circular frequency of the vibration, we have

$$\left(\frac{dx}{dt}\right)^2 + p^2x^2 = \text{constant} \tag{19.25}$$

Equation (19.25) is characteristic of simple harmonic motion; it may be obtained directly from (19.5) by multiplying both terms by $2(dx/dt)$ and integrating.

The principle of conservation of energy provides a convenient way for determining the period of vibration of a rigid body or of a system of rigid bodies possessing a single degree of freedom. Choosing an appropriate variable, such as a distance x or an angle θ, we consider two particular positions of the system:

1. *The displacement of the system is maximum*; we have $T_1 = 0$, and V_1 may be expressed in terms of the amplitude x_m or θ_m (choosing $V = 0$ in the equilibrium position).

2. *The system passes through its equilibrium position*; we have $V_2 = 0$, and T_2 may be expressed in terms of the maximum velocity $(dx/dt)_m$ or $(d\theta/dt)_m$.

We then express that the total energy of the system is conserved and write $T_1 + V_1 = T_2 + V_2$. Recalling from (19.15) that for simple harmonic motion the maximum velocity is equal to the product of the amplitude and of the circular frequency p, we find that the equation obtained may be solved for p.

As an example, we shall consider again the square plate of Sec. 19.5. In the position of maximum displacement (Fig. 19.6*a*), we have

$$T_1 = 0 \qquad V_1 = W(b - b\cos\theta_m) = Wb(1 - \cos\theta_m)$$

or, since $1 - \cos\theta_m = 2\sin^2(\theta_m/2) \approx 2(\theta_m/2)^2 = \theta_m^2/2$ for oscillations of small amplitude,

$$T_1 = 0 \qquad V_1 = \tfrac{1}{2}Wb\theta_m^2 \tag{19.26}$$

As the plate passes through its position of equilibrium (Fig. 19.6*b*), its velocity is maximum and we have

$$T_2 = \tfrac{1}{2}m\bar{v}_m^2 + \tfrac{1}{2}\bar{I}\omega_m^2 = \tfrac{1}{2}mb^2\left(\frac{d\theta}{dt}\right)_m^2 + \tfrac{1}{2}\bar{I}\left(\frac{d\theta}{dt}\right)_m^2 \qquad V_2 = 0$$

or, recalling from Sec. 19.5 that $\bar{I} = \frac{2}{3}mb^2$,

$$T_2 = \tfrac{1}{2}\tfrac{5}{3}mb^2\left(\frac{d\theta}{dt}\right)_m^2 \qquad V_2 = 0 \tag{19.27}$$

Substituting from (19.26) and (19.27) into $T_1 + V_1 = T_2 + V_2$, and noting that the maximum velocity $(d\theta/dt)_m$ is equal to the product $\theta_m p$, we write

$$\tfrac{1}{2}Wb\theta_m^2 = \tfrac{1}{2}\tfrac{5}{3}mb^2\theta_m^2p^2 \tag{19.28}$$

which yields $p^2 = 3g/5b$ and

$$\tau = \frac{2\pi}{p} = 2\pi\sqrt{\frac{5b}{3g}} \tag{19.29}$$

as previously obtained.

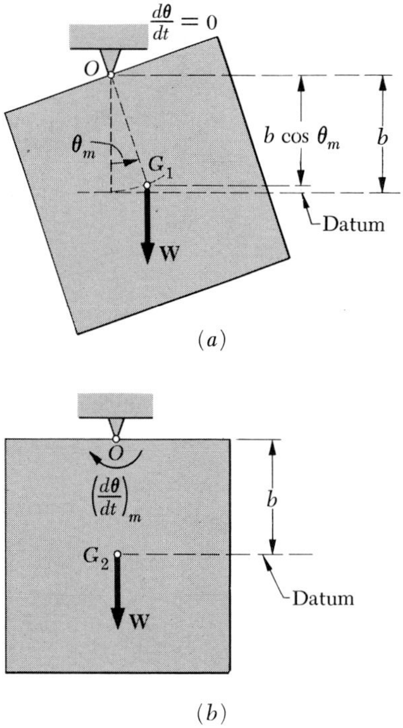

FIG. 19.6

SAMPLE PROBLEM 19.4

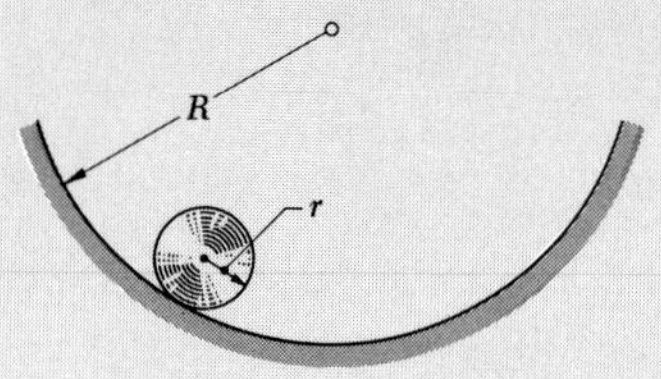

Determine the period of oscillation of a cylinder of radius r which rolls without slipping inside a curved surface of radius R.

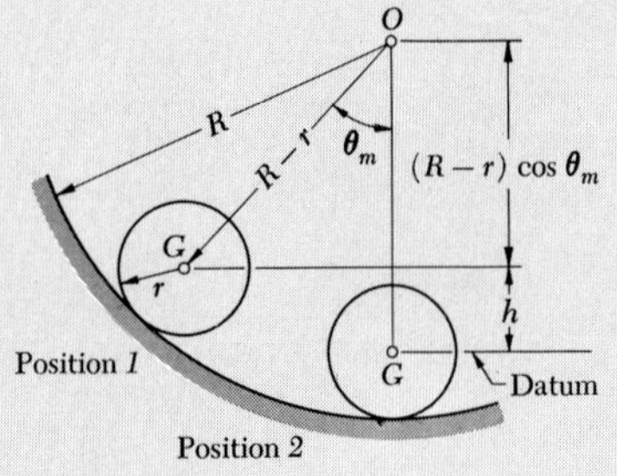

Solution. We denote by θ the angle which line OG forms with the vertical. Since the cylinder rolls without slipping, we may apply the principle of conservation of energy between position *1*, where $\theta = \theta_m$, and position 2, where $\theta = 0$.

Position *1*. *Kinetic Energy.* Since the velocity of the cylinder is zero, we have $T_1 = 0$.

Potential Energy. Choosing a datum as shown and denoting by W the weight of the cylinder, we have

$$V_1 = Wh = W(R - r)(1 - \cos\theta)$$

Noting that for small oscillations $(1 - \cos\theta) = 2\sin^2(\theta/2) \approx \theta^2/2$, we have

$$V_1 = W(R - r)\frac{\theta_m^2}{2}$$

Position 2. Denoting by $(d\theta/dt)_m$ the angular velocity of line OG as the cylinder passes through position 2, and observing that point C is the instantaneous center of rotation of the cylinder, we write

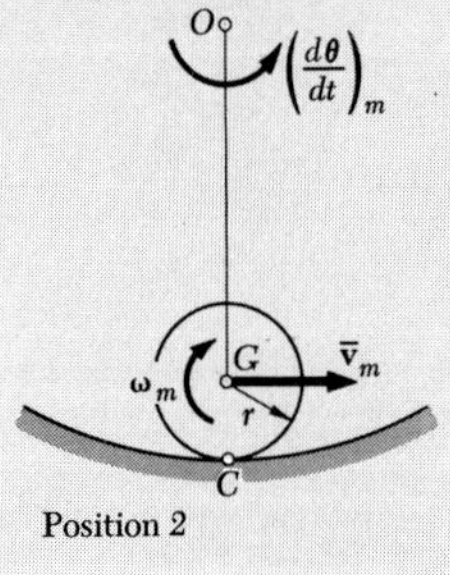

$$\bar{v}_m = (R - r)\left(\frac{d\theta}{dt}\right)_m \qquad \omega_m = \frac{\bar{v}_m}{r} = \frac{R - r}{r}\left(\frac{d\theta}{dt}\right)_m$$

Kinetic Energy:

$$\begin{aligned} T_2 &= \tfrac{1}{2}m\bar{v}_m^2 + \tfrac{1}{2}\bar{I}\omega_m^2 \\ &= \tfrac{1}{2}m(R - r)^2\left(\frac{d\theta}{dt}\right)_m^2 + \tfrac{1}{2}(\tfrac{1}{2}mr^2)\left(\frac{R - r}{r}\right)^2\left(\frac{d\theta}{dt}\right)_m^2 \\ &= \tfrac{3}{4}m(R - r)^2\left(\frac{d\theta}{dt}\right)_m^2 \end{aligned}$$

Potential Energy: $V_2 = 0$

Conservation of Energy

$$T_1 + V_1 = T_2 + V_2$$

$$0 + W(R - r)\frac{\theta_m^2}{2} = \tfrac{3}{4}m(R - r)^2\left(\frac{d\theta}{dt}\right)_m^2 + 0$$

Since $(d\theta/dt)_m = p\theta_m$ and $W = mg$, we write

$$mg(R - r)\frac{\theta_m^2}{2} = \tfrac{3}{4}m(R - r)^2(p\theta_m)^2 \qquad p^2 = \frac{2}{3}\frac{g}{R - r}$$

$$\tau = \frac{2\pi}{p} \qquad \tau = 2\pi\sqrt{\frac{3}{2}\frac{R - r}{g}} \quad ◄$$

PROBLEMS

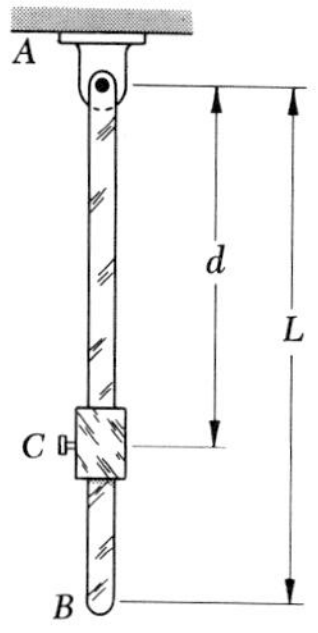

FIG. P 19.50

19.50. A small collar weighing 2 lb is rigidly attached to a 6-lb uniform rod of length $L = 3$ ft. Determine the period of oscillation of the rod when (*a*) $d = 3$ ft, (*b*) $d = 2$ ft.

19.51. Solve Prob. 19.50 assuming that the collar weighs 1 lb.

19.52. Using the method of Sec. 19.6, solve Prob. 19.5.

19.53. Using the method of Sec. 19.6, solve Prob. 19.9.

19.54. Using the method of Sec. 19.6, solve Prob. 19.10.

19.55. Using the method of Sec. 19.6, solve Prob. 19.11.

19.56. Using the method of Sec. 19.6, solve Prob. 19.12.

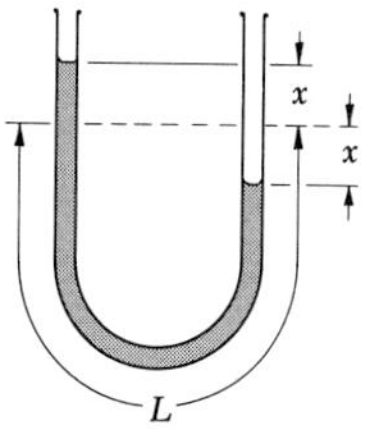

FIG. P 19.57

19.57. Neglecting fluid friction, determine the frequency of oscillation of the liquid in the U-tube manometer shown. Show that this frequency is independent of the density of the liquid and of the amplitude of the oscillation.

19.58. Two small weights w are attached at A and B to the rim of a uniform disk of radius r and weight W. Denoting by τ_0 the period of small oscillations when $\beta = 0$, determine the angle β for which the period of small oscillations is $2\tau_0$.

19.59. Two $\frac{1}{10}$-lb weights are attached at A and B to the rim of a 3-lb uniform disk of radius $r = 4$ in. Determine the frequency of small oscillations when $\beta = 60°$.

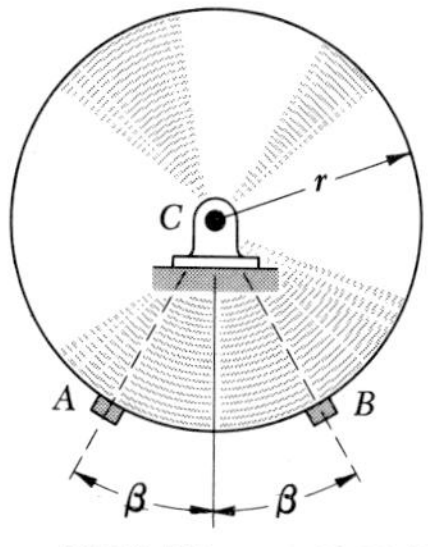

FIG. P 19.58 AND P 19.59

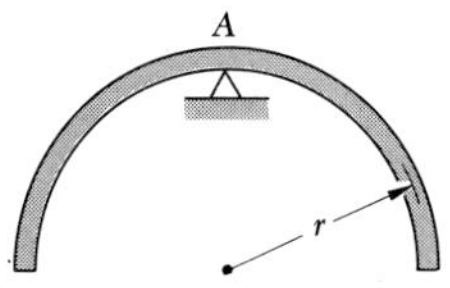

FIG. P 19.60

19.60. A half section of pipe is suspended as shown. Determine the frequency of small oscillations. Assume that μ is sufficiently large to prevent slipping at A.

19.61. Using the method of Sec. 19.6, solve Prob. 19.41.

19.62. The motion of the uniform rod AB is guided by the cord AC and by the small roller at B. Determine the frequency of oscillation when the end B of the rod is given a small horizontal displacement and released.

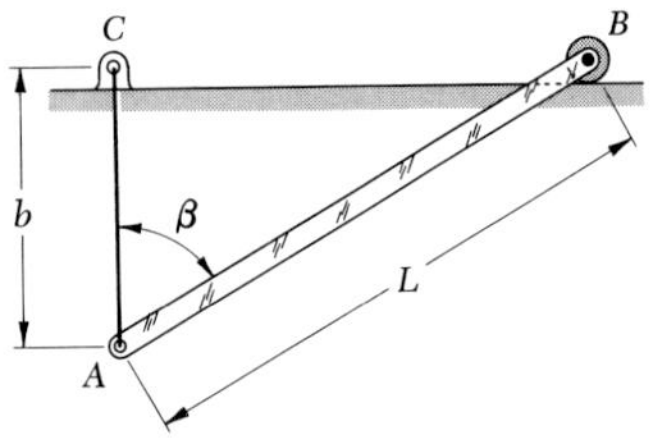

FIG. P 19.62

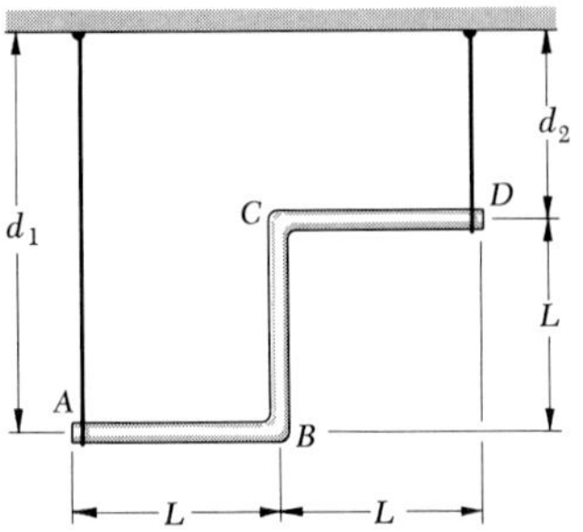

FIG. P 19.63

19.63. A section of uniform pipe bent in the shape shown is suspended from two vertical cables attached at A and D. Determine the period of oscillation when point D is given a small horizontal displacement to the right and released.

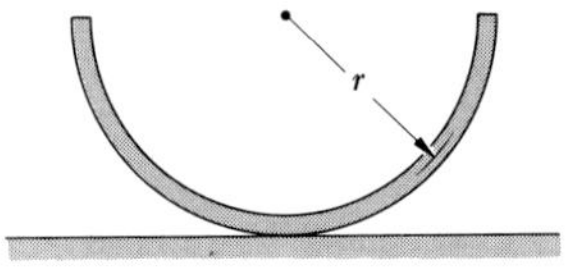

FIG. P 19.64

19.64. A half section of pipe is placed on a rough surface, rotated through a small angle, and then released. Assuming that μ is sufficiently large to prevent sliding, determine the period of oscillation.

19.65. Using the method of Sec. 19.6, solve Prob. 19.25.

19.66. Solve Sample Prob. 19.4 assuming that the cylinder is replaced by a sphere of radius r.

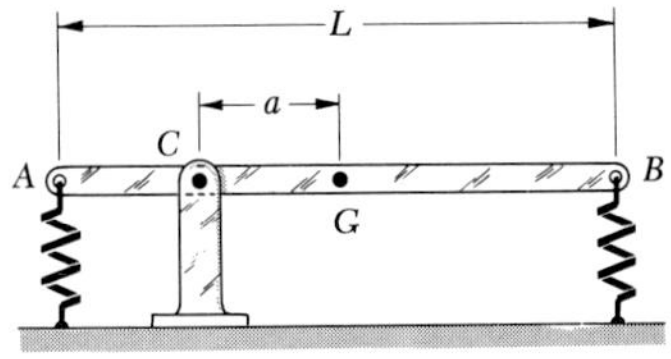

FIG. P 19.67

19.67. A slender bar of weight W and length L is attached to a pin support at C and to two springs each of constant k. Knowing that end B is depressed slightly and then released, determine the frequency of vibration if (*a*) $a = 0$, (*b*) $a = \frac{1}{4}L$, (*c*) $a = \frac{1}{2}L$.

19.68. Solve Prob. 19.67 assuming $W = 20$ lb, $L = 5$ ft, and $k = 10$ lb/in.

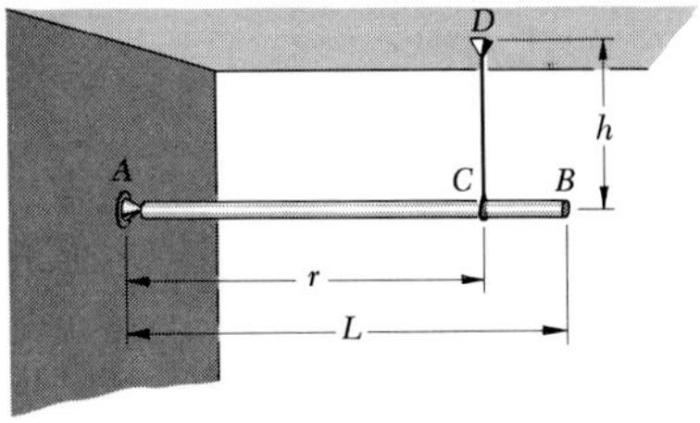

FIG. P 19.69

19.69. A uniform rod of length L is supported by a ball-and-socket joint at A and by the vertical wire CD. Derive an expression for the period of oscillation of the rod if end B is given a small horizontal displacement and then released.

19.70. Using the method of Sec. 19.6, solve Prob. 19.44.

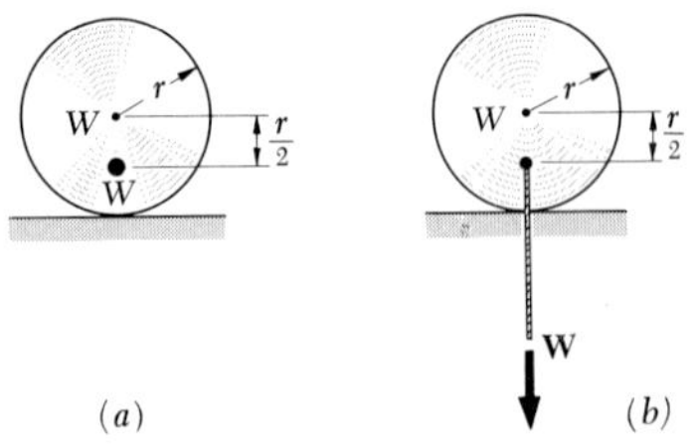

FIG. P 19.71

19.71. A uniform disk of weight W and radius r may roll on the horizontal surface shown. In case a, a weight W of negligible dimensions is bolted to the disk at a distance $\frac{1}{2}r$ from the geometric center of the disk. In case b, a vertical force of constant magnitude W is applied to a cord which is attached to the disk at a distance $\frac{1}{2}r$ from the center of the disk. Determine the ratio τ_b/τ_a of the two periods of oscillation.

***19.72.** As a submerged body moves through a fluid, the particles of the fluid flow around the body and thus acquire kinetic energy. In the case of a sphere moving in an ideal fluid, the total kinetic energy acquired by the fluid is $\frac{1}{4}\rho V v^2$, where ρ is the mass density of the fluid, V the volume of the sphere, and v the velocity of the sphere. Consider a 1-lb hollow spherical shell of radius 3 in. which is held submerged in a tank of water by a spring of constant 3 lb/in. (*a*) Neglecting fluid friction, determine the period of vibration of the shell when it is displaced vertically and then released. (*b*) Solve part *a* assuming that the tank is accelerated upward at the constant rate of 10 ft/sec².

FIG. P 19.72

***19.73.** The shell of Prob. 19.72 is held submerged by an inextensible cord of length 3 ft instead of a spring. (*a*) Neglecting fluid friction, determine the period of small oscillations of the shell when it is moved slightly to the side and then released. (*b*) Solve part *a* assuming that the tank is accelerated upward at the constant rate of 10 ft/sec².

***19.74.** A thin plate of length l rests on a half cylinder of radius r. Derive an expression for the period of small oscillations of the plate.

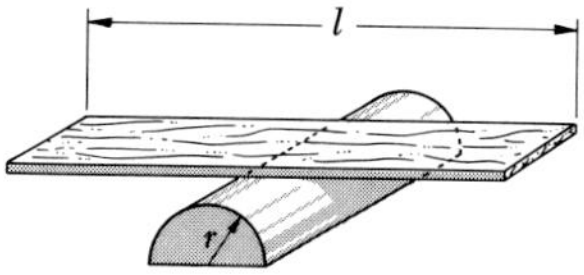

FIG. P 19.74

19.7. Forced Vibrations. The most important vibrations from the point of view of engineering applications are the *forced vibrations* of a system. These vibrations occur when a system is subjected to a periodic force or when it is elastically connected to a support which has an alternating motion.

Consider first the case of a body of mass m suspended from a spring and subjected to a periodic force **P** of magnitude $P = P_m \sin \omega t$ (Fig. 19.7). This force may be an actual external force applied to the body, or it may be a centrifugal force produced by the rotation of some unbalanced part of the body. (See Sample Prob. 19.5.) Denoting by x the displacement of the body measured from its equilibrium position, we write the equation of motion,

$$+\downarrow\Sigma F = ma: \qquad P_m \sin \omega t + W - k(\delta_{\text{st}} + x) = m\frac{d^2x}{dt^2}$$

Recalling that $W = k\delta_{\text{st}}$, we have

$$m\frac{d^2x}{dt^2} + kx = P_m \sin \omega t \tag{19.30}$$

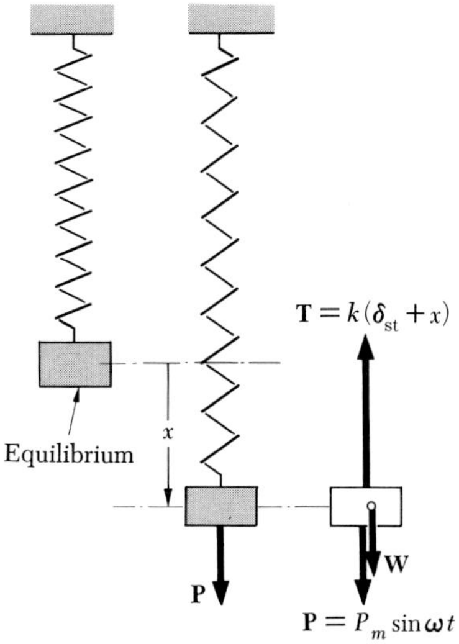

FIG. 19.7

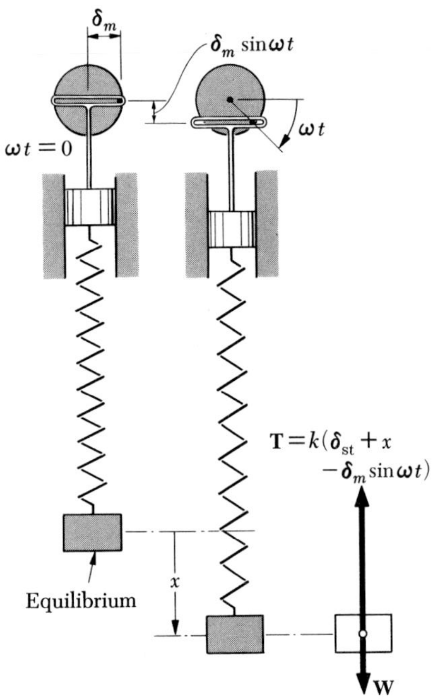

FIG. 19.8

Next we consider the case of a body of mass m suspended from a spring attached to a moving support whose displacement δ is equal to $\delta_m \sin \omega t$ (Fig. 19.8). Measuring the displacement x of the body from the position of static equilibrium corresponding to $\omega t = 0$, we find that the total elongation of the spring at time t is $\delta_{st} + x - \delta_m \sin \omega t$. The equation of motion is thus

$$+\downarrow \Sigma F = ma: \qquad W - k(\delta_{st} + x - \delta_m \sin \omega t) = m\frac{d^2x}{dt^2}$$

Recalling that $W = k\delta_{st}$, we have

$$m\frac{d^2x}{dt^2} + kx = k\delta_m \sin \omega t \tag{19.31}$$

We note that Eqs. (19.30) and (19.31) are of the same form and that a solution of the first equation will satisfy the second if we set $P_m = k\delta_m$.

A differential equation like (19.30) or (19.31), possessing a right-hand member different from zero, is said to be *nonhomogeneous.* Its general solution is obtained by adding a particular solution of the given equation to the general solution of the corresponding *homogeneous* equation (with right-hand member equal to zero). A *particular solution* of (19.30) or (19.31) may be obtained by trying a solution of the form

$$x_{\text{part}} = x_m \sin \omega t \tag{19.32}$$

Substituting x_{part} for x into (19.30), we find

$$-m\omega^2 x_m \sin \omega t + kx_m \sin \omega t = P_m \sin \omega t$$

which may be solved for the amplitude,

$$x_m = \frac{P_m}{k - m\omega^2}$$

Recalling from (19.4) that $k/m = p^2$, where p is the circular frequency of the free vibration of the body, we write

$$x_m = \frac{P_m/k}{1 - (\omega/p)^2} \tag{19.33}$$

Substituting from (19.32) into (19.31), we obtain in a similar way

$$x_m = \frac{\delta_m}{1 - (\omega/p)^2} \tag{19.33'}$$

The homogeneous equation corresponding to (19.30) or (19.31) is Eq. (19.3), defining the free vibration of the body.

Its general solution, called the *complementary function*, was found in Sec. 19.2,

$$x_{\text{comp}} = A \sin pt + B \cos pt \tag{19.34}$$

Adding the particular solution (19.32) and the complementary function (19.34), we obtain the *general solution* of Eqs. (19.30) and (19.31),

$$x = A \sin pt + B \cos pt + x_m \sin \omega t \tag{19.35}$$

We note that the vibration obtained consists of two superposed vibrations. The first two terms in (19.35) represent a free vibration of the system. The frequency of this vibration, called the *natural frequency* of the system, depends only upon the constant k of the spring and the mass m of the body, and the constants A and B may be determined from the initial conditions. This free vibration is also called a *transient* vibration since, in actual practice, it will soon be damped out by friction forces (Sec. 19.9).

The last term in (19.35) represents the *steady-state* vibration produced and maintained by the impressed force or impressed support movement. Its frequency is the *forced frequency* imposed by this force or movement, and its amplitude x_m, defined by (19.33) or (19.33′), depends upon the *frequency ratio* ω/p. The ratio of the amplitude x_m of the steady-state vibration to the static deflection P_m/k caused by a force P_m, or to the amplitude δ_m of the support movement, is called the *magnification factor.* From (19.33) and (19.33′), we obtain

$$\text{Magnification factor} = \frac{x_m}{P_m/k} = \frac{x_m}{\delta_m} = \frac{1}{1 - (\omega/p)^2} \tag{19.36}$$

The magnification factor has been plotted in Fig. 19.9 against the frequency ratio ω/p. We note that, when $\omega = p$, the amplitude of the forced vibration becomes infinite. The impressed force or impressed support movement is said to be in *resonance* with the given system. Actually, the amplitude of the vibration remains finite because of damping forces (Sec. 19.9); nevertheless, such a situation should be avoided, and the forced frequency should not be chosen too close to the natural frequency of the system. We also note that for $\omega < p$ the coefficient of $\sin \omega t$ in (19.35) is positive, while for $\omega > p$ this coefficient is negative. In the first case the forced vibration is *in phase* with the impressed force or impressed support movement, while in the second case it is 180° *out of phase.*

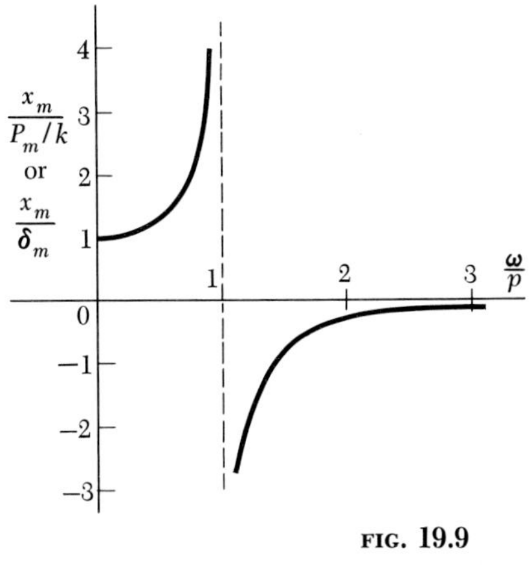

FIG. 19.9

SAMPLE PROBLEM 19.5

A motor weighing 350 lb is supported by four springs having each a constant of 750 lb/in. The unbalance of the rotor is equivalent to a weight of 1 oz located 6 in. from the axis of rotation. Knowing that the motor is constrained to move vertically, determine (*a*) the speed in rpm at which resonance will occur, (*b*) the amplitude of the vibration of the motor at a speed of 1,200 rpm.

a. **Resonance Speed.** The resonance speed is equal to the circular frequency (in rpm) of the free vibration of the motor. The mass of the motor and the equivalent constant of the supporting springs are

$$m = \frac{350 \text{ lb}}{32.2 \text{ ft/sec}^2} = 10.87 \text{ lb-sec}^2\text{/ft}$$

$$k = 4(750 \text{ lb/in.}) = 3{,}000 \text{ lb/in.} = 36{,}000 \text{ lb/ft}$$

$$p = \sqrt{\frac{k}{m}} = \sqrt{\frac{36{,}000}{10.87}} = 57.5 \text{ radians/sec} = 549 \text{ rpm}$$

Resonance speed = 549 rpm ◄

b. **Amplitude of Vibration at 1,200 rpm.** The angular velocity of the motor and the mass of the equivalent 1-oz weight are

$$\omega = 1{,}200 \text{ rpm} = 125.6 \text{ radians/sec}$$

$$m = (1 \text{ oz})\frac{1 \text{ lb}}{16 \text{ oz}}\frac{1}{32.2 \text{ ft/sec}^2} = 0.00194 \text{ lb-sec}^2\text{/ft}$$

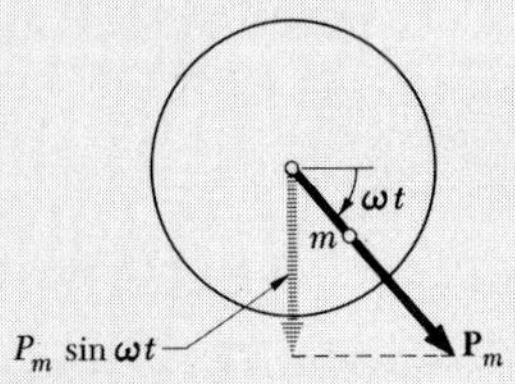

The magnitude of the centrifugal force due to the unbalance of the rotor is

$$P_m = ma_n = mr\omega^2 = (0.00194)\left(\tfrac{6}{12}\right)(125.6)^2 = 15.3 \text{ lb}$$

The static deflection that would be caused by a constant load P_m is

$$\frac{P_m}{k} = \frac{15.3 \text{ lb}}{3{,}000 \text{ lb/in.}} = 0.00510 \text{ in.}$$

Substituting the value of P_m/k together with the known values of ω and p into Eq. (19.33), we obtain

$$x_m = \frac{P_m/k}{1-(\omega/p)^2} = \frac{0.00510 \text{ in.}}{1-(125.6/57.5)^2}$$

$x_m = 0.00135$ in. ◄

PROBLEMS

19.75. A block of weight W is suspended from a spring of constant k and is acted upon by a vertical periodic force of magnitude $P = P_m \sin \omega t$. Determine the range of values of ω for which the amplitude of the vibration exceeds twice the static deflection caused by a constant force of magnitude P_m.

19.76. In Prob. 19.75, determine the range of values of ω for which the amplitude of the vibration is less than the static deflection caused by a constant force of magnitude P_m.

19.77. A simple pendulum of length l is suspended from a collar C which is forced to move horizontally according to the relation $x_C = \delta_m \sin \omega t$. Determine the range of values of ω for which the amplitude of the motion of the bob exceeds $2\delta_m$. (Assume δ_m is small compared to the length l of the pendulum.)

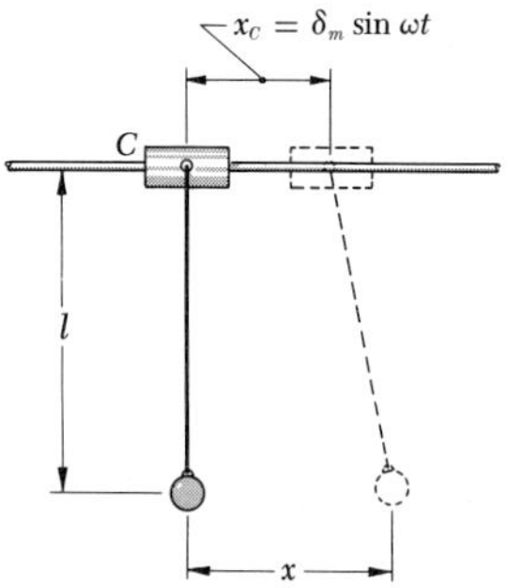

FIG. P 19.77

19.78. In Prob. 19.77, determine the range of values of ω for which the amplitude of the motion of the bob is less than δ_m.

19.79. A motor weighing 200 lb is supported by four springs having each a constant of 50 lb/in. The unbalance of the rotor is equivalent to a weight of 2 oz located 5 in. from the axis of rotation. Knowing that the motor is constrained to move vertically, determine (*a*) the speed (in rpm) at which resonance will occur, and (*b*) the amplitude of the steady-state vibration of the motor at a speed of 240 rpm.

FIG. P 19.79

19.80. Solve Prob. 19.79 assuming now that the 200-lb motor is directly supported by a light horizontal beam and that the static deflection of the beam due to the weight of the motor is 0.250 in.

19.81. A motor weighing 300 lb is supported by four springs having each a constant of 300 lb/in. The motor is constrained to move vertically, and the amplitude of its movement is observed to be 0.090 in. at a speed of 600 rpm. Knowing that the rotor weighs 120 lb, determine the distance between the mass center of the rotor and the axis of the shaft.

19.82. In Prob. 19.81, determine the amplitude of the vertical movement of the motor at a speed of (*a*) 100 rpm, (*b*) 800 rpm, (*c*) 375 rpm.

19.83. Rod AB is rigidly attached to the frame of a constant-speed motor. When a collar of weight W is placed on the spring, it is observed to vibrate with an amplitude of 0.10 in. When two collars, each of weight W, are placed on the spring, the amplitude is observed to be 0.12 in. What amplitude of vibration should be expected when three collars, each of weight W, are placed on the spring? (Obtain two answers.)

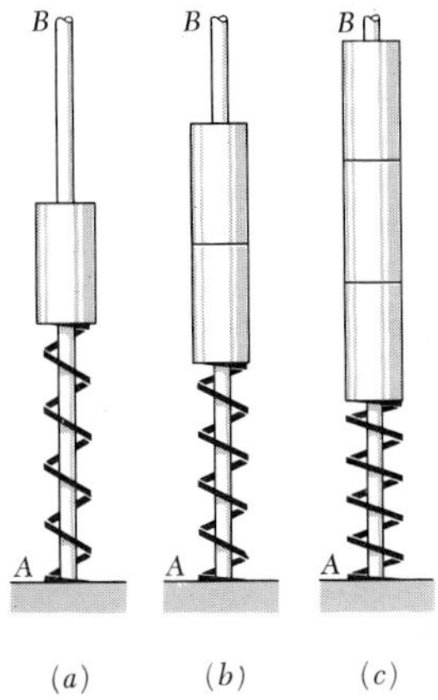

FIG. P 19.83

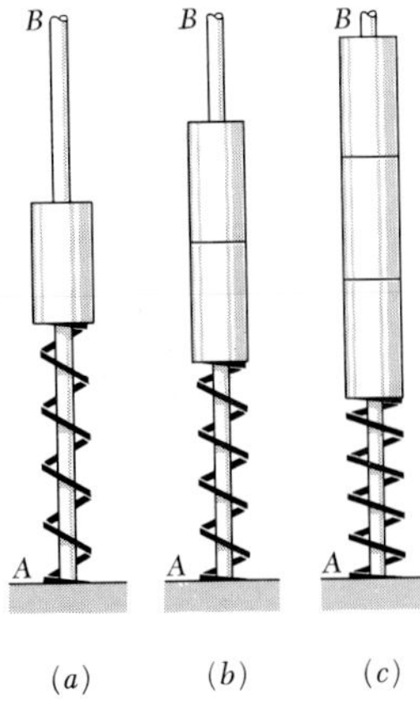

FIG. P 19.84

19.84. Rod AB is rigidly attached to the frame of a constant-speed motor. When a collar of weight W is placed on the spring, it is observed to vibrate with an amplitude of 0.30 in. When two collars, each of weight W, are placed on the spring, the amplitude is observed to be 0.10 in. What amplitude of vibration should be expected when three collars, each of weight W, are placed on the spring? (Obtain two answers.)

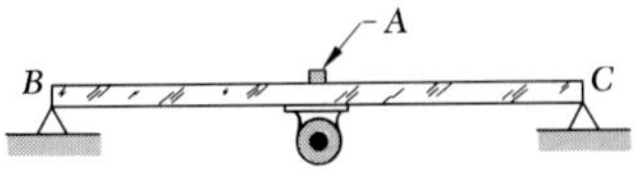

FIG. P 19.85

19.85. A variable-speed motor is rigidly attached to the beam BC. The rotor is slightly unbalanced and causes the beam to vibrate. When the speed of the motor is less than 1,000 rpm or more than 2,000 rpm, a small object placed at A is observed to remain in contact with the beam. For speeds between 1,000 and 2,000 rpm the object is observed to "dance" and actually to lose contact with the beam. Determine the amplitude of the motion of A when the speed of the motor is (*a*) 1,000 rpm, (*b*) 2,000 rpm.

19.86. In Prob. 19.85, determine the speed at which resonance will occur.

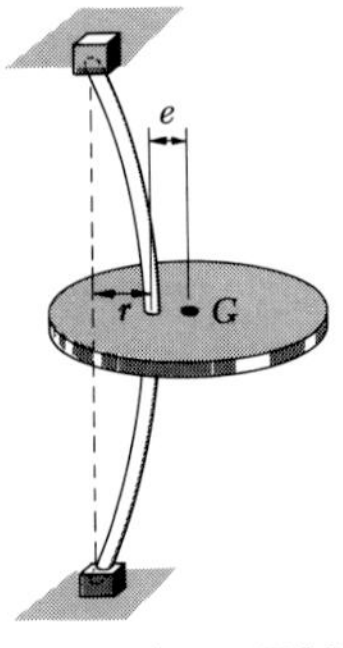

FIG. P 19.87 AND P 19.88

19.87. A disk of mass m is attached to the mid-point of a vertical shaft which revolves at an angular velocity ω. Denoting by k the spring constant of the system for a horizontal movement of the disk and by e the eccentricity of the disk with respect to the shaft, show that the deflection of the center of the shaft may be written in the form

$$r = \frac{e(\omega/p)^2}{1 - (\omega/p)^2}$$

where $p = \sqrt{(k/m)}$.

19.88. A disk weighing 75 lb is attached to the mid-point of a shaft. Knowing that a static force of 100 lb will deflect the shaft 0.050 in., determine the speed of the shaft in rpm at which resonance will occur.

19.89. Knowing that the disk of Prob. 19.88 is attached to the shaft with an eccentricity $e = 0.075$ in., determine the deflection r of the shaft at a speed of 800 rpm.

FIG. P 19.90

19.90. A certain vibrometer used to measure vibration amplitudes consists essentially of a box containing a slender rod to which a mass m is attached; the natural frequency of the mass-rod system is known to be 5 cycles/sec. When the box is rigidly attached to the casing of a motor rotating at 600 rpm, the mass is observed to vibrate with an amplitude of 0.060 in. relative to the box. Determine the amplitude of the vertical motion of the motor.

19.91. Solve Prob. 19.90 assuming that the speed of the motor is 150 rpm and that the other data are unchanged.

19.92. A small trailer weighing 600 lb is supported by two springs, each of constant 100 lb/in. The trailer is pulled over a road, the surface of which may be approximated by a sine curve of amplitude $1\frac{1}{2}$ in. and of period 16 ft (i.e., the distance between two successive crests is 16 ft, and the vertical distance from a crest to a trough is 3 in.). Determine (*a*) the speed at which resonance will occur, (*b*) the amplitude of the vibration of the trailer at a speed of 40 mph.

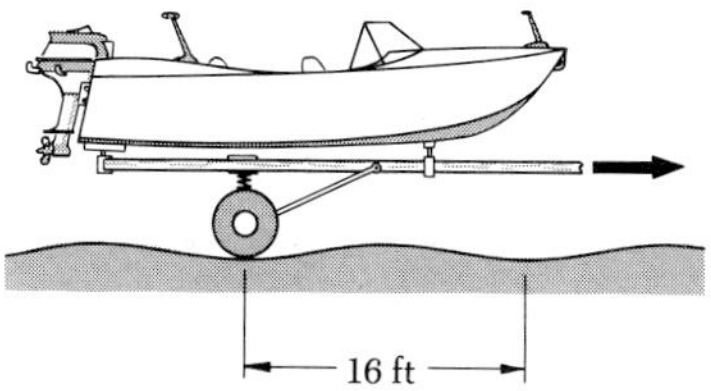

FIG. P 19.92

19.93. Knowing that the amplitude of the vibration of the trailer of Prob. 19.92 is not to exceed $\frac{3}{4}$ in., determine the smallest speed at which the trailer can be pulled over the road.

19.94. The amplitude of the motion of the pendulum bob in Prob. 19.77 is observed to be 2 in. when the amplitude of the motion of collar *C* is 1.0 in. Knowing that the length of the pendulum is $l = 36$ in., determine the two possible values of the frequency of the horizontal movement of the collar *C*.

DAMPED VIBRATIONS

***19.8. Damped Free Vibrations.** The vibrating systems considered in the first part of this chapter were assumed free of damping. Actually all vibrations are damped to some degree by friction forces. These forces may be caused by *dry friction*, or *Coulomb friction*, between rigid bodies, by *fluid friction* when a rigid body moves in a fluid, or by *internal friction* between the molecules of a seemingly elastic body.

A type of damping of special interest is the *viscous damping* caused by fluid friction at low and moderate speeds. Viscous damping is characterized by the fact that the friction force is *directly proportional to the speed* of the moving body. As an example, we shall consider again a body of mass *m* suspended from a spring of constant *k*, and we shall assume that the body is attached to the plunger of a dashpot (Fig. 19.10). The magnitude of the friction force exerted on the plunger by the surrounding fluid is equal to $c(dx/dt)$, where the constant *c*, expressed in lb-sec/ft and known as the *coefficient of viscous damping*, depends upon the physical properties of the fluid and the construction of the dashpot. The equation of motion is

$$+\downarrow \Sigma F = ma: \qquad W - k(\delta_{st} + x) - c\frac{dx}{dt} = m\frac{d^2x}{dt^2}$$

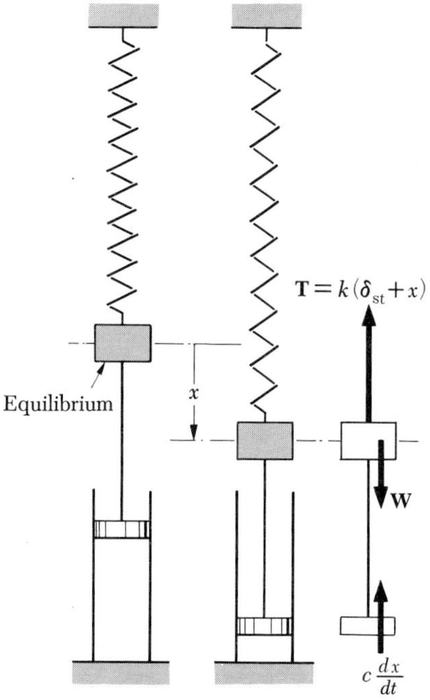

FIG. 19.10

Recalling that $W = k\delta_{st}$, we write

$$m\frac{d^2x}{dt^2} + c\frac{dx}{dt} + kx = 0 \tag{19.37}$$

Substituting $x = e^{\lambda t}$ into (19.37), we write the *characteristic equation*

$$m\lambda^2 + c\lambda + k = 0 \tag{19.38}$$

and obtain the roots

$$\lambda = -\frac{c}{2m} \pm \sqrt{\left(\frac{c}{2m}\right)^2 - \frac{k}{m}} \tag{19.39}$$

Defining the *critical damping coefficient* c_c as the value of c which makes the radical in (19.39) equal to zero, we write

$$\left(\frac{c_c}{2m}\right)^2 - \frac{k}{m} = 0 \qquad c_c = 2m\sqrt{\frac{k}{m}} = 2mp \tag{19.40}$$

where p is the natural frequency of the system in the absence of damping. We may distinguish three different cases of damping, depending upon the value of the coefficient c.

1. *Heavy Damping:* $c > c_c$. The roots λ_1 and λ_2 of the characteristic equation (19.38) are real and distinct, and the general solution of the differential equation (19.37) is

$$x = Ae^{\lambda_1 t} + Be^{\lambda_2 t} \tag{19.41}$$

This solution corresponds to a nonvibratory motion. Since λ_1 and λ_2 are both negative, x approaches zero as t increases indefinitely. However, the system actually regains its equilibrium position after a finite time.

2. *Critical Damping:* $c = c_c$. The characteristic equation has a double root $\lambda = -c_c/2m = -p$, and the general solution of (19.37) is

$$x = (A + Bt)e^{-pt} \tag{19.42}$$

The motion obtained is again nonvibratory. Critically damped systems are of special interest in engineering applications since they regain their equilibrium position in the shortest possible time without oscillation.

3. *Light Damping:* $c < c_c$. The roots of (19.38) are complex and conjugate, and the general solution of (19.37) is of the form

$$x = e^{-(c/2m)t}(A \sin qt + B \cos qt) \tag{19.43}$$

where q is defined by the relation

$$q^2 = \frac{k}{m} - \left(\frac{c}{2m}\right)^2$$

Substituting $k/m = p^2$ and recalling (19.40), we write

$$q = p\sqrt{1 - \left(\frac{c}{c_c}\right)^2} \tag{19.44}$$

where the constant c/c_c is known as the *damping factor.* A substitution similar to the one used in Sec. 19.2 enables us to write the general solution of (19.37) in the form

$$x = x_m e^{-(c/2m)t} \sin(qt + \phi) \tag{19.45}$$

The motion defined by (19.45) is vibratory with diminishing amplitude (Fig. 19.11). Although this motion does not actually repeat itself, the time interval $\tau = 2\pi/q$ corresponding to two successive points where the curve (19.45) touches one of the limiting curves shown in Fig. 19.11 is commonly referred to as the period of the damped vibration. Recalling (19.44), we observe that τ is larger than the period of vibration of the corresponding undamped system.

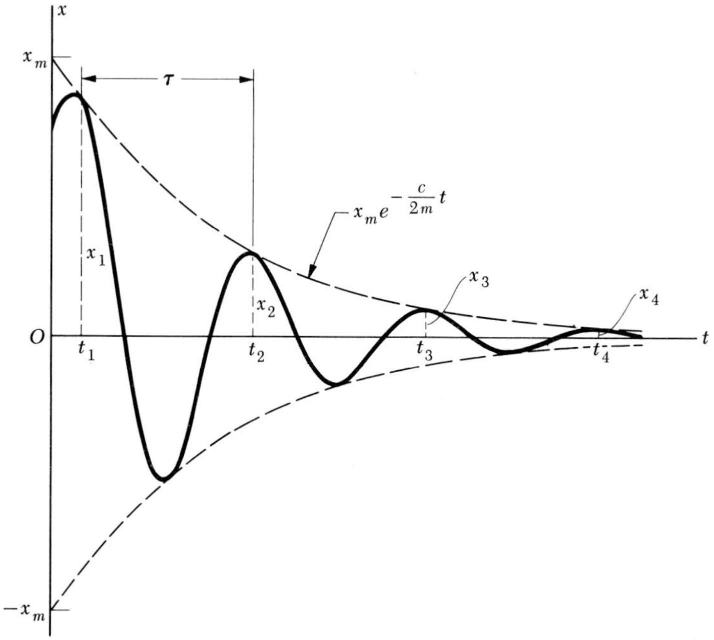

FIG. 19.11

*19.9. Damped Forced Vibrations.

If the system considered in the preceding section is subjected to a periodic force **P** of magnitude $P = P_m \sin \omega t$, the equation of motion becomes

$$m\frac{d^2x}{dt^2} + c\frac{dx}{dt} + kx = P_m \sin \omega t \tag{19.46}$$

The general solution of (19.46) is obtained by adding a particular solution of (19.46) to the complementary function or general solution of the homogeneous equation (19.37). The complementary function is given by (19.41), (19.42), or (19.43), depending upon the type of damping considered. It represents a *transient* motion which is eventually damped out.

Our interest in this section is centered on the steady-state vibration represented by a particular solution of (19.46) of the form

$$x_{\text{part}} = x_m \sin(\omega t - \varphi) \tag{19.47}$$

Substituting x_{part} for x into (19.46), we obtain

$$-m\omega^2 x_m \sin(\omega t - \varphi) + c\omega x_m \cos(\omega t - \varphi) + kx_m \sin(\omega t - \varphi) = P_m \sin \omega t$$

Making $\omega t - \varphi$ successively equal to 0 and to $\pi/2$, we write

$$c\omega x_m = P_m \sin \varphi \tag{19.48}$$

$$(k - m\omega^2)x_m = P_m \cos \varphi \tag{19.49}$$

Squaring both members of (19.48) and (19.49) and adding, we have

$$[(k - m\omega^2)^2 + (c\omega)^2]x_m^2 = P_m^2 \tag{19.50}$$

Solving (19.50) for x_m and dividing (19.48) and (19.49) member by member, we obtain, respectively,

$$x_m = \frac{P_m}{\sqrt{(k - m\omega^2)^2 + (c\omega)^2}} \qquad \tan \varphi = \frac{c\omega}{k - m\omega^2} \tag{19.51}$$

Recalling from (19.4) that $k/m = p^2$, where p is the circular frequency of the undamped free vibration, and from (19.40) that $2mp = c_c$, where c_c is the critical damping coefficient of the system, we write

$$\frac{x_m}{P_m/k} = \frac{x_m}{\delta_m} = \frac{1}{\sqrt{[1 - (\omega/p)^2]^2 + [2(c/c_c)(\omega/p)]^2}} \tag{19.52}$$

$$\tan \varphi = \frac{2(c/c_c)(\omega/p)}{1 - (\omega/p)^2} \tag{19.53}$$

Formula (19.52) expresses the magnification factor in terms of the frequency ratio ω/p and damping factor c/c_c. It may be used to determine the amplitude of the steady-state vibration produced by an impressed force of magnitude $P = P_m \sin \omega t$ or by an impressed support movement $\delta = \delta_m \sin \omega t$. Formula

(19.53) defines in terms of the same parameters the *phase difference* φ between the impressed force or impressed support movement and the resulting steady-state vibration of the damped system. The magnification factor has been plotted against the frequency ratio in Fig. 19.12 for various values of the damping factor. We observe that the amplitude of a forced vibration may be kept small by choosing a large coefficient of viscous damping c or by keeping the natural and forced frequencies far apart.

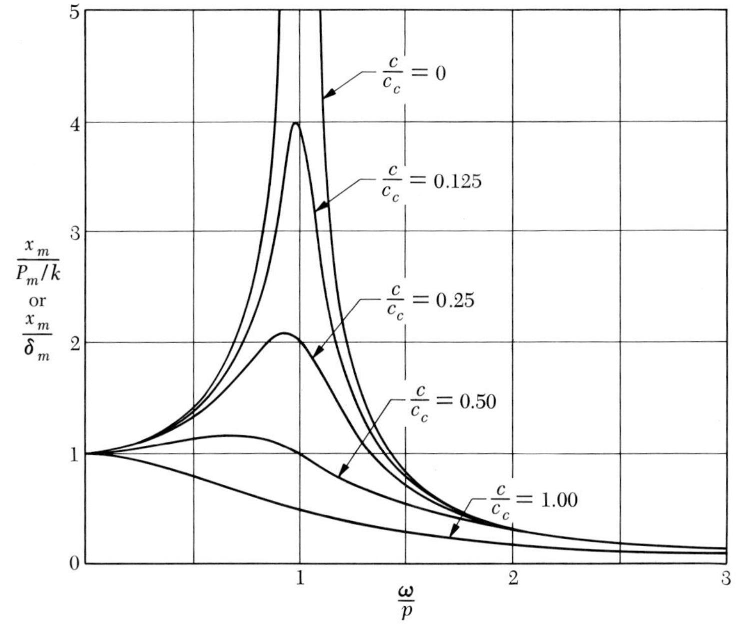

FIG. 19.12

***19.10. Electrical Analogues.** Oscillating electrical circuits are characterized by differential equations of the same type as those obtained in the preceding sections. Their analysis is therefore similar to that of a mechanical system and the results obtained for a given vibrating system may be readily extended to the equivalent circuit. Conversely, any result obtained for an electrical circuit will also apply to the corresponding mechanical system.

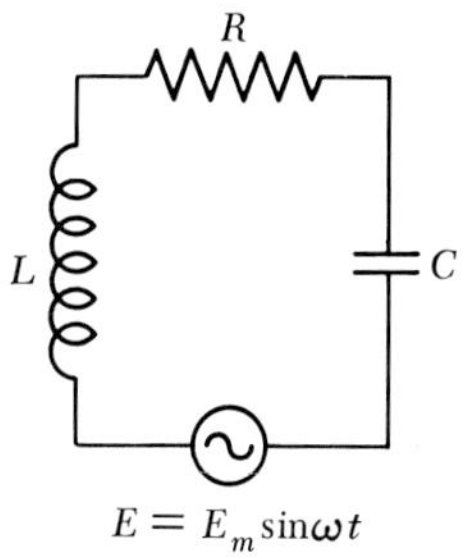

FIG. 19.13

Consider an electrical circuit consisting of an inductor of inductance L, a resistor of resistance R, and a capacitor of capacitance C, connected in series with a source of alternating voltage

$E = E_m \sin \omega t$ (Fig. 19.13). It is recalled from elementary electromagnetic theory† that, if i denotes the current in the circuit and q the electric charge on the capacitor, the drop in potential is $L(di/dt)$ across the inductor, Ri across the resistor, and q/C across the capacitor. Expressing that the algebraic sum of the applied voltage and of the drops in potential around the circuit loop is zero, we write

$$E_m \sin \omega t - L\frac{di}{dt} - Ri - \frac{q}{C} = 0 \qquad (19.54)$$

Rearranging the terms and recalling that, at any instant, the current i is equal to the rate of change dq/dt of the charge q, we have

$$L\frac{d^2q}{dt^2} + R\frac{dq}{dt} + \frac{1}{C}q = E_m \sin \omega t \qquad (19.55)$$

We verify that Eq. (19.55), which defines the oscillations of the electrical circuit of Fig. 19.13, is of the same type as Eq. (19.46), which characterizes the damped forced vibrations of the mechanical system of Fig. 19.10. By comparing the two equations, we may construct a table of the analogous mechanical and electrical expressions.

TABLE 19.2.
Characteristics of a Mechanical System and of Its Electrical Analogue

Mechanical System	Electrical Circuit
m Mass	L Inductance
c Coefficient of viscous damping	R Resistance
k Spring constant	$1/C$ Reciprocal of capacitance
x Displacement	q Charge
v Velocity	i Current
P Applied force	E Applied voltage

Table 19.2 may be used to extend to their electrical analogues the results obtained in the preceding sections for various mechanical systems. For instance, the amplitude i_m of the current in the circuit of Fig. 19.13 may be obtained by noting that it corresponds to the maximum value v_m of the velocity in the analogous mechanical system. Recalling that $v_m = \omega x_m$, substituting for x_m from Eq. (19.51), and replacing the constants of the mechanical system by the corresponding electrical expressions, we have

† See Hammond, "Electrical Engineering," McGraw-Hill Book Company, Inc., chap. 1.

$$i_m = \frac{\omega E_m}{\sqrt{\left(\frac{1}{C} - L\omega^2\right)^2 + (R\omega)^2}}$$

$$i_m = \frac{E_m}{\sqrt{R^2 + \left(L\omega - \frac{1}{C\omega}\right)^2}} \tag{19.56}$$

The radical in the expression obtained is known as the *impedance* of the electrical circuit.

The analogy between mechanical systems and electrical circuits holds for transient as well as steady-state oscillations. The oscillations of the circuit shown in Fig. 19.14, for instance, are analogous to the damped free vibrations of the system of Fig. 19.10. As far as the initial conditions are concerned, we may note that closing the switch S when the charge on the capacitor is $q = q_0$ is equivalent to releasing the mass of the mechanical system with no initial velocity from the position $x = x_0$. We should also observe that, if a battery of constant voltage E is introduced in the electrical circuit of Fig. 19.14, closing the switch S will be equivalent to suddenly applying a force of constant magnitude P to the mass of the mechanical system of Fig. 19.10.

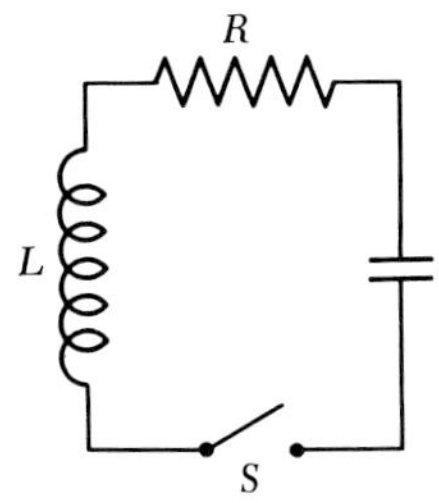

FIG. 19.14

The above discussion would be of questionable value if its only result were to make it possible for mechanics students to analyze electrical circuits without learning the elements of electromagnetism. It is hoped, rather, that this discussion will encourage the students to apply to the solution of problems in mechanical vibrations the mathematical techniques they may learn in later courses in electrical circuits theory. The chief value of the concept of electrical analogue, however, resides in its application to *experimental methods* for the determination of the characteristics of a given mechanical system. Indeed, an electrical circuit is much more easily constructed than a mechanical model, and the fact that its characteristics may be modified by varying the inductance, resistance, or capacitance of its various components makes the use of the electrical analogue particularly convenient.

To determine the electrical analogue of a given mechanical system, we shall focus our attention on each moving mass in the system and observe which springs, dashpots, or external forces are applied directly to it. An equivalent electrical loop may then be constructed to match each of the mechanical units thus defined; the various loops obtained in that way will form together the desired circuit. Consider, for instance, the mechanical system of Fig. 19.15. We observe that the mass m_1

is acted upon by two springs of constants k_1 and k_2 and by two dashpots characterized by the coefficients of viscous damping c_1 and c_2. The electrical circuit should therefore include a loop consisting of an inductor of inductance L_1 proportional to m_1, of two capacitors of capacitance C_1 and C_2 inversely proportional to k_1 and k_2 respectively, and of two resistors of resistance R_1 and R_2, proportional to c_1 and c_2 respectively. Since the mass m_2 is acted upon by the spring k_2 and the dashpot c_2, as well as by the force $P = P_m \sin \omega t$, the circuit should also include a loop containing the capacitor C_2, the resistor R_2, the new inductor L_2, and the voltage source $E = E_m \sin \omega t$ (Fig. 19.16).

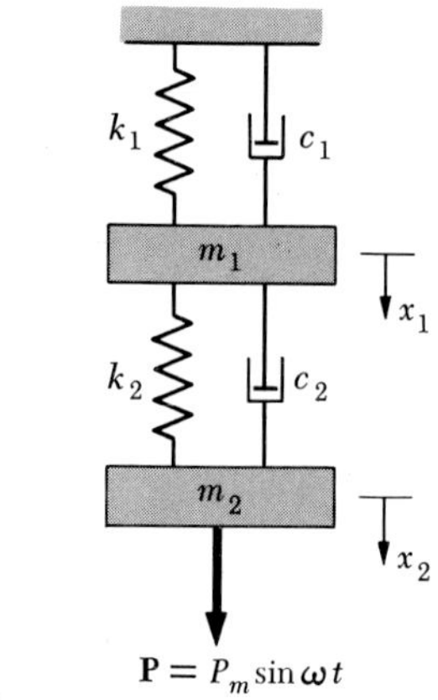

FIG. 19.15

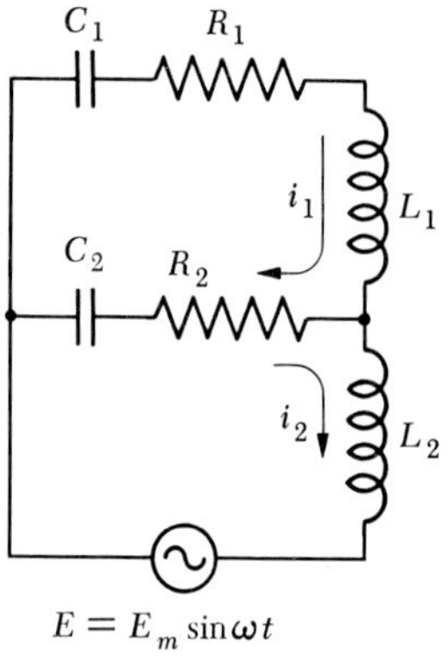

FIG. 19.16

To check that the mechanical system of Fig. 19.15 and the electrical circuit of Fig. 19.16 actually satisfy the same differential equations, we shall first derive the equations of motion for m_1 and m_2. Denoting respectively by x_1 and x_2 the displacements of m_1 and m_2 from their equilibrium positions, we observe that the deflection of the spring k_1 (measured from the equilibrium position) is equal to x_1, while the deflection of the spring k_2 is equal to the relative displacement $x_1 - x_2$ of m_1 with respect to m_2. The equations of motion for m_1 and m_2 are therefore

$$m_1 \frac{d^2x_1}{dt^2} + c_1 \frac{dx_1}{dt} + c_2 \frac{d}{dt}(x_1 - x_2) + k_1 x_1 + k_2 (x_1 - x_2) = 0 \qquad (19.57)$$

$$m_2 \frac{d^2x_2}{dt^2} + c_2 \frac{d}{dt}(x_2 - x_1) + k_2 (x_2 - x_1) = P_m \sin \omega t \qquad (19.58)$$

Consider now the electrical circuit of Fig. 19.16; we denote respectively by i_1 and i_2 the current in the first and second loops, and by q_1 and q_2 the integrals $\int i_1\, dt$ and $\int i_2\, dt$. Noting that the charge on the capacitor C_1 is q_1, while the charge on C_2 is $q_1 - q_2$, we express that the sum of the potential differences in each loop is zero:

$$L_1 \frac{d^2q_1}{dt^2} + R_1 \frac{dq_1}{dt} + R_2 \frac{d}{dt}(q_1 - q_2) + \frac{q_1}{C_1} + \frac{q_1 - q_2}{C_2} = 0 \qquad (19.59)$$

$$L_2 \frac{d^2q_2}{dt^2} + R_2 \frac{d}{dt}(q_2 - q_1) + \frac{q_2 - q_1}{C_2} = E_m \sin \omega t \qquad (19.60)$$

We easily check that Eqs. (19.59) and (19.60) reduce to (19.57) and (19.58), respectively, when the substitutions indicated in Table 19.2 are performed.

PROBLEMS

19.95. Show that, in the case of heavy damping ($c > c_c$), a body never passes through its position of equilibrium O (*a*) if it is released with no initial velocity from an arbitrary position or (*b*) if it is started from O with an arbitrary initial velocity.

19.96. Show that, in the case of heavy damping ($c > c_c$), a body released from an arbitrary position with an arbitrary initial velocity cannot pass more than once through its equilibrium position.

19.97. In the case of light damping, the displacements x_1, x_2, x_3, etc., shown in Fig. 19.11 may be assumed equal to the maximum displacements. Show that the ratio of any two successive maximum displacements x_n and x_{n+1} is a constant and that the natural logarithm of this ratio, called the *logarithmic decrement,* is

$$\ln \frac{x_n}{x_{n+1}} = \frac{2\pi(c/c_c)}{\sqrt{1 - (c/c_c)^2}}$$

19.98. In practice, it is often difficult to determine the logarithmic decrement defined in Prob. 19.97 by measuring two successive maximum displacements. Show that the logarithmic decrement may also be expressed as $(1/n) \ln (x_1/x_{n+1})$, where n is the number of cycles between readings of the maximum displacement.

19.99. In a system with light damping ($c < c_c$), the period of vibration is commonly defined as the time interval $\tau = 2\pi/q$ corresponding to two successive points where the displacement-time curve touches one of the limiting curves shown in Fig. 19.11. Show that the interval of time (*a*) between a maximum positive displacement and the following maximum negative displacement is $\frac{1}{2}\tau$, (*b*) between two successive zero displacements is $\frac{1}{2}\tau$, (*c*) between a maximum positive displacement and the following zero displacement is greater than $\frac{1}{4}\tau$.

19.100. The barrel of a field gun weighs 1,400 lb and is returned into firing position after recoil by a recuperator of constant $k = 10{,}000$ lb/ft. Determine the value of the coefficient of damping of the recoil mechanism which causes the barrel to return into firing position in the shortest possible time without oscillation.

19.101. A critically damped system is released from rest at an arbitrary position x_0 when $t = 0$. (*a*) Determine the position of the system at any time t. (*b*) Apply the result obtained in part *a* to the barrel of the gun of Prob. 19.100, and determine the time at which the barrel is halfway back to its firing position.

19.102. Assuming that the barrel of the gun of Prob. 19.100 is modified, with a resulting increase in weight of 400 lb, determine the constant k of the recoil mechanism which should be used with the same recuperator if the system is to remain critically damped.

19.103. In the case of the forced vibration of a system with a given damping factor c/c_c, determine the frequency ratio ω/p for which the amplitude of the vibration is maximum.

19.104. Show that for a small value of the damping factor c/c_c (*a*) the maximum amplitude of a forced vibration occurs when $\omega \approx p$, (*b*) the corresponding value of the magnification factor is approximately $\frac{1}{2}(c_c/c)$.

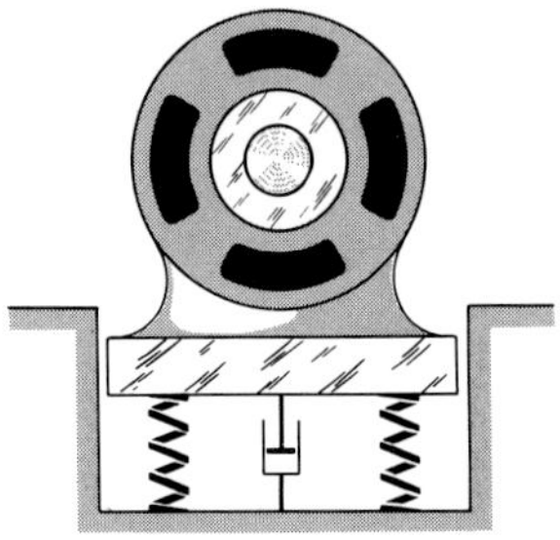

FIG. P 19.105

19.105. A motor weighing 50 lb is supported by four springs having each a constant of 1,000 lb/in. The unbalance of the rotor is equivalent to a weight of 1 oz located 5 in. from the axis of rotation. Knowing that the motor is constrained to move vertically, determine the amplitude of the steady-state vibration of the motor at a speed of 1,800 rpm, assuming (*a*) that no damping is present, (*b*) that the damping factor c/c_c is equal to 0.125.

19.106. Assume that the 50-lb motor of Prob. 19.105 is directly supported by a light horizontal beam. The static deflection of the beam due to the weight of the motor is observed to be 0.230 in., and the amplitude of the vibration of the motor is 0.02 in. at a speed of 400 rpm. Determine (*a*) the damping factor c/c_c, (*b*) the coefficient of damping c.

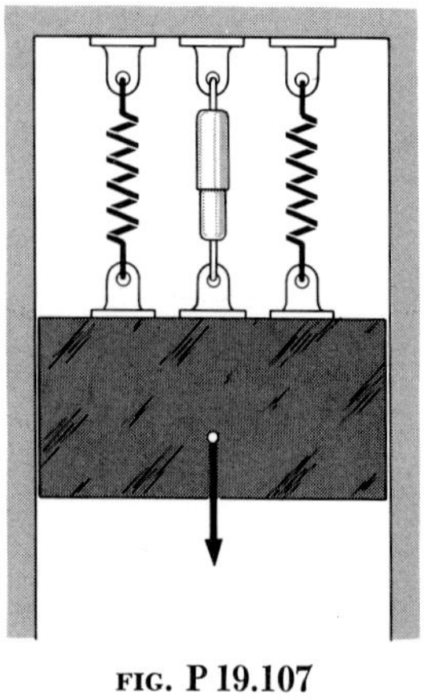

FIG. P 19.107

19.107. A machine element weighing 800 lb is supported by two springs having each a constant of 200 lb/in. A periodic force of maximum value 20 lb and of frequency 2.5 cycles/sec is applied to the element. Knowing that the coefficient of damping is 8 lb-sec/in., determine the amplitude of the steady-state vibration of the element.

19.108. In Prob. 19.107, determine the required value of the coefficient of damping if the amplitude of the steady-state vibration of the element is to be 0.15 in.

19.109. A platform of weight 200 lb, supported by a set of springs equivalent to a single spring of constant $k = 400$ lb/in., is subjected to a periodic force of maximum magnitude 100 lb. Knowing that the coefficient of damping is 10 lb-sec/in., determine (*a*) the natural frequency in rpm of the platform *if* there were no damping, (*b*) the frequency in rpm of the periodic force corresponding to the maximum value of the magnification factor, assuming damping, (*c*) the amplitude of the *actual* motion of the platform for each of the frequencies found in parts *a* and *b*.

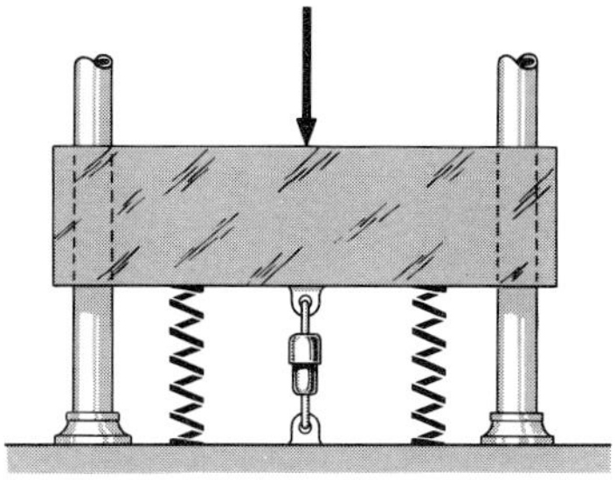

FIG. P 19.109

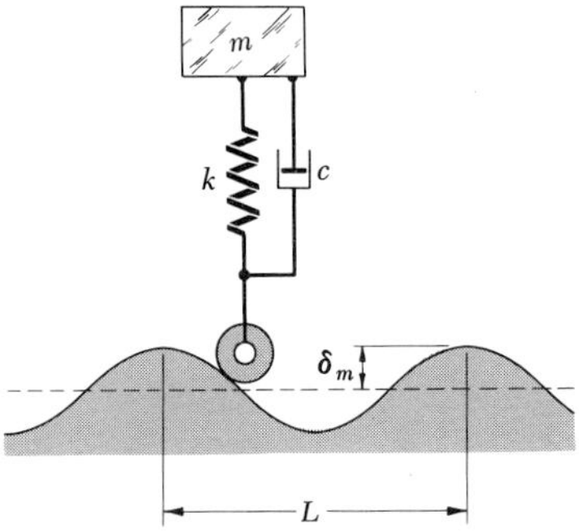

FIG. P 19.110

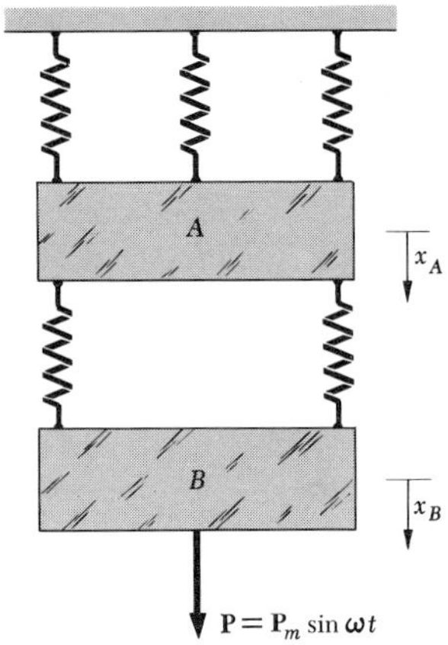

FIG. P 19.111

***19.110.** The suspension of an automobile may be approximated by the simplified spring-and-dashpot system shown. (*a*) Write the differential equation defining the absolute motion of the mass m when the system moves at a speed v over a road of sinusoidal cross section as shown. (*b*) Derive an expression for the amplitude of the absolute motion of m.

***19.111.** Two loads A and B, each of mass m, are suspended as shown by means of five springs of the same constant k. Load B is subjected to a force of magnitude $P = P_m \sin \omega t$. Write the differential equations defining the displacements x_A and x_B of the two loads from their equilibrium positions.

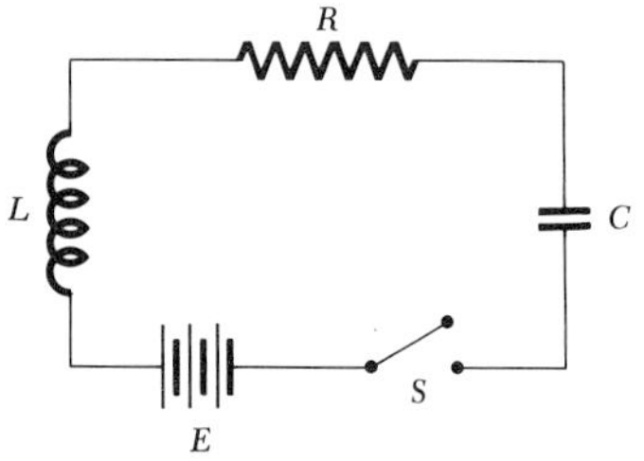

FIG. P 19.112

19.112. Determine the range of values of the resistance R for which oscillations will take place in the circuit shown when the switch S is closed.

19.113. Consider the circuit of Prob. 19.112 when the capacitance C is equal to zero. If the switch S is closed at time $t = 0$, determine (*a*) the final value of the current in the circuit, (*b*) the time t at which the current will have reached $(1 - 1/e)$ times its final value. (The desired value of t is known as the *time constant* of the circuit.)

19.114 through 19.117. Draw the electrical analogue of the mechanical system shown. (*Hint.* In Probs. 19.114 and 19.115, draw the loops corresponding to the free bodies m and A.)

19.118 and 19.119. Write the differential equations defining (*a*) the displacements of mass m and point A, (*b*) the currents in the corresponding loops of the electrical analogue.

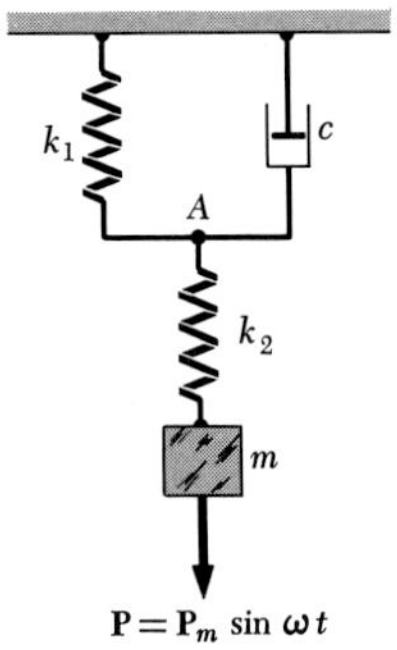

FIG. P 19.114 AND P 19.118

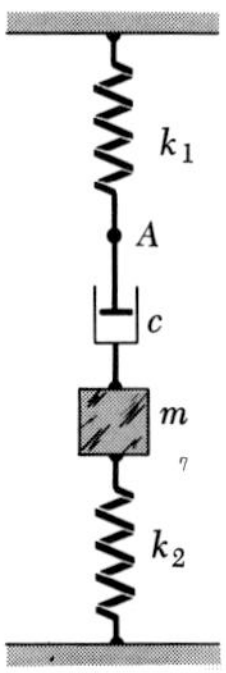

FIG. P 19.115 AND P 19.119

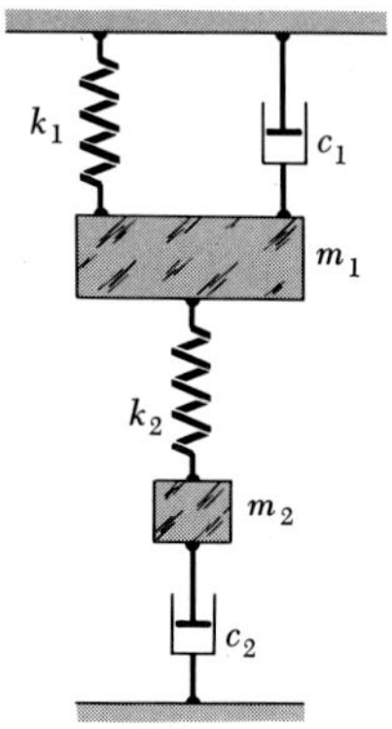

FIG. P 19.116 AND P 19.120

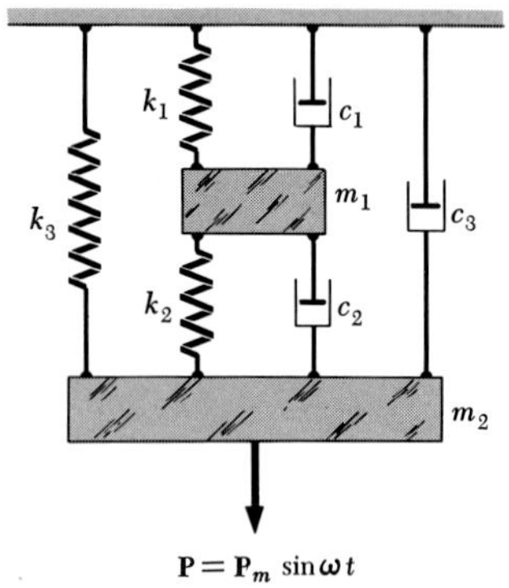

FIG. P 19.117 AND P 19.121

19.120 and 19.121. Write the differential equations defining (*a*) the displacements of the masses m_1 and m_2, (*b*) the currents in the corresponding loops of the electrical analogue.

REVIEW PROBLEMS

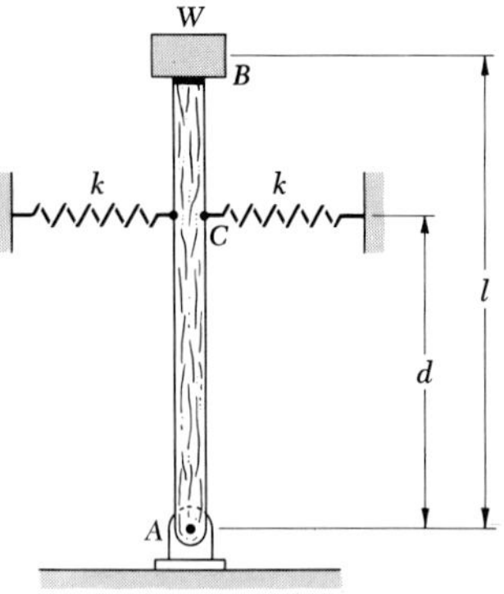

FIG. P 19.122 AND P 19.123

19.122. The rod AB is attached to a hinge at A and to two springs each of constant k. When $l = 20$ in., $d = 15$ in., and $W = 225$ lb, determine the value of k for which the period of small oscillations is (*a*) 1 sec, (*b*) infinite. Neglect the weight of the rod and assume that each spring can act in either tension or compression.

19.123. If $d = 16$ in., $l = 24$ in., and each spring has a constant $k = 4$ lb/in., determine the load W for which the period of small oscillations is (*a*) 0.50 sec, (*b*) infinite. Neglect the weight of the rod and assume that each spring can act in either tension or compression.

19.124. A simple pendulum of length l is suspended in an elevator. A weight W is attached to a spring of constant k and is carried in the same elevator. Determine the periods of vibration of the pendulum and of the weight if the elevator has an acceleration **a** directed (*a*) upward, (*b*) downward.

19.125. The centroidal moments of inertia $\bar{I}_x$ and $\bar{I}_z$ of an airplane weighing 1,600 lb are determined by letting the airplane oscillate as a compound pendulum. In the arrangement shown, the distance from the mass center G to the point of suspension O is known to be 6 ft. Knowing that the observed periods of oscillation about axes through O parallel to the x and z axes are, respectively, 3.10 sec and 3.25 sec, determine the centroidal moments of inertia $\bar{I}_x$ and $\bar{I}_z$.

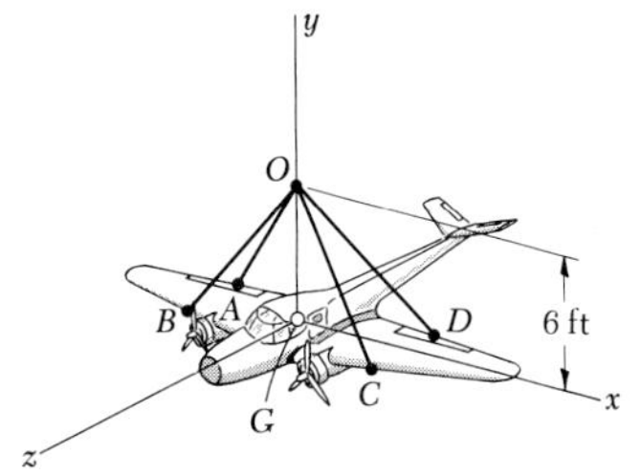

FIG. P 19.125

19.126. The centroidal moment of inertia $\bar{I}_y$ of an airplane weighing 1,600 lb is determined by suspending the airplane by two cables of length 6 ft as shown. The airplane is rotated through a small angle about the vertical through G and then released. Knowing that the observed period of oscillation is 2.60 sec, determine the centroidal moment of inertia $\bar{I}_y$.

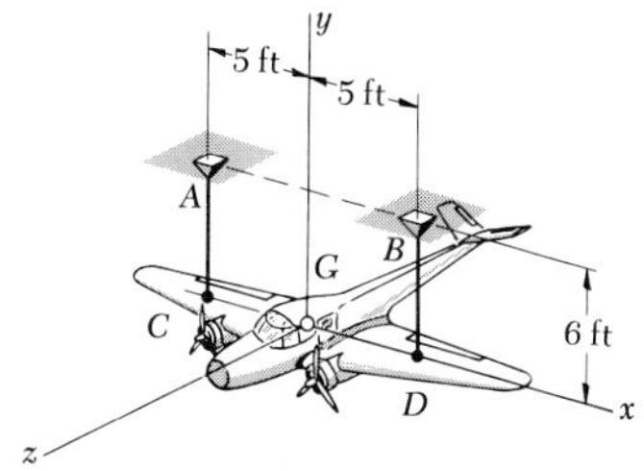

FIG. P 19.126

19.127. As the speed of a spring-supported motor is slowly increased from 150 to 200 rpm, the amplitude of the vibration due to the unbalance of the rotor is observed to decrease continuously from 0.150 to 0.080 in. Determine the speed at which resonance would occur, assuming no damping.

19.128. In Prob. 19.127, determine the speed of the motor for which the amplitude of the vibration is 0.200 in.

19.129. A slender rod AB of length 6 ft and weight $W = 40$ lb is attached to a pin at O and to a spring of constant $k = 40$ lb/in. at B. Determine (*a*) the distance b for which the largest frequency of vibration occurs, (*b*) the corresponding value of the frequency.

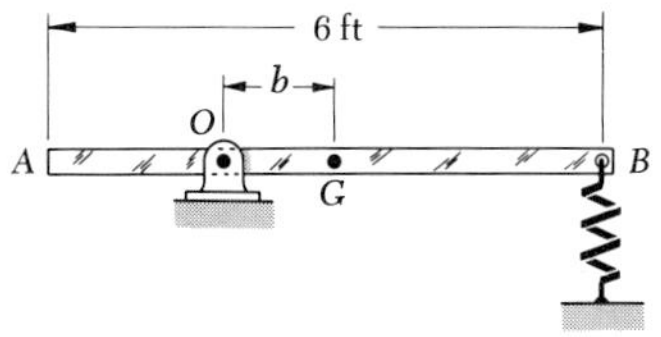

FIG. P 19.129

19.130. If either a simple or a compound pendulum is used to determine experimentally the acceleration of gravity g, difficulties are encountered. In the simple pendulum, the string is not truly weightless, while, in the compound pendulum, the exact location of the mass center is difficult to establish. In the case of a compound pendulum, the difficulty may be eliminated by using a reversible, or Kater, pendulum. Two knife-edges A and B are placed so that they are obviously not at the same distance from the mass center G, and the distance l is measured with great precision. The position of a counterweight D is then adjusted so that the period of oscillation τ is the same when either knife-edge is used. Show that the period τ obtained is equal to that of a true simple pendulum of length l and that $g = 4\pi^2 l/\tau^2$.

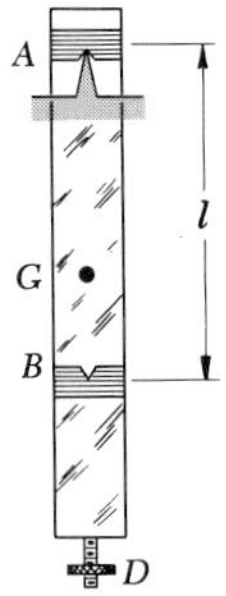

FIG. P 19.130

19.131. A period of 4.10 sec is observed for the angular oscillations of a 1-lb gyroscope rotor suspended from a wire as shown. Knowing that a period of 6.20 sec is obtained when a 2-in.-diameter steel sphere is suspended in the same fashion, determine the centroidal moment of inertia and the centroidal radius of gyration of the rotor. (Specific weight of steel = 490 lb/ft^3.)

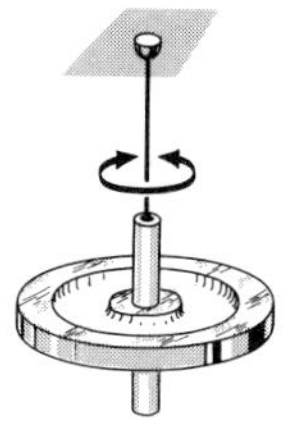
FIG. P 19.131

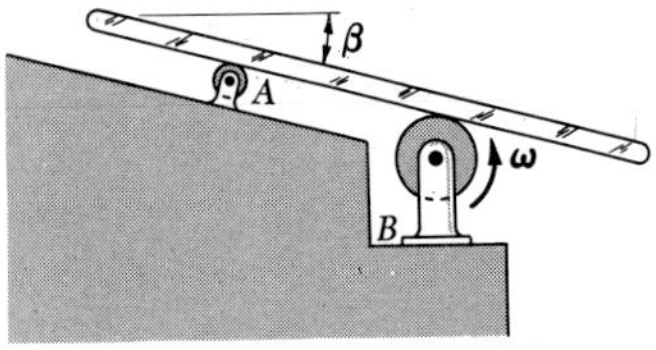

FIG. P 19.132

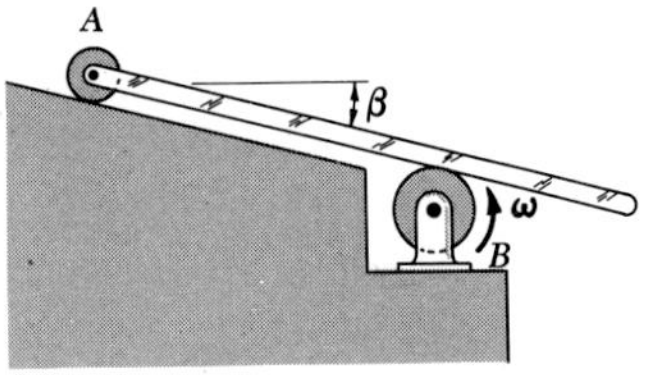

FIG. P 19.133

19.132 and 19.133. A plank of weight W is supported by a small wheel A of negligible weight and by a wheel B which rotates with a large counterclockwise angular velocity. The coefficient of friction between wheel B and the plank is μ and the distance between the two wheels is L. If the plank is displaced slightly from its equilibrium position, (*a*) show that the resulting motion is simple harmonic, (*b*) derive an expression for the frequency of the vibration.

Slender rod	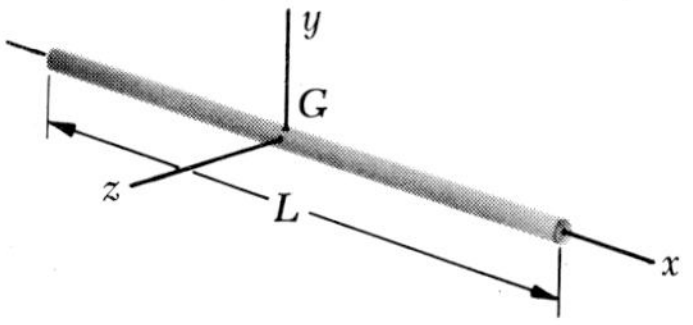	$I_y = I_z = \frac{1}{12}mL^2$
Thin rectangular plate	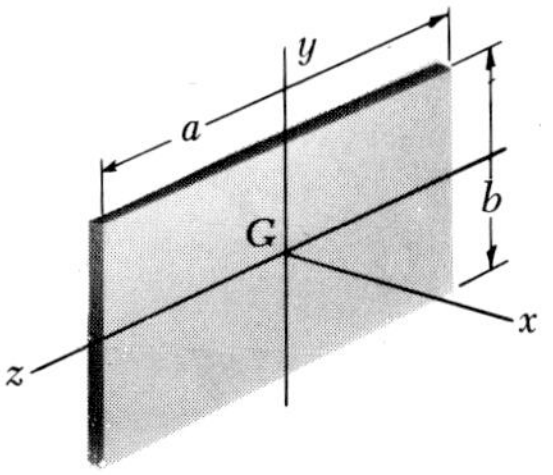	$I_x = \frac{1}{12}m(a^2 + b^2)$ $I_y = \frac{1}{12}ma^2$ $I_z = \frac{1}{12}mb^2$
Rectangular prism	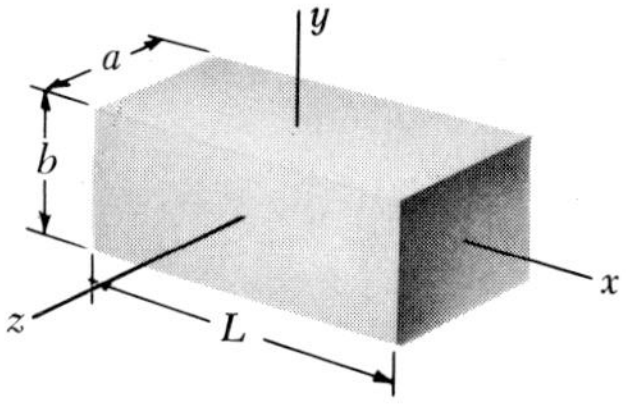	$I_x = \frac{1}{12}m(a^2 + b^2)$ $I_y = \frac{1}{12}m(a^2 + L^2)$ $I_z = \frac{1}{12}m(b^2 + L^2)$
Thin disk	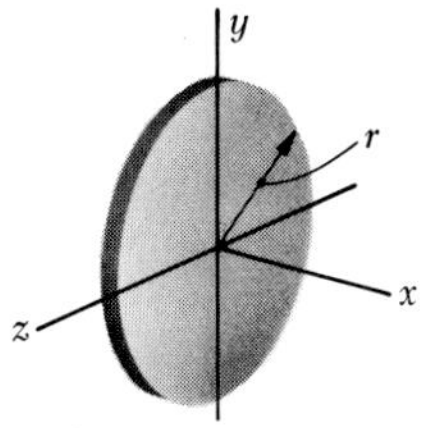	$I_x = \frac{1}{2}mr^2$ $I_y = I_z = \frac{1}{4}mr^2$
Circular cylinder	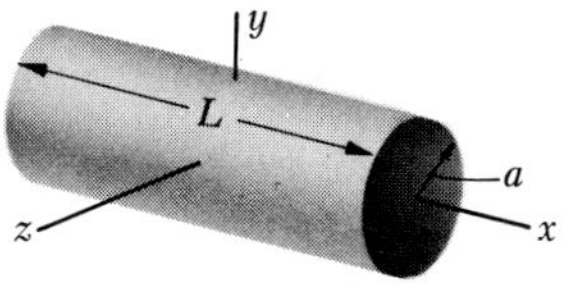	$I_x = \frac{1}{2}ma^2$ $I_y = I_z = \frac{1}{12}m(3a^2 + L^2)$
Circular cone	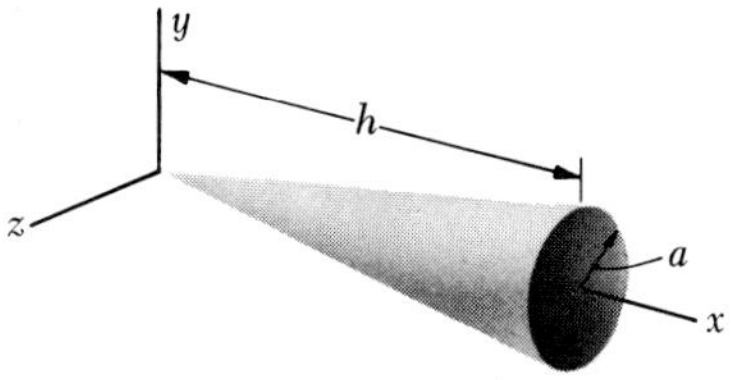	$I_x = \frac{3}{10}ma^2$ $I_y = I_z = \frac{3}{5}m(\frac{1}{4}a^2 + h^2)$
Sphere	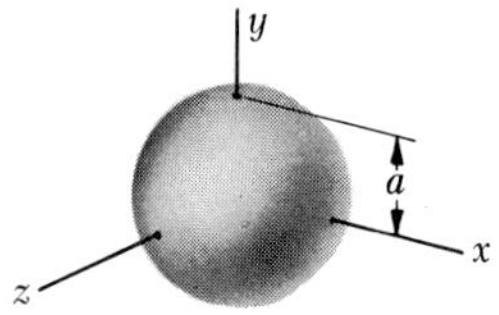	$I_x = I_y = I_z = \frac{2}{5}ma^2$

Mass moments of inertia of common geometric shapes

INDEX

ANSWERS TO EVEN-NUMBERED PROBLEMS

CHAPTER 11

11.2. $t = 2$ sec, $s = 1$ in., $a = -6$ in./sec^2;
$t = 3$ sec, $s = 0$, $a = 6$ in./sec^2.

11.4. 6 sec, -13 ft, 46 ft.

11.6. $a = 2t$, $v = t^2 - 9$, $s = \frac{1}{3}t^3 - 9t + 18$.

11.8. (*a*) 3 sec. (*b*) 5 ft, -28 ft/sec. (*c*) 32.5 ft.

11.10. (*a*) 9.17 ft/sec. (*b*) 5 ft. (*c*) 2.89 ft.

11.12. (*a*) 80 in.^{3}/sec^2. (*b*) 12 in./sec.

11.14. (*a*) 10 ft. (*b*) Infinite. (*c*) 0.230 sec.

11.16. (*b*) $v^2 = (1/k^2)(1 - e^{-2k^2gs})$.
(*c*) The velocity approaches this value as a limit for large values of *t*.

11.18. (*a*) $v = (kT/\pi)(1 - \cos \pi t/T)$,
$s = (kT^2/\pi^2)[(\pi t/T) - \sin(\pi t/T)]$.
(*b*) $v_{max} = 2kT/\pi$. (*c*) $s = 2kT^2/\pi$.
(*d*) $v_{av} = kT/\pi$.

11.20. (*a*) 15,540 ft. (*b*) 1,677,000 ft. (*c*) Infinite.

11.22. (*a*) 25,950 ft/sec. (*b*) 34.5 min.

11.24. (*a*) 15 ft/sec. (*b*) 45 ft/sec. (*c*) 225 ft.

11.26. (*a*) 1.115 sec, 35.9 ft/sec.
(*b*) 2.74 sec, 14.57 ft/sec. (*c*) 59.1.

11.28. (*a*) 314 ft. (*b*) 13.60 ft/sec.

11.30. (*a*) 14.93 sec, 334 ft. (*b*) $v_A = 44.8$ ft/sec,
$v_B = 51.7$ ft/sec.

11.32. 0.816 sec, 276 ft below ground level.

11.34. (*a*) 24 ft/sec ↓. (*b*) 12 ft/sec ↓.
(*c*) 36 ft/sec ↓. (*d*) 24 ft/sec ↓.

11.36. (*a*) 12 in./sec ↓, 12 in./sec ↑, 36 in./sec ↓,
36 in./sec ↑. (*b*) 48 in./sec ↑.
(*c*) 48 in./sec ↑.

11.38. (*a*) 6 sec. (*b*) $s_A = 54$ in. →, $s_B = 72$ in. →,
$s_C = 18$ in. ↓.

11.40. $v_A = 24$ in./sec →, $v_B = 28$ in./sec →.

11.42. $v_A = 5$ ft/sec ↓, $v_B = 1$ ft/sec ↑,
$v_C = 8$ ft/sec ↑.

11.44. (*a*) 40 ft/sec. (*b*) 288 ft.

11.46. (*a*) 120 in. (*b*) 0, 8, 16, and 22 sec.

11.48. (*a*) 5.33 ft/sec^2. (*b*) 22.7 mph.

11.50. 15 sec.

11.52. (*a*) 2 sec. (*b*) 1,500 ft.

11.54. 55.4 mph.

11.56. 22.5 ft/sec^2.

11.58. 25 sec.

11.60. (*a*) 135 in./sec. (*b*) 540 in. (*c*) 90 in./sec.

11.62. (*a*) 8 sec. (*b*) 72 ft.

11.64. (*a*) 12.00 sec. (*b*) 383 ft.

11.66. (*a*) -63 ft/sec^2. (*b*) -73 ft/sec^2

11.68. 288 ft.

11.70. (*a*) 60 in. (*b*) 120 in.

11.74. $\mathbf{v}_{min} = 2.828$ ft/sec ∡ 45°, $t = 1.500$ sec,
$x = y = -1.500$ ft.

11.76. (*a*) $x = y = 0$, $\mathbf{v} = 14.14$ in./sec ∡ 45°,
$\mathbf{a} = 22.4$ in./sec^2 ∡ 63.4°. (*b*) $x = 6.32$ in.,
$y = 5$ in., $\mathbf{v} = 4.45$ in./sec ∡ 34.2°,
$\mathbf{a} = 4.45$ in./sec^2 ∡ 34.2°.

11.78. (*a*) $\pm 90°$. (*b*) Ap. (*c*) Circle of radius A with center at the origin.

11.82. (*a*) 42.4°. (*b*) Directly above target.

11.84. 3.47 ft/sec $< v_0 <$ 11.57 ft/sec.

11.86. 25.8 ft.

11.88. $d <$ 19.1 ft.

11.90. 8.0° or 72.5°.

11.92. $R = v_0^2/g$, $\alpha = 45°$.

11.94. 36.5 ft.

11.96. (*a*) 93.1 ft. (*b*) 75.9°.

11.100. (*a*) 26.0 ft. (*b*) 22.4°.

11.102. 18.54 mph from 62.8° west of south.

11.104. (*a*) 30.8 mph ∡ 76.9°. (*b*) 452 ft ∡ 76.9°.
(*c*) 818 ft.

11.106. 35.1 ft/sec ∡ 81.2°.
11.108. (*a*) 63.9°.
(*b*) 1,195 ft/sec ↑, 32.2 ft/sec^2 ↓.
11.110. (*a*) 6.21 ft/sec ↖. (*b*) 1.153 ft/sec ↖.
11.112. (*a*) 4.84 ft/sec^2. (*b*) 63.6 mph.
11.114. 299,000 ft/sec^2.
11.116. 347 ft.
11.118. 43.8 sec.
11.120. 14,580 ft.
11.124. 17,060 mph.
11.126. 17,690 mph.
11.128. $v = 4$ in./sec, $\gamma = 0°$; $a = 64.5$ in./sec^2, $\gamma = 82.9°$; where γ is measured counter-clockwise from the positive r axis.
11.130. (*a*) $v = k\pi/\sqrt{2}$, $\gamma = 135°$; $a = \sqrt{5}\,k\pi^2/4$, $\gamma = -116.5°$. (*b*) $v = 0$; $a = k\pi^2/4$, $\gamma = 0°$.
11.132. $a = d\sec^2\theta\,[(d^2\theta/dt^2) + 2\tan\theta\,(d\theta/dt)^2]$.
11.134. $v = b\sqrt{1+\theta^2}\,(d\theta/dt)$.
11.136. $v = e^{b\theta}\sqrt{b^2+1}\,(d\theta/dt)$.
11.138. $a = (b\omega^2/\theta^3)\sqrt{4+\theta^4}$.
11.140. (*a*) $d\theta/dt = v_0/17$, $v_r = 0$.
(*b*) $d\theta/dt = 5v_0/169$, $v_r = -12v_0/13$.
11.142. (*a*) 15.83 ft/sec ∠ 50°. (*b*) 0.983 sec.
11.144. (*a*) 42 sec. (*b*) 1.848 ft.
11.146. (*a*) 4.50 sec. (*b*) 101.25 in./sec.
11.148. $\alpha = 5.7°$, $\beta = 1.0°$ (or $\alpha = 84.3°$, $\beta = 10.0°$).
11.150. ($\alpha = 29.5°$) $\rho = 22{,}900$ ft;
($\alpha = 70.0°$) $\rho = 58{,}100$ ft.
11.152. 240 ft/sec.

CHAPTER 12

12.2. 16.50 lb, 100.00 lb, 3.11 lb-sec^2/ft.
12.4. 3.86 ft/sec^2 ↓, 25 lb.
12.6. (*a*) 150.3 ft. (*b*) 18.97 mph.
12.8. (*a*) 0.152. (*b*) 16.00 ft/sec.
12.10. 4.4°.
12.12. Block A: (*a*) 3.43 ft/sec^2. (*b*) 34.3 ft/sec. (*c*) 18.52 ft/sec. Block B: (*a*) 6.00 ft/sec^2. (*b*) 60.0 ft/sec. (*c*) 24.5 ft/sec.
12.14. (*a*) 11.3°. (*b*) 6.69 ft/sec^2.
12.16. $F_{AB} = 2{,}000$ lb *C*, $F_{BC} = 3{,}000$ lb *C*.
12.18. (1) 33.3 lb added, (2) 33.3 lb taken away, (3) 1,367 lb added.
12.20. $g = \dfrac{v^2}{2h}\dfrac{m_2 + m_1}{m_2 - m_1}$.
12.22. (*a*) 7.00 ft/sec ↑. (*b*) 22.9 ft.
12.24. (*a*) 59.7 lb. (*b*) Impossible, since a_B cannot be greater than g.
12.26. $T_1 = 502.5$ lb, $T_2 = 47.5$ lb.
12.28. 2 min 59 sec.
12.30. 13.23 ft/sec ←.
12.32. (*a*) 75 lb. (*b*) 8.05 ft/sec^2 ←.
12.34. (*a*) 16.10 ft/sec^2 ←. (*b*) 4.83 ft/sec^2 ←.
(*c*) 11.27 ft/sec^2 ←.
12.36. 14.18 ft/sec →.
12.38. $s = (Wv_0^2/2gF_0)\ln 2$.
12.40. $v = \sqrt{gk/W}\,[\sqrt{x_0^2 + l^2} - l] \leftrightarrow$.
12.42. $\mathbf{a}_A = 13.25$ ft/sec^2 ↑, $\mathbf{a}_B = 1.889$ ft/sec^2 ↓, $\mathbf{a}_C = 9.47$ ft/sec^2 ↓;
block *C* strikes ground first.
12.44. $W_A = 11.25$ lb, $W_B = 22.5$ lb.
12.46. $\mathbf{a}_A = \frac{1}{2}g$ ↑, $\mathbf{a}_B = \frac{1}{4}g$ ↓, $\mathbf{a}_C = 0$.
12.48. (*a*) 22.7 ft/sec. (*b*) 2.62 ft.
12.50. 10.56 ft/sec.
12.52. 3.74 lb.
12.54. (*a*) $T_{CD} = W$. (*b*) $T_{CD} = \frac{1}{2}W$, $\mathbf{a} = 0.866\,g$ ∢ 60°.
12.56. (*a*) 947 ft. (*b*) 219 lb.
12.58. 19.4°.
12.60. $v_{\min} = \sqrt{gr\tan(\theta - \phi)}$,
$v_{\max} = \sqrt{gr\tan(\theta + \phi)}$.
12.62. 31.7°.
12.64. $1/h - 1/y = c^2\ln(x/b)$.
12.66. (*a*) 59.9 mph. (*b*) 139.1 mph.
12.68. 9.96 ft.
12.70. Length of plates must be doubled.
12.72. $x = L$, $y = 0$, $z = -eBL^2/2mv_0$.
12.74. (*a*) $F_r = -1.242$ lb, $F_\theta = 0$.
(*b*) $F_r = 0.932$ lb, $F_\theta = -1.242$ lb.
12.76. (*a*) $F_r = -4.60$ lb, $F_\theta = 0$.
(*b*) $F_r = -1.533$ lb, $F_\theta = -3.07$ lb.
12.78. $n = 0$: uniform circular motion;
$n = 1$: uniform rectilinear motion.
12.80. 1.317×10^{25} lb (or 4.09×10^{23} lb-sec^2/ft).
12.82. 5.32 ft/sec^2.
12.84. (*a*) 16,860 mph. (*b*) 1.2 per cent.
12.86. 22,300 mph, 3,240 mph.
12.88. (*a*) 5,790 mph. (*b*) 2,640 mph.
(*c*) 10,020 mph.
12.90. 12 hr 42 min.
12.92. 3 hr 5 min.
12.94. (*a*) $8r_0$. (*b*) 9.54.
12.96. (*a*) 24,000 mph. (*b*) 164.6°.
(*c*) 3,220 mph, 7.7°. (*d*) 50 hr 48 min.
12.98. A: 12.86 ft/sec^2. B: 25.8 ft/sec^2.
C: 19.32 ft/sec^2.
12.100. $\bar{v} = \sqrt{2gh(1 - h/l)}$, $v_{\max} = \sqrt{gl/2}$.

12.102. $t = (m/\sqrt{Tk})\,[\tanh^{-1}(v\sqrt{k/T}) - \tanh^{-1}(v_0\sqrt{k/T})]$. If v were greater than $\sqrt{T/k}$, the drag would be larger than the thrust and the speed could not be maintained.
12.104. $a = (P/m)\,e^{-kt/m}$.
12.106. 0.665.
12.108. 26,200 miles.

CHAPTER 13

13.2. 376×10^6 ft-lb.
13.4. 321 lb.
13.10. 143.2 ft, $F_{AB} = 12.6$ kips T, $F_{BC} = 5.40$ kips T.
13.12. 2.27 ft.
13.14. 15.10 ft/sec.
13.16. 2.51 lb.
13.22. 21 1°.
13.24. 77 mph.
13.26. 2.8 ft.
13.28. 3,520 lb/in.
13.30. (*a*) 8 in. (*b*) 0. (*c*) -1 in.
13.32. Loop 1: (*a*) $\sqrt{5gr} \leftarrow$. (*b*) $3W \rightarrow$.
Loop 2: (*a*) $\sqrt{4gr} \leftarrow$. (*b*) $2W \rightarrow$.
13.36. (*a*) 29.7 ft/sec. (*b*) 20.2 in.
13.38. (*a*) 7,580 mph. (*b*) 5 per cent.
13.40. 8,730 mph $\uparrow$.
13.42. (*a*) $\frac{1}{2}kl^2[(5 - 4\cos\theta)^{\frac{1}{2}} - 1]^2$.
(*b*) $-Wl\sin\theta$.
13.44. 12.07 in. above floor.
13.46. (*a*) 19.69 in. (*b*) 14.40 in.
13.50. (*a*) 11.58 ft/sec. (*b*) 19.79 ft/sec.
13.52. 45.4 ft/sec.
13.54. 7.04 ft/sec.
13.56. 6.82 ft/sec.
13.58. $1.091\sqrt{gl}$.
13.60. (*a*) 41.8°. (*b*) 3.38 ft.
13.62. 0.615 lb $\rightarrow$.
13.64. 1.600 in., 16 lb $\uparrow$.
13.66. (*a*) $\frac{1}{2}L$. (*b*) $\frac{1}{4}L$.
13.68. 36,700 ft/sec.
13.70. (*a*) $\frac{1}{2}mgR$. (*b*) mgR.
13.72. (*a*) 87.4×10^8 ft-lb. (*b*) 6.72×10^8 ft-lb.
13.74. 0.818 hp, 0.955 hp.
13.76. $t < 14.67$ sec: $1{,}708t$ ft-lb/sec;
$t > 14.67$ sec: 3,170 ft-lb/sec.
13.78. (*a*) 36.4 hp. (*b*) 60.1 hp.
13.80. (*a*) 9.09 hp. (*b*) 42.8 hp.
13.82. (*a*) Zero. (*b*) 720,000 hp.
13.84. 27.4 sec, 1,525 ft.
13.86. (*b*) $s = (W/3kg)\ln[(P_2 - kv_0^3)/(P_2 - kv_1^3)]$.
13.88. (*a*) 3.11 ft-lb. (*b*) 6.21 ft-lb. (*c*) Part *b* includes both the work done by the boy and the work done by the elevator motor in maintaining the constant velocity.
13.90. (*a*) 533 hp.
(*b*) 7.37 mph, 984 hp.
(*c*) 5.93 mph, 33,700 lb.
13.94. (*a*) $\frac{1}{2}mgR$. (*b*) $\frac{3}{4}mgR$.
13.96. $W(1 + h/L)$.
13.98. (*a*) 60.0 ft. (*b*) 0.161.

CHAPTER 14

14.2. 34,200 lb-sec.
14.4. (*a*) 151.8 sec. (*b*) 151.8 sec.
14.8. 1,800 ft/sec.
14.10. (*a*) 1.553 sec. (*b*) 3.11 sec.
14.12. (1) 25.8 ft/sec $\downarrow$. (2) 42.9 ft/sec $\downarrow$.
(3) 2.86 ft/sec $\downarrow$.
14.16. 33.6 ft/sec $\searrow$.
14.20. (*a*) 29.1 ft/sec. (*b*) Zero.
14.24. 4,270 lb.
14.26. 45.2 lb $\searrow$ 20.1°.
14.28. 10.42 ft/sec.
14.30. (*a*) 2,188 ft/sec $\rightarrow$. (*b*) 1,548 ft/sec $\rightarrow$.
14.32. 0.40 mph, 7,290 lb.
14.34. (*a*) 3 ft/sec $\leftarrow$. (*b*) 3 ft/sec $\leftarrow$.
14.36. (*a*) 4 ft/sec $\leftarrow$. (*b*) 49.7 lb $\leftarrow$.
14.38. (*a*) 3.47 mph $\rightarrow$. (*b*) 2.88 mph $\rightarrow$.
(*c*) 2.60 mph $\rightarrow$.
14.40. (*a*) 24.9 lb-sec. (*b*) 19.94 lb-sec.
14.42. (*a*) $\mathbf{v}_A = 23$ ft/sec $\leftarrow$, $\mathbf{v}_B = 1$ ft/sec $\rightarrow$.
(*b*) 13.04 ft-lb.
14.44. 0.400 lb.
14.46. $\mathbf{v}_D' = \frac{1}{8}v_A(1 + e)^3 \rightarrow$.
14.48. (*a*) $1.621\mathbf{v}_1$. (*b*) $1.333\mathbf{v}_1$. (*c*) $0.571\mathbf{v}_1$.
14.50. $a = r\sqrt{2}$, $\mathbf{v}_B' = v/\sqrt{2} \measuredangle 45°$.
14.52. 0.330.
14.56. (*a*) $\tan\theta = \sqrt{e}$. (*b*) $\sqrt{e}\,v$.
14.58. (*a*) 0.945. (*b*) 12.94 in.
14.60. $d/(1 - e^2)$.
14.62. $\theta_A = 79.7°$.
14.64. 1.331 ft.
14.66. (*a*) 1.890 in. (*b*) 6.67 ft-lb.
14.68. $W_A = W_B$.
14.70. (*a*) 200 ft-lb. (*b*) 160 ft-lb.
14.72. (*a*) 3.98 ft-lb. (*b*) 3.62 ft-lb.
14.74. 2.86 in., 20.2 in.

14.76. (a) 12.50 in./sec. (b) $T_{\text{final}} = \frac{1}{16}T_1$. (c) Straight line, $x = 5$ in.
14.78. (a) $v_2 = 2v_1$. (b) +100 per cent. (c) Zero. (d) +300 per cent.
14.80. (a) 27.3 ft/sec. (b) 1.099 ft.
14.82. 22.7 ft/sec.
14.84. 8.01 in.
14.90. $3r_0$.
14.92. 30°.
14.94. 11,280 miles, 1,018 miles.
14.96. 26,700 ft/sec, 26.9°.
14.98. (b) $\frac{1}{3}\sqrt{6}\,v_{\text{esc}}, \frac{1}{2}\sqrt{2}\,v_{\text{esc}}$.
14.100. 776 lb ⦪ 30°.
14.102. 69.9 lb.
14.104. (a) 26.0 lb ←. (b) 0.698 ft/sec² →.
14.106. 327 lb.
14.108. wv_0/g →.
14.110. ρQv ⦩ θ.
14.112. (a) 7,360 lb. (b) 21,090 hp. (c) 12,750 hp.
14.114. 7.5°.
14.116. (a) $F = (w/g)(u - v)$.
14.118. (a) 4,100 lb. (b) 6,450 lb.
14.120. (a) $\gamma Av^2/g$. (b) $\gamma Av^3/2g$.
14.122. 11.86 lb →.
14.124. 278 ft³/sec.
14.126. 40.9 ft/sec ↓.
14.128. (a) 1,138 lb. (b) 136.6 hp.
14.130. (a) wv/g. (b) 9.32 lb.
14.132. (a) $w(l - vt)$. (b) $wvt + wv^2/g$.
14.134. u/g.
14.136. (a) 180 ft/sec². (b) 720 ft/sec².
14.138. 10,060 ft/sec.
14.140. (a) 1,540 ft/sec. (b) 11,600 ft/sec.
14.142. (a) 30,320 ft/sec →. (b) 13,680 ft/sec →
14.144. (a) $\frac{1}{2}v_1$ →. (b) Max power $= \frac{1}{4}A\rho(1 - \cos\theta)v_1^3$. (c) $\eta = 2(V/v_1)(1 - V/v_1)(1 - \cos\theta)$.
14.146. 80,700 ft.
14.152. (a) 6 oz. (b) 75 per cent.
14.156. $\sqrt{hg}$.
14.158. $v^2 = (2PgL/W)\ln 2$.
14.160. (a) 0.388 sec. (b) 0.518 sec.

CHAPTER 15

15.2. (a) 2 sec. (b) +1.600 radians, −1.200 radians/sec².
15.4. (a) 0, +0.200 radian/sec, −0.050 radian/sec². (b) 0.506 radian, +0.0736 radian/sec, −0.01839 radian/sec². (c) 0.800 radian, 0, 0.
15.6. (a) 2.98 radians/sec². (b) 34,200 revolutions.
15.8. 551 revolutions.
15.10. 66,700 mph, 0.01947 ft/sec².
15.12. 1.362 sec, 5.45 radians/sec.
15.14. (a) 20 ft/sec². (b) 80.2 ft/sec². (c) 200 ft/sec².
15.16. (a) 1.047 radians/sec². (b) 19.44 revolutions.
15.18. (a) 3.95 radians/sec². (b) 3.18 sec.
15.20. (a) $\alpha_A = 8.38$ radians/sec² ↻, $\alpha_B = 13.96$ radians/sec² ↻. (b) 2.25 sec.
15.22. (a) $a_B = r\theta_0(2\pi/T)^2\sqrt{\theta_0^2\cos^4(2\pi t/T) + \sin^2(2\pi t/T)}$. (b) Maximum: For $\theta_0 \leqslant 1$, $a_B = r\theta_0(2\pi/T)^2$, at $\theta = \pm\theta_0$; for $\theta_0 \geqslant 1$, $a_B = r\theta_0^2(2\pi/T)^2$, at $\theta = 0$. Minimum: For $\theta_0^2 \leqslant \frac{1}{2}$, $a_B = r\theta_0^2(2\pi/T)^2$, at $\theta = 0$; for $\theta_0^2 \geqslant \frac{1}{2}$, $a_B = r(2\pi/T)^2(\theta_0^2 - \frac{1}{4})^{\frac{1}{2}}$, at $\theta = \pm(\theta_0^2 - \frac{1}{2})^{\frac{1}{2}}$.
15.24. $\mathbf{v}_B = 176$ ft/sec →, $\mathbf{v}_C = 0$, $\mathbf{v}_D = 170.0$ ft/sec ∠ 15°, $\mathbf{v}_E = 124.5$ ft/sec ⦪ 45°.
15.26. (a) 1.121 radians/sec ↻. (b) 22.0 in./sec ⦫ 60°.
15.28. $\mathbf{v}_D = 2v$ →, $\mathbf{v}_F = \sqrt{2}\,v$ ∠ 45°.
15.30. (a) $\frac{1}{4}\omega_A$ ↺. (b) $\frac{1}{2}\omega_A$ ↻.
15.32. $\omega_B = 40$ rpm ↺, $\omega_C = 20$ rpm ↻.
15.34. (a) 0, 26.2 radians/sec ↻. (b) 209 in./sec ↓, 0. (c) 0, 26.2 radians/sec ↺.
15.36. 205 in./sec ↓, 13.41 radians/sec ↻.
15.38. $\omega_{BD} = 5$ radians/sec ↺, $\omega_{DE} = 3$ radians/sec ↻.
15.40. $\omega_{BD} = 1.5$ radians/sec ↻, $\omega_{DE} = 4$ radians/sec ↻.
15.42. (a) 0, 0. (b) 0.934 radian/sec ↺, 4.60 ft/sec →.
15.46. $v_P = b\omega\sin\omega t\,[1 + (b\cos\omega t)/\sqrt{l^2 - b^2\sin^2\omega t}]$.
15.48. Vertical line intersecting zx plane at $x = 0$, $z = 5.25$ ft.
15.50. (a) 1 in. to right of A. (b) 4 in./sec ↓. (c) 16 in./sec unwrapped on outer pulley, 8 in./sec unwrapped on inner pulley.
15.52. 0.462 radian/sec ↻, 4.16 ft/sec ∠ 73.9°.
15.54. (a) 5 radians/sec ↻. (b) 40 in./sec ↑. (c) 25 in./sec ⦩ 53.1°.
15.58. (a) 3 radians/sec ↺. (b) 27 in./sec ↑.
15.66. (a) 22 in./sec →. (b) 0.833 radian/sec ↻.
15.72. 12 ft/sec² ↑, 0.500 radian/sec² ↻.

15.74. (*a*) 12 in./sec^2 ←. (*b*) 12 in./sec^2 →.
15.76. $\mathbf{a}_C$ = 7,150 ft/sec^2 ↑.
$\mathbf{a}_D$ = 7,150 ft/sec^2 ⦩ 60°.
15.78. $\mathbf{a}_A$ = 6 in./sec^2 →,
$\mathbf{a}_B$ = 25.1 in./sec^2 ⦢ 85.4°,
$\mathbf{a}_C$ = 37.5 in./sec^2 ↑.
15.80. $\mathbf{a}_A$ = 6 in./sec^2 ↓,
$\mathbf{a}_B$ = 66.5 in./sec^2 ⦩ 15.7°.
15.82. $\boldsymbol{\omega}_{AB} = 0$, $\boldsymbol{\alpha}_{AB} = \frac{1}{4}\omega_0^2$ ↺,
$\boldsymbol{\omega}_{BC} = \frac{1}{2}\omega_0$ ↻, $\boldsymbol{\alpha}_{BC} = 0$.
15.84. (*a*) 877 ft/sec^2 ←. (*b*) 233 ft/sec^2 →.
15.86. $\mathbf{a}_D$ = 36 in./sec^2 ↑, $\mathbf{a}_E$ = 36 in./sec^2 ↓,
$\mathbf{a}_F$ = 36 in./sec^2 ←.
15.88. (*a*) 30.0 radians/sec^2 ↻.
(*b*) 54.0 radians/sec^2 ↺.
15.90. (*a*) 2.81 radians/sec^2 ↺.
(*b*) 18 in./sec^2 ←, 150.5 in./sec^2 ↑.
15.92. (*a*) $\boldsymbol{\alpha}_{BC}$ = 40 radians/sec^2 ↺,
$\boldsymbol{\alpha}_{CD}$ = 20 radians/sec^2 ↺.
(*b*) $\mathbf{a}_C$ = 256 in./sec^2 ⦩ 51.3°, $\mathbf{a}_D = 0$.
15.94. (*a*) $\boldsymbol{\alpha}_{BC}$ = 40 radians/sec^2 ↺,
$\boldsymbol{\alpha}_{CD}$ = 5 radians/sec^2 ↺.
(*b*) $\mathbf{a}_C$ = 167.6 in./sec^2 ⦩ 17.4°, $\mathbf{a}_D = 0$.
15.96. $v_x = v(1 - \cos vt/r)$, $v_y = v \sin vt/r$.
15.98. $\omega = (v_B \sin \beta)/(l \cos \theta)$.
15.100. $v_B = r\omega \cos \theta$, $a_B = r\alpha \cos \theta - r\omega^2 \sin \theta$.
15.102. $v_B = R\omega \sec^2\theta$,
$a_B = R \sec^2\theta\,(\alpha + 2\omega^2 \tan \theta)$.
15.104. $\alpha = -2(v_A^2/b^2) \sin \theta \cos^3 \theta$.
15.106. $v_P = 2r\omega \sin \omega t$, $a_P = 2r\omega^2 \cos \omega t$.
15.108. (*a*) 10.47 ft/sec ↓, (*b*) 9.07 ft/sec ↓, (*c*) 0.
15.110. 24.1 radians/sec ↻, 180°.
15.112. (*a*) 1.933 radians/sec ↺.
(*b*) 17.10 in./sec ⦪ 20°.
15.114. $\boldsymbol{\omega}_{BP}$ = 2.92 radians/sec ↺,
$\boldsymbol{\omega}_{EF}$ = 1.130 radians/sec ↺.
15.116. (*a*) $\boldsymbol{\omega}_{EF} = \boldsymbol{\omega}_{BD}$, $\mathbf{v}_{P/BD} = l\omega$ ←, $\mathbf{v}_{P/EF} = 0$.
(*b*) $\boldsymbol{\omega}_{EF} = \boldsymbol{\omega}_{BD}$, $\mathbf{v}_{P/BD} = l\omega/\sqrt{3}$ ⦪ 30°,
$\mathbf{v}_{P/EF} = l\omega/\sqrt{3}$ ⦢ 30°.
15.118. $\mathbf{a}_1 = [r\omega^2 \rightarrow] + [2u\omega \uparrow]$,
$\mathbf{a}_2 = [r\omega^2 \downarrow] + [2u\omega \leftarrow]$,
$\mathbf{a}_3 = [r\omega^2 \leftarrow] + [u^2/r \leftarrow] + [2u\omega \rightarrow]$,
$\mathbf{a}_4 = [r\omega^2 \uparrow] + [2u\omega \downarrow]$.
15.120. $a = R\omega^2\sqrt{1 + (2u/R\omega)^2}$.
15.122. (*a*) 0.00582 ft/sec^2 west.
(*b*) 0.00446 ft/sec^2 west. (*c*) Same as *b*.
15.124. 83.8 ft/sec^2 ⦪ 60°.
15.126. (*a*) 790 ft/sec^2 ⦪ 72.6°.
(*b*) 891 ft/sec^2 ⦪ 57.8°.
15.128. 1.124 radians/sec ↺, 8.07 radians/sec^2 ↻.
15.130. 1.266 radians/sec^2 ↺.
15.132. 709 ft/sec^2 ⦩ 81.5°.
15.134. 18.4°.
15.136. (*a*) $\boldsymbol{\alpha}_{AB} = \boldsymbol{\alpha}_{BC} = 0$,
$\boldsymbol{\alpha}_{BD}$ = 1.333 radians/sec^2 ↻.
(*b*) $\mathbf{a}_A$ = 32 in./sec^2 →,
$\mathbf{a}_B$ = 16 in./sec^2 →.
15.138. (*a*) 166.7 rpm ↻. (*b*) 21.8 ft/sec ↘.
15.140. (*a*) 0. (*b*) 58.9 in./sec ←.
(*c*) 94.3 in./sec ←.
15.142. (*a*) 8.33 revolutions. (*b*) Infinite.
(*c*) 1.151 sec.
15.144. 1.964 sec, 3.93 sec, 7.85 sec.

CHAPTER 16

16.2. (*a*) 64.4 ft/sec^2 →. (*b*) **A** = 5.387 lb ↑,
B = 0.387 lb ↓.
16.4. (*a*) 6.44 ft/sec^2 →. (*b*) 44.0 in.
16.6. (*a*) 15.22 ft/sec^2. (*b*) 2.50.
16.8. (*a*) 21.5 ft/sec^2 →, 10.0 lb.
(*b*) 1.25 in. $\leqslant h \leqslant$ 8.75 in.
16.10. 16.1 ft/sec^2 ↑.
16.12. 36.8 ft.
16.14. 256 lb →, 305 lb ↑.
16.16. (*a*) 3.02 ft/sec^2 →.
(*b*) $\mathbf{A}_x$ = 31.3 lb ←,
$\mathbf{A}_y$ = 156.3 lb ↑, **B** = 43.7 lb ↑.
16.18. $\mathbf{B}_y = \mathbf{C}_y$ = 40.3 lb ↓.
16.20. (*a*) $\bar{\mathbf{a}}$ = 31.0 ft/sec^2 ⦩ 85.8°.
(*b*) **A** = 0.288 lb ⦢ 30°, **B** = 0.520 lb ⦢ 30°.
16.22. (*a*) 0.500 g ⦩ 30°.
(*b*) Platform: 1.250 g ⦩ 30°, block: 0.625 g ↓.
16.24. V_B = −20.1 lb,
M = −150.7 lb-in. at center of *BC*.
16.26. 4,340 revolutions.
16.28. 31.9 radians/sec^2 ↻.
16.30. Case 1: 56.2 radians/sec^2 ↺.
Case 2: 61.8 radians/sec^2 ↺.
16.32. 8.05 ft/sec.
16.34. (1) 25 radians/sec^2 ↺, 50 radians/sec ↺,
22.4 radians/sec ↺; (2) 14.07 radians/sec^2 ↺,
28.14 radians/sec ↺, 16.77 radians/sec ↺;
(3) 6.09 radians/sec^2 ↺, 12.18 radians/sec ↺,
11.04 radians/sec ↺; (4) 9.79 radians/sec^2 ↺,
19.58 radians/sec ↺, 9.89 radians/sec ↺.
16.36. 73.0 lb.

16.38. $\alpha = \dfrac{2g}{r} \dfrac{\mu(1 + \mu)}{1 + \mu^2}$ ↻.
16.40. α_A = 15.46 radians/sec² ↺, α_B = 7.73 radians/sec² ↻.
16.42. (*a*) 13.72 radians/sec² ↺. (*b*) 4.58 sec.
16.44. $\alpha = \dfrac{2\mu g \sin\phi}{r(\sin 2\phi - \mu \cos 2\phi)}$ ↺.
16.46. $\bar{k}^2\alpha/\bar{a}$
16.48. 3 in. from A on line AB, 12.88 radians/sec² ↻, 6.44 ft/sec² →.
16.50. T_A = 442 lb, T_B = 522 lb.
16.52. $\mathbf{a}_A$ = 14 ft/sec² ↑, $\mathbf{a}_B$ = 26 ft/sec² ↑.
16.54. T_A = 25 lb, T_B = 30 lb.
16.56. (*a*) 30 lb. (*b*) 42.9 radians/sec² ↻. (*c*) 64.4 ft/sec² ↑.
16.58. (*a*) $\bar{\mathbf{a}} = \mu g$ ←, $\alpha = \dfrac{5}{2}\dfrac{\mu g}{r}$ ↻. (*b*) $t = \dfrac{2}{7}\dfrac{v_0}{\mu g}$. (*c*) $s = \dfrac{12}{49}\dfrac{v_0^2}{\mu g}$. (*d*) $\bar{\mathbf{v}} = \dfrac{5}{7}v_0$ →, $\omega = \dfrac{5}{7}\dfrac{v_0}{r}$ ↻.
16.60. $P = 4\mu W/\sqrt{58}$.
16.62. Inside a circle of radius 1 ft with center at x = 1.5 ft, z = 2.5 ft.
16.64. (*a*) 45.3 radians/sec² ↺. (*b*) $\mathbf{A}_x$ = 15 lb →, $\mathbf{A}_y$ = 16 lb ↑
16.66. 1.600 ft $\leqslant h \leqslant$ 3.73 ft.
16.68. 0.120 in.
16.70. (*a*) $4wL/7$. (*b*) $9g/7$ ↓.
16.72. 6.33 in.
16.74. (*a*) 11.62 radians/sec² ↻. (*b*) $\mathbf{A}_x$ = 34.1 lb ←, $\mathbf{A}_y$ = 27.0 lb ↑.
16.76. (*a*) $\frac{3}{4}g/l$ ↻. (*b*) $\mathbf{N} = 13W/16$ ↑, $\mathbf{F} = (3\sqrt{3}/16)W$ →. (*c*) 0.400.
16.80. $\tan\beta = 3\mu$.
16.82. 2.55 ft.
16.84. (*a*) 10.30 radians/sec² ↻, 10.30 ft/sec² →. (*b*) 0.180.
16.86. (*a*) 5.15 radians/sec² ↻, 5.15 ft/sec² →. (*b*) 0.340.
16.88. (*a*) Does not slide. (*b*) 10.30 radians/sec² ↻, 10.30 ft/sec² →.
16.90. (*a*) Slides. (*b*) 2.86 radians/sec² ↺, 9.66 ft/sec² →.
16.92. 3.08 lb.
16.94. (*a*) 4.03 ft/sec² ←. (*b*) μ_A = 0.25, μ_B = 0.
16.96. (*a*) 0.298. (*b*) $15g/28$ →.
16.98. 9.92 lb.
16.100. (*a*) 4.32 lb. (*b*) $\mathbf{A}$ = 10.93 lb ↑, $\mathbf{B}$ = 2.71 lb ←.
16.102. 5.41 lb →.
16.104. (*a*) $3g/4L$ ↺. (*b*) $\mathbf{A} = 3W/8$ →, $\mathbf{C} = 13W/8$ ↑.
16.106. T_{BD} = 19.89 lb, T_{CE} = 31.3 lb.
16.108. 61.5 lb ↑.
16.110. (*a*) 11.95 radians/sec² ↻. (*b*) 36.8 ft/sec² ↘. (*c*) 2.47 lb ↗.
16.114. $\mathbf{A}_x$ = 8.70 lb ←, $\mathbf{A}_y$ = 10.07 lb ↑, $\mathbf{B}$ = 0.613 lb ←.
16.116. α_{AB} = 12.87 radians/sec² ↻, α_{BC} = 12.87 radians/sec² ↺, $\mathbf{A}_x$ = 4.66 lb ←, $\mathbf{A}_y$ = 6.16 lb ↑, $\mathbf{C}$ = 0.666 lb →.
16.118. (*a*) α_{disk} = 17.05 radians/sec² ↺, α_{AB} = 8.52 radians/sec² ↻. (*b*) $\mathbf{A}_x$ = 14.71 lb ←, $\mathbf{A}_y$ = 6.77 lb ↓.
16.120. Cylinder: $\mathbf{a}_c = a/3$ →, $s = 3d/2$. Sphere: $\mathbf{a}_s = 2a/7$ →, $s = 7d/5$.
16.122. (*a*) 1.456 lb →. (*b*) 2.66 lb →.
16.124. α_{AB} = 16.56 radians/sec² ↺. α_{BC} = 24.8 radians/sec² ↻.
16.126. (*a*) $\alpha_A = 2g/5r$ ↺, $\alpha_B = 2g/5r$ ↻. (*b*) $W/5$. (*c*) $4g/5$ ↓.
16.128. $\frac{1}{2}L$.
16.130. (*a*) $\alpha_{AB} = \alpha_{CD} = \dfrac{3g}{2l}\left[1 + \dfrac{3h^2}{2l^2}\right]^{-1}$ ↻. (*b*) $\mathbf{a}_B = l\alpha_{AB}$ ↓, $\mathbf{a}_D = [h\alpha_{AB}$ ←$] + [l\alpha_{AB}$ ↓$]$.
16.132. $M_{\max} = +wL^2/27$, at $2L/3$ to right of A.
16.134. $V_B = -5W/8$, $M_B = -WL/4$.
16.136. 86.9 mph.
16.138. (*a*) Each outside wheel: 1,074 lb ↑; each inside wheel: 426 lb ↑. (*b*) 0.541.
16.140. (*a*) 0.50. (*b*) $\mathbf{A}_n$ = 841 lb ←, $\mathbf{B}_n$ = 361 lb ←.
16.142. (*a*) 15.7°. (*b*) 0.28.
16.144. $\mathbf{A}$ = 183.9 lb ↑, $\mathbf{B}$ = 183.9 lb ↓.
16.146. (*a*) $\mathbf{C}$ = 183.7 lb →, $\mathbf{D}$ = 61.3 lb →. (*b*) W_C = 0.750 lb, θ_z = 180°; W_D = 0.250 lb, θ_z = 180°.
16.148. On disk B; 6.25 in. below shaft; on disk C, 3.125 in. above shaft.
16.150. (*a*) 3.35 radians/sec². (*b*) A_x = −24 lb, A_z = −2.25 lb, B_x = +24 lb, B_z = −0.25 lb.
16.152. 15.74 lb-ft.
16.154. (*a*) 55.2°. (*b*) 15.86 lb-ft.
16.156. $\mathbf{A}$ = 26.9 lb ↑, $\mathbf{D}$ = 26.9 lb ↓.
16.158. (*a*) 76.0°. (*b*) 4.91 radians/sec.

16.160. (*a*) $2wr^3\omega^2/g$. (*b*) 0. (*c*) $wr^3\omega^2/2g$.
16.162. (*a*) $\alpha = \dfrac{Pg}{2Wr}\dfrac{\pi}{(\pi-2)}$ ↻. (*b*) $\frac{1}{2}P/(W+P)$.
16.164. (*a*) $\mathbf{a}_A = 2g/5$ ←, $\mathbf{a}_B = 2g/5$ ↓.
(*b*) $\mathbf{a}_A = 2g/7$ ←, $(\mathbf{a}_B)_x = 2g/7$ ←,
$(\mathbf{a}_B)_y = 2g/7$ ↓.
16.166. (*a*) $\bar{r} = \bar{k}$. (*b*) $\frac{1}{2}W$ ↑.
16.168. 5.52 lb ↑.
16.170. (*a*) 8.05 radians/sec² ↻. (*b*) 90.1 lb.
16.172. (*a*) 2.29 radians/sec², 0.
(*b*) 1.717 radians/sec²,
0.664 ft/sec² along negative *x* axis.

CHAPTER 17

17.2. 7,900 revolutions.
17.4. $L^3 = 24I_0g/w$.
17.6. (*a*) 292 rpm. (*b*) 15.92 revolutions.
17.8. 14.60 lb-ft.
17.12. 7.62 ft, 38.1 ft-lb.
17.14. (*a*) 211 lb. (*b*) 178.9 lb.
17.16. 19.77 revolutions.
17.18. (*a*) 13.74 revolutions. (*b*) 11.49 lb ↖.
17.20. (*a*) 12.85 revolutions. (*b*) 0.711 lb.
17.22. 25.1 lb-ft.
17.24. $\mathbf{v} = (4gs/3)^{\frac{1}{2}}$ ↓.
17.26. 2.55 ft.
17.28. (*a*) $\omega = 1.074\sqrt{g/r}$ ↻. (*b*) 1.433*W* ↑.
17.30. (*a*) $\sqrt{3g/l}$, 2.50*W*. (*b*) 4.01 radians/sec,
50 lb.
17.32. 7.18 radians/sec ↺.
17.36. $\sqrt{g/2r}$.
17.38. (*a*) $\omega = 0, \bar{v} = \sqrt{gr}$.
(*b*) Vertical position with end *A* at *D*.
17.40. (*a*) $\mathbf{v}_A = 8.51$ ft/sec ↓, $\mathbf{v}_B = 4.91$ ft/sec ←.
(*b*) $\mathbf{v}_A = 0$, $\mathbf{v}_B = 13.90$ ft/sec ←.
17.42. (*a*) 16.05 ft/sec →. (*b*) **A** = **C** = 300 lb ↑.
17.44. (*a*) 45.3 rpm ↻.
(*b*) 81.3 rpm ↻.
17.46. $\mathbf{v}_B = 0$, $\mathbf{v}_D = 34.0$ ft/sec ↓.
17.48. 10.76 ft/sec ↙ 45°.
17.50. 7.35 radians/sec ↻.
17.52. 12.94 ft/sec ←.
17.54. 20,100 ft-lb/sec.
17.56. (*a*) 76.2 hp. (*b*) 381 hp.
17.58. 21.8 ft/sec ↓.
17.60. 6.75 ft/sec ←.
17.62. (*a*) $\mathbf{v}_A = 7.36$ ft/sec ↓, $\mathbf{v}_B = 5.52$ ft/sec →.
(*b*) $\mathbf{v}_A = 18.39$ ft/sec ↓, $\mathbf{v}_B = 0$.
17.64. 143.0 rpm.
17.66. 1.304 ft.
17.68. (*a*) 3*W*/2. (*b*) 3*W*/4.

CHAPTER 18

18.2. 0.335 lb-in.
18.4. $v(1+\mu)/2g\mu$.
18.8. (*a*) 6.58 sec. (*b*) 10.83 lb, 4.17 lb. (*c*) 0.304.
18.14. $gr^2t/(r^2 + \bar{k}^2)$ ↓.
18.16. (*a*) 3 in. (*b*) $\bar{\mathbf{v}} = 32.2$ ft/sec →,
$\omega = 64.4$ radians/sec ↻.
18.18. 11.71 ft/sec ↑.
18.20. (*a*) $2\bar{v}_0/7\mu g$. (*b*) $5\bar{v}_0/7$ →.
18.22. 0.385 lb-ft ↻.
18.24. Pipe: $\bar{\mathbf{v}} = g/10$ →, $\omega = g/5$ ↺.
Plate: $\mathbf{v} = 3g/5$ →.
18.26. 36.9 rpm.
18.28. 41.1 rpm.
18.30. $\omega_A = \omega_B = 159.1$ rpm ↻, $\omega_P = 20.9$ rpm ↺.
18.32. (*a*) 57.1 rpm. (*b*) 57.1 rpm.
18.34. $v_r = 15.84$ ft/sec, $v_\theta = 11.96$ ft/sec.
18.36. (*a*) $\bar{\mathbf{v}}_1 = mv_0/M$ →, $\omega_1 = mv_0/MR$ ↺.
(*b*) $mv_0/3M$ →.
18.38. (*a*) $\bar{\mathbf{v}}_1 = mv_0/3M$ →, $\omega_1 = mv_0/3MR$ ↻.
(*b*) $mv_0/3M$ →.
18.40. (*a*) 2.25 radians/sec ↺.
(*b*) $\mathbf{R}_x = 11{,}650$ lb →, $\mathbf{R}_y = 17{,}470$ lb ↑.
18.42. 2*L*/3.
18.44. $h_A = h\left(\dfrac{6W}{6W + W_P}\right)^2$
18.46. 2*L*/3.
18.48. 1.5°.
18.50. $\omega = 3\bar{v}_1/2b$ ↻, $\bar{\mathbf{v}}_x = \bar{v}_1/4$ ←, $\bar{\mathbf{v}}_y = 3\bar{v}_1/4$ ↑.
18.52. (*a*) $\mathbf{v}_A = \bar{v}_1$ ↑, $\mathbf{v}_B = 2\bar{v}_1$ ↓.
(*b*) $\mathbf{v}_A = \bar{v}_1$ ↓, $\mathbf{v}_B = 2\bar{v}_1$ ↑.
18.54. 31.0° ↘.
18.56. $\mathbf{A}\Delta t = W\sqrt{l/3g}$ ↑, $\mathbf{B}\Delta t = W\sqrt{l/12g}$ ↑.
18.58. (*a*) Downward. (*b*) To the left.
18.60. 5.60 lb ↑.
18.62. $A_y = 0$, $A_z = +813$ lb, $B_y = 0$,
$B_z = -813$ lb.
18.64. (*a*) 58.7 rpm. (*b*) 58.7 rpm.
18.66. (*a*) Zero. (*b*) $C_x = 0$, $C_y = +122.6$ lb,
$D_x = 0$, $D_y = -122.6$ lb.
18.68. (*a*) $\Omega = 2.5\dfrac{h}{r^2}\dfrac{(g-a)}{\omega}$. (*b*) Same as *a*.
18.70. (*a*) 38.6 ft/sec →. (*b*) 20 lb ←.

18.72. (*b*) $\omega_2 = 2\bar{v}_1 r/(r^2 + \bar{k}^2)$.

18.74. (*a*) $\omega = \dfrac{6\bar{v}_1}{l} \dfrac{\sin\beta}{3\sin^2\beta + 1}$ ⤸.

(*b*) $\mathbf{v}_A = 3\bar{v}_1 \dfrac{\sin\beta\cos\beta}{3\sin^2\beta + 1} \leftarrow$.

18.76. (*a*) $\mathbf{v}_A = \dfrac{2m}{2m + M}\sqrt{2gh}\downarrow$,

$\omega = \dfrac{2m}{2m + M}\dfrac{\sqrt{2gh}}{R}$ ⤸.

(*b*) $\mathbf{v}_A = \dfrac{2m - M}{2m + M}\sqrt{2gh}\downarrow$,

$\omega = \dfrac{4m}{2m + M}\dfrac{\sqrt{2gh}}{R}$ ⤸.

18.78. Gyroscopic couple will tend to turn motorcycle clockwise (when viewed from above).

18.80. 5,400 rpm.

CHAPTER 19

19.2. 2.79 ft/sec, 23.4 ft/sec^2.

19.4. (*a*) 4 lb/in. (*b*) 2.21 cps.

19.6. 300 lb, 5.71 cps.

19.8. (*a*) 0.1065 sec. (*b*) 1.419 ft/sec ↑, 8.05 ft/sec^2 ↑.

19.10. (*a*) 0.431 sec, 2.32 cps. (*b*) 3.65 ft/sec, 53.1 ft/sec^2.

19.12. 3.27 lb.

19.14. (*a*) 2.52°. (*b*) 5.04°.

19.16. 1.400 ft.

19.20. (*a*) 2.21 sec. (*b*) 2.37 sec. (*c*) 3.03 sec.

19.22. 16.3°.

19.24. (*a*) 0.533 sec. (*b*) 0.491 radian/sec.

19.26. (*a*) 5 in., 0.594 cps. (*b*) 1.554 ft/sec.

19.28. $\tau = 2\pi\sqrt{2W/3gk}$.

19.30. 1,022 lb/in.

19.36. (*a*) $f = (1/2\pi)\sqrt{g/2r}$.
(*b*) $f = (1/2\pi)\sqrt{6g/11r}$.

19.38. 0.707.

19.40. (*a*) $r_a = 7.09$ in. (*b*) 3.42 in.

19.42. $\tau = 2\pi\sqrt{L/6g}$.

19.44. (*a*) $\tau = 2\pi\sqrt{h/2g}$. (*b*) $\tau = 2\pi\sqrt{h/g}$.

19.46. 0.760 lb-ft-sec^2, 8.66 in.

19.48. 0.1774 lb-ft-sec^2.

19.50. (*a*) 1.715 sec. (*b*) 1.566 sec.

19.52. (*a*) 5.71 cps, 0.20 in., 7.18 in./sec.
(*b*) 100 lb.

19.58. 75.5°.

19.60. $f = (1/2\pi)\sqrt{g/2r}$.

19.62. $f = (1/2\pi)\sqrt{g/2b}$.

19.64. $\tau = 2\pi\sqrt{r(\pi - 2)/g}$.

19.66. $\tau = 2\pi\sqrt{7(R - r)/5g}$.

19.68. (*a*) 5.42 cps. (*b*) 4.58 cps.
(*c*) 3.83 cps.

19.72. (*a*) 0.322 sec. (*b*) 0.322 sec.

19.74. $\tau = \pi l/\sqrt{3gr}$.

19.76. $\omega > \sqrt{2kg/W}$.

19.78. $\omega > \sqrt{2g/l}$.

19.80. (*a*) 375.3 rpm. (*b*) 0.00216 in.

19.82. (*a*) 0.00420 in. (*b*) 0.0711 in. (*c*) ∞

19.84. 0.060 in. or 0.0429 in.

19.86. 1,085 rpm.

19.88. 969 rpm.

19.90. 0.045 in.

19.92. (*a*) 19.70 mph. (*b*) 0.480 in.

19.94. 0.369 cps, 0.639 cps.

19.100. 1,320 lb-sec/ft.

19.102. 7,780 lb/ft.

19.106. (*a*) 0.1582. (*b*) 20.1 lb-sec/ft.

19.108. 4.73 lb-sec/in.

19.110. (*a*) $m\dfrac{d^2x}{dt^2} + c\dfrac{dx}{dt} + kx$
$= (k\sin\omega t + c\omega\cos\omega t)\delta_m$.

(*b*) $x_m = \dfrac{\sqrt{k^2 + c^2\omega^2}\,\delta_m}{\sqrt{(k - m\omega^2)^2 + (c\omega)^2}}$,
with $\omega = 2\pi v/L$.

19.112. $R < 2\sqrt{L/C}$.

19.118. (*a*) $m\dfrac{d^2x_m}{dt^2} + k_2(x_m - x_A) = P_m\sin\omega t$,

$c\dfrac{dx_A}{dt} + k_1x_A + k_2(x_A - x_m) = 0$.

(*b*) $L\dfrac{d^2q_m}{dt^2} + \dfrac{(q_m - q_A)}{C_2} = E_m\sin\omega t$,

$R\dfrac{dq_A}{dt} + \dfrac{q_A}{C_1} + \dfrac{(q_A - q_m)}{C_2} = 0$.

19.120. (*a*) $m_1\dfrac{d^2x_1}{dt^2} + c_1\dfrac{dx_1}{dt}$
$+ k_1x_1 + k_2(x_1 - x_2) = 0$,

$m_2\dfrac{d^2x_2}{dt^2} + c_2\dfrac{dx_2}{dt} + k_2(x_2 - x_1) = 0$.

(*b*) $L_1\dfrac{d^2q_1}{dt^2} + R_1\dfrac{dq_1}{dt} + \dfrac{q_1}{C_1}$
$+ \dfrac{(q_1 - q_2)}{C_2} = 0$,

$L_2\dfrac{d^2q_2}{dt^2} + R_2\dfrac{dq_2}{dt} + \dfrac{(q_2 - q_1)}{C_2} = 0$.

19.122. (*a*) 30.4 lb/in. (*b*) 10 lb/in.

19.124. (*a*) $\tau = 2\pi\sqrt{l/(g + a)}$, $\tau = 2\pi\sqrt{m/k}$.
(*b*) $\tau = 2\pi\sqrt{l/(g - a)}$, $\tau = 2\pi\sqrt{m/k}$.

19.126. 1,141 lb-ft-sec^2.

19.128. 141.4 rpm or 109.5 rpm.

19.132. (*b*) $f = (1/2\pi)\sqrt{(\mu g/L)\cos\beta}$.